MW00772721

Moving Forward

Reflections on Autism, Neurodiversity,
Brain Surgery, and Faith

Jacki Edry

Cover design by Studio Liat Perry
Edited by Sarah Rosenbaum, Adina Moryosef
Formatting by Heather Osborne
ISBN 978-965-599-523-7

Jacki Edry
www.jackisbooks.com

Dedication

This book is my humble offering to all whom it may assist, with the hopes that you will find it to be inspiring, empowering, and educational.

Special thanks to Professor Steven Gross for all your guidance, support, and inspiration, from the day we first met. May you and your family always be blessed with the wonderful things you dream of.

Table of Contents

Introduction

During the last number of years, I have been on a fascinating and often challenging journey. It began about seven years ago, when I was diagnosed with a large and extremely dangerous brain tumor.

Within weeks, I found myself in the hospital awaiting a surgery I was not certain I would survive. I knew that if I did, the process of recovery was going to be long and complicated.

Due to the grace of G-d,* I did survive. But when I awoke in the ICU, I found that my body had become completely unfamiliar to me. I experienced extremely distorted and scrambled sensory processing and was in significant pain.

This was quite a harrowing experience. Despite this, I slowly began to realize I had been gifted with a rare opportunity to experience firsthand the unusual sensory-based phenomena I had been observing for many years, both through my professional experience and as a parent of children with neurodiversity.

It took me quite a while to figure out how to navigate my

---

* Observant Jews follow the custom of writing G-d's name by omitting the "o" as it is a biblical commandment to avoid erasing or destroying the name of the Ineffable.

i

new reality. It was extremely challenging to learn how to function using my somewhat dysfunctional body.

The road to rehabilitation proved to be rocky and complex. Yet, at the same time, I found it highly enlightening.

Throughout this process, I spent many hours pondering the meaning of life, my identity, and my place in the world.

I sought to gain an understanding of the inner workings of the brain, sensory perception and processing, and how they affect one's ability to learn and function.

In addition, I questioned how mindset and faith influence our ability to heal and cope with pain.

I kept a journal of my thoughts and insights throughout my recovery. Over time, it became clear to me all the issues I had been grappling with appeared to be somehow interrelated.

It took me many years to figure out how to transcend my limitations and begin to move forward. This book is a compilation of the reflections and discoveries I made along the way.

I am honored to share this journey with you. I hope it will enable you to gain new understandings about the world of neurodiversity, and you will find them to be useful, intriguing, and empowering.

In addition, I hope by the time you have reached the end of this book, you will come to believe things can always change and improve, and with hard work and faith, you can overcome great challenges and enjoy a wonderful and meaningful life.

Part I:

Autism and Neurodiversity

Encountering Autism

My journey with autism began shortly after I started high school. At the time, along with all the typical teenager stuff, I volunteered at a local veterinarian's clinic. I had always had a tremendous love for animals, and it was clear to everybody that I was destined to become a vet.

Then, when I was fourteen, I heard about a family who was seeking help for their son Mark, who had been diagnosed on the autistic spectrum. Back in the early '80s, autism was considered a relatively rare disorder.

I was curious about their program, so I went to a meeting at their home. The minute I saw Mark, a beautiful five-year-old boy, I instantly fell in love. I decided to join the team of volunteers working with him in their home-based, child-centered program.

Every session with Mark proved to be fascinating and challenging. We spent hours teaching him to communicate, perform basic tasks, and speak by imitating his movements and methods of play. Progress was slow, so every time he looked me in the eye or gave me a hug, I felt as if my heart was exploding. It was an amazing experience, and I learned a tremendous amount from those few years with him.

As was expected, once I completed high school I went off to college to study a pre-vet curriculum. As summer vacation approached, one of my friends told me they were looking for staff at a summer program for autistic children that he worked at in Upstate New York. The camp was designed to give inner-city kids the opportunity to enjoy the summer at a sleep-away camp in the country.

I jumped at the opportunity. A few months later I found myself living with a group of outstanding counselors in the middle of the woods, near a lake, with a group of twelve mostly nonverbal adolescent autistic boys. We did many things that were considered revolutionary with them. They learned how to whitewater canoe, make food, camp out, and most of all, to communicate.

I worked with the same group of boys for three consecutive summers, and it was amazing to see how they went from being nonverbal inner-city kids to country campers who, each in his individual way, communicated with each other and functioned. We treated them like capable children, and they did their best to live up to our expectations. I have very fond memories of mud fights in the pouring rain, running through the fields, and braving the rapids on the river. It was a far cry from the NYC experiences – behavioral programs, Individual Educational Plans, and the like – that they were used to. It was extremely challenging and great fun; a truly amazing experience.

After my second summer, I became keenly aware that I

had been "barking up the wrong tree," so to speak, for most of my life, and destiny was taking me in a different direction. I abandoned all my science courses and changed my major to education, including in my course load special education, psychology, photography, Jewish studies, and dance – all things I felt I needed to find out who I really was and to work with these incredible children.

At my university, fourth-year students conducted extensive research projects and then wrote an undergraduate thesis or completed a year-long project in their area of interest. I decided to examine the effects of exercise on self-stimulatory behavior in autistic children for my thesis. I was overjoyed when one of the first behavior modification schools in the US invited me to do my research at their center. I took a semester off from my regular studies, relocated, and started what was to be a shocking, sobering experience.

One of the first surprises I encountered there was seeing Mark, now a teenager, who had also relocated and was enrolled in this school. His parents had always tried to find the best programs for him, and since behavior modification was just taking off and considered very successful, they decided to switch gears and give it a chance.

Behavior modification was the antithesis of the child-centered approach they had been using when I was working with him. It was a "scientifically documentable behavioral approach," where primary (food) and secondary (social) reinforcers were used. Every sentence we said was pre-programmed, reinforcers were predictable, and words were backed up by sign language. If he put a puzzle piece in the proper place, he was given a piece of candy. If he couldn't sit still, a soft felt belt would help him stay seated in his chair. If he was aggressive and frustrated, he was placed into a small padded room to calm down.

My sweet little Mark had turned into a frustrated, aggressive teenager. He was one of many. He was still putting pieces into simple puzzles, just as he had been doing eight years previously. My heart broke for him, and for all the other children I saw there. I couldn't make any sense of the program; it was as if the children were being trained to become "functional robots" rather than learning the skills they needed to lead happy and productive adult lives. Everything I saw was the complete opposite of what I had experienced up to that point, and the totally artificial, cold, and scientific environment frustrated me (and them) to no end.

I was instructed to work with a group of children according to a pre-programmed agenda. I wasn't permitted to simply pick them up and hug them when they needed assistance calming down, or to do things like playfully color their hands by slapping fingerpaint on them to help them to understand where they were relative to their body. If they couldn't sit, we just gave them more sweets (not exactly conducive to helping a child sit still) and forced them to stay put.

No real learning was taking place; it was all about training them how to behave and extinguishing unacceptable behaviors. But when one was extinguished, another one would take its place, as the root of the problem was never addressed. My heart broke again and again.

Within a few weeks, I decided to change the subject of my research project from exercise and self-stimulatory behavior to finding ways to help autistic children progress and communicate using natural and loving techniques. After everything I had experienced through Mark's program and my three summers at camp, none of the things I saw at this school appeared to be logical, or beneficial, for the children.

There was one trend I discerned that I found to be quite interesting. Using behavior modification techniques, some of the children would initially make some "quick progress." However, over time, they would usually get stuck and become totally dependent on the reward-punishment, right-and-wrong system. As a result, they became afraid of making mistakes and ceased to initiate anything for fear of doing something the wrong way. In addition, they still didn't develop social relationships, because they were never taught how.

In real life, we are seldom immediately rewarded with a piece of candy or a pat on the back. When the staff decided to reduce the number of reinforcements that were given, they were often faced with an aggressive child.

When parents would begin to complain that their child had stopped making progress, or they remained disconnected, they would quickly be assured that it was because the child was autistic and incapable of developing social relationships.

However, after my previous experiences, I couldn't buy into these theories. I had seen too many children progress and appear to be happy by doing the exact opposite of what I was witnessing at the school. It simply didn't make sense to me to work with children in this manner. As far as I was concerned, children, whether they are autistic or not, needed to learn to play, have fun, make friends, and create. I did not see a pre-programmed behavioral educational setting as the right environment for them to do any of these things or to thrive and be happy.

I realize this perspective goes against mainstream theories regarding the treatment of autistic children. It was true in 1986 and is true today. I also know every child is an individual, and every parent must decide what treatment program is appropriate for their own child. I must clarify that I am in no way attempting to convince anyone that what I concluded back then, and what I believe now, is correct. What I do know is that this viewpoint has helped me tremendously, both in my work with children over the years and in raising my own son, who was diagnosed on the spectrum many years after I wrote my thesis.

I am eternally grateful that I had very firm ideas about educating autistic children before my son was born. It would have been impossible for me to go against the mainstream had I not acquired this knowledge beforehand. It has proven to be invaluable to us in the many battles we fought throughout his childhood and are still fighting to date.

Defining Autism

If you ask people to define autism, you will receive many different answers. There is the traditional DSM (Diagnostic and Statistical Manual of Mental Disorders) definition. There is a definition from the assessment team that uses the DSM definition. There are professionals. There are parents. There are categories that have changed over time. In the past, there was PDD (pervasive developmental disorders), Kanner's syndrome, infantile autism, Asperger syndrome, and more. Now there is ASD (autism spectrum disorder), a broad-spectrum diagnosis. The criteria have changed over time, and I imagine it will continue to change.

It usually takes a team of specialists to diagnose ASD. A person needs to demonstrate some of the difficulties defined in the DSM to receive a diagnosis. Many times, they only have a few of the symptoms listed. In these cases, they are often diagnosed with a mild case of autism or are considered high-functioning. A low-functioning child will need an immense amount of support. A high-functioning child might only need to work on social interactions, for instance. But they will both be considered to have ASD.

People on the spectrum might exhibit very different behaviors. There are also instances, such as in the case of my son, where the diagnosis changes as the child develops and makes progress. An example of this is that someone considered to be low-functioning can become high-functioning. In many cases, language is what is used to define whether someone is low- or high-functioning. Also, if a person has significant linguistic delays or complications, they might be considered to be low-functioning, even though their typical daily functioning or emotional sensitivity and makeup might be typical or even outstanding.

For the parent whose child has just been diagnosed, this can be extremely confusing. And to be perfectly honest, I find it difficult to define and understand autism to date, even though I have been around people on the spectrum for over forty years. So, rather than trying to make sense of the endless terminology and professional jargon, I propose what might be a more useful way to define autism. You can simply set the terminology aside and ask yourself a few questions about your child (or the person who has been diagnosed):

- What do I observe is difficult for them? Consider such things as overall communication, sensory processing issues, linguistic issues, motor organization issues, cognitive issues, etc.
- What do I observe are their strong points?
- What makes them happy?
- What is interesting to them?
- What annoys them?
- What is the easiest way to connect with them?

The answers to these types of questions can serve as the starting point for developing an understanding of who your child is and what they are coping with. They will provide you with practical information regarding their specific issues and better assess the best treatment options.

When your child receives a diagnosis, you will need to take action. You will only be able to do this if you understand what it means **for your particular child**. I might even go so far as to say that the diagnostic terminology is almost irrelevant. It is necessary primarily because it gives you a common language with professionals and will entitle you to funding and treatment programs. Other than that, it most likely won't assist you in any way to begin understanding or helping your child.

My Understanding of Autism

Before I even try to present you with my understanding of autism, I reiterate: I am not a diagnostician and am simply sharing with you what I have come to understand over the years. You might disagree with me. There will likely be professionals who will.

I am writing from my perspective as a parent and educator. In addition, thank G-d, I have survived complicated brain surgery to remove a tumor on my brainstem. The havoc it wreaked on my body and senses has taught me a tremendous amount, and helped me to "verify" my thoughts about autism over many years.

I believe it is important to observe each child as an individual when assessing their development. Many professionals measure progress in comparison to classmates or other people with similar characteristics or diagnoses. I think it is more beneficial to consider their unique challenges and needs, and to keep in mind everybody develops at their own pace.

In general, it would be helpful if all children were evaluated by professionals and parents in this manner, whether or not they have a diagnosis. Currently, in almost any typical classroom there are a number of children who are diagnosed with one thing or another. Some kids might have sensory processing issues which interfere with their ability to concentrate. Others might have social issues, learning disabilities, or suffer from depression. ADHD (attention deficit-hyperactivity disorder) appears to be incredibly prevalent.

As children are diagnosed and categorized, they become eligible for services from the medical and educational systems. In many instances, their eligibility for these services is determined by budgetary considerations, standardized allocations, and additional criteria, and not in accordance with their individual needs to the degree that is most beneficial for them.

I'm not sure what the statistics are worldwide. In Israel, there are many children who have trouble staying focused in class. There is a lot of pressure from educators (indirectly) and neurologists to give them medications such as Ritalin and Concerta. I know this is a provocative idea, but I suggest perhaps the solution for many of these children would be to simply educate them in a manner that excites and inspires them. My sons' neurologist actually agreed with me on this point.

He did, however, also suggest I medicate my children, claiming the educational system was not going to change in the near future and my kids needed to function within it. Fortunately, we were able to find alternative solutions that addressed their visual and auditory processing issues, and their concentration and performance in school improved without medication.

Giving children the opportunity to learn in engaging learning situations can also help them to thrive and, in some instances, might alleviate or reduce reliance on medication to learn. Methods like PBL (problem- or project-based learning), SEL (social-emotional learning), and settings that enable them to be creative and move around can be useful. But I am getting off track. Please forgive me. For as long as I can remember, I've had a tendency to go off on tangents, and I'm certain that if I were assessed as a child today, I would receive a diagnosis of ADHD and SPD (sensory processing disorder). Fortunately, as I was growing up, I acquired skills that enabled me to compensate for these difficulties and to reach the goals I set for myself.

So, let me refocus on the question at hand: What actually is my understanding of autism? The only answer I can come up with is, I wish I knew. I wish somebody knew. But I don't think there is any specialist who knows exactly what autism is, or can claim with certainty that they know what causes it. I also doubt there is any one root cause that is relevant to everyone on the spectrum.

It seems to me the professionals have clumped together a bunch of symptoms that may or may not be connected or have the same etiology. Hence, there are many different categories of autism, changing definitions, and, recently, the creation of a "spectrum" disorder.

I think it's clear that people with ASD have something

going on neurologically. People with autism are neurodiverse. They are autism-diverse. They might have some similar symptoms, but most people will have some symptoms which are unique to them. I imagine if you fill a room with people on the spectrum, it will be difficult for you to fully understand what their individual challenges are or why they all have the same diagnosis. I am fairly confident most people would agree with me about this.

I am also convinced most people on the spectrum will have some challenges relating to insufficient or scrambled sensory processing. It can be at any level or stage: input, processing, or output. Sometimes there will be hypo-sensitivity, sometimes hyper-, and sometimes a combination of both. In many instances, they will be accompanied by issues with motor processing or organization as well, which further complicates things.

People who experience any of these challenges may cognitively understand what others are requesting from them and want to respond accordingly, but may be unsuccessful because they are stuck in a body that has "a mind of its own" and does something else, or even freezes.

It appears that the human brain possesses a system of filters to prevent us from receiving too much information. For example, most of us will see pretty much what we expect to see, and hear what we expect to hear. We will not see everything that is going on in the room. We generally pay attention to the big picture. It's only when something unusual occurs that we take notice of it.

The same sort of thing happens with our sense of hearing. A person living on a noisy street will automatically tune out the ongoing din of traffic. If there is a sudden onslaught of fire trucks, it will likely capture his attention. If there is nothing unusual going on, the noise from the street will not even enter into his consciousness.

Now, I invite you to try to envision what life would be like if these filters were broken or dysregulated. Imagine you see every individual grain of sand at the beach or every tiny movement in the room. Or you notice if there are two different shades of lightbulbs in the room, and the fluorescent light is periodically flickering. At the same time, you hear every sound around you. The wind in the trees, a person walking by, people talking, dogs barking, babies crying.

In addition to this, you feel every texture around you, such as the itchy tag on your shirt, the wind on your face, grains of sand on the floor, and more. Then someone starts cooking something in the room. Another person comes in sweaty from a run, and someone else has put on strong perfume. Your olfactory senses have suddenly become bombarded.

Once the food is cooked, it's placed in front of you and you are expected to eat it. But all the textures are mixed up, the smell is too strong, and the color doesn't appeal to you. Do you think you would be able to eat?

What do you think your reaction would be to all of this? How long do you think you would be able to cope with such overstimulation without seeking a break? I imagine it wouldn't be for very long. Do you think you would be able to concentrate on completing a task at the same time as all this was happening, if somebody asked you to? If so, for how long? How do you think all of this would affect your mood and overall sense of well-being?

If the stimulation were to change or become irregular, it would exacerbate your state of sensory overload. You might experience something like you feel when you're standing next to someone who is fiddling with the volume button on the stereo. After a few seconds, there's a good chance you will yell at them to either leave it up or down because the inconsistent input has started to drive you crazy.

Now, let's take a look at the ways in which you might attempt to "turn off" the stimulation. Perhaps you would choose to run into a dark room and hide under the covers. You might put on some very loud music and close your eyes to shut out the other types of sensory input. Or you would decide to inspect every individual grain of sand in the park.

There is also a chance your body will begin to vibrate from the overload, so you might start rocking to calm yourself down. It's unlikely that you would be able to focus or be patient with people around you during this time.

Following my brain surgery, I began experiencing sensory overload, which is comparable to what happens to an electrical system during a power surge – the excess energy runs through the system and the circuit breaker trips. In humans, this might cause the person to jump, flap, or simply shut down. It might be their only way to cope. It also might be a completely automatic reaction to calm down the system.

If, in the midst of a system overload, someone began to make demands of you, how do you think you would react? Do you think a system of rewards and punishments would help you manage the power surges in your circuit breaker? If so, do you think they would help you solve the problem in the long-term, or might they only help you to curb your reactions temporarily, in order to receive a "reward" or to please others?

Would not wanting to disappoint those around you help you to control your reactions to your sensory overload? Would you feel like a failure if you were unable to stop the surges?

As a person who has both observed and experienced sensory overload, I wholeheartedly believe the solution is to try to balance out the systems that are not regulated. There are many ways to address these issues, including things like sensory diets (which are specialized activities designed to help regulate children's sensory imbalances), auditory training, Irlen spectral filters, finding quiet places to turn off the environment, and more. I'm unable to list all the options or solutions. But I have noticed when systems become balanced (whether sensory, vestibular, or any combination of things going on in the body and brain), the need to "behave strangely" lessens or disappears on its own. I have found behavioral interventions are insufficient for regulating these systems in the long term. Balancing the systems is what helps.

It's often assumed that people on the spectrum are not interested in forming relationships or communicating with others. I believe this isn't usually the case. It might not have anything to do with the lack of will to communicate. It might have everything to do with their ability at that moment – and in some cases, the lack of communication or social interaction might boil down to the person experiencing "technical difficulties."

I'll give you an example. My son has severe auditory processing issues. If there are two conversations going on in the room at the same time, the sentences being spoken will likely merge together. In many instances, he will completely misunderstand what is being said to him because he has picked up words from both conversations. The things he hears make no sense to him. This might cause him to lose track of the conversation or to answer a question incorrectly. He might say something completely off the subject because he attempts to join in on the conversation but has no clue as to what people are talking about. So, he gives it his best shot – but many times he is really off the mark.

In addition, he thinks in pictures, not words. Language is something he is forced to use because he truly wants to communicate with others. But for him, using language is an ongoing struggle. In order to answer a question, he must first search through his library of pictures and movies (which takes much longer than accessing words). Once he has found the picture he's looking for, he needs to translate it into words. Then he needs to organize his mouth to produce them. As he also has motor organization challenges, this also takes a significant amount of time.

In short, by the time he manages to find an answer to a question and to figure out a way to express himself, the person who has asked the question has usually repeated it several times and then decided he either didn't understand it or doesn't know the answer. This results in frustration on both sides. He often tells me the words get stuck in his mouth. Sometimes he stutters, and sometimes he simply opts out and doesn't answer – it's much easier for him to either gesture or not make the effort at all. He will often try to figure something out on his own without asking for assistance or telling people what his plans are. His willingness to make the effort to communicate depends upon how much motivation or energy he has available for this on any particular day.

Fortunately, as he is growing older, he is developing writing skills and other forms of communication. But his knowledge and understanding of things are far superior to his ability to share them with others. His receptive language, if the auditory input is clear, is much better than his expressive. But if the auditory input is unclear, then both types of communication are insufficient.

I honestly don't know how he manages to cope with these difficulties. I often see the pain in his eyes as he feels people are losing patience with him, underestimating his abilities, or simply talking around him, for him, or about him. I have the utmost respect for him because he keeps trying. I can't imagine how hard it must be for him. He has so much inside, and so many thoughts that are stuck in his head without any way to express them. He has so many desires he can't tell us about. I pray one day he will. But I must say one thing is absolutely clear to me: he wants to communicate. He desires friendships and relationships. He will do everything he can to ensure that people around him feel good. But his linguistic abilities are extremely limited at this point.

Something that greatly frustrates me is when people make the assumption about him, or others on the spectrum, that they prefer to be in their own world and are uninterested in those around them. I don't understand why people make these assumptions. Perhaps it is because that's what professionals have told them.

I have learned that what is apparent to the eye doesn't necessarily have anything to do with what is going on inside the person's mind or heart. Diagnostic manuals tend to be based on observations and assumptions regarding those who are experiencing difficulties. But these are subjective observations, made by practitioners. They are not firsthand descriptions of things that are experienced by the people facing the challenges.

I am convinced there are times when people have such complex processing and organizational issues that their ability to connect with others or to establish relationships is severely impaired. It's important to keep in mind that ability and functioning are not static. They can change with every minute of every day, depending on the environment in which a person is present. Ability can also be worked on and improved because our brains have plasticity, and cognition is changeable.

I am also certain people on the spectrum, as well as people

with many other types of challenges or disabilities, are similar to neurotypical people in many ways. I am absolutely convinced that beyond their challenges, people with autism are filled with desires, hopes, and dreams. They might not be able to tell us what they are, but that doesn't mean they don't exist. They may need to find alternative methods of communication, but that doesn't mean they are uninterested or don't want to connect with others. Sometimes their challenges are so great they are unable to break through their barriers to express themselves or to form relationships with others.

It is our job to help them to overcome these hurdles. We must do our best to try to figure out the root causes of their difficulties and to come up with solutions that can help them balance and organize their perceptions and abilities. But I always work under the assumption that, despite their challenges, they are whole, loving people who yearn to build warm and healthy relationships with others. They are simply bogged down and distracted due to the "technical difficulties" with which they are coping.

Diagnoses put limitations on people and categorize them. They are primarily used by educational and medical systems to allocate funding and services. Please try to see the person before the diagnosis. I have always told parents that their child is the same child they loved before they received the diagnosis. If they keep this in mind, it will help them to keep searching for the loving soul they have been gifted with, even if the road might be long and difficult.

Raising an Autistic or Neurodiverse Child

Parenting a child on the spectrum, or with any neurodiversity or disability, can be a fascinating and often challenging journey. There will likely be moments of great frustration, and of tremendous excitement and satisfaction. There is a fair chance you will readjust your perspectives on life. Your sense of freedom might change, as well as your set of friends.

Developmental milestones you may have taken for granted might suddenly appear to be as significant as climbing Mt. Everest. If you are fortunate, you will learn to appreciate and revel in the little things. You will likely need to assess and reorganize your priorities and your finances.

It may take a lot of time and effort to bring about change. However, all your family members will have the opportunity to grow from the experience and to become better people throughout the process. Every little step forward will enable you to understand you have embarked on an amazing journey.

We have always found it empowering to try to keep in mind that great challenges serve as wonderful opportunities for growth. With a lot of love, persistence, and hard work, amazing things can happen.

A Few Practical Suggestions

When planning this book, my intention was to give you a glimpse into the world of neurodiversity as I have experienced it, with the hope it will assist those who read it. As a parent, it wasn't my aim to write a professional-type guidebook for raising kids with disabilities. I did feel, however, that it would be beneficial to offer some practical suggestions I have found to be helpful over the years. I hope they will serve you well.

Coping with Diagnosis

As parents, I think one of the most important things you will need to do after receiving a diagnosis is to take a deep breath and take some time to digest the news. Even if you instinctively knew your child would be diagnosed with ASD or neurodivergence it usually takes a while to internalize the news once it has been confirmed.

Please try to avoid blaming each other because something has "gone wrong." Nobody really knows what causes autism or neurodivergence, and it's likely due to several factors. Because of this, I suggest you simply leave the "why" behind and focus on doing your best to support each other and to investigate your next steps together.

It is important to realize that each of you will cope with the diagnosis differently. Being patient with each other and seeking common ground will help you get through the initial period of adjustment. And, after you have become involved with the whirlwind of therapies and the like, I recommend that you stop periodically and make time for yourselves – recharging your batteries and enjoying quiet time is critical and empowering.

Devising a Treatment Plan

Once you have landed on your feet, you will need to establish a treatment plan. This can prove to be extremely difficult. You will likely find yourselves bombarded with tons of information that you will somehow need to make sense of. The internet is full of materials and support groups. Medical professionals, therapists, school districts, family members, and friends will all try to offer advice and influence your decisions. At times, it will seem as if everyone is pulling you in different directions. This can be extremely confusing and stressful.

I suggest trying to listen to your inner voice. If a program or treatment setting looks or feels wrong to you, or if your child appears to react badly to it, then it probably isn't suitable. Sometimes the most commonly used or acclaimed methodologies might be wrong or ineffective for your child. You might want to keep in mind there will always be trends or "popular" treatment methods. In many instances, they will turn out to be passing fads.

Over time, you will learn to feel out what works best for you and your child. It is also essential to consistently monitor how things are going as your child develops and changes. Sometimes things that were successful at a particular stage of development become less effective over time.

As parents, you know your children better than anybody who works with them. You will need to learn to advocate for them, and for yourselves. You are the people who are ultimately responsible for your child. No school district authority or medical professional has the right to take this responsibility away from you. Unfortunately, my husband and I have come across many over the years who have tried.

There were times when we encountered professionals who thought they should have the exclusive rights to make all decisions regarding our child's treatment plan. They would do things such as ask us to simply sign off on their plans and follow their instructions, or to forfeit our rights to give our opinions or intervene. Some went so far as to state that we weren't qualified to have a say in the decision-making process.

We have always found this to be incredibly annoying and offensive. In addition to having better knowledge of our child, I was, in fact, a "professional." I had written a thesis on educating autistic children many years before my child was born, and I ran support groups for parents and teachers of kids on the spectrum. However, there were professionals who considered this to be irrelevant because I was dealing with my own son and therefore wasn't "objective." This type of claim is completely off-base and illogical. My knowledge in the field is something to be tapped into, not disregarded.

Some of the professionals we encountered went so far as

to forbid us from entering the treatment room with them, even when our child was young and nonverbal. One of them even stated that she thought my son, who was only three years old, was "too attached" to me and needed to become " more independent." This was absolutely absurd. At that point, he was extremely disconnected from everyone and had no communication skills. We had to work really hard to get him to pay attention even to us.

When we encountered professionals of this sort and were unable to avoid working with them (such as people from the school district), we were faced with no other option but to remind them that we, as parents, are ultimately responsible for our child. Parents are the people who will need to cope with any problems which may arise from an unsuccessful or irrelevant treatment plan – the professional won't be sitting beside the children at three in the morning when they can't sleep or handling a meltdown outside of their clinical setting.

It is important to listen to professional opinions and to follow their advice if it's suitable for your child. But, at the same time, parents have the right and the ultimate responsibility to make decisions regarding the treatment plans or educational settings which will be most appropriate for their child.

I also would like to suggest that if a professional doesn't see you as a team member, and you have the option of doing so, you might want to consider choosing someone else to work with your child. It will benefit all parties if you pick a team of professionals who understands this and will be willing to work with you hand-in-hand. There'll be a lot of trial and error along the way, and ongoing respect, cooperation, and communication between parents and professionals is essential. Everyone needs to work together as a cohesive team for a treatment program to succeed.

Scheduling

One common phenomenon I have noticed is that the schedules for neurodivergent children tend to be extremely intense. I sometimes get the feeling people believe if these types of children are given some downtime, it will waste precious moments and they will somehow regress due to a lack of stimulation.

A large percentage of these children spend long days in special classes. Their days are filled with intensive learning and therapies. Upon arrival at home, they are often given additional tutoring and treatments. They have very little time to simply "do nothing" throughout the day.

I understand the parents' fear that if the child isn't being stimulated then she will likely just "stim out" or play inappropriately. Or, she might just stare at the TV, cell phone, or do absolutely nothing. And, in many instances, this might be the case.

I would like to suggest, however, that you consider that sometimes this might not be such a bad thing. For example, most neurotypical kids will choose to have some downtime after school. Many adults will kick off their shoes and plug into the TV after a hectic day at work. People tend to need some unscheduled "do nothing" time to process information and to let off some steam at the end of the day.

In many instances, neurodivergent children are just like everybody else in this area. They might even need this type of break more than the average person because they have to work much harder than their neurotypical counterparts to accomplish basic daily activities. A bit of unscheduled time can help them slow down, recharge their batteries, and process what they have experienced throughout the day.

A little bit of quiet can go a long way – even if it means the child might occasionally engage in some "non-productive" behaviors.

Doing Your Best

There are times it can be extremely challenging to raise a child with autism or other disabilities. Sometimes parents might feel as if they are juggling too many things: caring for their child, running to treatments, trying to make time for work, their other children, their marriage, and anything else that pops up along the way.

This becomes more complicated when parents feel that no matter how hard they try, it isn't enough. They feel frustrated because they believe if they were able to make more of an effort, or if they had more economic resources, they could give their child just one more treatment. These feelings tend to worsen if the child is going through a difficult period.

Almost every parent I know has experienced these emotions. My husband and I certainly have not been exceptions. Over the years, we have learned to be kinder to ourselves. It took us some time to realize that we can only do our best at any particular time. Sometimes we can provide more, and sometimes less. There are a lot of different factors involved that can limit or enhance our ability to accomplish what we would like to do.

We have always made it a priority to do whatever we could to help our special child. But we have also learned it is no less important to meet the needs of the entire family and to remain calm, positive, and hopeful. If we had continued beating ourselves up about not accomplishing all our goals, then we would simply have wound up being frustrated, drained, or bitter. These are not positive mindsets, and they have a negative effect on everyone involved.

Life is a delicate and ever-changing balancing act. In light of this, I encourage you to try to be gentle and patient with yourselves. You will always be faced with changing resources and abilities. It's important to let go of the "If I only had more _____, I could have done _____" types of thoughts. They are detrimental and will cause you to feel drained and frustrated. On the other hand, if you remain positive and go with the flow, it will give you the strength you need to help your entire family.

A Few Words About Siblings

I can't possibly begin to consolidate my thoughts about siblings of "special" children into a few concise paragraphs; the topic is so complex and important it requires an entire book to do it justice.

I would, however, like to raise a few points for consideration. It's very easy to become fully involved with tending to the needs of your "special" child. This is completely understandable. However, it is extremely important to try to find the time and energy to dedicate to your neurotypical children as well. They will need your support and guidance as they grow and develop. In addition, they will need help to cope with the unique issues which will arise because they are a sibling of a "special" child.

Their needs can often be quite complex. They might experience feelings of guilt, jealousy, anger, or embarrassment regarding their special sibling. They might also feel they must protect them. It is possible they will be concerned that they will one day be responsible for their well-being.

This can be confusing or stressful for them, and they will need you to listen to their concerns and to help them to find ways to cope. Sometimes, as parents, you will have to do a bit less for your special child in order to provide your other children with the things they require. When every child receives the care, attention, and guidance they need, the entire family benefits.

Another thing to keep in mind is that siblings can be

wonderful teachers and friends for your "special" child. They can become an integral part of your therapeutic team. Children can naturally do many things that adults need to learn how to do. They can be extremely creative in coming up with ways to communicate and play with a sibling who is having difficulties in these areas. If you provide them with gentle guidance and support, you will likely see amazing, spontaneous things happen.

I remember how incredible it was to watch my younger sons playing with their older neurodivergent brother, who didn't play in an ordinary fashion when he was young, and missed going through a number of typical developmental and social stages. I would often sit and observe the boys playing together. They looked like different-sized children of the same age who were having fun. My younger children somehow enabled my older child to "relive" the developmental stages he had missed. They all seemed to pass through them together.

It was beautiful to watch them sitting on the floor and building with blocks or Lego, painting, sculpting with Play-Doh, or rolling a ball back and forth to each other. They would talk, laugh, and engage in spontaneous eye contact and games. My younger sons helped their brother tremendously, even though they had no idea they were doing so. They were very persistent, and he couldn't help but take part in their activities.

These early relationships have grown deeper as they have matured. They all enjoy being in each other's company and have a lot of respect for one another. I pray that, G-d willing, they will continue to remain good friends who will look after each other throughout their lifetimes.

Teaching to Enable

There are many different ways you can teach your neurodivergent child. I'm certain you will discover what works best for you. However, I suggest you try to teach in a manner that enables your child. This is quite different from "doing for" your child.

When teaching skills, it's helpful to create situations where children will learn to take initiative and to try new things on their own. Educating them in this manner will help them to develop independence, which is imperative for their future.

This process can be quite difficult and time-consuming. For example, it's much easier to button a shirt for them in the morning rush than to take the time to teach them to push the buttons through the buttonholes. The same goes for choosing the clothes for your child, as opposed to enabling them to choose (and to mismatch or pick seasonally inappropriate items along the way) for themselves.

Showing children how to make a sandwich is far more complicated than doing it for them. Teaching reading, typing, and computer skills will likely require tremendous investment, but they will enable your child to communicate and learn independently.

It's important to begin educating toward independence as

early as possible, even if your child might need a considerable amount of support throughout the process. It will help facilitate the development of the skills which will empower them to become as self-confident and successful as possible.

Significant Change Takes Time

As parents, you will likely want your child to progress and develop as quickly as possible. In addition, many educational systems tend to emphasize the importance of swift and steady progress. At times they might even compare the development of your child to another child in the same class or with the same diagnosis. This may cause you to feel pressured, especially if your child is progressing slower than expected.

However, there are instances where slower development isn't necessarily negative. I have found this to be particularly true when children are learning in programs that focus on the development of independence and cognitive, linguistic, and social skills. Acquiring these types of skills is a complex process. It therefore might take some time before the results of the intervention become apparent.

I doubt there are any shortcuts that can effectively circumvent this process. However, once these skills become internalized, they serve as the building blocks for further development. This, in turn, can lead to the child making far more progress than was originally anticipated.

I suggest patience when assessing your child's progress. There will be many ups and downs along the way. Sometimes the child will develop quickly, then suddenly things might slow down for a while. You will likely experience these types of changes many times as your child develops. However, with patience and hard work, things usually continue to progress over time.

Humor is Priceless

There is nothing like a good sense of humor to help you get through a difficult day. Laughter is great medicine. And, when raising a child with challenges, maintaining the ability to laugh about some of the unique situations you will inevitably find yourself in can be lifesaving. As they say, a little humor goes a long way!

In addition, teaching your child to have a good sense of humor can be helpful. People tend to enjoy being around someone who is light-spirited and who knows how to have a laugh. I have found that even non-verbal kids can develop a wonderful sense of humor. Giving them this gift can greatly benefit them.

Remember to Have Fun and Enjoy Life

Life is a beautiful thing. Every day is an opportunity to learn and experience new things, to love, and to laugh. Don't forget to take the time to do the things you enjoy and to appreciate all the good things around you. This will help you to revitalize when times get tough.

Be Hopeful and Optimistic!

One of the most empowering suggestions I can offer you is to do your best to stay hopeful and optimistic that things will improve over time. Please try not to listen to anyone who tries to convince you otherwise. Nobody knows what the future will bring. I'm certain you will feel much happier if you choose to believe things will work out for the better, and remember that new medical, technological, and educational advances are being made all the time. So, even if things don't look entirely rosy right now, there is always a chance something new will come along that will flip the cards. Maintaining hope for a brighter future will help you motivate yourself to do the best you can with your abilities at the time.

Many professionals, or others, might try to fill your head with worries or take away your hope. I can't understand why they do this. Perhaps it's because they want to make sure you won't be disappointed, or they want to prevent you from complaining to them later if things don't work out as expected.

No matter what the reason, exposure to these types of attitudes can make you feel distraught and pessimistic about the future. If you can, I suggest you do your best to ignore it, or just avoid encounters with people who make these types of predictions. They will only make you feel discouraged and lose faith in your child and yourself.

My husband and I had a negative experience of this type with a doctor who evaluated our son when he was about four years old. We had taken him to a highly reputable neurologist for an assessment. We had barely sat down in the examination room when he said, "Your child is autistic. If he has not learned how to speak by now, he will never speak. As you are religious, if you would like, you can try praying for him. Maybe it will help."

If we had been inexperienced parents, we would likely have been traumatized by such a prognosis. A statement like that could have taken away all hope. We might have believed there was no point in continuing to work hard to help him because we had been told that our efforts would prove fruitless.

By the time we left the examination room, we felt frustrated, angry, and offended. Hearing this type of prognosis can be devastating. Fortunately, we didn't believe a word he said. We both agreed that doctor had no clue what he was talking about, even though he had a great reputation and a lot of degrees. In our opinion, he was a complete twit.

By the next day, we already had proof that our understanding of the situation had been accurate.

At about five in the morning, just before sunrise, we suddenly heard a small, unfamiliar voice calling out, "Mommy...Mommy." It startled us out of our sleepy haze. Our son, who had never addressed us spontaneously before, was standing over our bed and trying to get my attention. We both jumped out of bed and hugged him with all our might. It was an unforgettable moment. This was the breakthrough we had been praying and working for.

Moving Forward

I have lost count of the times I have heard people make negative prognoses which have turned out to be completely inaccurate. Nobody is truly capable of predicting the future. So, once again, I propose you try to remain optimistic.

For sure, some days will be better than others. But, in general, if you are armed with faith and hope that your child will continue to grow and develop, it will empower you to keep working hard and moving forward.

Part II:

Sensory Perception and Processing

Visual Perception and Processing

As human beings, we are highly dependent on our senses to understand the goings-on in our environment and to function safely, accurately, and efficiently. All our senses are important – but it is commonly agreed that vision is our dominant sense. A simple internet search will link to many medical and neurological resources that claim that about 70% of our sensory receptors are in the eye.

This being the case, I would like to explore a bit more in-depth how deficient or inefficient visual processing might affect overall functioning and communication abilities.

There are many different types of visual impairments. Some of them are rooted within the eye (such as anatomical problems, muscular issues, or coordination between the eyes). I'm not a doctor and not qualified to address these types of issues.

What I would like to consider are neurologically or sensory-based visual perception and processing issues. Once again, I am not a medical specialist in this area. I have, however, both witnessed and experienced firsthand the effects of scrambled or deficient visual perception and processing. I hope that sharing some of these experiences with you will enable you to gain some insight as to how these types of issues can affect a person's overall quality of life, as well as their ability to learn, communicate, and function.

Please keep in mind I am offering you a glimpse into personal experiences, which will likely not be relevant to everyone. I do hope, however, that they will serve as food for thought for anyone who might be experiencing or is in contact with someone who is coping with, these types of issues.

Perhaps one of the biggest hurdles related to difficulties with visual processing is to actually discern that they exist and that they might be the root cause of many other, different types of problems. Receiving an accurate diagnosis can be challenging; it's one of those things that often "slips through the cracks." I imagine this happens because these types of problems are not usually detectable through a typical examination by an eye doctor or neurologist, and at times, not even a neuro-ophthalmologist or didactic assessments can detect them.

There are instances where it may be apparent there is a problem, but it's unclear as to why it's occurring. For example, when one of my sons was in kindergarten, his teacher noticed he was having difficulties with writing and drawing. She suggested we go to an occupational therapist for an assessment. During our first meeting, it became very clear something unusual was going on. He was cooperative and willing to do whatever was asked of him, but he experienced extreme difficulty doing apparently simple tasks. He couldn't identify a specific-colored crayon in a box of different colored crayons. He avoided putting puzzles together at all costs. He was unable to copy or write evenly, efficiently, or in straight lines.

It was unclear why this was happening, as he had been fitted with glasses and was even doing eye exercises to improve coordination between his eyes. We continued looking for answers, but no specialist was able to detect what was going on with him. It wasn't until mid-way through fifth grade that we found the answer, after years of frustration and ineffective private tutoring.

By the time we had reached this point, he had been diagnosed with ADD (attention deficit disorder) and dyslexia. And even though he was intelligent and knew technically how to read, he was unable to comprehend what he was reading or to read more than a few sentences without them scrambling. He was incapable of writing a sentence without errors and had incredible difficulty learning even basic mathematics.

In addition, he was a child who was athletic and loved to run, but was unable to score a goal in a soccer game or to ride a bike. Kids in school would make fun of him and refuse to allow him to play on their teams. This in itself was strange, due to his athletic build and love for sports. He became socially isolated and lost belief in his abilities. He had no motivation to learn because even though he knew the material extremely well, he couldn't pass an exam if it wasn't given to him orally. And the Ministry of Education usually didn't permit him to take oral exams, despite all our efforts to negotiate otherwise. It was an extremely painful and trying situation for all.

Around this time, we were also engaged in a tremendous struggle with the educational system regarding his older brother. He had the same diagnoses and was in a similar academic situation, but in eleventh grade. While he was preparing to take his final, Regents-type exams, the Ministry of Education notified us they wanted him to be tested without any accommodations. This would have caused him to fail miserably. We had to wage an all-out war to overturn their decision. The problem was, like his brother, his type of difficulties did not have a "name" or diagnosis which would enable him to be eligible for the types of accommodations we all – including the administration of his school – knew he needed.

Discovering Irlen

One day, amidst all these challenges, a good friend handed me an article about Irlen syndrome. Irlen syndrome is a neurological phenomenon related to visual perception and processing. According to the Irlen Institute,

> Irlen Syndrome (also referred to at times as Meares-Irlen Syndrome, Scotopic Sensitivity Syndrome, and Visual Stress) is a problem with the brain's ability to process visual information. This problem tends to run in families and is not currently identified by other standardized

educational or medical tests. This largely unknown and undiagnosed disorder affects approximately 15% of the general population, 50% of individuals with reading and learning difficulties, 30% of individuals with ADHD and autism, and a significant portion of individuals with brain injury, chronic headaches, and migraines. (https://irlen.com/isaw/)

Immediately upon reading the article, I booked an appointment for the kids to get an assessment. We figured if we were stuck between a rock and a hard place, we had nothing left to lose by getting tested. The worst-case scenario would be the waste of a few hours and some money – something we had done many times before in attempts to better their situation.

The assessment process was very different from that of a typical didactic or psychological assessment. The examiner checked their reading and visual perception abilities while asking them a bunch of questions about how they see things, whether the light in the room irritated them, and how they felt during the process of the assessment and while reading.

I stood aside and observed them throughout the process. At one point, she asked my younger son to point to an object on the page. He pointed to a spot on the table. She repeated the instruction. He was by that time quite tired and a bit irritated, and he answered he was touching the object she had requested. His visual perception was so off he was convinced he had placed his finger on the object, as opposed to on the table.

I must admit it was extremely difficult for me to stand by and watch them struggle. It was even worse to gain an understanding of how inconsistent and distorted their visual perception was. It brought tears to my eyes just thinking about how difficult it was for them to read. And how frustrated and horrible they must have felt every time a teacher criticized them for being "lazy" or for not making the effort to read. They both had been making a tremendous effort to do their best and succeed. They simply had been unable to, as things began moving all over the page whenever they tried.

Midway through the assessment, the examiner began to place colored overlays on the page. She went through a process of checking whether they improved their ability to read, and then of finding a combination of colors they thought were most helpful for them. When they had settled on a color, she asked them to read a page.

I was more than shocked when, suddenly, both of my sons began to read quickly and fluently! If somebody had told me that this would be possible, I wouldn't have believed them. I knew they knew how to read, technically, but they hadn't been able to put their knowledge into practice until that moment. It seemed almost ridiculous that a simple colored overlay was the key to reading!

At this point, I felt the tears begin to well up in my eyes again. This time, they were tears of relief and joy about having found a solution. There were also more tears of frustration, and even anger. How was it possible something so simple had not been recommended to us? I had met with endless teachers, school officials, doctors, therapists, didactic assessors – and nobody had suggested I check them for Irlen syndrome. It was discovered many years ago, and there are many studies that have verified its validity. None of this made sense to me until I started telling professionals about it and heard their reactions.

I must admit I was shocked by their negativity or passivity when I told them about what we had experienced. The eye doctors I consulted with thought it was interesting, but didn't show particular interest in learning too much about it. The neurologist who had been trying to prescribe them Ritalin and the like for years immediately discredited it. School professionals thought it interesting, and even got excited when they saw them reading; however, none of them made any effort to learn more about it or to suggest to parents of other children who were having reading difficulties that they take their children to get assessed. I consider this extremely unfortunate because many years of suffering could be prevented if children were referred for assessment at an early age.

When my youngest son was in first grade, his teacher mentioned he was reading slowly. I immediately took him to get assessed. And as there is a genetic component to Irlen syndrome, I was completely unsurprised when he was diagnosed as well. He was fortunate because he didn't have to endure the difficulties in school his siblings did – he didn't develop the academic gaps or require the years of remedial instruction that they did.

I would therefore like to suggest this to professionals and parents alike: if a child is experiencing reading difficulties, please check them for Irlen syndrome as early as possible. It could save them from years of frustration, failure, and unhappiness. If it turns out they do have Irlen syndrome, it might even save them from things like a (mis)diagnosis of dyslexia or of ADHD and the medications which often accompany it.

Once the children received their diagnoses, I set up an appointment for the second stage of the assessment, where overlays are replaced with tinted spectral lenses. The overlays are useful but are limited to improving reading. Since Irlen syndrome affects every aspect of visual input, the overlays provide a partial solution at best.

Watching their reactions to the colored spectral filters was amazing. In addition to achieving fluency in reading, they were relaxed and didn't need to shade their eyes from the lights that had always annoyed them. When they went outside, we discovered their visual fields had expanded significantly. So had their ability to go up and down stairs safely, as their depth perception had improved. In addition, they were able to play catch without missing the small ball that was thrown at them. We discovered that the reason that my son was lousy at soccer was he had been unable to track the ball. It would disappear from his field of vision and then suddenly hit him in the face, or he would try to kick the ball, but miss it completely instead.

It turned out another one of my children, who had often experienced fear or discomfort in different situations, had an extremely limited field of vision. It was almost tunnel vision. He was stunned when, suddenly, his visual field widened significantly. He finally understood why he would occasionally think he had been "imagining" people appearing and disappearing around him. They had simply stepped in and out of his visual field (in situations like walking down a sidewalk, for example). Needless to say, his level of fear and discomfort diminished significantly as soon as he began wearing his Irlen filters.

Once the children started wearing their lenses, their lives began to improve dramatically. Within a few months, my fifth grader turned into a bookworm. He would go to sleep at night with piles of books on his bed. He began to improve his soccer skills and obtained a better social standing and sense of security. My eleventh grader also began to improve over the next year and a half, and successfully completed his matriculation exams. His self-confidence also increased tremendously.

Perhaps more significant than their academic achievements were the changes in their overall sense of calm and well-being. Their moods stabilized, and they settled down. In addition, their ability to concentrate has improved significantly. Two conversations I had with my fifth grader's private tutor summed the change up perfectly.

A week before he received his lenses, she took me aside and

suggested I reconsider my objections to giving him Ritalin. She had been working with him for a few years and said he was never able to concentrate for more than five minutes, and it was a pity to leave him "without treatment" for his difficulties.

I told her I believed the problem was rooted in deficient visual or sensory processing, and therefore would not be solved with medication. I preferred to wait to see if there would be any improvement once he received his lenses.

Much to her surprise, during their next session, and equipped with his blue-gray tinted lenses, he sat for an entire 45 minutes without attempting to leave the room or even take a break. She was left speechless. From that day on, they began to make significant progress and started closing the academic gaps he had acquired over the years leading up to this life-changing diagnosis.

Irlen and Autism

Because there is a genetic component to Irlen, I also decided to test my son who is on the autistic spectrum. I didn't really think he had it because he is a visual thinker. He did, however, tend to lose track of or skip words after reading a few paragraphs. He was already a high school student.

After checking a number of different colored lenses, he tried the yellow ones. The minute he put them in front of his eyes, his entire body language changed. He turned around, looked at me, and said, "Mom, buy these for me!" I don't know if, before that moment, he had ever asked me to buy him anything. If he had, it had not been assertively or directly. I was shocked. He repeated himself again, and we assured him we would order them for him.

He could not, and to date is still not, able to describe to me how the lenses improve his visual perception. I often wonder if he had been experiencing the world to that day in bits and pieces or distorted, as Donna Williams (a well-known autistic woman, who was an author and artist) described in her books. When he was young, he used to stare and squint at the lights. He also used to have significant problems making eye contact. I hope one day he will be able to tell us what his visual perception is like. I'm sure it is somewhat non-traditional.

The moment he received his lenses, he began to read fluently, without skipping words. His teachers even began to request he read things aloud to the class. He also suddenly became aware of his location in space, which was a surprise to us all.

From the time he was young, he had always been very clumsy. He would often knock things over, or spill or bang into things. In addition, he tended to stand way too close to people. I remember trying to teach him to take a few steps back whenever he was conversing with people. There were also times where he would go to sit down next to someone on the couch and accidentally sit on them. This could be extremely embarrassing for everyone. All these things improved dramatically the minute he received his tinted lenses.

As a parent, I think it worth checking how kids on the spectrum or kids with any form of suspected sensory dysregulation react when they look through Irlen filters. It might even be worth giving kids with ADHD but without reading issues the opportunity to "feel the lenses." I stress they should be given a chance to look through the filters (and not necessarily go through the entire assessment process) to see if they appear to help them or make them "feel good."

In the case of my son, it wasn't clear he even needed the lenses. He read fairly well without them. If he hadn't been given the opportunity to look through the lenses or to experience how they made him feel, I imagine we wouldn't have picked up on his possibly severe case of Irlen syndrome. The lenses haven't made his autism disappear, but they have significantly improved his quality of life and his ability to function and progress.

I would like to stress that if a person has been experiencing visual perceptual problems from birth, they would likely be unaware they have a problem – it's the way they have always experienced reality. There may be instances where they could be aware they are having some difficulties, but they might not understand what the problem is. It's only when they are given the opportunity to peer through the lenses that they will come to realize there are other and perhaps more complete ways of seeing things.

My Journey with Irlen

If I remember correctly, the first thing my sons said to me when we left the examiner's room was, "Mom, when are you getting assessed? You really need to. We know that you have it. You have to check!" As kids often have great insights, I listened to their hearts and scheduled an appointment.

I'm not sure if I had Irlen syndrome as I was growing up. If I did, it didn't affect my reading abilities. For as long as I can remember, I have had a pile of books beside me. This was true before my surgery, and afterward. I never felt I had any difficulties consuming books. Perhaps I had a very mild form of it as a child, because I had problems with night vision, and in particular while navigating steps (depth perception) in the dark.

As I got older, I began to experience difficulties driving at night. I hated the glaring oncoming headlights and found it hard to concentrate and focus my eyes. I would avoid night driving whenever possible. Aside from this, I didn't experience any other visual irregularities.

This all changed the minute I opened my eyes after my surgery. First of all, I was seeing double. I was not surprised by this because my surgeon had explained this was going to happen and would likely improve within a few months. But in addition to this, my vision became completely fuzzy, and all the lights had halos around them. They would also send out streaks of light as I blinked my eyes. My whole visual field became unstable and confusing. Any type of fast movement aggravated this situation.

I found myself getting completely dizzy and confused whenever I was pushed in a wheelchair down the corridor, or while sitting as a passenger in a car. I would have to close my eyes to avoid getting nauseous or experiencing vertigo in these situations.

I also had to pace myself when I was walking. If I attempted to walk at a somewhat normal pace, I would immediately lose my balance. I was unable to make any sudden movements or even turn my head from side to side without getting dizzy. And even though my left vestibular nerve had been damaged, it didn't justify this type of disability. I took to walking with a cane just to provide myself with some sort of stability.

As if this wasn't enough, I became completely intolerant of light. I was diagnosed with photophobia. Light simply irritated me. If I was in a place with different types of lighting, such as a combination of natural and fluorescent, or yellow and white lighting (typical in hospitals and schools), I would immediately lose visual clarity and depth perception.

I became unable to enter any place with bright or flashing lights without getting completely disoriented and overwhelmed. I avoided all places where these things were prevalent: shopping malls, performances, concerts, weddings. I was essentially forced to become an antisocial hermit. I paid a heavy price for any attempt to be otherwise.

I began to fully understand why some kids on the spectrum have tantrums in places with irregular lighting. I'm sure that if I had been a child with this issue and someone tried to force me to enter a place with strong, colored, or flashing lighting, I would have had a complete meltdown. As an adult with self-control and understanding, I avoided putting myself into situations where I would need to cope with these types of lighting. When I found myself in situations where I had no other option, I had to fight an intense urge to run away.

When these things started happening to me, I recalled an incident when my son with autism was about 11 years old. We had been invited to a celebration. The hall was fitted with fluorescent lights, and a defective one was flashing irregularly. As we crossed the doorframe, he asked us to go home. As it was the middle of the Sabbath, about to rain, and it had taken us 45 minutes to walk there, we told him we would stay for a short while.

I doubted he had any concept of what a short while meant at that point, but he agreed to sit down at the table with us. After a few minutes, he repeated his request to leave. We again put him off a bit. And then, suddenly, he was gone. We couldn't find him anywhere. We began to panic. He was practically nonverbal at the time, and would not usually respond when his name was called.

A team of people started running in every direction to find him. It took about half an hour. He had left the compound and started walking home alone, which was completely unsafe. Needless to say, we were scared, and also traumatized by the situation. He had asked us to leave, and we had refused – so he took matters into his own hands. He simply could not tolerate the flashing lights. We couldn't understand why he had done such a thing, as he was always very complacent. We knew the lights were annoying, but had no idea they were intolerable enough to cause him to attempt to navigate the way home on his own.

After my surgery, I began to understand why he had chosen to run away, even if it meant he would be out in the world on his own. For a person with hypersensitive or dysregulated visual perceptions, these types of lighting have the potential to cause a person to feel as if he were in the middle of a war zone, under attack. And when people find themselves in the middle of a war zone, they often will flee.

I have found, in many instances, people assume people on the spectrum have tantrums for no apparent reason. I have often heard people saying these types of things. I doubt this is accurate. I imagine in most instances, something real is going on, and perhaps in more cases than not, the culprit is likely sensory dysregulation or distortion.

After my surgery, I began to experience very strange visual disturbances in addition to the photophobia. People's faces would suddenly begin to distort in the middle of a conversation. Light spears would fly out of lampposts. Spots, waves, and halos would appear around things. All of this became much worse around artificial lighting, and at night. Going for a walk in the early evening was completely disorienting because the changing light caused my vision to blur.

Perhaps one of the most difficult things for me to do was

to navigate stairs. Whenever I entered a stairwell, I would be reminded of a famous Escher painting where the stairs were painted in a way that created an optical illusion. For me, in real life, they became quite disorienting, and would regularly transform into something like a scene from the Hitchcock movie *Vertigo*. The only way I could walk down a flight of stairs was to keep my head facing straight ahead and feel my way slowly down with my feet.

If I hadn't already known how to walk down a flight of stairs, there is no way on this earth I would have attempted to do so after my surgery. I imagine if I were a child with similar visual distortions, I would have had a full-blown tantrum if anyone would have attempted to take me into a stairwell. It would have been terrifying.

Four Years 'til Freedom

I suffered from visual instability for nearly four years. In general, I preferred to stay home. If I got lucky, a trip to a quiet spot in nature would also elevate my mood. I did my best to avoid crowds, busy environments, stores, or any places with high sensory or visual stimulation.

I learned to plan every outing carefully. Public transportation was exhausting, as were any car trips. I always kept my eyes closed while traveling, or I would lose my orientation and my lunch. I was highly dependent on my cane because I never knew when I would experience vertigo or lose track of where my feet were going.

Moving Forward

After every outing, I needed to recover in bed for hours. Things were frustrating and exhausting. On the one hand, I wanted to leave the safety of my home and to interact with people or see interesting places. On the other hand, dealing with all my sensory issues outside of my familiar environment was so incredibly challenging it took too much out of me to do it on a regular basis.

During this entire time, I actively sought a solution. I went to three different eye doctors, two neuro-ophthalmologists, several neurologists, and even conversed with my neurosurgeon about the issue. None of these specialists offered me any insight as to how to solve the problem. Their usual response was something like, "What do you expect? You had complex brain surgery. You'll have to make the best of the situation." For me, making the best of the situation meant staying at home and missing many important events, including weddings, graduations, and everything in between.

I will never forget the day I first experienced what colored filters felt like. Shulamit Elad, the founder of Irlen Israel, patiently helped me to choose the mix of filters that suited me. They gave me a "nice feeling" and the light in the room ceased to annoy me. I felt calmer and more focused.

We then left the examination room and stepped outside. I was shocked that nothing seemed unstable or was in motion. We stood on a path that had cracks between the tiles, and the lines were not moving. The trees on the side of the path were not leaning at unusual angles. I took a few slow steps and then realized I was not experiencing any dizziness or vertigo, so I increased my speed. The environment remained stable.

We continued down the path and then approached a two-tiered, uneven staircase. She asked me if I could ascend it. I realized it was not in motion. I climbed both tiers easily and at a regular pace, and then turned around to go back down. I was floored. There were no Escher designs! I felt a rush of excitement run through my body. I didn't even want to hold on to my cane. It was the first time in four years I was certain where my feet were! I was able to see perfectly clearly, my depth perception was intact, and nothing was distorted or moving. I couldn't believe my eyes!

Right after the surgery, I decided to stop wearing glasses. I preferred to view everything in soft focus. I found that when I experienced visual distortions or irregularities, it was much easier to bear if they were a bit blurry. I hadn't had the pleasure of seeing a human face or a bird in a tree in focus for years. I suddenly rediscovered that clarity can be a beautiful thing.

I was so excited and overwhelmed, I had the urge to run! After years of walking at a turtle's pace, leaning on my cane, I couldn't help but attempt to dash into the small field near the path. I felt the exhilaration flowing through my veins and had difficulty containing myself. No words I can write accurately describe how I was feeling. All I can say is I realized G-d had given me back the gift of stable visual perception. And it was a wonderful gift, indeed.

Auditory Processing

Auditory processing issues, such as CAPD (central auditory processing disorder) are reminiscent of the types of visual processing issues I described in the previous chapter. They are not the types of hearing impairments that can be measured in decibels. Rather, they fall into the category of neurological issues. They occur when, for some reason, the brain doesn't detect and process sounds in a typical or efficient manner.

As with visual processing, there are instances when it is difficult to accurately identify and diagnose the problem. For example, a parent may feel their child has problems hearing. They take him for a hearing test, and they are informed his hearing is considered within "normal" range.

Chances are, the parent was correct, but the hearing test didn't detect the problem. It's important to understand that a test result indicating a person has hearing within "normal" range doesn't necessarily mean he is capable of hearing things properly, it only demonstrates he is able to detect the sounds and words that are spoken during the test with the level of accuracy that was expected.

Typical hearing assessments don't test for auditory processing issues. Therefore, if a parent feels the results of a hearing test were inaccurate or insufficient, they should ask the ENT (ear, nose, and throat) doctor to refer their child (or themselves, if they are the ones experiencing the problem) for a specialized APD (auditory processing disorder) assessment.

In order to undergo the APD evaluation, a person must be capable of responding to the questions the examiner will ask. If the person being tested is too young, nonverbal, or unable to understand and follow instructions, it might not be possible to conduct the assessment.

There are instances where auditory processing problems can be mistakenly diagnosed as attention problems. For example, if a child is sitting in class and misses a key word every few sentences, within a few minutes they will have lost track of what the teacher is saying. The teacher might think they are daydreaming, having problems focusing, or lazy.

The teacher might then advise the parents to take the child for a screening. If the parents had already been to an ENT and been told their child has "normal" hearing, they will likely turn to a neurologist to check for ADHD. The neurologist would ask if the child has difficulty paying attention in class or at home, and the parents would affirm that.

Since a diagnosis of ADHD depends on many factors, including teachers' viewpoints or parental opinion, there is a fair chance that's the diagnosis the child will receive. The child, in fact, does have attention issues. But the root cause is not because the child is incapable of paying attention – it is because essential pieces of information are lost due to inefficient auditory processing, and as a result can't keep track of things.

In many cases, the neurologist would prescribe a drug to help the child concentrate. The only problem is this would not solve the issue, because medications such as Ritalin cannot cure auditory processing problems. Perhaps they might help the child to remain seated in class, but they won't help hearing issues.

Unfortunately, there are no "Irlen lenses" for auditory processing problems. Things like FM transmitters can help improve hearing in noisy environments such as classrooms, but they aren't a cure. They are also not usable in every environment.

Recognizing an Auditory Processing Disorder

Some of the things that are indicative of an APD are if the child has difficulty understanding parts of words, loses track of conversations, or is unable to pay attention for any length of time in class. They may also speak very loudly without being aware of it or mispronounce words.

Sometimes they might pick up on auditory stimuli at inconsistent levels. They might hear things too loudly or detect every noise in their environment (hypersensitive hearing). They might also miss parts of the conversation or hear incomplete words. These types of inconsistencies may vary throughout the day, depending on environmental factors or how tired they are at the time.

If they have hypersensitive hearing, every small noise can

lead to sensory overload. This may cause them to do things like shout at people during mealtime because they hear them chewing and it irritates them. They might also think people are shouting at them, even though they have addressed them in a regular tone, and then may either get insulted or shout back, which can lead to an argument.

Another thing that might be indicative of an APD is if the child hears partial instructions or mixes up words with similar sounds. For example, a parent asks the child to go to their room to fetch a book. The child runs to his room to get it and returns with a toy truck in his hand.

Children with an APD may also have difficulty learning to read properly or have a poor auditory memory because they are not interpreting sounds correctly.

In addition, an APD might be accompanied by other neurological or sensory processing issues, such as Irlen syndrome or any of the other sensory areas.

APD in the School Environment

APDs can make things extremely difficult for children in school. Learning in the classroom setting may be exhausting and complex. Trying to decipher what the teacher is saying from a different side of the classroom requires a tremendous amount of energy. If, at the same time, the child sitting behind the child with an APD says something to the teacher, they will now need to try and adjust their auditory focus. This may take time, and they may or not succeed in adjusting their focus to the other student, and then back to the teacher, in time to follow the discussion. If there is a class discussion, this will exacerbate the situation. In addition to shifting their auditory attention, they will have to try to understand what is being said from multiple locations, and in many instances, simultaneously.

In such situations, the child will likely lose track of what is being said. If, in the middle of the discussion, the teacher calls on the child, he will likely either be incapable of answering, answer incorrectly, or simply feel embarrassed.

Background noise in class might complicate things further. If kids are whispering, shuffling feet, or moving around, a child with an APD will have difficulty deciphering what the teacher is saying above the din.

If the APD is undiagnosed, or if the teacher is unaware of the problem or insensitive, she might assume the child is not motivated to learn or has an attention problem.

Educators need to understand that children with an APD need to work much harder than an average child to understand what is going on and to compensate for their difficulties. If the teacher lacks patience or underestimates the students' abilities, it will lower their motivation to continue making an effort and can be damaging to their self-image. This, in turn, will likely lead to low academic performance.

Children with an APD should learn in an acoustic classroom, and perhaps with an FM system or appropriate hearing device. They will also require accommodations in class. They will need to sit in a strategic location to reduce the amount of noise around them. In addition, they will need to take more breaks than the average student, and may need a reduction in their academic requirements and/or specialized tutoring. They should also be provided with the option of receiving written materials to supplement the information that was discussed in class, so they will not be entirely dependent on their auditory abilities.

Children with auditory processing problems may also develop social problems. They may miss parts of the conversation, intonation, and social cues, or "get in someone's face" in order to hear them better or to read their lips.

They may miss part of the rules during playtime, which can lead to disagreements and frustration. If they hear parts of conversations, they may misinterpret social situations or think other children are talking about them.

Situations like this may cause a child to react in a hurt or angry manner. This, in turn, will likely cause the other children in the group to become confused because suddenly, in the middle of a game, their friend might begin to shout at them, cry, or run away – and they have no idea why.

These types of misunderstandings make it difficult for children with an APD to maintain positive relationships with peers and may even lead to social alienation. They may begin to "act out" to gain the attention of others or to improve their social standing. Unfortunately, this tends to complicate things further rather than make them better.

In light of this, it is critical to try to receive an accurate diagnosis as early as possible. This will enable children with an

APD to receive the understanding, support, and accommodations they need to excel academically, develop a positive self-image, and achieve good social standing.

Making Sense of a Few More Senses

All our senses contribute to our ability to accurately interpret stimuli from the environment. If even one of our senses isn't functioning properly, there is a direct effect on our entire system. Sensory perception also varies between individuals. For example, one person might consider a meal salty that another person might consider bland. Sensory perception also varies throughout the day. If a person is tired, irritated, or excited, his sensory perception may become either hypo- or hypersensitive, or even a combination of the two.

I have already delved into how our senses of sight (visual) and hearing (auditory) influence our perception. I would now like to take a brief look at how processing irregularities in some other senses can affect behavior and functioning.

The Sense of Touch (Tactile Sense)

The tactile sense helps us to understand how our environment feels. It plays a significant role in keeping us safe by providing us information about pain, pressure, temperature, and vibrations. We also learn about texture through the tactile sense.

The tactile sense also is involved with the way that we connect with others. A hug may cause us to feel loved or generate a warm feeling. But a hug that is too strong may be painful or invasive. A handshake can provide us with a lot of information about a person we have just met. A cuddle can soothe us after a tiring day.

Dysregulations in the tactile sense can be problematic in many areas, and particularly in the area of safety. If a person has a lack of tactile sensitivity, he might not be aware he has sustained an injury or burn.

In addition, he might tend to seek out deep tactile stimulation or pressure (such as massage, bear hugs, wrestling, etc.). There are instances where this might irritate others, and he might not be aware of it, especially in the case of peers at school. In extreme cases, he might resort to self-injury to compensate for his inability to "feel" stimulation.

The opposite situation occurs when people experience a hypersensitive sense of touch. They might be irritated by anything that touches their skin. If they have a scratchy tag in their clothing, it can ruin their concentration and mood for the entire day. Many children with this issue prefer to wear only soft, worn-out clothing made of cotton or similar materials. My children had a wardrobe full of beautiful clothing they refused to wear because they didn't like their texture.

For us, it was always preferable to make accommodations for this sensitivity rather than force them to wear uncomfortable clothes. If I had made them dress more "stylishly," they wouldn't have been able to function in school due to the constant prickling on their skin. As they grew older, the situation improved to a degree, but not entirely.

Another area in which a hypersensitive tactile sense can cause difficulties is social interactions. If a friend in class brushes by a child with a hypersensitive sense of touch in the hallway, the child might think the other one is picking a fight and retaliate. A fistfight in school may break out in response to a child placing their bag too close to a hypersensitive child, or if they touch them (or push them) in a game of tag.

The Sense of Smell (Olfactory Sense)

The olfactory sense also provides us with a lot of information as to what is going on around us. In addition to providing us enjoyment when there is a pleasant scent in the air, it can help us remain safe if something is amiss in foods we eat or if there are noxious fumes in the air. A loss of the sense of smell can be dangerous.

A hypersensitive sense of smell can make things highly uncomfortable for the person who is experiencing it. Strong odors, even if they are pleasant, can lead to nausea or headaches. If they are unpleasant, they may cause a person to flee a room.

If a classroom is stuffy, and there are many children who have just returned from a gym class, and have unwrapped their sandwiches for lunch, it may be completely unbearable for a child whose olfactory sense is working overtime. He might refuse to sit next to a child whose odor indicates he might have put on strongly perfumed hair gel or forgotten to brush his teeth or change his socks.

If he is forced to remain around an odor that doesn't suit him, he might feel physically ill. He definitely will not be able to concentrate or to learn. It is therefore helpful to keep this in mind and enable him to change his seating or open a window if needed.

The Sense of Taste (Gustatory Sense)

The gustatory sense, or the sense of taste, is affected by several different areas of sensory input. First, there is the tongue, which picks up on the different tastes. Input from the taste buds may be inconsistent. If they lack sensitivity, the person might add a lot of salt or spice to their food to detect their taste.

In addition to this, the tactile and the olfactory senses also affect the way things taste. A stuffy nose may make someone lose their appetite or cause the food to "taste weird." If a food doesn't appeal to the person's sense of smell, they will be unable to eat it.

The tactile sense, in combination with the visual sense, can also affect the child's willingness to eat particular types of food. Many children will refuse to eat foods if they don't "look right" to them, or if the texture doesn't appeal to them. Sometimes they might have trouble mixing textures, such as cereal with milk, yogurt with fruit, or mashed potatoes with peas. Lots of kids I know refuse to mix different types of food on the same plate. Some kids prefer to eat only crunchy foods.

When my son was young, he would only eat dry cereal, yogurt, apples, bananas, and a few other things. Fortunately, our doctor said we shouldn't be overly concerned with this because cereal is fortified with vitamins. This piece of advice prevented a lot of conflicts surrounding food. When people try to force a child with sensory issues to eat foods that don't appeal to them, it can turn mealtime into a war zone. This is a sad and unfortunate situation. When there is a power struggle around food, nobody wins.

We tried to help our son by exposing him to different types of food without pressuring him to eat them. We would place things in bowls around where he was playing, or on the tray connected to his highchair, and he would play with them and experiment with them. It could be very messy, but after a while, he began to taste things here and there. Around the time he reached puberty, his senses became a lot more organized, and he began to try many more different types of foods. And now, as a young adult, he eats a healthy and well-balanced diet.

Concluding Words About Senses

Perhaps the most important point I would like to make about senses is you can't fight with them. I believe it is impossible to force somebody to do something that negates their "sensory alarm system" and expect them to feel good and remain focused and productive throughout the process.

My experience has shown me that more often than not, behavioral treatment of sensory issues is unsuccessful in the long run. I suggest finding a solution for the sensory problem itself will likely be a far more effective approach.

If the sensory imbalance can be solved simply and effectively, such as with Irlen lenses, then it makes things much easier. However, in most cases, the solution is not so quick or efficient. It might require employing things such as sensory diets, occupational therapy, or customized clothing to assist a child with a dysregulated sensory system to become balanced.

Treating sensory issues can be a lengthy process that requires considerable effort. However, it is essential to find ways to regulate the sensory system. Without a balanced system, learning and daily functioning will remain impaired, and the child will lack an overall sense of comfort and well-being.

Part III:
Brain Surgery, Faith, and Healing

Diagnosis: Brain Tumor

For the longest time, I had been experiencing weakness and the overall feeling that "something is wrong." My bloodwork was perfect, and my physical exam was completely normal, so my doctor was not overly concerned. In addition, I was always running on turbo speed, so I thought perhaps I was just in dire need of a vacation.

At the time, my days were filled with tending to my children, each with his own special challenges, waging war with an educational system that was not granting them the programs and services they needed, and running a challenging educational program for students from disadvantaged backgrounds. Logic told me these were enough reasons for me to feel exhausted.

Logic is logic, but intuition sometimes defies it. My inner voice wouldn't rest, and it kept sending me the message that something was terribly wrong. I felt as if I were "a car that is running out of gas." I also started getting terrible tinnitus in my left ear, which was becoming extremely loud. My neck was suddenly really stiff, and I would wake up in the middle of the night with bad headaches at the base of my skull. It was all very strange.

Moving Forward

Over the course of a year, I went to my ENT again and again with complaints that my hearing was deteriorating. It tested in the normal range, but I felt as if I were hearing through a wad of cotton or underwater and couldn't make out what was said to me. The ringing was ever-present and growing louder all the time. Since it was all inexplicable, and my hearing tests were showing there was a slight deterioration on the left side only, my doctor finally sent me to do an MRI.

Five days later, sitting in the living room as my children milled about, I got an email that the results had arrived. I downloaded the file and opened it. I began to read things like "a placeholder 5 centimeters in diameter" (they use the term placeholder in Hebrew, rather than tumor), essential nerves involved, acoustic neuroma or meningioma...and lots of other words I needed to google to understand. I took a deep breath and tried to pretend nothing unusual was going on. It was very difficult to fake it, as I realized I had a huge and very dangerous tumor sitting on my brainstem. I had no clue if it was cancerous or not. Brain cancer was a scary concept for me, as a few people who I dearly loved had died from it, one while I was holding his hand.

I took another deep breath and decided to go to my neighbor to use her printer, as mine was broken. I walked like a zombie to her house, downloaded the document, and printed it without explanation. When I returned home a few minutes later, I noticed my daughter was crying. I had closed the document on the computer, but it seems she learned the hard way that peeking over a parent's shoulder when they are reading a personal document is not necessarily a good idea. I hadn't been able to digest the news myself before I had to start helping her cope with it.

What happened afterward was a complete blur. We had been in the process of moving house and suddenly found ourselves in the middle of a whirlwind of trying to understand what we were up against and what type of treatment was required. We were extremely fortunate that my sister-in-law knew of a rabbi who had expertise in directing people to the medical expert who would be best able to help them.

He sent us to a neurosurgeon in Jerusalem, a fine surgeon who had the reputation of being one of two doctors in the country who knew how to treat such a complicated tumor located on the base of the skull. We made an appointment for a few days later and tried to keep our spirits up. Needless to say, it was incredibly difficult. I was frightened and stressed, and had no idea what was going to happen.

A few nights before my appointment, I had a dream that was so real and triggered such a strong emotional reaction it woke me up. I dreamed Rabbi Mordechai Eliyahu,* blessed be his memory, appeared before me and said the following words: "It is not what it looks like, and it will be okay." I felt his loving and kind energy warm my soul.

I immediately awoke and felt certain what I had

---

* Rabbi Mordechai Eliahu OBM was a noted Torah scholar, educator, and kabbalist who served as Sephardi Chief Rabbi of Israel from 1983 to 1993. I follow his teachings closely.

experienced was not an ordinary dream. I was certain he had chosen to help me get through my difficult time. I was very puzzled by his choice of words, which I remembered very clearly. I couldn't understand why he said, "it is not what it looks like..." I kept hearing him say that sentence over and over in my head. It was a bit strange for me, but after the dream, I felt a lot calmer and more confident that things were going to be okay. I am eternally grateful to him that he appeared in my dream to assist me.

A few days later we drove up to Hadassah hospital in Jerusalem. I have always loved the mountains there and feel a tremendous connection to them. They fill me with a sense of spirituality and healing. Jerusalem was the driving force behind my return to Israel; it was the place where I had been taking my son for therapies for over eight years. And now, suddenly, it was going to be in the mountains of Ein Kerem that I was seeking treatment. I felt there was no coincidence in this fact.

A short time later, we found ourselves sitting across from the professor, an experienced neurosurgeon who had done many complicated surgeries of this type. He explained my tumor was a meningioma, which is usually not cancerous. That was the good news. The difficult news was the tumor was on my brainstem, which was a problematic location to reach. It was very large and had engaged with some critical nerves surrounding it. It had also begun to enter my ear canal, which was why my hearing became impaired.

He was very surprised I was still on my feet, and informed

us I needed immediate surgery. He wasn't certain if I would be able to retain the hearing in my left ear after the procedure, but that was the least of the complications to be expected. He discussed the many other possible complications I might encounter and stated it was going to be a very long and difficult surgery. Both the room and his words began to blur. I rested my head in my hands, closed my eyes, and began to wonder if I was going to die, or if I would live but remain cognitively and physically impaired.

I gathered my courage and lifted my head to ask him if he thought I would be able to get through the surgery and if my cognitive facilities would be intact afterward. It was a terrifying moment. I didn't feel ready to say goodbye to my loved ones, and I didn't want to become a burden on them or to lose my ability to understand what was going on around me.

He looked at me and then turned the computer screen around so I could see it. I was suddenly faced with the image of a huge glowing tumor sitting on my brainstem. It was shocking. He began explaining to me I needn't worry about cognition because it was sitting in a different area of my brain. As he was speaking, I suddenly felt as if a lightbulb went on in my head... Rabbi Mordechai Eliyahu's words reappeared in my thoughts... "It isn't what it looks like, it will be okay..."

My question had been answered. I felt as if I finally understood why he had chosen those particular words when he appeared to me in my dream. The image in front of me was shocking and terrifying, but things were going to be okay.

Some of the terrible stress I was feeling started to diffuse. His words echoing in my head gave me tremendous strength and enabled me to get through that incredibly difficult moment.

I took a deep breath, tried to focus my thoughts, and managed to tune back into the conversation, only to hear the professor's voice in the background saying, "You will get through this. But *how* you will get through this depends on three things: the surgeon, G-d, and your level of determination." My husband paused for a moment and then gently answered him. "Professor, I truly agree with you. But you mixed up the order of things: G-d comes before the surgeon."

The professor disregarded his comment and continued to explain the procedure to us. He said I would likely sleep for a few days after the surgery and might have a breathing tube in my throat after I woke up. He told me I would feel as if I had been hit by a train after I regained consciousness. He said many more things but they all became a giant blur for me. I was too preoccupied with trying to figure out how I was going to manage to get through the incredibly difficult challenges I knew were in store for me. I kept thinking of my family and I knew I had no choice but to keep myself together and to brace myself for a difficult surgery and recovery.

I couldn't bear the thought of things going otherwise.

Finding Strength Through Faith

As you probably have come to realize over the course of this book, I am a person with a deep and abiding sense of faith. I can't write about autism or brain surgery and recovery without sharing a bit more about my Jewish faith, a faith that helped me face significant challenges and to heal. It has brought me great joy and strength and given me deep meaning in life.

I am thankful to G-d and believe He has been incredibly merciful to me. I consider myself to be extremely fortunate. I have been blessed with the ability to learn and experience new and beautiful things every day. Living a religious Jewish lifestyle has brought me tremendous satisfaction and peace of mind. I have discovered life is filled with so many amazing things that are right in front of our eyes, if we just recognize and appreciate them. Every moment we have the ability to perform *mitzvot* (acts in accordance with G-d's will), show loving-kindness to one another, or do something that benefits others in this world is a blessing.

There have been times during the last few years I have had to fight hard to live and heal. It has been difficult to attain quality of life in the face of constant pain and limited mobility. But seeing a twinkle in a child's eye, giving a hug to a loved one, doing mitzvot, creating, learning, and appreciating the miracles in the littlest things in life have made it worth fighting the battles I have been faced with.

Without faith, I am certain this journey would have been far more difficult. I imagine I would have suffered from long bouts of sadness or even desperation. Not every day is perfect, and I certainly have my ups and downs. However, the Jewish outlook on life is filled with purpose, hope, and optimism – all of which help me to get back on track when I waver.

Judaism

I began to explore Judaism as a young adult, shortly after completing college. It was the summer of 1987, and I was on my first visit to Israel. I had chosen to visit the Holy Land because I had many questions about my Jewish identity. I had been raised to take pride in the fact I was Jewish, but I had no real understanding of what that truly meant. I was taught Judaism is more of a cultural identity than a religion. We celebrated the high holidays, Passover, and Chanukah, as most "cultural" Jews did. However, we did not observe the Jewish laws (*halachot*) relating to the holidays or the Sabbath.

The Holocaust also had some influence on me, as it was something that was part of our lives, though from a distance. We knew about the family members who had been killed in the war and had somewhat of a connection with the few remaining survivors. It wasn't something that was discussed or explored deeply, but it definitely motivated me to begin exploring my roots. I even took a course in college to learn about it more in depth.

In addition to this, for as long as I could remember, I had an unexplained curiosity and drive to visit Israel to "see what it's like." Immediately upon graduation, I booked a flight and spent a summer on a kibbutz "discovery" program.

One evening, a few soldiers invited me to do some sightseeing around Jerusalem. It was a beautiful August evening, and we went to eat falafel near the gates of the Old City. The air was refreshingly crisp, and the walls of the Old City were golden and breathtaking. When I stepped out of the car and planted both feet on the ground, I was quite surprised to hear myself saying, "I'm home. Finally, I'm home."

Needless to say, I was shocked to hear the words that had slipped out of my mouth. I didn't quite know what to do about it...so I simply tried to ignore the whole incident and get on with things. I ordered my falafel and joked around with the guys on the way back to the kibbutz. A short time later, I found myself back in New York City with a good job in an advertising agency. Everything was perfect for a young woman, fresh out of college, with a bright future ahead of her in the Big Apple.

Everything was perfect – except for one thing. That night in Jerusalem kept replaying in my head. I kept feeling those golden walls calling me to come back home. I couldn't focus on anything else for a long time. Everything else seemed to be so empty. Even though I had been born and raised in New York, all I wanted to do was to go back home – to Israel. It made absolutely no sense at all, but my inner restlessness grew day by day. I began to question if there was such a thing as spirituality and if it lived somewhere inside of me.

After about seven months, I purchased a one-way ticket to Tel Aviv. I planned to stay in the country until I figured out what I was looking for. Gradually, my restlessness turned into curiosity. I decided to learn about Judaism and faith.

One of the good things about being in Israel is you don't have to work exceptionally hard to learn the basics of Jewish practice; the names of the holidays and their meanings are part of even non-religious circles. And, considering that I only knew the names of maybe half of the holidays and hadn't a clue what I was supposed to do in a synagogue, this helped spare me quite a lot of embarrassment in the beginning.

Most of my learning was accomplished through a slow, osmotic process. It was a fascinating journey. Over time, I gradually began to live a religious lifestyle. It has brought me so much contentment, purpose, and inner joy I can no longer imagine living any other way.

Discovering My Jewish Identity

In addition to my gradual spiritual awakening, I pondered questions about the Jewish identity I was raised with. I was puzzled as to why my family had felt it important for us to hang on to our cultural affiliation if we were completely non-religious. I couldn't figure out *why* we considered ourselves to be "proud Jews." What were we proud of? Why were (and are) assimilated Jews persecuted for being Jewish, even if they don't identify with or practice Judaism? Why did the Holocaust happen, and what did it mean for the generations that followed? All these unresolved questions caused me inner turmoil, and I began to seek answers.

Statistically, Jews make up only about 0.002 percent (two people per thousand) of the general population. Yet, for some reason, everything about us seems to be of great interest to the world. Everything that happens in Israel, our tiny country, is broadcast globally every day.

There is also an ongoing dialogue about dividing up our nation, which is no larger than the size of the state of New Jersey. In addition, we have been surrounded by enemies who have sought to annihilate us for thousands of years. Yet somehow, despite this, we have survived and flourished.

None of this made sense to me until I began to study the Torah.* I learned G-d is our Creator, and He gives life to all things. He holds the fate of the Jewish people, and of all people, in His hands.

I also discovered being a Jew is far more than simply having a cultural affiliation. Judaism is a religion, with laws and rich traditions. It is a nation. At times, we have been fortunate enough to live in our homeland. For the most part, we have been forced to survive in the diaspora, where we have

---

* The five books of Moses: *Bereshit* (Genesis), *Shemot* (Exodus), *Vayikra* (Leviticus), *Bamidbar* (Numbers), and *Devarim* (Deuteronomy).

suffered from ongoing and often systematic persecution.

The Torah lays out a very clear set of guidelines we are expected to live by. Today, however, not all Jews are familiar with Jewish law or choose to abide by it. There are also many different factions prevalent in Judaism today, due to different interpretations as to how to follow Jewish law.

Not everybody who is Jewish wishes to be affiliated with their Judaism. Some people don't even believe in the existence of G-d. Others might even believe that religion, including Judaism, is the cause of all wars. This is an unfortunate misunderstanding, because love, not war, is the essence of Judaism.

One thing I have noticed regarding Judaism is if a person is born Jewish, in my experience, they will find it practically impossible to disassociate themselves from it. I'm not sure if this is the case with other religions, but if a person is Jewish, it's likely that at some point someone will remind them of their affiliation, even if they are completely non-religious. For some reason, people find the need to make it clear to us that we are a part of the Jewish people. It doesn't appear to be relevant to them if we are interested in practicing or identifying with our Judaism or not. For them, in many cases, it is something that's important to take note of. This may turn out to be either positive or negative, depending upon whether they are pro- or anti-Jewish.

HaShem ("The Name") Oversees the World

A fundamental concept in Judaism is that G-d oversees everything. In Hebrew, this is called *hashgacha*. He knows our thoughts and is aware of everything we experience. Whatever happens in the world is a part of His master plan, whether it appears to be a trivial detail or is of universal proportions.

When I was learning about this concept, I was told to imagine myself observing a master painter at work. He initially takes a blank canvas and a palette full of colors, and then makes a few brush strokes. There may or may not appear to be a connection between the lines. Some colors appear to go together, and others might clash. The observer has no idea what the painter is planning. He only has the privilege of standing by and waiting to see what happens next.

The painter continues painting, layer after layer. He mixes the colors and changes the details and lighting. Slowly, over the course of time, the painting takes form. It is amazing how all the details suddenly merge together and unify into a beautiful composition. During this process, the painter makes decisions, changes course, and re-adjusts his plans.

This image of a painter can be used metaphorically as an infinitely small illustration of what G-d does on a universal level. We have no idea what He is planning for us. We can only respond to things as we experience them. What we plan for ourselves is not always on par with what He decides is right for us. The only way we can begin to understand how the puzzle fits together is through hindsight.

There is a well-known expression in Judaism that goes,

"Not everything is good, but it is all for the best." There are times when things happen that appear to be completely unpalatable or unclear. Despite this, I have come to understand I must try to acquiesce to His will with dignity. Even if I don't always understand why, I must endure the particular challenges G-d has set out for me. I'm not always successful at this. But I do my best to keep trying.

Prayer and determination can be extremely helpful in the face of tribulations. I have seen and felt their power over the years. They have led me to understand that inner peace and joy can be achieved despite external or physical challenges.

It took me many years and life experiences to understand that I should embrace and celebrate my Judaism. I consider myself extremely blessed and fortunate to have come to this realization. It has enabled me to connect to my Creator, my people, and the Land of Israel. I now, thank G-d, lead a more fulfilling and peaceful life than I did years ago. Faith is what fuels me to drive on in the face of strife, and fills me with love, opportunity, and hope.

May we all be blessed with the things that are best for us, and for the world.

Part IV:

Regeneration and Recovery

Adjusting to a New Reality

At the beginning of April 2013, I underwent an almost twelve-hour brain surgery to remove the tumor. By the time it had been diagnosed, it was extremely large and had wound itself around several critical nerves. Fortunately, the biopsy confirmed it was benign. But even though I knew the process of recovery was going to be difficult, nothing could have prepared me for the challenges awaiting me.

When I woke up from surgery, I felt as though I were in a completely unfamiliar body. All my senses had become scrambled. I needed to learn how to walk, talk, and even eat again. The tiniest movements I had always taken for granted took a monumental effort. It was difficult to even attempt to figure out how to begin the process of regaining my senses, focus, and the use of my body.

At the time, a dear friend of our family suggested I keep an ongoing diary about my journey to recovery. For the first nine months, I wrote regularly about my experiences. After that, I continued to note things on occasion if I considered them to be significant. I kept track of them in an organized and dated journal to keep track of my progress.

I have chosen to share some of these writings with you to

enable you to have a glimpse into the world of someone who is struggling through the journey to recovery in the face of unusual neurological phenomena and deficient and scrambled sensory processing.

I would like to stress that although the process of recovery was long and difficult, it was also filled with joy, beauty, and hope. There were times I managed to get through it with grace and understanding, and there were occasions when I was unsure if I would succeed in getting through the day. I imagine that at times, it won't be easy for the reader to accompany me on this journey.

I did my best to illustrate the process as it was. I hope by the time you finish reading this journal, you will have reached the understanding, as I have, that life is an incredible and beautiful thing and worth fighting for. I have learned a tremendous amount over the last number of years, and firmly believe everything happens for a reason.

Before I get started, I would like to say a few words about my family. The process of my diagnosis, surgery, and recovery was complicated for all of us. We all did our best to help and understand each other. My husband, with a lot of help from G-d, family, and friends, somehow managed to juggle everything and to remain supportive and optimistic throughout it all. He has taught us all how powerful faith, a good hug, and a great sense of humor can ease the process of healing.

At the time, my oldest child was finishing high school, and my youngest was in preschool. Each of the children had to work through feelings of fear, confusion, frustration, and insecurity. It was difficult for them to focus in school and to maintain a typical daily routine. It was a serious challenge for every one of them, and each learned to cope with their new reality in their own individual way.

We did our best to support them, even though we, ourselves, were entangled in the throes of the whirlwind. We weren't always as successful as we would have liked, but we tried our best to ease their burdens and to maintain some semblance of "normalcy" in our home throughout the process.

It would take an entire book to even attempt to delve into the complex process we all underwent. In addition, I'm not sure the members of my family would appreciate it if I were to divulge the particulars with the world. I will therefore concentrate on sharing my process of healing with you, leaving them the option of sharing their stories later if they choose to.

I am certain all our family members have come to understand that with enough love, hard work, determination, faith, and support, it is possible to overcome immense challenges and to grow and prosper. This is a lesson, G-d willing, that will serve us all well throughout our lives.

A Journal of Healing: Exploring Recovery, Faith, Autism, and Neurodiversity

2013

Home again

April 17

It's been a few days since I returned home from the hospital, and I'm having a really rough day. I'm okay, but I woke up and realized something has gone wrong with my facial nerves. The left side of my face is pretty much paralyzed. My lips are partially functioning and my eyelid is not closing all the way. I hope it recovers. The upside is it looks like I had a facelift on the damaged side, all my wrinkles have disappeared!

I'll get myself together and make my way to the emergency room to make sure I'm not having a brain bleed or some other unexpected complication.

Despite this recent development, I'm glad I returned home, even though it's extremely challenging. Some of the kids are having a hard time, which makes things really difficult for me. I hope they start to feel more balanced and secure soon, and I won't need to leave them again in order to recover in a therapeutic setting.

May 27

I'm experiencing increased clarity of thought. It's challenging to deal with my physical limitations and the frustration of not being able to set proper limits for the children. I need to pray more and to keep in mind it is a miracle I am here and able to think.

I'm going through so much – it's hard to comprehend it all and to make sense of things. I have no idea what my husband feels. We are in this together, but each of us is also alone. There is so much distance between us, with each one having to deal with such different things. He needs to deal with logistics, children, work, and finances. I need to relearn to use my body again, to overcome fears and physical challenges, to cope with pain, fatigue, and frustration...where do we meet up? Physical challenges make spiritual focus difficult. I need to leave my body behind to focus on my spirit...

Reflections on Surgery and Life

June 2

Once again, I am reliving the day of the surgery. I keep having flashbacks to the moments when they wheeled me down that corridor. It wasn't a long one, but those few minutes were both eternally long and incredibly short.

I heard the surgeon briefing the staff. They discussed the position they would place my body in, the hours of surgery anticipated, and a list of incomprehensible medical jargon I did not understand.

I found myself listening and I knew this was the end of the road, a test of my belief in my Creator. I interrupted them, quite loudly, said the prayer, "Shema Israel"* and asked G-d to please send guardian angels to help the doctors succeed with their task.

The entire team all looked at me for a moment, and not one of them said a word. Within minutes, they proceeded to wheel me into the room, transfer me to the operating table, put an oxygen mask onto my face, and hook a burning IV drip into my arm. It was time to say goodbye to the existence I had been familiar with. I knew that if I woke up, I would face a great unknown reality. The medical release form I had signed had given me no promises for a bright future.

Before the surgery, I tried to tell everyone I loved something that they would remember, something that would give them strength if I didn't have the opportunity to see them again. No words I can write can describe that experience. It is too painful to remember.

I did wake up, thank G-d. I immediately realized my surgeon hadn't been exaggerating when he said I would feel as

---

* The "Shema" prayer , a declaration of faith, is recited upon arising and upon retiring: "Hear O Israel, the Lord is our God, the Lord is One" (*Shema Yisrael Adonai eloheinu Adonai ehad*) (Deuteronomy 6:4). It is recited upon arising and upon retiring.

if a train ran into me. It did. All I could feel was pain. I found myself trapped inside a body that didn't seem to know exactly what I wanted from it. I tried to sleep to escape from the pain, but found myself unable to. Everything was in a haze. It was hard to make sense of anything, due to the surgery, the medication, and a body that didn't want to do what I told it to.

I was in the hospital for about ten days. For the first two days, I was in the ICU. I don't remember too much about it, other than the pain and the nurse who tended to me with tough love. He made me sit in the chair against my wishes, and tried to get me to eat. The thought of food was unreasonable to me, I couldn't imagine myself eating anything, chewing, swallowing, or keeping anything down. Despite this, my sister somehow managed to spoon some Jell-O into my mouth.

It was lucky they didn't try to force me to try to eat anything else, because I was still unaware that I was unable to swallow anything but liquids and soft, mushy stuff. It would be a few weeks before I could swallow anything solid without choking on it. The endoscope* they inserted through my nose showed I had some damage to my vocal cords. Fortunately, this improved to a level which enabled me to swallow soft food fairly quickly.

In spite of the pain, I found myself searching for the meaning of life, and what I was meant to do. I knew I had

---

* An endoscope is a thin tube with fiber-optic cables used to look inside the nose, back of the nose, voice box, and back of the throat and tongue.

survived for a reason and if G-d had given me the opportunity to live, I must have a task to do. I was surrounded by love and prayers.

I have no way of knowing how many people had been praying for me, but I knew there were a lot of them. Groups of children and adults would gather to learn Torah and pray for my recovery. I was amazed – I could actually feel how the prayers affected my healing process. It was if a cloud of energy would suddenly engulf my hospital bed and work its way throughout my body. It would give me the strength to fight. What was interesting about this is there were many times I would receive word people had been praying for me at that very moment.

The hospital was a fascinating place. It was filled with so much pain, love, and care. People forgot their differences, religious affiliations, culture, and economic status. Everyone there was in pain, terrible pain, and everyone prayed to heal. We all helped each other and wished each other well. If only those lessons would continue outside of the hospital walls, the world would be a much better place.

When the time to go home arrived, I was both relieved and terrified. My body was weak, confused, and unstable. My children were waiting, but I had no idea how I would be able to take care of them. I needed to focus on recovery, they needed a mommy. The two things didn't necessarily go hand in hand. It was going to be a challenge.

In addition to uncomfortable side effects, the steroids I was taking to reduce the swelling in my brain decided to mess up my system. It took a few weeks to wean my body off them, during which time I was convinced I had become a complete nervous insomniac. I prefer not to describe my behavior while "under the influence." It was not charming, to put it mildly. I guess a good way to sum it up was the neurologist who examined me and politely asked my husband if I "was like this before the surgery." You can imagine how I felt hearing that.

Another week went by and I still wasn't functioning. My left side was weak, I had no sense of balance, and was seeing double. The physical therapist who arrived at my home to treat me wasn't trained in neurological PT and was of no help. My kids were testing me, and my husband was trying to be mommy, daddy, and superman. It was not an easy feat.

I couldn't help but ask myself difficult questions. Where was the light at the end of the tunnel? How was I going to get through this? Was I going to heal? There had been so many prayers, so much effort, yet I felt as if I was going backward, not forward. Everything was getting confusing. I was crying to the heavens, waiting for answers, and watching my family react to the situation, one after the other. What was I to do?

***

At almost two months after surgery, my body was pulling strongly to the left. It felt as if weights were dragging me to the side, which I needed to counter, only I wasn't sure how.

I found myself standing in the kitchen, rocking. I was beginning to develop a "firsthand" perspective on autism. It reaffirmed all my thoughts throughout the years about how behavior modification is problematic because it doesn't deal with sensory issues. I could feel in my body how simply "extinguishing" behaviors would be insufficient and temporary; no provisions are made for sensory irregularities.

The rocking calmed the left pull and somewhat centered my body for short periods of time. It lessened the waves of weights running through my body. How strange it was to be doing the things I have seen my son do, and so many of the children I had worked with and taught over the years.

The interesting part about it was my cognition had remained untouched. I was not "disconnected" from the world, but my body required some kind of repetitive movement to soothe the sensory disorganization I was experiencing. I was both experiencing the sensation while analyzing it from the sidelines and wondering what was in store for me next.

I must say, I've gained a lot more understanding and respect for the people who deal with scrambled sensory input. It's very difficult to separate "perceptions" from "reality." The fact that I had had a good sense of reality, having experienced "typical" sensory input prior to my surgery, enabled me to recognize that my sensory input had become scrambled and deficient. My previous sensory experience assisted me to try to sort out what was going on around me on a cognitive level.

This situation helped me to imagine what it must be like for children who didn't have a "typical" head start. For them, unusual sensory input was their reality. It's no surprise they demonstrate strange behavior.

Jacki Edry

Thoughts about *chesed* (doing good)
June 4

On the night before surgery, the house was packed full of people who came to bless us for our recent move to a new house˙ and to pray for the success of the operation. People were praying, singing, and being supportive. At times, they were tearful. Everyone tried to preserve the joy and keep faith that everything was going to be okay.

This was the beginning of what was to become an ongoing phenomenon: people would show up at our doorstep – many of whom we didn't even know – with hot meals for the family, to make Shabbat dinners, to clean the house, and to help with the children. They would give anonymous envelopes with money to our friends, knowing we would feel uncomfortable taking them. They wanted to support us financially because they knew the surgery had cost a significant amount of money and I was going to be unable to work for a number of months.

It's now already close to two months since surgery and the doorbell is still ringing. It was strange becoming accustomed to this type of reality. We were a family who was used to giving, not receiving. For us, giving was natural and easy. Receiving was complicated. Our prayers have always been,

---

˙ It is customary in Judaism to convene a minyan for a *channukat ha-bayit* ("home dedication") to affix the mezuzah in the door post, rather like a Jewish housewarming party.

101

and still are, that we will have the ability to give and not receive.

The thing that made this situation bearable – as opposed to embarrassing – was it was an opportunity to experience how wonderful *Am Israel** is. People have a tremendous desire to do *chesed* (good deeds). The beauty of it is people love to do mitzvot. They do them out of love, not pity, and without the expectation they will receive something in return.

Life can be hard, and there are many situations where we see the unpleasant sides of things. The news is so packed with negative information it's very easy to forget that, in general, people aim to do good. Rabbi Levi Yitzchak of Berdichev, blessed be his memory, was a great defender of Israel. He would always seek to find the positive deeds of the people. Over the last few months, I have found myself thinking of him often...how right he was, and how we all need to spend a lot more time thinking positively about each other and loving each other.

When given the opportunity, *Am Israel* shows kindness to one another and we go out of our way to do mitzvot.

---

* *Am Israel*, lit. the "Nation of Israel," is a term in Hebrew that refers to people of Jewish origin, who are considered a nation. It can also refer to the "People of Israel."

Focusing on the positive things

June 10

It seems natural to focus on all the negative things which go on in the world. There is no shortage of them, unfortunately. When you speak with people, more often than not the conversation turns into a long list of complaints about human nature and how lousy it is.

One thing I have experienced throughout my illness is actually the opposite: human nature can be wonderful, giving, caring, and beautiful.

Day after day, for the last few months, people have been going out of their way to assist me. Some of them I knew beforehand, and some not. They all sought to do mitzvot, to make my day better and easier, and to lift my morale.

A new form of entertainment

June 13

I wake up in the morning and it takes me a while to get mobile. I find myself lying propped up on a bunch of pillows, waiting for my system to organize itself. It takes about half an hour before I can sit up and dangle my feet.

The time passes quickly: thoughts run through my head, and the pain receptors throughout my body begin to wake up and say good morning. They want to make sure I feel all my organs.

Moving Forward

As I slowly become aware of my environment, I find myself staring at the lights on the ceiling. It's very easy to get lost playing with them. There are two fixtures, simple dangling light bulbs. A few months ago, I never could have imagined they could be such a source of entertainment.

As I look at them, they begin to dance around the ceiling. Each one of them slowly divides into two, and then they begin to move around. It looks like a slow waltz. They gradually move together, and then apart, merge into one, and then separate again. The dance repeats itself over and over, each time with a slight variation. If I don't catch myself, I can disappear into the performance, forgetting the outside world around me.

Nighttime fun

June 14

It's the middle of the night, one of the many times I have found myself wide awake, listening to my heart racing way too fast. I slowly started walking across the floor, checking that my balance is in place. My left shoulder was pulling me sharply left, and I needed to counteract this by leaning my right side into the wall.

Suddenly, the lower part of my left leg became extremely heavy, as if someone had slipped an iron band just above my ankle. It was a huge effort to lift my foot off the floor. It's far safer to drag it and to try to achieve some stability.

At times, I wish I still had a catheter in, or that I was a male so I could find an easier solution than trying to reach the bathroom in the middle of the night without hitting the floor. Once I finally do arrive there, I need to make a serious effort to sit down. Trying to get back up without flying into the opposite wall is an even more interesting challenge.

By the time I get back to bed after one of these adventures, I know I will need to spend the next four hours trying to entertain myself, because I won't be able to sleep for a good while. It's a good thing I have relatives overseas – the time difference enables me to converse with my mom or sister instead of trying to pass the time speaking to my fears and pain.

When I finally did lie down, the roller coaster began. It's interesting to play the part of the tracks. The room looks like it's going up and down. The walls and windows realign at all different angles. After a while, I feel the cars passing over me. Large, heavy weights move like waves over my body. They travel through my chest, down my midriff, and over my legs until they reach my toes. When they hit the bottom of my feet, they either disappear out of the soles or travel back up my legs in reverse, depending on how long they decide to keep me awake. I have never been a huge fan of roller coasters, but I imagine this kind is somewhat reasonable, as at least it doesn't make me nauseous.

Making sense of my senses – My new reality

June 17

My vision is playing serious tricks on me. I spend most of the day looking at the world from a different angle. The flat road and sidewalk from the other side of the street suddenly rise up and turn into a steep hill. Nothing is stable, and I usually can't look at any object for too long or I lose my perspective of where I am in relation to it. It's very hard to balance.

The world looks really strange at times. The walls and ceiling meet up in diagonal lines, like in a model of a 3-D room I once saw in a movie about Temple Grandin.˙ The lines of grout between the tiles on the floor separate into two, as if they are dividing train tracks across the floor. If I look out the window and watch someone walking down the street, his or her "identical twin" follows right behind at the same pace.

It's even weirder to watch someone's face "clone itself" while I am holding a conversation with them. It's really difficult to concentrate on what they are saying while they suddenly become double. I'm certain that if I were a child, I would never look at people directly because it would be terrifying to see their faces distort and become monster-like right before my eyes....

˙ Mary Temple Grandin, an American scientist, is a prominent advocate for the humane treatment of livestock for slaughter. Diagnosed as autistic as a child, she advocates for autism and neurodiversity rights and is the subject of the Emmy- and Golden Globe-winning semi-biographical film, *Temple Grandin*.

It's amazing how many things fall on the floor in one day. I guess I never really noticed how many times my young children drop things all around the house. I used to just pick them up. But now that I can't do that so easily, if at all, I notice they have strewn toys and shoes all over the house. In addition to this, my left hand isn't working properly and my hand-eye coordination is off, so I keep knocking things over or missing the counter.

I don't try to bend down to pick things up, because then vertigo sets in and I will find myself kissing the tiles if I make the attempt. I have learned to become an expert at using my toes to pick things up while holding on to a counter or table to keep me from falling.

My left shoulder is becoming limper and more deformed each day. It's hanging significantly lower than my right shoulder. I started researching the cause, and it appears I have damage to my accessory nerve. My muscle bulk is disappearing and the physical therapy doesn't help. I can't raise my arm to the side above my shoulder. It's frustrating; it keeps getting worse rather than improving. My whole body looks as if it is on the offside.

I've made a new rule for myself: Don't look down. If I look down, I will inevitably get vertigo and need to find a wall or couch immediately to keep myself from falling. If I want to try to sweep, I must keep my head straight and eyes looking forward. I must "feel my way" around the room with my feet.

I'm so tired all the time. There are no words to describe how exhausted I feel. If I try to do something that takes (a very long) five minutes to do, like make a sandwich for my son, I need to rest for a good half hour afterward. If I take a shower and get dressed, I need to rest for two hours. I can't shower and have a physical therapy session on the same day. It's way too much for me.

It's extremely difficult to attempt to manage the house from my couch. It is almost impossible to keep calm and positive while the kids are going nuts and jumping on the furniture like superballs. I feel as if I'm fighting a losing battle.

I think most people's bodies function in some sort of "autopilot" mode most of the time – or at least mine used to. Our bodies don't usually require planning to carry out most everyday physical actions. They simply respond to a thought or command automatically.

It's become clear to me that the autopilot on my left side has become dysfunctional. It takes an extreme effort to plan every physical action. For example, if my physical therapist stands facing me with her hands held up in front of her and tells me to "punch her hands" using my left hand, my brain immediately understands the request, but my body has no clue how to do it. By the time I process my thoughts and try to organize my body to move, she has already repeated the request several times.

This situation reminds me of what I have observed watching my autistic son, who is already a teenager but can't coordinate his movements to tie his shoes or to hold his pencil correctly. Cognitively, everything is clear, but motor planning is problematic.

For me, the situation becomes even more frustrating when I see the therapist thinks I don't understand the request or gets impatient. I can imagine how much pain and frustration – and perhaps humiliation – my son has experienced throughout his life because of his poor motor planning abilities. It greatly saddens me to think about this.

June 18

My scalp woke up today. It is a very strange feeling after being numb for so long. My skull also woke up, and it has changed shape. It's full of indentations, bumps, and pathways. The strangest thing I am experiencing is itching. It feels like my scalp is itching – until I touch it and realize the itching is coming from the inside of my skull, and I can't scratch it. It's really weird.

My vision is still not improving. I still spend most of my day looking at a slanted room.

Vegging Out

June 19

My body doesn't want to move today. Everything is slow. Painfully slow, as if working against the force of gravity. My brain, however, is in overdrive. My thoughts are running way too fast, and then they get stuck in a traffic jam in my body. I am frustrated, tired of endless pain, and waiting for my energy to return. It's really challenging to experience such a huge difference between my thoughts, desires, and physical abilities.

I have composed an entire book in my head, but it's too painful to sit and write it. Nothing is comfortable, and I can't even dictate my thoughts to a speech-to-text program. I'm looking for freedom – the freedom to move, to do things independently, to care for my kids, and even to clean my house. I have gone from being extremely independent and in chronic overdrive to being stuck on the couch waiting for people to do things for me. I'm finding this to be quite a challenge. I must have a serious lesson to learn about patience and being thankful for every movement I am capable of making. I hope I will succeed.

June 25

One of the hardest things to deal with is sadness and frustration. The need to manage the household from my couch is incredibly frustrating, to put it mildly. Educating kids who test my limits while I am stuck in a bed is outrageously challenging. It's so difficult to be patient or nice when everything hurts. Sometimes I just want to walk out the door and come back when I'm strong. However, this is impossible.

Sometimes I feel as if I have no more energy to continue fighting. But I refuse to give up.

June 26

The lower left side of my head keeps telling me to lie down. It lets me move around for a while, then says, "Enough! Put me back on the pillow." The rest of my body is fed up, aching to become mobile, but the back of my head and neck stubbornly refuse. They start pulling me sideways, sending waves up to my head, and take away my balance.

After a short while on the bed, the rest of my body starts to protest, so I get back up. Ten minutes later, the fight begins again. I'm really learning about how we mustn't take anything for granted – and how much we need to thank G-d for every minute we can stand on our feet!

July 2

I still have a lump behind my ear at the base of my skull. It's swollen, liquidy, painful, and limits my ability to move my neck.

Every day has new challenges and pain. I feel like I have knives running through my neck and head and down to my shoulder, which has atrophied. My vision is improving slightly and I don't see double all the time. The left side of my skull is still sore and sensitive. I still can't look or bend down and have terrible problems balancing. I can't walk in a straight line very well. The pain is exhausting and makes it difficult sometimes to maintain a positive attitude. I really need a good laugh...

I am looking for strength and wishing things would improve faster...and am always surprised at the number of things I can't do.

Thoughts about sadness

July 5

I have come to realize getting sad is another *middah ra'ah* – bad trait – that drains all my energy to fight and to get better. It's very easy to let sadness creep over me when everything hurts, the house looks as if a tornado has passed through it, the kids are fighting, and I am unable to do anything to change the situation.

How can I pick myself up and shake myself off in order to get on with things? I beg HaShem sends me guidance and understanding about what all this means, what I am supposed to learn from it, and what to do with it.

***

Learning how to clean

I have discovered filling the washing machine with my toes is an excellent leg and balancing exercise! Sweeping the floor without looking directly down is also interesting. The same goes for scrubbing pots...although it is harder to ensure I have cleaned every spot without looking at them at the same time.

Thoughts about anger

I have always known getting angry is detrimental, but now I pay an immediate and nasty price if I lose my cool. When someone shouts at me, I no longer have any defenses and I feel as if their vocalizations stab through my body and make it vibrate. If I lose my cool and shout, knives run up and down my neck and through my head. My whole system wants to close down, run away, and hide in a cave. I pray to HaShem and beg Him to have mercy on me and to save me from this *middah ra'ah*.

What's in a lump?

July 21

It turns out the lump on the back of my head is leaking CSF (cerebrospinal fluid), which is a really charming thought. I had a huge scare a week and a half ago, when I went to the emergency room, and a CT confirmed there was a leak. The doctors decided to admit me to the neurosurgery unit and to drain the fluid. This might sound simple, but the gist of it was to put a tube in my spinal cord for 5 days to let the fluid drain out. I was to expect to be in considerable pain, at risk for infection, in need of antibiotics and close observation. All in all, I was in for a real party.

Fortunately, a few minutes before the doctor on call was about to begin the procedure, my surgeon came out of the OR and decided he preferred to leave things as they were. He didn't want to take the risk and stated that even if the procedure was successful, there were no guarantees it wouldn't refill anyway. He ordered us to go home and keep an eye on it instead. We are praying it will disappear, or at least not grow.

Reason to celebrate

July 25

Today is my birthday. It's a miracle to be alive! I am so grateful to G-d I am here. I'm a bit broken, crooked, and in constant pain – but I can hug my kids, do HaShem's will, and love my family. My body is not particularly cooperative, but I can think and talk clearly. I am eternally grateful for this. When I get overly worn out and frustrated, I need to remind myself where I could be and how lucky I am. It's so important to keep things in proportion...

Learning to rock

August 1

Balance has become an issue. I have lost stability, and find it difficult to walk without going off-kilter. My physical therapist was working with me today, and she told me I should hold on to a chair and rock back and forth to balance out my vestibular system (the sensory apparatus of the inner ear). I must say I had a good laugh when I realized she was teaching me to rock...seeing as autistic kids are told *not* to rock because it's considered to be a form of stimming.

It was very strange for me to discover the PT knows rocking can solve a sensory or vestibular problem, and teachers of behavioral modification consider it to be a behavioral issue. If I have learned one thing through my own body, it's that it's not a behavioral problem. It is a necessary activity that helps reorganize the system when it goes out of whack. When everything gets back in order, the drive to rock diminishes.

Behavioral therapists will often tell you a major flaw in their method is that when you "extinguish" a behavior, another one often develops in its place. I imagine this occurs because there is a need to balance the system. A much better treatment would be to figure out what has gone off-balance, and then find a way to help it reorganize. Once the root cause is stabilized, the behaviors disappear on their own.

August 3

I now realize I have no need to go to amusement parks anymore...I have one inside of my head...

The bigger picture

August 12

I am tired today and thinking about life and how careful we need to be to appreciate everything, and how, in an instant, things can completely change. G-d plans our challenges for us, and we need to try to understand what to do with them. It's not always easy to figure things out.

How do we come to understand what our task is in the large scheme of things? How do we know we are going down the right path and fulfilling G-d's will?

August 22

It's mid-August, five months after surgery. It's the first time I will spend an entire night alone in years. The silence is weird. Everyone is on vacation. I stayed home in order to rest and to enable them to enjoy their vacation without having to take my limitations into consideration.

I have been having lots of flashbacks lately. Suddenly, the neurosurgery unit becomes alive... I get brief glimpses of the week after surgery, the pain, the unfamiliarity with my body that was once so easy to use.

I wonder when – or if – my body will ever work again the way it used to. The pain feels like it is never-ending, although I know it is less intense than it was. It just makes me feel so tired sometimes.

I don't know where to channel my energies, as they are so limited and I have so much to do. I wish I didn't have to worry about finances. It would make the process of healing much simpler, and it would be easier to relax and go with the flow.

My inner voice tells me to stop everything, to begin writing, and to dedicate myself to trying to figure out what G-d really wants from me, what my real *shlichut* (mission) is. I want to neutralize myself from all the distractions of this confused world, to spend my time raising my kids and learning and sharing what HaShem allows me to figure out. Projects, work, students, and all the other stuff I used to tend to seem so far away from me now. My energies want to go inward and upwards, rather than to be diverted to other places in accordance with other people's priorities.

Appreciation

August 23

At times I feel as if I have been transported to another planet, and I need to learn how to "land" and to function in this world again. My priorities have been rearranged, and my perspective has totally changed. I have no idea how to build bridges of communication with people who live on a more "regular" plane of existence, as there is such a huge distance between us now.

It is very hard to imagine how I will be able to find the patience to deal with so many of the "usual" types of things people are preoccupied with: power, pride, their appearance, wealth, materialism, and things of the like. My focus is on connecting with G-d, finding out what my true mission in life is, rehabilitation, and raising my children. How will I be able to find a place in my heart to deal with all the "stuff" most people are busy with? Is that what I am really meant to do? How do I bridge the gaps?

My process of healing is far from done, and I pray one day

I will completely recover. Physical limitations steal my independence and make it difficult for me to plan things, as I never know how much energy I will have, or whether I will see straight or be dizzy and off-balance.

My soul is fighting with my body to find inner peace and to connect with G-d. My mind is in overdrive, but I also recognize a calm inner power that knows I have so much to be thankful for, every second of the day.

Physical challenges are like baggage I am forced to deal with. They chain me down when I want to fly. I am not sad or depressed because I know G-d loves me and has given me the gifts of life, family, and love. These are such precious things and can be easily overlooked when faced with the daily challenges and distractions of life.

We mustn't take anything for granted; everything is a gift. Everything, from breathing to talking, holding a child, eating and swallowing food, is a gift. The ability to love and so show love is a privilege. Being able to smile or ask a question is a blessing. Nothing is certain, and the ability to do the simplest things in life must be appreciated.

The blessings in *birkot hashachar* (part of the morning prayers) are not simply words – they must be stated with great care. They teach us to be grateful for every little thing we have. It's so easy to let life pass us by, and so important to stop and appreciate it.

I'm in too much pain now to keep writing, the knife is twisting in the lump at the back of my neck. It's time to lie down.

September 12

It's a few days before Yom Kippur, and just after Rosh Hashana,˙ during the period of the ten holy days where one delves into the inner workings of one's soul. It is a time of judgment and decision-making, where people examine the things they need to do to become closer to HaShem and to carry out their mitzvot throughout the upcoming year.

A few weeks ago, during the quiet of a Shabbat afternoon, an unusual image suddenly popped into my head. I felt as if the Redemption – the *Geula* – was just out of reach, and if I were to just extend myself and make an effort, I might be able to grab it and pull it toward us. It was a fleeting image, requiring action.

I actually almost thrust my hand forward to try to catch it, but then I remembered I was sitting at the dining room table with my family, and I didn't quite know what they would think if I suddenly started grabbing the air. I felt confused and surprised, and was unsure as to what it meant or what I was supposed to do.

On the first day of Rosh Hashana, I had another unsettling experience. I had taken some painkillers, fought with the strong desire to stay in bed, and forced myself to go

---

˙ During Rosh Hashana, the Jewish "New Year," where the Jewish people proclaim G-d as their King, it is said that G-d inscribes the names of the righteous in the Book of Life. Then follows the Ten Days of Repentance, when we atone for our mistakes and are sealed into the Book of Life with fasting and prayer on Yom Kippur, the Day of Atonement.

to a synagogue near my house.

In the middle of prayers, I once again found myself overwhelmed. I was listening to the shofar, standing with my eyes closed. Every hair on my body stood on end. The tears started flowing down my cheeks, and I saw an intense image of all the letters of all the prayers floating up to the sky, only to crash into dark clouds and then scatter in all different directions, stopped by an invisible barrier.

I immediately changed the tone of my prayers. The sweet melodies of the songs disappeared from my lips. I was overcome by the desire to plead, to shout to HaShem to free all of *Am Israel*, to accept all our prayers, and to bring about the Redemption for every individual and for the nation as a whole.

I must have stood there for a long time, rocking, with my eyes closed. And, as was said about Chana, I was moving my lips while silently shouting and pleading to HaShem. I was completely transported into a private world in the middle of the synagogue. Sounds of the shofar carried my thoughts higher and higher. The letters struggled to penetrate the clouds, driving me to intensify my prayers.

As the service came to an end, I felt shaken, not knowing if I had done enough. I opened my eyes and saw that everyone around me looked just as they always did. They were smiling and chattering, completely unaware of the drama that had unfolded in my heart, or the intense struggles and difficulty I

---

* I Samuel 1:13.

had experienced.

As soon as the service finished, I left the synagogue and walked home alone. I proceeded very slowly, leaning on my cane, seeking balance. My lips were still moving, wondering how to make sense of such unexpected experiences that were so much bigger than me.

Ready to venture out into the big world...or not

September 18

Two days after Yom Kippur, I was still really weak and shaky after my unsuccessful attempt to fast. All throughout the holy day, I drank a limited amount of water, but by 5:30 p.m. I was seeing giant black spots in front of my eyes. I decided this wasn't a good sign, as I was looking after my two small children. I started to drink large quantities of water and the spots went away, but I still felt so horrible I didn't know what to do with myself. I managed to drink some tea and eat some cake, take some painkillers and crawl into bed until the following day.

All the next day, I felt weak, but I did my best to try to function. My belly was really sore, not allowing me to eat enough to give my body the energy it needed. I stayed around the house, drank a lot, and tried to rest. I went to bed a bit late, because of all the excitement of putting up our sukkah. Sukkot* is such a beautiful holiday, and I felt my batteries

---

* Sukkot is a weeklong Jewish holiday that comes five days after Yom

121

begin to recharge just thinking about it.

The next day I made my first attempt to attend a celebration and mingle with people. Unfortunately, my body had been screaming at me all day and telling me to get in bed and not go anywhere. I tried to rest and recover because I didn't want to miss the bat mitzvah party of my good friend's daughter. I had decided to attend for a short time to try to participate in their joy. I knew how much it meant to them for me to be there.

When evening came around, I took some painkillers and walked out the door. At the entrance to the hall, I already sensed I was in trouble. My vision immediately blurred from the lights and the people milling about. I started seeing double, or something like that, and began experiencing distorted depth perception. The loud music assaulted my ears. My instincts warned me to back up and exit. I didn't heed them.

I took a deep breath and tried to plan how I would manage to get across the room to our table without crashing into anyone or falling. People started coming up to me, pleased to see me, wishing me well. I was in complete sensory overload, trying to breathe slowly and organize my environment. I managed to sit down, eat a bit, and speak to a few close friends when the music allowed for it.

Kippur. Sukkot celebrates the gathering of the harvest and commemorates the miraculous protection G-d provided for the children of Israel when they left Egypt. We celebrate Sukkot by dwelling in a foliage-covered booth (known as a _sukkah_).

I kept it somewhat together for about an hour, and then my brain said, "Get out of here, NOW!" I didn't obey the command, as my friends were in the middle of speeches, and it would have been really impolite to just walk out. Ten minutes passed and they were still talking. I put my head on the table and closed my eyes. It took another fifteen minutes before I was able to make my exit.

A friend of mine volunteered to drive me home. As soon as we left the hall, I realized how mixed up my senses had become. I hardly felt the ground and tried to stabilize myself by leaning on my cane. It was a good thing my arms had not turned into Jell-O, as my legs certainly had.

It was extremely difficult for me to balance and to propel myself in the direction of the car. The minute we were seated, tremors and waves started to run through my entire body. I began shaking uncontrollably. I tried to relax and breathe deeply, but the waves of tremors continued. I was fully conscious, talking to my friend, but my body had gone ballistic, and I had absolutely no control over it.

When we arrived home, I somehow managed to fumble my way through the door, despite my knees collapsing periodically. I held back the need to vomit. Luckily, I managed to keep my thoughts calm, because my body was going nuts. I sipped some water, propped myself up quietly on the couch, and waited for my "conscious seizure" to finish.

It took about 40 minutes for my body to begin to regulate, and another hour to finally fall asleep. When I woke in the morning, my entire body was sore and weak, as if I had run a marathon. I wondered if I had experienced what an autistic child feels when they are in sensory overload. If it was anything like what I had gone through, I can completely understand why they tantrum when they encounter flashing lights or hear loud or inconsistent auditory stimuli.

It was another two days before my body began to regulate itself. I was amazed by how traumatized I had become from what most people would have considered to be a "good party."

Perspective

October 16

It's six months after surgery. I made a long list of everything that is still wrong in my body and took it to the doctor to get his opinion. It was stuff I didn't believe was particularly superficial: I have a pool of cerebrospinal fluid in my head and neck, a remaining bit of the tumor in my brain, double and distorted vision, and the inability to bend my head down. In addition, I have a lack of balance, problems swallowing, weakness on my left side, partial facial paralysis, and plenty of pain. The list is longer than what I have just written, but I won't bother elaborating further.

I wasn't looking for sympathy, nor expecting him to offer me any magic solutions for my problems. I was seeking information. I wanted to know if the symptoms I have been experiencing are dangerous. I have been suffering from an ongoing, subliminal fear my situation was deteriorating. This exacerbates my stress and pain and prevents me from progressing and healing.

An example of this is I keep imagining I have a swimming pool of CSF growing inside my head. I thought perhaps this was part of the reason I often wake up in the middle of the night with an intense pressure headache, fearing I'll need to make another trip to the emergency room.

I wanted the doctor to confirm I am slowly, perhaps painfully, getting better and the symptoms I am experiencing are "normal" for someone who has been through such an abnormal experience.

After hearing a few of the items on the list, my surgeon looked at me and stated quite bluntly, "You should have died from that tumor. You didn't. Everything that is still wrong is trivial compared to that. I'm sure if you start thinking that way, you will feel much better."

I guess this was his way of putting things into perspective for me. Immediately. And hopefully permanently.

2014

Speechless

January 14

I need to learn to coordinate my thought process with my speech. Sometimes, particularly if I'm upset or angry, my brain runs in super-fast mode and then I discover my mouth can't keep up with it. The words get stuck in my mouth, and the syllables jam up and collide. It's a terrible feeling when the words get lost or tangled up. My brain keeps running on overdrive, and my speech struggles to keep up. At times I am successful and other times, I am not. My thoughts get confused in the struggle, and my level of frustration mounts.

To become suddenly aware I can't communicate as successfully as I used to is weird and unsettling. When I spoke to a friend about this recent change, she said she thought for the first few months after surgery I was for the most part silent, so perhaps now that I am speaking much more, I'm noticing the difference.

I'm not sure, but either way, it will take some readjusting to accommodate this change. Getting a message from my brain in the middle of a conversation that says, "Hey, wait a minute, there's a traffic jam in your mouth, so you better stop talking until you make sense of things" is extremely difficult to process. Life can be very strange sometimes.

I can't help thinking about my autistic son, who for most of his life could not speak his thoughts. Even now, as a teen, I'm certain he can only express a very small percentage of what he is thinking. Whether it be due to a lack of understanding of language, a lack of motor organization, or both – the end result is difficult and I don't know how he manages to have as calm a personality as he does. Maybe he is unaware things should be different, as he has always lived in a somewhat uncooperative body and that is his reality.

All this makes me think about what I need to do to help

myself, and all those wonderful children on the spectrum or who are experiencing difficulties formulating speech to work through and around the traffic jams in our collective brains.

January 15

My speech messed up again this morning. I have this shocking feeling something is going wrong in my brain. I was certain I said something, a simple sentence referring to my sister, and then suddenly my children asked what it had to do with my daughter. I said I had said "my sister," and they said I had mentioned my daughter's name. "*Achoti*" ("my sister") and "Ravid" don't really sound alike. It was two against one, and I realized I must have confused the names, and thought one and said the other.

The kids saw I was stressed about the situation and tried to make light of it. They claimed everyone makes this type of mistake sometimes. And yes, I had been somewhat distracted, because my daughter had a swollen eye and needed to go to the emergency room. But I still felt this horrifying feeling creeping through my body that said, "Ha! I told you so! Your head and mouth and thoughts are all mixed up!"

I thank G-d I have an inkling when something goes wrong. I also imagine if I just slow down and focus when I'm stressed, my brain will behave itself. It's not that I'm completely distraught and lack hope or faith. I do hope and pray all this is a "normal" part of the healing process. A few months ago, the room was slanted sideways and the floor tilted up to meet me; now, my language center is playing tricks on me.

I remember reading accounts of people on the autistic spectrum describing how they would give their body a command to do one thing, but it would do something else. One man described how he would sometimes find himself "fusing with sounds," such as a dog howling. He would only become aware he was repeating the sounds when the people in his environment would point it out to him. There were times when these people were aware of what their bodies were doing, but it was as if they had no control over them because their bodies had minds of their own.

I find these situations very interesting. I try to place myself in the role of the objective observer of my own body. I attempt to figure out what's going on and how to fix it. I find myself asking my brain if I should just shut up for a few days and see what happens. Or if I should practice slowing down. I try to remember what my son does when his words get stuck. I thank G-d I can write down my thoughts so I am not entirely dependent on my brain and mouth to coordinate themselves when I am in need.

This is turning out to be a fascinating journey. And, despite the fact that the last nine months have been incredibly challenging, I believe I have gained a lot of amazing insights and perspectives on life. I hope I am making progress and I'm beginning to heal.

Finding the strength to carry on

February 10

This morning I took a few painkillers, put a skirt and jacket on over my pajamas, grabbed my cane, and walked my kids to school. Even though it was only a few blocks away, it took me about 20 minutes to walk the distance. By the time I arrived, I had tears in my eyes from the frustration and pain.

At the entrance, I ran into the father of a girl from my son's kindergarten. He is a kind man with three lovely girls. His wife passed away a few months before I got sick. Every time I see him, my heart sinks into my belly. I keep an eye on him, and he observes me. I notice he is beginning to straighten up his gait and to carry on with his life. His girls are slowly beginning to smile again. And, despite his difficulties, he is always grateful to G-d.

I realized he was also observing me, trying to size up if I am improving. He asked me if I'm feeling better, and I said yes, despite the pain, I am slowly getting stronger. He questioned how long I thought it would take for me to heal, and I answered that only HaShem knows – perhaps a year and a half or more, if the doctors are right. He then stated, "it's difficult for all of us, but we must carry on." I affirmed his words, and then we hugged our children and parted ways, each thinking of the other's pain.

Every time I see him, it reminds me I could so easily be under a gravestone, and despite all my difficulty and pain, I am incredibly thankful and lucky I can hug my children and husband and be there for them. G-d has given me many challenges, but I am here to do my very best to live up to them.

Calming the storm

October 29

I have a storm in my belly today. A lack of quiet. I keep searching for something to calm the turbulence. My brain is going full speed ahead, and my body is stuck in reverse. Or perhaps not reverse, but crawling very slowly forward. Either way, I don't feel I am getting anywhere. How much inner searching can I do to find my place? How can I shake off the chains that lock me into one spot? How can I prevent sadness from riveting me to the bed when my body hurts too much to move?

I have so much joy in life, my spirit thrives with the love of my husband and beautiful children, G-d, and all the amazing things around me. I have so many gifts – how can I get trapped for even a second in a downward spiral because of my deficient body?

I know I have tremendous resilience, and an intense desire to live and thrive. But then the carpenter ants start dancing around the campfire inside of my skull and my shoulder begins to scream at me for picking up my arm too many times in a row. Progress is unbearably slow because in the midst of doing what I want to do, my body suddenly says, "Sorry, Woman, I'm going on strike today. Go find someone else to party with."

It has been over a year and a half since surgery, and I can't get used to living inside of this alien body that never ceases to surprise me. There is such an incredible difference between "me" and "my body." Two ends of the spectrum have been forced into one small, somewhat dysfunctional package. It will be amazing if I somehow manage to find the balance between the opposing poles, a middle ground where I can be at peace and somehow accomplish the things I strive to do.

2015

The altar

March 16

During my last MRI, it became apparent that the part of the tumor left in my brain had started to grow again. Perhaps this is part of the reason I have been feeling so down and out. The surgeon determined the only way to treat it was for me to undergo radiosurgery (radiation). This is a process of bombarding a tumor with radio waves in the hopes it will cause it to somehow implode and die. The major benefit of radiosurgery is they don't have to cut open your skull and tinker around in there. It's supposed to be extremely precise and therefore shouldn't kill too many surrounding cells or the nerve that enables me to swallow and just happens to run right down the middle of the tumor. After a single zapping session (namely, five separate zaps over a short period of time, each zap hitting the tumor from a different angle), the process begins to work, and only after a year or more will it be apparent if the treatment has been effective.

It was clear the procedure was not going to be any picnic. However, it was certainly better than letting the tumor continue to grow and risking death.

So, once again, I knew I had to buckle down and go through another surgery, but thankfully one that was going to be less invasive and with fewer side effects. I simply had no other option.

A month has passed since I underwent the radiosurgery procedure, and I still have a really hard time trying to digest what the experience was like. The protective device in my soul just wants me to bury it somewhere in the "too painful to deal with" file. However, the rest of me keeps trying to somehow relive it, to try to learn something from it, if possible.

As I sat on the hospital bed, the surgeon explained to us they would be screwing an external frame onto my head and it would be there all day. He detailed the plan, testing, and procedure I was about to undergo. He then quite casually mentioned that in another month, they would be using another frame that doesn't need to actually be screwed onto the skull.

As he was about to inject the local anesthetic into my scalp, I gently asked, "Umm, Doctor...? Perhaps it would be better to wait another month?" Somehow the thought of screws in my skull didn't appeal to me. But he just smiled and looked at me with his kind eyes and said, "Sorry, it's not suitable for you...this procedure is more precise, and with your nerve in the center of the tumor, this is the only way to go." In short, I interpreted his words as, "Too bad, you're screwed. Sit back and enjoy the ride."

I won't describe in detail what he did, but let's just say within a short period of time my skull became unified with a tightly fitted external frame for the rest of the day. The frame was kept stable by two screws in my forehead and two in the back of my skull. I was pleased someone had invented the straw so I could drink without wetting my shirt. It was quite a strange experience to feel my forehead slowly puffing up around the screws. My husband and I joked around a lot about me looking like the Bride of Frankenstein that day.

The pain was, let's say, significant and progressive. The climax of it was, of course, to be at the end of the day, because I would need to lie flat on my back in order to undergo the treatment. Since the surgery to remove my tumor, I had been unable to lie flat on my back because it caused me to experience tremendous pressure in my head. I have taken to sleeping like a character from a fairy tale, propped up on lots of pillows.

Throughout the day, I kept trying to convince myself I would somehow manage to get through it. The doctors reassured me there was no reason for me to panic because the procedure only took about half an hour.

When evening approached, I was finally summoned to the treatment room. As I walked down the long hall and entered the darkened room, the only thing I could do was begin to pray. The team of doctors and technicians was wonderful and gentle. They supported my hands and head in order to place me on the table. The frame was too heavy for me to mobilize alone.

Once they settled me down, they started to lower the top end of the table. I realized I was not going to be lying flat on my back...my head was going to be tilted backward for the entire procedure. The pressure started immediately building up in my brain, causing me intense pain. In the midst of this, I heard them screwing the frame onto the table. Images of the altar from *Akeidat Yitzchak* (the sacrifice of Isaac) in the Bible suddenly popped into my head. Only this time, it felt as if I was the one who was about to be sacrificed...

There is a point where there is nothing left to do but surrender. This was the second time I have had to do it, but this time they didn't put a mask over my face and send me off to sleep. The only thing I could do was to try to separate my soul from my body and try to get through the treatment somehow.

I started to pray *Shema Israel*. Blank pictures mingled with the sounds of the doctors placing a hood over my head, laser beams flashing. They checked the coordinates and removed the hood. And then suddenly there was silence. Everyone left the room and I was alone with G-d and the machine doing its job.

I kept asking Him to send me some light to penetrate the black pain that was exploding in my head. I begged Rabbi Mordechai Eliyahu to visit me as he had in my dream a few years ago. I once again remembered his words, "It's not what it looks like, it will be okay." I looked for his face through the blackness, or for some light, somewhere. I could feel the pressure building in my head, and the doctor's steady touch on my arm. I heard his voice gently saying, "Only three more to go, we're almost finished..."

When it was all over, they sat me up, rolled me to the treatment room, and started removing the screws. When they put them in, they used a local anesthetic. When they removed them, they didn't. As the pressure from the frame was released and I was permitted to sit up again, alleviating the pressure in my brain, I started to feel so strange I was certain I was going to faint. The nurse tended to my wounds and gave me a cup of tea, and I tried to regain my bearings. I realized that although my senses were okay, my body was definitely in shock. I tried to reason with it somehow, but it wasn't listening.

That shock lasted for a number of days. The swelling in my forehead gradually spread down my face, and I looked like a Neanderthal who had undergone Botox treatment. At least all my wrinkles had disappeared again!

I've discovered there is something very interesting about reaching the point of complete surrender. I think for the most part, people feel they are somewhat in control of their lives. I have realized we are not. We are in control of what we do, the choices we make, for sure, but we never know what's in store for us.

For me, it's a constant reminder of what I believe is our task in life: to try to live by G-d's will and to try to better the world around us. Perhaps I will not have the strength to change the world, but I can certainly begin with the people who are dear to me. I hope to infect those around me with the desire to do good. I can only pray I succeed in doing mitzvot and spreading as much love, assistance, positive energy, and hope as possible to those around me, for as long as I am around. And, G-d willing, it will be for a long time, and may I be able to make a significant impact.

Mortality

June 16

The passing of a number of people in the last few weeks has, once again, made me think about life and death, and what we are meant to do with the time we have been given on this earth. It's a topic that seems to be all too familiar lately.

I am torn by the burning desire to accomplish things before my time runs out and the limitations I am forced to live with because of my somewhat dysfunctional body. I'm constantly battling to find this balance without letting life slip by. There is so much I want to do, yet I can't commit to anything. I always try to reserve my energy for the children, for they are far more important than anything else.

Life's challenges can be so difficult. When I look at those around me, many seem to be close to their wits' end because they can't cope with the difficulties they are faced with. My heart breaks from the stories I hear around me. I can only try to be supportive and to provide them with as much guidance or consolation as I have, to the best of my abilities. Of which I wish I had a lot more.

Understanding neurology and sensory overload

July 11

Last night I had a very interesting (although not particularly fun) experience that I think might help others gain some insight into how it feels to deal with sensory overload and strange neurological processing.

I am now about three-and-a-half years past neurosurgery, and several months past radiosurgery to zap the remaining tumor on my brainstem. I have achieved a somewhat reasonable level of day-to-day functioning (although everything is relative, and I only mean "reasonable" in comparison to the state I was in the first few years after surgery). However, I am still pretty much incapable of going to any place that has a combination of different types of lighting, or noise, or multiple types of sensory input. Hence, I don't go to any weddings, performances, crowded events, shopping malls, etc. Most of the time, this is a somewhat manageable inconvenience.

Last night, however, my son had a very special event at school. It was the second grade *chumash*˙ ceremony, and they

˙ Hebrew for the printed form of the five books of Moses, also known as the Pentateuch. A typical *chumash* comprises the five books of Moses (Genesis, Exodus, Leviticus, Numbers, and Deuteronomy) in Hebrew with vowels and cantillation marks, divided into the

were putting on a performance that ended with a communal prayer ceremony. It was one of those times, as a parent, I felt I had to be there for him. I believed that I would somehow manage to get through the evening.

Unfortunately, I once again found myself in a situation where there was a huge abyss between what I desired to do, what I thought I could do, and what I was actually capable of doing.

My level of sensory overload started out at a somewhat tolerable level as we paraded down the road after the van that was blaring music for all the neighborhood to hear. The procession was crowded, led by drummers who were periodically blowing shofars, and flashing lights. I tried to keep myself at a reasonable distance from the tumult, and I also put in earplugs, so I was able to manage.

I then decided it would be okay for me to sit in the amphitheater. It was a difficult climb to the top, but I figured I would be best off there because it was far from the speakers. I was quite pleased with myself that I was able to wade through the crowd and climb the stairs, aided only by my cane.

I positioned myself in the middle of the top row, near good friends, and waited for the performance to begin. That's when the action started...

For some reason, in almost every setting in Israel, the people who control the soundboard feel the performance will

---

weekly Torah portions.

only be effective if they turn up the volume to an extremely high level. Many people dislike this tendency, and at many weddings, people leave the hall to converse and socialize. The same thing happens at performances, and even more so if they are outdoors. It doesn't seem to bother them if the sound quality is poor, it simply needs to be really loud. So, they turned up the volume, and no ear plugs could stop the intense pounding of the music.

To make things worse, there were flashing white and colored lights throughout the performance, plus laser beams that periodically flashed through the audience. There were moving white "stars" projected over the kids and the floor as they were singing. Everything was moving, flashing, and colorful. I covered my eyes, but I could still see and feel the lights and music penetrating my senses. After about five minutes, I knew I had to make an immediate escape.

I then realized that the steps were full of people, lights were flashing all over the audience, and my legs had turned to jelly. There was no way I was going to be able to remove myself from the situation, even if I was assisted by someone. I was going to have to stick it out.

For the next hour (yes, hour!) I sat with my eyes covered, ears plugged, and tried to somehow tune out the environment. Every time I peeked through my fingers, all I saw was an ocean of moving colors and flashing lights. Straight lines became waves, everything was moving in all directions, and I had no idea where I was in space.

When the performance finally ended and the

amphitheater emptied out, I slowly got up. I positioned myself facing the wall, and, leaning sideways, began progressing down the stairs while holding on to the railing. There was no way I could have gone down the stairs looking forward, even though people were holding out their hands and offering me assistance.

I made my way into the hall, and then continued to stagger out toward the night air like a drunk. I couldn't feel my feet, I simply dragged them out in front of me. Once I finally made it outside, I found a quiet place next to a fence I could lean on. I had to remain there for about twenty minutes until the world stopped moving around me.

I then realized I should attempt to get home, which was all of three blocks away. I wanted to go, but my body had shut down. My legs were like lead, completely uncooperative.

I stumbled forward, leaning heavily on my cane. All this time, my husband had been waiting patiently for me outside the school building. We hadn't found seating next to each other throughout the performance and he knew I might need assistance on the way home. I decided to send him to the car and suggest he just drive it home without me. I preferred trying to walk, figuring a few blocks in the chilly night air might help clear out my brain. I knew riding in a car would be far worse than walking. I also doubted I would have been able to climb into the car, even with assistance.

I started heading home. My left side had gone on strike. I took one step forward with my right leg, and then leaned on my cane and dragged my left leg forward. My knee bounced twice. I then repeated the process again. Progress was slow. After half a block, my right leg decided it would be going on strike as well. I realized I was stuck and the only thing I could do was to find the humor in the situation. I began to laugh out loud. And to sing.

I must have looked like a madwoman. I was staggering down the road, leaning on my cane, and stopping every few steps while laughing and singing. My young son had walked about a block ahead of me and was sitting on a wall, waiting for me to arrive. Who knows what he must have been thinking. I explained to him my body was "stuck," and there was no reason to worry. I guess because I was laughing and singing, he felt it was okay to make fun of me and wasn't nervous or frightened. I'm sure he thought I had gone a bit nuts.

I suddenly became aware a young child was walking down the block behind me. I could sense he was afraid to pass me on the sidewalk. I turned to him and explained I was having a problem with my leg and all was okay, that he didn't need to be afraid. He muttered "be healthy" under his breath and scooted past me.

It took me well over half an hour to walk those three blocks home. All I wanted to do was sit on the couch and drink a cup of hot, sweet tea. My adrenaline levels slowly decreased, and after about 30 minutes I was able to shuffle around the living room. I started to stutter and got a terrible headache. It took about another full hour and some painkillers before I was able to fall asleep. Thank G-d, when I woke up in the morning, my system had more or less recovered.

I certainly don't recommend this type of nightly entertainment to anyone. However, I must say, it was quite amazing and interesting to see how the brain goes into crisis mode and shuts off areas of the body. Throughout the entire experience, my cognition had remained completely intact. In addition to undergoing the physical experience, I felt as if I had become a silent observer of myself. I was fascinated by how my mind would attempt to give my body an order to propel itself forward, and it would flat-out refuse.

I have read many accounts of people on the spectrum describing similar things. I now completely understand them. It is quite weird to have your mind think one thing and your body do another. I had to rock, bounce, and sing in order to get my body to move forward. My left leg would get stuck after every step if I didn't bounce it up and down twice. I also had to employ singing and laughing at myself to release my physical and emotional stress. I also found them to be far more useful and entertaining than the alternative, crying.

I'm very lucky in that I don't give a hoot what people think of me. If I had been concerned about how I appeared to others, I would have really been up a creek, with no paddle to get me home. And considering the situation I was in, I really needed to get home...

2016

The little things

February 10

It's in the little things a person feels the loss of independence the most. And sometimes it can be extremely painful.

Before my surgery, I never really thought twice about doing what I want to do, or about my ability to accomplish anything. However, since my surgery, this reality completely changed. Not only have I lost a significant amount of mobility, I've also lost a lot of my independence. There are many things I need assistance to do, including tending to the house or mobilizing from place to place. My energy conks out in the middle of things, or my senses get overloaded and I need to find a quiet place to rest. This can be extremely frustrating and restricting.

At times, this reality is hard to live with. I miss out on things that are important to me or to others. There are instances where I'm unable to be there for the ones I love. This can be extremely frustrating. And even though I'm eternally grateful for every moment I am alive, I sometimes have difficulty accepting the situation as it is.

One thing I find to be extremely irritating is when people decide I will be unable to attend an event without asking me what I feel I am capable of doing or would like to do. I don't blame anyone for preferring I avoid a situation they think will be difficult for me; that makes sense. The difficulty I have is when people make the choice *for* me. Perhaps it's just my pride. I'm not sure. But it's important for me to take part in the decision-making process. I want to judge for myself whether a situation is suitable for me. Most people are free to do as they choose – I wish that for myself, as well.

So much has been taken away from me. I try to accept this with as much grace as I am capable of. Thank G-d, my mind and cognitive facilities have not been impaired. So, I want to be the one to make the call regarding my abilities and preferences. People can rest assured I won't hold them responsible for me in any given situation. I don't want to be a burden on anyone. It's not beneficial for either party.

If my wings have been clipped, that doesn't mean I don't want others to fly. The opposite is true. I want them to soar higher than ever before, and to send me a breath of fresh air from above.

2017

Discoveries about my vision

January 11

It's close to four years after my initial surgery, and I'm finally able to decide to try to rehabilitate my vision. Since my surgery, I've seen everything in soft focus, and often experience double or warped vision. I decided to get regular prescription lenses because I need to see in focus to get tested for Irlen syndrome.

A few days ago, I received my new glasses and put them on, and although I had sensed that something was really wrong beforehand, I was quite surprised at how badly my visual perception had become impaired. Since the surgery, every time I wore my old glasses I felt disoriented and confused. I found it was easier to manage blurry vision than irregular vision in clear focus.

When I put on my new glasses, I discovered something very interesting. The world was in perfect focus, which was a beautiful thing. But at the same time, everything looked flat, as if it were a 3-D drawing on a 2-D surface (like a cube sketched on a piece of paper) instead of a real 3-D world. I had lost my sense of depth perception.

This completely disoriented me. I was afraid to move because I was unable to accurately judge how far away things were from me. I sat at the table and looked at the kitchen, and although the walls and sink looked farther away than the refrigerator, I couldn't actually assess how far either of these objects was from me or from each other.

I began to feel very strange and lost my bearings. I tried to walk around the living room but got dizzy. After about ten minutes, I felt completely exhausted and needed to remove the glasses.

Colored Irlen lenses might help me with my irregular visual perception.* I believe there's a fairly good chance I have

---

* Once I was assessed and diagnosed with Irlen syndrome, I began wearing custom-colored spectral filters and my sense of visual clarity was restored. The lenses don't cure the problem, but when I wear them, they

it. I definitely feel annoyed by light, and my kids just got tested and diagnosed with it, and they are absolutely certain I need tinted lenses as well. Brains can be really strange at times!

Compatible with life

March 2

About a month ago, thank G-d, the doctor informed me that the MRI showed the remaining tumor in my brain has shrunk about a millimeter in depth. This was a great sign, and I hope on our upcoming yearly visit, we will learn that things continued to follow this direction.

We had a very short discussion, during which I questioned him about the remaining side effects of the treatment: the problems with my vision, the cerebrospinal fluid leaking out of my brain into my neck, sensory overload, vestibular issues, and slight facial paralysis.

He looked at me kindly and suggested I attempt to see things as he does. My pre-surgery brain scans indicated a situation that was incompatible with life. When he analyzes my current ones and looks at me, he sees some side effects of the process, but it's a far cry from being a situation that is incompatible with life. And that is something to be very pleased about. As for the leftovers, I need to learn to live with them, but I should try to focus on the fact I am *able* to live with them...

---

regulate the symptoms. See " Visual Perception and Processing" in Part II.

His abrupt statement knocked me a bit off guard. But once I managed to organize my thoughts, I realized he was right. I must never forget that, despite my disabilities, I am eternally grateful to be alive and to share my life with the people I love.

Part V:

Navigating New Pathways

Observations About
Brain-Body Connections

Conducting Traffic in My Brain

In the last few years, my body underwent a couple of experiences that proved extremely challenging to adjust to. The first was the surgery to remove the tumor from my brainstem and its aftermath. The second was a serious bout of viral-induced vertigo in 2019 that required hospitalization, after which it took months of recovery for my vestibular system to even begin to stabilize.

As I've recounted, living with a somewhat dysfunctional or distorted sensory system is a complex and interesting experience. It can be uncomfortable and frightening. There are many instances when I receive unstable or inaccurate sensory input from my environment, which can lead to confusion or lack of control over my body.

Inaccurate depth perception can cause me to trip or become dizzy when I look at a flight of stairs. Vertigo can make me lose my balance or my dinner. Distorted visual perception can make a person suddenly look like a monster or a kaleidoscope in the middle of a conversation. All these things combined can make it virtually impossible to concentrate or function.

In order to compensate for some of these inadequacies, my brain seems to have created new pathways that bypass the dysfunctional areas. They enable me to regulate some of my sensory input and automate my motor functioning. I believe they were developed during the rehabilitation process.

There are times when I'm able to order my brain to disregard irregular sensory input and to use cognition to gain control of my actions. It's almost as if I can press the "ignore sensory input" button and then tell one of my limbs to perform a specific operation – at which point I can almost feel how a different area of my brain starts taking over in order to bypass the inefficient pathways.

As I was recovering from my bout with vertigo, I began to retrain my vestibular system by attempting to ignore the distorted sensory input and employing muscle memory to teach myself to regain more natural body movements. I began to "talk to my limbs" and to tell them to move fluidly, even though it felt weird and unsafe. By forcing myself to move naturally, my muscle memory helped me to reacquire my natural gait. It took me months to get back on track, and even now I occasionally experience recurring instances of vertigo.

One of the things that helped me overcome these dysregulations was that I had previously experienced typical sensory processing. This enabled me to recognize what I was experiencing then was irregular, and I would attempt to stabilize myself.

I imagine if had I been a child, and unfamiliar with regulated sensory processing, it would have been practically impossible for me to develop methods to balance my sensory systems on my own without the recollection of muscle memory that had helped me so much.

It's therefore not surprising that it takes a tremendous amount of time and effort to teach children who have these types of issues how to self-regulate. It can present an enormous challenge to break through the walls of sensory distortion and to overcome the types of impairments they might be living with.

Writing and Brain-Body Pathways

I believe I have finally found a way to compensate for the difficulties I experience while writing. They stem from the damage to my accessory nerve,* and affect the functioning of my left shoulder and arm. My shoulder is permanently slouched forward and has limited mobility. I can't stretch my arm out in front of me to type on the computer as I sit at the table for more than a few minutes.

While searching for a solution, I decided to try a speech-to-text program. It seemed like a logical solution until I actually tried it. I was surprised to discover I was completely

---

* The (spinal) accessory nerve provides movement to two muscles essential to movement in the neck and shoulders, larynx (voice box) and other structures in the throat.

unable to write in this manner.

It did prove to be a worthy experiment, however, because it helped me to gain some insights into how my brain is wired and what pathways it employs while composing text.

As a rule, I think very quickly. I can't speak or write at even close to the speed that I think. However, until my surgery, I had always pretty much been able to keep up with my thoughts when I type. When typing, it feels as if my thoughts travel directly from the speech center in my brain to my fingertips.

I don't think about this in real time as it happens. It's completely automatic. I can also actually feel the front portion of my brain heat up as I work. It sends messages to my hands, which move accordingly.

My oral speech and hearing centers are not involved in this process. It might sound strange, but when I write, I feel as if I am having a conversation both inside of and with my brain. It's a very quick and efficient system that requires minimal effort on my part.

In contrast to this, when I attempted to dictate my ideas, I discovered I was unable to focus my thoughts or to express myself. It felt as if oral communication involved a completely different area of my brain.

Initially, I would attempt to write something, and then my thoughts would become jumbled and the words would get stuck. It was as if I were experiencing a traffic jam somewhere between my brain and my mouth. In addition, when I would hear myself speaking, I would get distracted and lose my train of thought.

It appears to me that somehow the brain-hand connection that bypasses my oral speech center frees up my cognitive and organizational resources, enabling me to compose efficiently. It's amazing how much impact this bypass has on the quality, clarity, and speed of my writing.

I have also noticed that when I type, my writing becomes more accurate, and I have access to a significantly larger, subconscious vocabulary.

I gave up trying to use the speech-to-text method after a few attempts and resorted to typing while sitting in bed with my laptop resting on my legs. This enables me to compensate for the lack of ability to raise my arms to type. It's difficult to sit in this position for long, but it's far better than having a pain-induced ten-minute time limit at a desk.

As with everything else, I've had to search for a non-traditional solution to compensate for my disabilities. I think this has been an important part of my healing process.

I'm certain if I had simply given up and accepted my limitations, I would have begun to feel quite frustrated and miserable. I've discovered that if I am persistent enough, I can usually come up with a creative solution that enables me to live a more satisfying life.

Whenever I get really discouraged, I try to remember the mantra my son's incredible teacher drilled into his head:

"Never, ever give up!" (Even when the going gets tough!)"

Thoughts About Pain and Recovery

Aside from the sensory and neurological issues I have described, one of the biggest challenges is figuring out how to balance my daily activities in a manner that enables me to experience the least amount of pain and fatigue as possible. At times, this has been – and still is – extremely challenging.

I've experienced many different types of pain over the years. For the most part, I'm able to keep it under control and function at a reasonable level. However, there are days where I'm completely unsuccessful and I must simply give my body a rest. Fortunately, the frequency and the intensity of these incidents have decreased significantly over the last few years.

I've also come to understand that my attitude, along with my general state of mind, affect the intensity and types of pain I am faced with, as well as my overall quality of life.

Figuring Out Back Pain

My first major bout of chronic pain occurred about 15 years ago, in the midst of an extraordinarily stressful period of my life. I had been driving several hours a day to take my son for therapies, working in the evenings, taking care of the house and kids, and trying to make ends meet. I was a stressed-out mess, doing my best to get through each day. My life was in chronic overdrive.

One day, I suddenly found myself with a terrible backache. I was virtually unable to move. The pain got worse day by day, and it became incredibly difficult to function. After a few months, I was told I was suffering from a slipped disc in my lower back.

I think I reached my lowest point one morning when, after struggling for 45 minutes to find a way to get out of bed, I managed to throw on some clothes to walk my son to the bus stop. It was only a few blocks away, but it took a while due to the severe pain and pins and needles in my leg. These symptoms were supposedly caused by the disc that was putting pressure on my sciatic nerve.

At the time, I was also suffering from a miserable cough, which exacerbated the situation. On the way back home, I leaned into a hibiscus bush during a coughing fit. As I continued to progress slowly along my way, I noticed all the cars passing by me slowed down a bit and the drivers peered at me. I knew I was limping and dressed sloppily, but I couldn't figure out why this was so interesting to passers-by.

It wasn't until I arrived back home that I understood what people had been looking at. When I had leaned into the hedge, a huge flower had gotten stuck to my hair at the top of my head. I had been so occupied with the pain I didn't even feel it. I looked like a disheveled mess decorated with a dangling flower crown. People must have thought I was nuts. I remember standing in front of the mirror, laughing and crying. I couldn't believe how pathetic I looked and felt.

Throughout that entire period, I had been desperately looking for some relief from the pain. I tried massage, acupuncture, chiropractic treatments, physical therapy, and traditional medical doctors – but nothing helped.

At some point, the professor who was treating my son told me about the work of Dr. John Sarno. Even though I didn't identify with everything he said, it did make sense to me that stress (which he claims stems mostly from repressed anger – the part I had difficulty relating to) causes the brain to release chemicals that lead to mild oxygen deprivation in our muscles. This, in turn, causes extreme cramping and intense pain. He suggested that things like slipped discs don't necessarily need to be painful, rather it was the oxygen deprivation that was the culprit.

His cure was to understand this concept, stop fearing the pain, and begin to move and act regularly without seeking additional medical treatments. (He did stress that it was critical to confirm that there were no underlying or dangerous medical issues causing the pain.)

Much to my surprise, by the time I finished the book, most of the pain had disappeared, and so had the sciatica and nerve-related symptoms. And, in general, I haven't had any re-occurrences of my "disc pain."

Coping with Post-Surgery Pain

My second bout of chronic pain began after the operation. On top of the sensory issues, my days were filled with intense, unremitting pain. I would take a dose of paracetamol (acetaminophen) every three to four hours – day and night – to stop the twisting of the knives in my head, neck, and shoulder. Even though it wasn't enough to dramatically reduce my pain, I refused to take any other types of painkillers. I figured I had enough problems to deal with and wasn't willing to risk additional side effects or possible addiction from the narcotics almost every doctor I visited offered me.

I began to believe I would never again experience a normal, pain-free moment. It was very frustrating and at times, depressing. There were days when it was hard for me to muster the strength to continue to struggle and to function.

Fooled Again!

One morning, a few years after the surgery, a lightbulb went off in my head. I realized that since the surgery, most of my days had been filled with fear and thoughts about pain, stress, and worries about my body. I had a flashback that reminded me I had been in this state of mind when I had my "slipped disc" years before. It suddenly dawned on me my brain had likely been playing tricks on me and I had once again fallen into the cycle of chronic pain. I was really annoyed at myself and couldn't believe I had been "fooled" once again.

From that moment on, my life began to improve tremendously. I began to understand what was going on with me. I concluded I suffer from two types of pain: legitimate pain, and stress- or thought-induced pain.

My legitimate pain stems from the fact that a piece of my skull base on the left side is missing. This makes that part of my head and neck extremely sensitive to cold and movement. I also have a cerebrospinal fluid leak into that soft, empty space, creating a lump on the back of my head. The size and shape of the lump vary throughout the day, depending on my activities.

Pressure from fluid buildup in that area can cause pain in my skull base and neck. In addition, my left shoulder is somewhat out of place and atrophied due to nerve damage. If I try to use my arm too much, it pulls down even more and adds to the strain and pressure on my neck and skull base.

This type of pain can be managed for the most part if I keep my head and neck warm, reduce the number of times I try to raise my left arm to the side, and avoid bending down or lying on my left side. All in all, if I "behave myself," then I will have minimal or no pain. However, if I don't listen to my body or work too hard, I pay the price.

The other type of pain I experience appears to be rooted in stress or thinking too much about my body and life. I would find myself in a loop of worrying about all my problems and physical symptoms and then trying to figure out what to do about them. I noticed when I was preoccupied with this type of thinking or focused on the goings-on in my body, my legitimate pain would intensify and reach severe levels. This would happen even if I hadn't done anything that would normally trigger the pressure in my head and neck to develop.

Due neurological irregularities resulting from the surgery, I can also experience some very strange or even frightening symptoms. I have discovered that bodies can do some very weird things. This is particularly true for me if I am stressed, in sensory overload, or have a mild virus or fever.

When the types of things I just mentioned occur, I try to slow down and relax as much as possible. I then try to assess whether I need medical intervention. I check my vital signs and temperature, rest a bit, drink water. If my vitals appear to be normal, and things calm down a bit when I begin to relax, I assume nothing dangerous is going on.

At this point, I usually just try to take it easy and disregard the weird symptoms or pain. I noticed if I do this, in most cases, the symptoms fade quite quickly. However, if I focus on them or stress out about them, they tend to get worse.

Once I realized this was going on, it broke the cycle of intense chronic pain and worry. I learned I shouldn't take my pain, moods, or thoughts too seriously. I realized if I didn't dwell on them, and if I simply recognized their existence and then left them alone and got on with things, they usually improved.

I came to understand that if it wasn't necessary for me to take action in order to change my situation, then I was best off changing my pattern of thought and concentrating on things that were truly productive or interesting. This decreased my pain level by about 80 percent. At present, I only need to take painkillers if I ignore the signals my body gives me when I work too hard or bend down too many times. This has made an incredible difference in my quality of life and has enabled me to free up my body and mind from the miserable circle of ongoing pain and the search for unsuccessful treatments.

We Are Not Our Pain

Another factor that I think has helped me to move beyond my disabilities and chronic pain is that I don't feel they define me. They are not a part of my identity. They are something I have had to become accustomed to dragging around with me, but they aren't me. Sometimes I feel as if I am comprised of "me" (which includes my mind and soul) and "my body." They are two separate entities and are not always in sync. There are occasions when I feel trapped within a body that doesn't reflect my mindset or desire to do specific things at all (such as to dance or go hiking in the woods and climb a tree).

I believe the way people define themselves also has a direct influence on their overall state of mind and their ability to heal – or at least to move forward. It seems that a person coping with a chronic illness or disability who allows it to become an integral part of their identity will find it much harder to begin to move past it and to start healing.

For example, since my surgery, I have been forced to make some accommodations to compensate for my disabilities (such as using Irlen spectral filters, a cane, earplugs in noisy places, etc.). I also have to limit the number of things I attempt to do on any given day. In addition, I undergo periodic medical testing to confirm that the remaining tumor in my brain is still dormant. These things require some attention, but I just do what needs to be done and then turn my attention to the things I want to concentrate on.

I've come to terms with the fact I must live with my disabilities and deal with them, but they haven't become a part of my identity. They simply exist. Whenever possible, I ignore them. I definitely avoid focusing on them. I know that if I pay attention to them, I will feel them more intensively or I'll wind up being in a foul mood.

Over the last few years, I have run into many people who relate to these types of challenges differently. They have an illness or disability, and it takes over their entire life. They surround themselves with people who also have the same types of problems and they spend their days discussing their ailments. Over time, their ailments become an integral part of their identity.

I am in no way passing judgment on people who focus on their issues. Every person is an individual and must find the most comfortable way for them to cope with their challenges. I'm also not suggesting people should avoid seeking ways to find support or a group of people who have experienced similar challenges to gain knowledge and understanding about their situation. I have simply noticed, in many instances, if a person continually focuses on their ailments, problems, or disabilities, it can become more difficult for them to live contentedly.

In addition, I have encountered people whose problem ceased to exist and they suddenly felt empty inside. I think this might stem from the fact that sometimes even the loss of something painful or difficult can cause confusion or the feeling of losing purpose or identity. When this happens, it can become challenging to move beyond the problems and start healing.

One other thing I have observed is that people who are more focused on being productive and involved with things outside of themselves and their bodies appear to be happier and enjoy a better quality of life than those who are more inward-focused. It seems as if the more people concentrate on doing good or spending time with people they love, the less they focus on their internal goings-on. This can help them to free themselves from a lot of worries, pain, and sadness. Their identity is formed through their actions as opposed to their internal struggles.

In light of these understandings, I have attempted to adopt this type of mindset. There are times when this has proven to be difficult, but overall, it has helped me to see the positive side of life. It has freed up my mind to concentrate on the useful things I can do rather than focus on the frustrating or painful challenges of daily life.

A Message for Caregivers and Friends

I have experienced many situations in which kind, caring people unintentionally make it difficult for a person with an illness to shift their focus to more positive agendas. For example, I have always felt uncomfortable when people feel the need to ask me a million questions about how I am feeling and functioning. I know they do this out of true concern and wish to help me to feel better. However, these types of questions tend to put the focus on what is wrong with me, as opposed to inquiring about what my mindset is or simply engaging in everyday topics of conversation.

Perhaps this occurs because people might feel my physical challenges have become the most important thing on my mind or in my identity. They might not understand that for me, they are something I am forced to deal with, on as minimal a level as possible, and I prefer to ignore them whenever I can.

I think for me, and perhaps for other people in similar situations, it might be more helpful or empowering if caring people were to gently and non-invasively inquire about our physical issues and offer assistance if necessary, and then to move on to discuss other topics that are of mutual interest. This enables the friendship to continue as it was, as opposed to becoming a friendship that is focused on illnesses and challenges.

Thoughts About Professionals

I would like to raise a somewhat sensitive issue regarding medical professionals. There are many instances where they, I imagine unwittingly, encourage patients with complex illnesses or disabilities to believe they have no choice but to accept the fact their situation is permanent and unchangeable. To prevent people from developing false hopes about their prognoses, they lead people to believe whatever they have will remain with them for the rest of their lives, and they will have to accept this as part of their reality.

I believe this type of attitude propagates a mentality of illness, which, in turn, prevents healing. It takes away the patient's hope that their situation can improve over time. If a medical professional tells a patient they are suffering from a chronic illness or a type of chronic pain that is not likely to improve (in the best of cases), then they often will have no faith that they can or will find a solution for it. They might not even begin to seek one out. There are times when a person might fall into extreme depression or hopelessness in reaction to such a prognosis.

I implore medical professionals to take extreme care in defining illnesses in this manner or making such negative prognoses. I believe one of the most dangerous things that a professional can do is to take away hope from a patient, or from a parent of a child with a disability. No one has the ability to accurately predict what the future will bring, and there are times when statistics can do more harm than good. Technology and medicine are changing at lightning speed, and things that once seemed impossible are now commonplace. There is always a chance something will be discovered that will completely change a negative prognosis overnight.

I firmly believe hope and faith are two driving forces that can help to empower people to overcome great challenges. Professionals have been granted the opportunity and ability to help their patients to develop them both. They can encourage their patients to believe that, in many cases, with hard work and optimism things can improve over time. If professionals take the time to do so, they will greatly help their patients along their road to recovery.

Afterward:

Reflections on the Pandemic

It is the end of 2020, which has proven to be a highly tumultuous year for all. In the face of the worldwide pandemic and political and financial instability, I imagine many people have started to ask themselves questions about the meaning of life. They have begun to think about the changes they need to make in their lives and what needs to be done to improve society.

Many folks have been forced far out of their comfort zones. Individuals, families, and societies have been given no other option but to begin rebuilding their lives. There have been global shifts in power, and there will likely be more to come.

The world needs to begin to heal and to move forward. People are seeking ways to enable this to happen.

By the time you have reached this point in this book, it will have become clear to you I have been grappling with these types of questions for many years. They became even more relevant for me the moment I opened my eyes in the ICU and realized I was still present in this world.

In light of this, I would like to offer a few words of optimism for the future. Sometimes when we are forced to restart everything, it's an opportunity to reconsider our place in the world and a call to take action in face of significant challenges.

I have seen so many people struggling with the lockdowns and the restrictions on their personal freedom. Political and financial insecurity have made things even worse. They no longer have trust in their governments, and they do not believe the authorities and companies responsible for taking care of the public will actually do so. It appears many of these leaders espouse the values that personal gain, money, pride, and power are far more important to them than keeping the interests of the public in mind.

A lot of people have lost faith that things will improve. This can be a dangerous line of thinking.

I believe the remedy to this situation lies within each one of us. We can all start thinking about what we can do to improve things. Every individual has the power to make a difference.

There is no end to the good we can do. Even if we begin by taking the tiniest steps, we can have a positive influence on those around us. We can start anytime, and from anywhere, as technology enables us to reach each other in seconds, even from within the confines of our own homes.

Things will only get better if we begin to take things into our own hands and start changing the world by ourselves. No politicians or big business leaders will do this for us. It needs to come from within every one of us. We are all capable of contributing something, no matter how big or small.

I believe every person was born into this world with a mission at hand. If people take it upon themselves to discover what their unique calling is, and then see how they can use it to contribute to society, things will begin to improve.

If every individual would simply take a look around them, and then reach out to someone and to make their day just a little bit brighter, we will help each other build a better, healthier world. One step forward can set the ball in motion. And when a ball starts rolling, it can go quite a distance. It's well known that good deeds lead to other good deeds, and mitzvot lead to other mitzvot.

There is a statement in Judaism that says a tiny bit of light dispels a great amount of darkness. I imagine most people have seen how one small candle disperses light throughout an entire room.

In the face of these incredibly challenging times, I would like to propose that every one of us try to empower ourselves to become one of the candles that lights up the world.

It is said the darkest part of the night appears just before dawn. We might just be at the darkest part of the night. And, G-d willing, if we all make an effort, we can all help to bring about the dawn of a new era. Together, we can work toward the common good to build a better, more caring, and prosperous world.

Postscript:

Not Finished Yet

This is a prayer to you, my Creator.

A simple prayer, or maybe not.

You see, I believe I'm not finished yet.

I want more time. Lots more time.

There is so much more I want to do.

I am not yet ready to stop loving those around me.

I want to be accessible to them, for some of them will be
   unable to find me if they can't hear my voice or feel my
   arms around them.

If I am somewhere under the ground and my soul is floating
   beside You in the Heavens,
      those whom I love might feel only sorrow –
      and I might not be able to reach or console them.

I want to accomplish so much more while I am here on this
   Earth.

I want to reach many hearts and help them to become closer
   to You.

I aim to help to ease the pain of those around me,
      to assist them to see the good around them
      and to find meaning and purpose in life.

I so hope to successfully guide my children, to watch them
   grow and develop into beautiful, loving parents who work
   toward bringing good into the world.

I yearn to bring joy and laughter into the lives of others.

To assist them to feel strength and security.

I want to teach them to love You and all Your creations.

There is so much more I strive to accomplish.

To write and teach and learn.

I plead with You – please grant me clear thought and the opportunity to create, and to discover my true calling and to succeed in carrying it out in this world.

I believe I am not finished yet.

As each year goes by, I realize I have not yet even begun to come close to accomplishing what I aim to achieve.

Please, G-d, hear my prayers.

The challenges and pain are somehow manageable, as long as clarity and strength are present, to continue to do what I am only just beginning to discover I want to do.

Please stay with me and hear me.

Take good care of my loved ones as well as all of *Am Israel*, and I will do my best to discover and carry out my mission.

Life is beautiful and full of love.

As each year goes by, I cherish it more and more.

You have given me so many gifts, and I thank You for granting me the ability to realize and appreciate them.

Thank you, my Creator.

And please, hear my prayers.

Because I believe I have not yet completed my mission.

In fact, I believe (and even hope) I am only just getting started.

Acknowledgments

First and foremost, I would like to thank G-d for all of the good He has given me, and that He has enabled me to reach this point. With His blessing, this book will reach whomever it can benefit.

I would like to express infinite thanks to Prof. Steven Gross. I would not have been able to write this book without your ongoing support, invaluable teachings, and sense of humor throughout the years. You have been part of every page that I have written.

I am eternally grateful to my neurosurgeon, Prof. Sergey Spektor; to Prof. Yigal Shoshan, who performed my radiosurgery; to Dr. Idit Tamir and the medical and support staff at the Hadassah Ein Kerem hospital; to Dr. David Rahima, my ENT: and to Dr. Shmuel Kugler. If you hadn't all been such wonderful *shlichim,* I would not be where I am today.

I will always carry my love and appreciation for my dear friend and physical therapist, Lisa Hoze (blessed be her memory), close to my heart. May her soul ascend in the heavens and achieve eternal peace. I hope you are dancing in the heavens, just as you danced with me when I couldn't even walk! And I would like to thank Simone Shittrit for introducing us and for helping us all as a talented OT.

I would like to thank Michal Ozeri, who spent countless hours doing PT with me to try and ease my pain and teach me to walk in a straight line.

There are no words that can reflect how appreciative I am to all of my amazing friends, and their families, who have been supportive of me every step of the way: Meyrav Bar Haim, Einav Zohar, Lea Rotner, Simha Nizri, Adi Ziv, Dr. Leora Schachter, Hana Reller, Shira Greenbaum, Omer Shiloach, Michal Ganiel, Shuli Kalaora, Orna Koren, Esti Mauda, the members of the Neve Itamar Synagogue, the Kiryat HaSharon community, and Yaron Jacobs.

Special thanks to Shulamit Elad, founder of Irlen Israel, for helping us to view the world clearly and comfortably, and for all your support and inspiration over the last few years.

I would also like to offer endless appreciation to Tracy Stevens and all the therapeutic team at the Feuerstein Institute who worked with our son, under the direction of Prof. Gross; and to Prof. Reuven Feuerstein (of blessed memory) who helped guide us, and who enabled us to receive therapies at the most hopeful treatment center I have ever encountered.

Much gratitude to Drs. Uri Rubinstein and Yehuda Senecky, and Ilana, for all the wonderful medical care and assistance to our children over the years.

Warm thanks to Rabbi Yossi Munk, Etti Bekerman, and the amazing volunteers at Et La'asot for your support and for bringing so much joy into the lives of special children.

Endless appreciation to Rabbi Ahikam Getz, Amichai Grinwald, and the incredible team of rabbis at Mechinat Avner Akko, who enabled our son to blossom while proving that love, dedication, and hard work make inclusion possible.

Many thanks to my editors, Sarah Rosenbaum and Adina Moryosef; to Nir Bosco for the original cover design and website; Liat Perry for the cover redesign; Heather Osborne for proofreading and formatting; and Chana Studley for your guidance.

And last, but certainly not least, I would like to express my everlasting love and gratitude to my family. To my husband and soulmate, Avi (Avraham), and our precious children: Ravid Suzanne, Boaz Meir, Dan Shlomo, Levi Yitzchak, and Yehuda Eliyah.

To my mother, Sheila Tanenblatt, and my sister, Shari Tanenblatt Leventhal, for your endless support and for flying halfway across the world to help me through my surgery. To my father-in-law, R' Shlomo Edry (of blessed memory), for all your blessings and prayers; my sisters-in-law, Annette, Yaffa, and Yehudit, and my brother-in-law, David, and their families; and to my brothers, Michael and Danny, for always being there for us.

May G-d bless you all with health, happiness, comfort, and everything wonderful that will enable you to reach your dreams, and to accomplish the amazing things that you are meant to do!

About the Author

Jacki Edry is a graduate of Hampshire College and has an extensive background in education, writing, and marketing. She has been exploring the world of autism and neurodiversity for over thirty-five years. Jacki is a survivor of complex brain surgery that left a lasting imprint on her body, as well as her neurological and perceptual abilities. She is also a parent of neurodivergent children. She has spent many years advocating for inclusion programs in the educational system and providing support for families of children with disabilities.

Jacki spends most of her time learning about how young minds discover and interpret the world. She enjoys integrating this knowledge into her work and creative ventures. Jacki is particularly interested in the brain, mind-body connections, and inclusion of people with disabilities in society. She aims to integrate these different schools of knowledge to help better the world.

Jacki resides in Israel with her husband, children, and dog.

A

FIELD GUIDE TO

MUSHROOMS OF

THE CAROLINAS

ALAN E. BESSETTE

ARLEEN R. BESSETTE

MICHAEL W. HOPPING

A
Field Guide to
Mushrooms of
the Carolinas

THE UNIVERSITY OF

NORTH CAROLINA PRESS

Chapel Hill

A Southern Gateways Guide

Text © 2018 The University of
North Carolina Press

Designed by Richard Hendel
Set in Guardian and TheSans
by Tseng Information Systems, Inc.

Manufactured in the United States of America

The University of North Carolina Press has
been a member of the Green Press Initiative
since 2003.

Cover photo of *Stereum ostrea*
by Michael W. Hopping

Additional captions: p. x, *Hygrocybe
acutonica*; p. xii, *Amanita banningiana*;
p. xiv, *Amanita cokeri*; p. 38, *Lepista
subconnexa*; p. 40, *Amanita flavoconia*

Library of Congress
Cataloging-in-Publication Data
Names: Bessette, Alan, author. |
Bessette, Arleen R., author. |
Hopping, Michael, 1952- author.
Title: A field guide to mushrooms of the
Carolinas / by Alan E. Bessette, Arleen R.
Bessette, and Michael W. Hopping.
Other titles: Southern gateways guide.
Description: Chapel Hill : The University
of North Carolina Press, [2018] | Series:
A southern gateways guide
Identifiers: LCCN 2017042869|
ISBN 9781469638539 (pbk : alk. paper) |
ISBN 9781469638546 (ebook)
Subjects: LCSH: Mushrooms—North
Carolina—Identification. | Mushrooms—South
Carolina—Identification. | Mushrooms—
Southern States—Identification.
Classification: LCC QK605.5.S67 B47 2018 |
DDC 579.609756—dc23
LC record available at https://lccn.loc.gov
/2017042869

To the

Asheville Mushroom Club

that brought us together

CONTENTS

ACKNOWLEDGMENTS

This book would not have been possible without the valuable assistance from so many friends and colleagues:

Pat Buchanan's line drawings added visual clarity to key concepts explained in the introduction and in select group headers.

Color illustrations, both beautiful and accurate, were provided by Harley Barnhart, Jason Bolin, Fabrizio Bordo, Ryan Bouchard, E. J. Dwigans, Dan Guravich, Rosanne Healy, Josh Hutchins, Josh Kielsmeier-Cook, Marty Klein, Renée Lebeuf, David Lewis, Owen McConnell, John Plischke III, Alan Rockefeller, Bill Roody, Mary Smiley, Matthew Smith, Walt Sturgeon, Adelaide and Jeremy Ward, and Michael Wood.

Bruch T. Reed supplied specimens of *Laetiporus sulphureus* for us to photograph.

Retired park ranger Ron Anundson and all the staff of Morrow Mountain State Park, Albemarle, North Carolina, partnered and supported our work during our mycological surveying and provided us a home away from home.

Bart Buyck, Roy Halling, Jay Justice, Patrick Leacock, Brian Looney, Andy Methven, Otto Miettinen, Ron Petersen, John Plischke III, Bill Roody, Dianna Smith, Matt Smith, Walt Sturgeon, Rod Tulloss, and Bill Yule aided with mushroom identification.

Rytas Vilgalys reviewed portions of the manuscript and made sound suggestions for its improvement.

Michael Hopping owes his late-fruiting interest in mushrooms to Carroll Anderson, who taught him to see morels, and Charlotte Caplan for her patience with his novice curiosity.

We are especially grateful to Lucas Church, Mark Simpson-Vos, and the staff at the University of North Carolina Press. Always accessible when needed, ever supportive, they were instrumental in making this undertaking a true pleasure. Thank you for taking a chance on a "mushroom book" and making this possible.

If we have failed to mention anyone who should be acknowledged, it is an unintentional oversight for which we apologize.

A

FIELD GUIDE TO

MUSHROOMS OF

THE CAROLINAS

INTRODUCTION

Impatience is inherent to the human condition. So is excitement. Expect both to attend your mushrooming adventures. And if you're new to mycology, know this, right up front: Impatience is not your friend. We hope you'll rein it in a bit. Invest some of that thwarted energy and excitement in a curiosity about the basic concepts of mushroom identification. You'll thank yourself, again and again, for the success bookwork makes possible.

REGIONS AND HABITATS

The Carolinas are famously biodiverse. Temperate conditions and abundant rainfall support but don't fully explain this. Interactions between elevation and long-term climatological shifts played a role as well. The Ice Ages of the past 2.5 million years never pushed glaciers this far south, but arctic conditions at their feet did drive many northern species into our region. Some still persist at higher mountain elevations. Repeated glacial advances and retreats mixed and remixed the roster of animals, plants, and fungi.

Five major bioregions are recognized in the Carolinas. From northwest to southeast these are the Blue Ridge Mountains, the Piedmont, the Southeastern Plain, the Middle Atlantic Coastal Plain, and the South Atlantic Coastal Plain. A sixth, man-made ecoregion is also of interest to mushroomers: Cities, Towns, and Farmsteads.

Blue Ridge Mountains

The Appalachian mountain chain known as the Blue Ridge extends in a northeasterly direction from north Georgia to south-central Pennsylvania. The Blue Ridge is geologically ancient. Uplifts first occurred almost half a billion years ago, during the era when fungi were venturing onto land. More recently, a collision between North America and Europe made a crumple zone of the Appalachian landscape.

This is a region of contrasts. Elevations range from 1,500 ft. to 6,684 ft., the summit of Mt. Mitchell in western North Carolina. Our high mountains are the wettest in eastern North America, averaging almost 90 inches of annual rainfall. The nearby city of Asheville is the Carolinas' driest, averaging 37 inches. Temperate conditions in lower valleys cool above 5,000 ft. to a climate reminiscent of Maine's. Ecological communities include high-altitude spruce/fir forests, heath balds, bogs, and several variations of hardwood and mixed hardwood/conifer forests.

Piedmont

The rolling Piedmont plateau at the foot of the Blue Ridge escarpment stretches from Alabama to New Jersey. In the Carolinas it spreads southeastward from the mountains to a fall line roughly marked by Augusta, Georgia; Columbia, South Carolina; Raleigh; and Roanoke Rapids.

Elevations decrease with distance from the mountains, dropping from 1,500 ft. to approximately 200 ft. above sea level at the fall line. Annual rainfall averages about 45 inches. Thousands of years of human activity have shaped the natural history of the Piedmont. Indigenous peoples used intentional burning. Now the area is dotted with large-scale agricultural, industrial, and urban developments. Although this is our least biologically diverse zone, the Piedmont contains distinct communities dominated by hardwoods, conifer plantations, and cleared land—often in some stage of reversion to forest.

Southeastern Plain

The Southeastern Plain is an extensive, U-shaped bioregion with a northwestern terminus in west-central Tennessee. The region drops south through Mississippi and Alabama, takes a gradual northeastern turn through the Carolinas, and peters out in northern Virginia. In the Carolinas the Southeastern Plain fans out to the east and south of the Piedmont fall line, eventually intergrading with the Middle Atlantic Coastal Plain. The Southeastern Plain is occasionally hilly but predominantly flat and poorly drained. From southwest to northeast, population centers include Orangeburg, Sumter, Florence, Fayetteville, Ft. Bragg, and Rocky Mount.

Elevation ranges from a few hundred feet to near sea level. Rainfall averages 45-50 inches. Ecological communities include the drought-prone Sand Hills, crop and pasture land, pine plantations, and native forests in which conifers, hardwoods, or mixtures of both are found. A formerly dominant tree species, the longleaf pine, has largely been replaced by loblolly and shortleaf pines or hardwoods previously held in check by frequent, low-intensity fires.

Middle Atlantic Coastal Plain

The Middle Atlantic Coastal Plain is the poorly drained and often swampy expanse of land lying between the Southeastern Plain and the Atlantic coast from Myrtle Beach north to the Delmarva Peninsula. South of Myrtle Beach the region goes inland. Waterboro, Wilmington, Marine Corps Base Camp Lejeune, Greenville, N.C., and Elizabeth City are located in the Middle Atlantic Coastal Plain.

This region has average annual rainfall of 50-60 inches. Major acreage in the north is devoted to production of row crops. North Carolina's blueberry industry centers farther south in acid, sandy soils. As in the more westerly regions, pine plantations are common. Native communities include pine flatwoods, shrubby bogs known as pocosins, and the peculiarly elliptical Carolina bays. Swamps with bald cypress, tupelo, and Atlantic white cedar are found, along with maritime forests featuring live oak and dwarf palmetto. Coastal marshes and offshore barrier islands complete the picture.

South Atlantic Coastal Plain

A thin strip of South Carolina coast and its associated barrier islands represent the northern limit of the South Atlantic Coastal Plain. It sweeps southward across the Georgia and northern Florida coasts. Hilton Head, Charleston, and Georgetown are representative centers of population.

This flat, subtropical region typically gets about 50 inches of rain per year. It is a place of swamps, wide rivers, and semi-dry to dry land composed of muck, clay, or sand. Vegetation is adapted to flooding and hurricane winds. Plantations of slash and loblolly pine have replaced most of the longleaf pine community. Swamp forests contain water tupelo and bald cypress. Oaks inhabit some drier bottomlands. Sea islands grow live oak, cabbage palm, slash pine, and red cedar.

Cities, Towns, and Farmsteads

Regardless of geographic location, manmade landscapes often share a number of distinctive features. People enjoy mowed lawns, city parks, golf courses, orchards, and landscape plantings. Farm animals require pasture. These engineered habitats favor the growth of certain mushrooms, including some choice edibles.

But here, extra culinary caution is required; see "Can You Eat It?" on p. 6. Car exhaust should rule out eating mushrooms harvested next to busy roads. What pesticides and fertilizers has a municipality sprayed in its parks? Mushrooms found on golf courses have commonly been marinated in chemicals, iffy table fare at best. Also be advised that some state or federal land units ban mushrooming or require a collecting permit.

Despite the drawbacks, mushroomers often do well in urban and suburban settings. Lawns or pastures are good habitats for agarics and puffballs. Maitake can be found at the base of old oak trees in city parks. Mulch supports both native and introduced species. Finally, engineered landscapes abound in woodland edges, trailsides, and islands of landscape plantings. Transitional or edge environments are prime mushroom hunting locations.

GETTING ORIENTED

Imagine a nature scene. Are you seeing mostly plants and animals? Ordinarily, they're the most obvious creatures around. But we're also surrounded by long-lived fungal networks residing for the most part invisibly underground, in wood, or on decaying matter. These networks are nondescript masses of tiny threads called **mycelia** (singular, **mycelium**). Once in a while, certain species of mycelia announce their presence by engaging in a reproductive act known as a **fruitbody**, or mushroom. This is connected to the parent mycelium by fibers occasionally thick enough to give a false impression of roots. Think of the linking threads as multiple, sometimes microscopic fruit stems. Mushrooms can be picked, if done responsibly, without damage to the mycelium.

Fungi are not plants. They are classified in kingdom Fungi. Like animals, mycelia must rely on outside sources to obtain the sugar needed to power their cellular engines. Certain fungi form beneficial **mycorrhizal** relationships with plant partners. The plant, often a tree, receives extra water and minerals from the fungus; in return the fungus receives plant sugar. Other fungi are **saprobes** or **saprotrophs**— recyclers of dead material—or **parasites**

The job of a fruitbody, whether or not it looks like or is commonly called a mushroom, is to generate and provide for the distribution of spores capable of producing new mycelia. Fruitbodies assume incredibly varied but species-specific shapes. For this, mushroomers are grateful.

feeding on an involuntary living host. The largest single organism on Earth might be a parasitic mycelium occupying 3.4 square miles in Oregon. It has an estimated age of 2,400 years.

Mushroom growers and plant pathologists are necessarily attuned to the mycelia they cultivate or battle. For the rest of us, it's more about the mushrooms and, of those, maybe only the minority we find useful or tasty. No shame in that. Utilitarian motives are as good a place as any to start. But before spending too many hours charging around with a basket on your arm, familiarize yourself with the lay of mushroom land.

Easter Eggs

Mushrooms normally fall into the category of inconsequential detail we overlook. Changing that habit is not as simple as deciding that fungi are interesting. Some mushroomers speak of putting on "morel eyes" in the spring. Come summer, they employ "black trumpet eyes" to reveal another delicacy hiding in moss banks. They have developed useful search images, revised a few visual priorities. But even for veteran mushroomers, the first find of the season tends to be the toughest. Sensitivity to fragmentary shapes and subtleties of color improves with a fresh specimen in hand.

Mushrooms hide in plain sight. Speed— remember impatience?—is another key to mushrooming success. Slower is better. On mushroom club forays the least successful participants are often folks who haven't learned to throttle down from hiking pace. It occasionally pays to be first into an area, but the tracks of the impatient are frequently littered with stomped mushrooms that went unnoticed.

Veteran mushroom hunters in hilly or mountainous regions take advantage of the terrain. Camouflaged mushrooms or those partially concealed by leaves, needles, or other obstructions are easier to spot the closer they are to one's eyes. Try hunting uphill. If nothing else, the leisurely pace reduces the misery of a long climb.

Finally, expect the return leg on an out-and-back trail to be as productive as the outbound portion. What was behind a tree trunk or partially hidden by an upturned leaf or branch is now standing in the open, visible.

An Embarrassment of Riches
The fossil record tells us that fungi appeared on land at least 440 million years ago. Since then, they've been a rapidly diversifying group. According to a recent estimate, Earth is home to approximately 298,000 plant species. Better than two-thirds of these are formally documented. The same study calculated 611,000 species of fungi, of which only 43,271 had been scientifically described. More than 5,000 are found in the southeastern United States. Intrepid mycologists needn't travel to Borneo to discover new species. They're reported from the Carolinas on a regular basis.

Fungal diversity presents mushroom enthusiasts with challenges seldom faced by botany buffs or birders. A reputable guide to North American birds can be expected to include all wild species found here. Wildflower books aren't quite as comprehensive, but users can at least get close. With mushrooms, forget that expectation. General field guides, including this one, mention only a fraction of the species known or expected to occur

Mushrooming is like an Easter egg hunt. Proceed accordingly and you'll come closer to filling your basket.

in their area of coverage. There's simply not enough space to discuss them all. Selective incompleteness is compounded by the presence of species as yet unknown to science.

Voices of Experience
The value of access to experienced mushroom hunters is hard to overemphasize. For the vast majority of human history, personal instruction was *the* means of transmitting mushroom skills. We ate what our mamas ate and started fires with the types of tinder conk known to our people. Generations of village shamans passed along recipes for using the psychonautic fungi that empowered their visits to nonmaterial realms for purposes of divination or healing. Today, foraging for mushrooms remains a cultural tradition in several contemporary societies. While that's not true in most regions of the United States, mushroomers rarely complain about a lack of competition.

Field guides do not render person-to-person instruction obsolete. Far from it. No book can look at your mushroom and respond when you ask, "This could be poisonous but I'm supposed to taste it anyway?" or "This spore print is *pink*? You're joking; it looks brown to me."

Join a mushroom club. Participate in the field trips known in mycological circles as forays. The torrents of information that initially befuddle you will gradually coalesce into useful concepts.

MUSHROOMING GEAR
The general idea when hunting mushrooms is to observe, collect, and transport fungi in a manner that gets you and the goods home intact. Barring the

necessity of a GPS unit, this is not a gear-intensive proposition.

You will want a basket. Half-bushel peach baskets are readily available, rigid, and sized to carry a few pounds of mushrooms. The woven wood construction doesn't catch rainwater. Peach baskets aren't glamorous, but they are cheap to replace. Wire, plastic mesh, wicker, and other stiff, rot-resistant baskets are also good choices. Pick something that won't stink after marinating in fungal juices.

You'll want some small bags or a roll of waxed paper. Although mushrooms can be carried loose in a basket, that's not ideal. Paper or waxed paper bags keep your finds separate—crucial when collecting a mixture of edible and potentially toxic species. Bags also provide a second layer of damage protection. When harvesting morels, mesh laundry bags are sometimes used. The open weave allows spores to pass and inoculate new territory. Avoid plastic bags; fungi rot fast in nonporous plastic. That said, a garbage or recycling bag will keep your basket dry during a cloudburst.

You'll want a cutting and digging tool. Many mushrooms can be picked by hand. Others must be cut or excavated. If you plan to identify an unfamiliar ground dweller, digging is the way to go. The base of the stalk often contains vital clues. A yellow staining reaction seen only in the base of the stalk distinguishes some poisonous relatives of grocery store agarics from their delectable cousins. Keys to *Amanita* species are useless without an intact stalk base. When harvesting known varieties for the table, the priorities are different: surgical and clean. Cutting mushrooms with a knife or scissors doesn't injure the parent mycelium and reduces kitchen prep chores. Precleaning edibles with a soft brush before bagging them is another timesaver.

You'll want to bring along your wits. Pay attention to where you are, even in the excitement of stumbling across a mother lode. You might like to visit that spot again. For species identification, it's important to remember whether a mushroom grew on wood, a cow pie, a magnolia cone, or the ground. Was it under conifers, beneath deciduous trees, or in grass? At the end of a long day, keeping that information straight can be tough. Consider memory aids. Some mushroomers write notes on bags or carry a notebook. They may take pictures to document settings or show how a mushroom looked before it bounced around for hours in a bag and spent the night in the fridge. Sharp photographs from multiple relevant angles are invaluable when you need online advice.

You will probably *not* want to trudge around with a field guide. Leave it in the car or at home. Do bring what you need to cope with weather, bugs, hunger, health issues, and such. A 10x loupe or hand lens is a nice extra. If you're out with a group, decide how you'll maintain communications. Nobody has fun if somebody gets lost. Do your phones have reception? Walkie-talkies are a pricey alternative. Loud whistles work; instructions or messages can be conveyed in patterns of toots.

WHAT'S IN A NAME?

Ever hear of the Tower of Babel? Names often say as much about the namer as the named. People in West Virginia eat a mushroom called a Bradley. Western North Carolinians don't find Bradleys; they collect Leatherbacks. Apricot Milk Caps are found in the mid-Atlantic region. These are but a few of the common names for a single species. Others include Fish Milk Cap, Weeping Milk Cap, Tawny Lactarius, and Voluminous-latex Milky.

During the eighteenth century, the Swedish taxonomist Carl Linnaeus imposed scientific order on such chaos. He devised a universal framework for naming and describing species in the language of Latin. In 1838, another Swede, Elias

Magnus Fries, dubbed our much-named milk cap *Lactarius volemus*. Linnaean taxonomy has the advantage of showing the relationships between life forms. Kingdom Fungi categorically distinguishes all fungi from plants, animals, and other types of organisms. Members of kingdom Fungi are then divided into subkingdoms based on distinguishing characteristics. (Fungi of interest to mushroomers belong to subkingdom Dikarya.) That same refining process is repeatedly applied downward through levels of phylum, class, order, and family to genus and species. The scientific name for a species is a two-word combination of a genus and a specific epithet. *Lactarius* is the genus name shared by most milk mushrooms, and *volemus* is the epithet referring to one member of the *Lactarius* group. Genus names are capitalized; epithets are not.

But the system has a weakness. Which characteristics should be used to separate subgroups? What if the early taxonomists had established a basic distinction between Land Animal and Sea Animal? What would have happened then? Within Sea Animal, all finned forms could have been grouped into subcategory Fish. Within Fish, scientists might then have distinguished between gilled fish, cuttlefish, penguins, whales, manatees, etc. The poorly chosen separation of Land Animal from Sea Animal would have resulted in the mistaken idea that manatees are closer kin to sharks than to elephants.

A gaffe of this magnitude originally assigned the fungi to kingdom Plantae. Classical mushroom descriptions were based on characteristics such as gills vs. pores vs. teeth vs. smooth. But the advent of DNA sequencing is wreaking havoc throughout the Linnaean hierarchies. Laboratory analysis of genetic similarity has become the accepted method for assigning positions on the tree of life. Traditional mycological concepts have been especially hard-hit. It turns out

that Berkeley's Polypore, a large shelving mushroom with pores rather than gills, is a polypore in name only. Genetic studies place it in the *Russulales*, an order of predominantly gilled mushrooms that includes the milk caps. Slime molds, those magnificent flash-mob performers, crawled all the way out of kingdom Fungi and dispersed. Where some of them will end up is anyone's guess.

Scientific names for mushrooms are, to put it politely, in a state of flux. Check any two field guides and you'll find discrepancies. A waxcap once known as *Camarophyllus pratensis* or *Hygrophorus pratensis* var. *pratensis* or *Hygrocybe pratensis* var. *pratensis* is currently known as *Cuphophyllus pratensis*—note the preservation of the epithet; this is often, but not always, the case when a species is renamed. Some guidebooks refer to the Eastern Black Morel as *Morchella elata*. Genetics says that's a European species. Black morels found in North Carolina are *Morchella angusticeps*.

Oh, and the milk cap Fries called *Lactarius volemus*? It was recently moved to the genus *Lactifluus* and became *Lactifluus volemus*.

CAN YOU EAT IT?

Mushrooms delight in violating simple edibility rules. Only two withstand scrutiny.

1. To reliably distinguish edible from poisonous species you must learn them individually, one by one.

Don't feel compelled to memorize every latest and greatest scientific name. Some stick. Others do not. Learn one and move on. Those used in this book were accepted by world authorities at the time of publication. We have tried to include alternate or former scientific names when possible.

Do not eat any mushroom that hasn't been positively identified as an edible species. Whenever possible, have your identification confirmed by a person experienced with that species. When in doubt, throw it out!

2. You won't be poisoned by a mushroom you don't eat.

Our knowledge of mushroom edibility and toxicity is far less complete than you might imagine. As with almost any other foodstuff, humanity has mainly learned what should or shouldn't be eaten by trial and error. A relative few mushroom species have a solid track record of edibility for most people. A few others are just as well known to cause serious illness or death. Several of the responsible mycotoxins have been identified and studied. But for the great majority of fungal species, information on edibility is sketchy, contradictory, or absent. We're still uncomfortably reliant on case reports that boil down to "Bob ate species X and got a horrible bellyache." Was it species X that made Bob sick? a delayed reaction to the airport sushi he had for lunch? or the ulcer he didn't know he had? What if Mrs. Bob also ate species X and felt fine afterward? Placebo-controlled, double-blind experiments could easily answer the question, but mycologists cannot ethically feed species X to a bunch of volunteers and study them to find out what happens.

The toxicology committee of the North American Mycological Association (NAMA) maintains records of mushroom poisonings and other adverse reactions to fungi. The reports make for reading that is both disturbing and reassuring. A few people and pets *do* die each year from eating poisonous mushrooms. Far more common are nonfatal cases of gastrointestinal distress, liver and/or kidney damage, unpleasant neurological

syndromes, dermatitis, allergic reactions, and miserable interactions with alcohol.

Perhaps the most unsettling NAMA finding is the relative frequency of illness associated with morels, a group of highly prized edibles. Of the 41 adverse events reported to the organization in 2009, morels accounted for 6 nonfatal cases. Let's dig into that.

As with other foods, people have variable reactions to mushrooms. A rating of "edible" is no guarantee of safety for everyone. The issue might be digestibility. Plants are given shape by cellulose, a complex carbohydrate we can't digest as such. Mushrooms get structural integrity from chitin, an equally indigestible carbohydrate also used by insects and crustaceans to build shells. Cooking a mushroom degrades chitin into fragments more suitable for human stomachs, though gluttony may overwhelm that benefit. While it *is* possible to enjoy small amounts of some species—not morels—raw and with relative safety, you've been warned.

Mushrooms pose other challenges to the human system as well. Children have incomplete immune defenses. That's said to be one reason for the overrepresentation of kids in mushroom poisoning statistics. The elderly is another higher-risk group. Old livers and kidneys don't handle toxins as efficiently as they once did.

Mushroom Edibility Test: When sampling a mushroom species for the first time, sauté a slice in butter, salt, and pepper. Eat only that piece. Save the rest, raw, in the fridge. If all goes well and the taste experience was worth repeating, cook the remainder of your find tomorrow or, better yet, the next day. If, heaven forefend, there are problems, you've got a show-and-tell item for the drop-in clinic or emergency room.

Morels should never be consumed raw because they contain a small quantity of hydrazine, a carcinogen used in rocket fuel. (Button mushrooms from the grocery store may contain trace amounts as well.) Hydrazine steams away during cooking—keep that in mind when sniffing your morels in the pan. Appropriate prep and cooking technique is also effective against certain other sources of potential trouble. Before chowing down on honey mushrooms or sticky-capped boletes from the genus *Suillus*, go online and read how to prepare them.

Be wary of morels collected from old orchards. Due to the pesticides in use decades ago, orchard morels may contain dangerous amounts of lead or arsenic. Morels and several other fungi accumulate heavy metals that don't break down with the passage of time. Cooking can't remove them either. It's best to avoid eating any mushroom harvested from an area where high concentrations of lead, arsenic, or other heavy metals are possible. This includes coal ash deposits, railroad tracks, and highway roadsides.

Eating certain types of mushrooms within two days of drinking alcohol can cause distressing reactions similar to the effect of disulfiram, a drug sometimes prescribed to deter alcohol consumption. *Coprinopsis atramentaria* (p. 180) is famous for it. In rare instances, other species have been implicated as well, including morels, honey mushrooms, shaggy manes, oyster mushrooms, and king boletes/porcini.

Were these sporadic reactions causally related to drinking alcohol? If so, the victims must have been born under a very unlucky star. Thousands upon thousands of people have safely combined morels, porcini, etc. with a glass of wine.

When adding wild mushrooms to your diet, the bottom line is this: Do it responsibly. If you aren't absolutely certain of your identification, throw the mushroom out. If it's rotting or full of maggots, throw it out. If you collected it in an unfamiliar part of the country or the world, get a second opinion from a local forager; that mushroom might not be what you think it is, and highly publicized poisonings have resulted from failure to take this precaution. Think twice before eating wild mushrooms prepared by others. How much do you trust their identification and cooking skills?

In addition to the cautions above, there's another level of answer to the question "Can I eat it?" and that is "Maybe, but do you *want* to?" Hundreds of species are listed as edible in one source or another. Desirability is a separate matter. The Mushroom Edibility Test above (p. 7) begins to answer that question for you. The aroma and flavors of sautéed butter, salt, and pepper are a constant. Everything else belongs to your mushroom. What if you enjoy the taste but are turned off by the texture? Many "edibles" cook up slimy, tough, or woody. Some texturally disadvantaged species make excellent broths, tinctures, or medicinal teas.

The first thing to know about identifying mushrooms is that many of the diagnostic features will probably be unfamiliar. Mushrooms don't have beaks, petals, fins, or fur. The telltale features distinguishing one species from another often reside in places you aren't used to looking. The underside of a cap may be festooned with the expected gills, but in some cases, you'll see a surface resembling sponge rubber or a field of icicles instead. You'll need to train yourself to notice details that may at first seem odd or overly picky.

PARTS OF A MUSHROOM

The mushroom of most people's imagination probably resembles Figure 1, a fruitbody with a cap and stalk, decorated with a color and some combination of smaller features. While this general idea does apply to many types of fungi, others abandoned it for something else or never adopted it in the first place. Their fruitbodies can appear as blobs, cups, balls, crusts, or branching corals, to name a few variations. Not to be outdone, species of cap-and-stalk fungi often get creative with the basic model, distorting it in various ways. Stalks might be laterally placed on the cap or eliminated. Spore-producing areas may look nothing like gills. These are meaningful variations. Let's examine them, beginning with the site on the fruitbody where spores are produced.

FERTILE SURFACES

Spore production occurs in sheets of microscopic factory units deployed on a "fertile surface." This could be the sides (faces) of gills, the lining of small tubes opening to the outside as pores, the teeth of a tooth fungus, the inner surface of a cup, or none of the above. Fertile surface type helps separate mushrooms into large

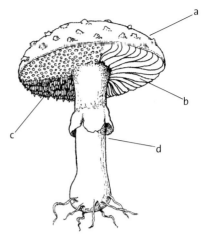

Figure 1. Parts of a mushroom: (a) cap with warts; (b) fertile surfaces with gills, (c) pores, or teeth; (d) stalk with a ring and rhizomorphs

related groups, but narrowing things down further requires closer inspection.

Gills

Gills are thin sheets of tissue suspended in a spokelike arrangement from the underside of many capped mushrooms. Gills may be jam-packed together (**crowded**) or widely spaced. Some species increase their fertile surface near the cap margin by having forked gills or adding **short gills** unconnected to the long ones.

Gills may or may not be anchored to the mushroom stalk, if it has one. The degree of gill attachment is another diagnostic clue.

The fertile surfaces of chanterelles and a few other species have ridges (false gills) that appear to be, but are not, true gills. The ridges are somewhat triangular in cross section, not sheetlike, but they can still be confusingly tall. To differentiate the tall ridges of a Cinnabar Chanterelle, for example, from the true gills of an orange waxcap, observe how the gills multiply near the cap margin. Chanterelle ridges

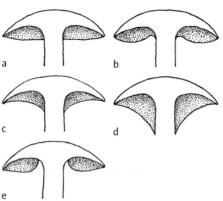

Figure 2. Types of gill attachments:
(a) attached, (b) notched, (c) decurrent,
(d) strongly decurrent, (e) free

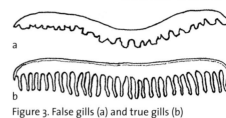

Figure 3. False gills (a) and true gills (b)

repeatedly branch. Waxcap look-alikes maximize fertile surface with short gills.

Milk mushrooms have gills that weep liquid (**latex**) when damaged. The amount and character of this "milk" are significant. What color is it at first? Does that change with exposure to air? Does it stain the gills or other surfaces? How does the latex taste? Peppery hot? Sweet? Because color changes may take seconds to more than half an hour to develop, cut a few gills when you harvest an unknown milk cap. Determine taste and initial color; watch a minute for early changes; then bag the specimen. If a delayed reaction is going to happen, it will probably be complete when you get home.

Gills yield other useful details. Usually they hang straight, but in a few species they're crinkled, **crisped**, like bacon. The gill edges of shiitakes and some other species aren't smooth; they are sawtoothed (**serrated**), fringed, or ornamented with tiny bumps or droplets. The edges might characteristically have a different color than the faces; these are **marginate** gills. Small folds, "**crossveins**," sometimes run across the underside of the cap, connecting adjacent gills. In some species, the gill faces are spotted or mottled. All of this has diagnostic significance.

Pores

Two large groups of mushrooms, the polypores and the boletes, produce spores inside hollow tubes and expel them through openings called pores. The underside of the cap is covered with them. Pore diameter and shape are species specific. Cut the mushroom perpendicular to the pore surface to see the tubes. They're packed together like soda straws in a box. The inner lining of the tubes is the fertile surface. Tube length can be important.

The pores, tubes, and entire fruitbody of a bolete remain fleshy throughout the mushroom's brief existence. Boletes typically grow on the ground and have a classic mushroom silhouette. The size, shape, color, and occasionally arrangement of pores are diagnostic features. So are color changes caused by damage to the pores. Lightly brush the back of a fingernail over the pore surface, being careful not to dig into or gouge it. Most "**bruising reactions**" occur rapidly, but some take quite a while to manifest. Rather than risk having to wait around when you get home, bruise the pores in the field and watch for a quick response before bagging the mushroom. If you get an early bruising reaction, take note. It may be different an hour later.

Polypores usually grow on wood, may lack a stalk, and tend toward woodiness themselves, at least in age. Perennial polypores, the bracket or conk fungi that live for years on the sides of trees, lay down a fresh layer of tubes and pores each season. You'll need to cut a specimen to observe that. Other species try to confuse things by presenting a pore surface that doesn't look like one. The Gilled Polypore, *Lenzites betulina*, has thick, tough "gills." The underside of a Maze Polypore resembles something out of Pac-Man. A pore surface might erode into a jagged field of tube remnants best distinguished from the uniform teeth of a tooth fungus with a magnifying glass.

Other Fertile Surfaces

Mushrooms need not have gills or pores. The spore factories of tooth fungi coat the teeth hanging under the cap. Flat coatings of fertile surface also occur. These may or may not be colored the same as other mushroom parts. The pits and ridges of morel caps are covered with fertile surface, as are the branches of coral mushrooms. In cup fungi, the fertile surface is located on top or inside the disc or cup, opposite the arrangements in gilled and pored species. Stinkhorns exude spores in a foul-smelling glop designed to draw flies and stick to their feet.

Truffles, puffballs, and other introverts house their fertile surfaces within. Vertically section a young specimen to inspect the interior layout and coloration. By the time a puffball is mature and puffing spores, these critical details are history.

SPORES

Spores are the single-celled beginnings of the next generation of mycelia. Mushrooms may launch spores into the air, arrange for transport by hungry animals, or in the case of the inkcaps, drip them in a slurry of dissolving, **deliquescing**, gill and cap tissue.

Microscopic examination of spores yields important information. Mature spores of a particular species are similar in size, shape, surface ornamentation, and internal features; see Microscopic Information, below (p. 15). Without microscopy, a few mushrooms resist identification, even to genus. Oh well.

But you don't need a microscope to determine spore color. That information is usually available to anyone with a spare sheet of paper or glass. Use it to make a **spore print**. What, you ask, is the fascination with spore prints? They remind you of a kindergarten craft project. Spore color is a no-brainer, right? White gills, white spore print; brown gills, brown spore print; yes?

No, not for a significant minority of species. Yellow Unicorn Mushrooms have yellow gills and pink spores. The spore print of the edible Blewit, a lavender mushroom with lavender gills, is listed as pink although it's closer to tan. Inedible or toxic silver-violet corts resemble Blewits right down to the gill color of young specimens, but *Cortinarius* spores are rusty brown. Purplish-black spores drop from the strangely yellow gills of hypholomas. The pale gills of the edible Parasol Mushrooms produce white spores; those of its poisonous look-alike, *Chlorophyllum molybdites*, are greenish. Species in the genus *Agaricus* have chocolate brown spores, but the young mushrooms have pale or pink gills—check out the button mushrooms, *Agaricus bisporus*, in the produce section at your supermarket.

Spore printing can go awry. Polypores are sometimes passive-aggressive and refuse to cooperate. Ditto for any overly dry specimen. Immature mushrooms often prefer to rot and present you with a wet

Spore printing is important. Learn to do it; then do it. Cut off the cap of a prime specimen. Set it gill- or pore-side down on a sheet of white paper. Take the precaution of placing an absorbent layer between the spore print paper and the surface of your table or countertop. Cover the cap with an overturned cup or bowl and check back after several hours or in the morning.

Figure 4. Making a spore print

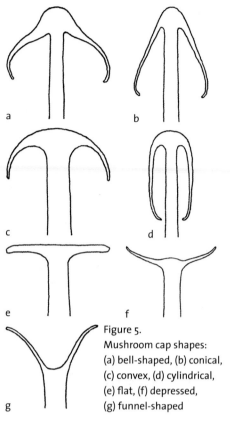

Figure 5.
Mushroom cap shapes:
(a) bell-shaped, (b) conical,
(c) convex, (d) cylindrical,
(e) flat, (f) depressed,
(g) funnel-shaped

brown stain. This can also happen with geriatric specimens and apparently prime boletes. A milk cap might bleed latex all over a spore print. Prevent juices from interfering with spore prints by cutting a hole in a 3 × 5 index card large enough to slide the stalk through but small enough to keep the cap from touching the card. Support the card and mushroom on the rim of a water glass with the stalk hanging down inside. Then cover and wait.

To see a white spore print on white paper, hold it at an angle to a bright source of light and look for telltale shadows behind ridges of heaped spores. Some mushroomers who anticipate white spores do their spore printing on half-white/half-black paper. Alternatives include clear glass, Mylar film, aluminum foil, or a mirror.

THE SUPPORT STRUCTURE

In a few types of fungi, a fertile surface is all that appears, presenting as a crust on the mycelium's food source. But in the vast majority of cases, the fertile surface occurs on, or is supported by, a superstructure: a cap and stalk, bracket, cup, gelatinous glob, or branched clump of tissue. The details of this support structure are crucial for mushroom identification.

General Appearance

Size matters. Oyster Mushrooms of the *Pleurotus ostreatus* group resemble fleshy, gilled shells projecting from logs or trees. Caps average 5-18 cm across. An inedible genus, *Crepidotus*, contains several members with a similar shape, color, and texture. But they are smaller, 1.5-5 cm wide—the spore color is also different.

Mushrooms have species-specific shapes. Caps might feature a characteristic central bump called an **umbo** or a central "**umbilicate**" dimple. The edge or **margin** of the cap may be "**inrolled**" (tucked under), **scalloped** like the rim of a pie crust, or decorated with hairs, veil fragments, or spokelike radial lines (**striations**). In side view, cap silhouettes run the gamut from a furled umbrella to one trashed by a gust of wind.

Color

You'd think this is straightforward, but no. The button stage of a brown bolete might be purple. Individuals of the same species often display slight, or not so slight, variations on a color theme as well. Nor are mushroom colors limited to those found in a box of crayons. Mycologists have dealt with these issues in different ways, some of which are incoherent to laypeople. The result is a hash of terms such as fuscous, pinkish-cinnamon, and sunburn (5D5). When a range of colors must be presented, the problem is compounded. To some extent that can't be helped, but when you are confused by color names, try two things. First, consult the photo of a species representing the color in question. Second, when a choice comes down to a difference of color ranges, is there a unifying constant? Are you being asked, in effect, to choose between colors tinted with yellow/orange vs. red/purple?

Species with naturally damp, translucent caps often fade and opacify at the first hint of drying. This trait is called **hygrophanous**.

Surface Features

Mushroom caps and/or stalks may be dry, sticky, or slimy. They may be smooth, lined, wrinkled, or cracked; bald or covered with scales, tufts, warts, powder, fuzz, or hairs. A cap or stalk covered with loose flaking scales is said to be **scurfy**. The caps of some species are **zoned**, showing concentric rings or bands of color. Most of these surface features are self-evident, at least with a hand lens. If a term confuses you, check the glossary or ask a mushrooming friend for help.

Flesh Characteristics

The fleshy interior of a mushroom's cap and stalk contains valuable information. Is it solid, hollow, or **stuffed** with pith of a different texture? What color is it? Does that change when exposed to air? If it does, where does the staining reaction occur? In the cap? At the base of the stalk? All over? The flesh of tooth mushrooms and polypores is often zoned, somewhat resembling grain lines in wood.

Stalk

Mushroom stalks are almost as variable and diagnostic as the caps. A stalk might be smooth, scurfy, hairy, spotted, or covered with a netlike pattern called **reticulation**. Surface textures range from dry to sticky or slimy. Some stalks maintain a similar diameter top to bottom (**equal**). Others are club-shaped or taper in one direction or the other. They can be solid, hollow, or stuffed. The color may or may not match the cap.

Some stalks supply developmental details that caps don't. Mushrooms begin as thickened clumps of mycelium. These organize into mushroom tissues, grow, and then, in gilled species at least, the umbrella of the cap opens. Mushrooms-to-be in the genus *Amanita* and a few others are initially encased in a membrane, the **universal veil**. This breaks open as the mushroom "hatches." In some species, veil fragments adhere to the cap as a large **patch**, as small **warts**, or as **powder**. In other varieties, the universal veil simply tears, remaining attached to the base of the stalk. The torn bag is known as the **volva**—note the spelling. Partly because the fate of the universal veil varies from species to species, stalk bases are of great interest. Some *Amanita* species also possess rooting **basal bulbs**.

Whether or not a universal veil is present, inspect stalks and cap margins for remnants of a more localized covering, the **partial veil**. Many species use them to protect immature fertile surfaces. Partial veils are anchored centrally to the stalk and peripherally to the cap margin. The classic mushroom "skirt" is a **membranous** partial veil that has separated from the cap margin but not the stalk. The area of stalk attachment and veil fragments found there are also referred to as a **ring** or **annulus**. At the supermarket, you'll be able to observe the membranous veil of button mushrooms, cremini, and portobellos at various stages of development.

A different style of partial veil resembles a radial cobweb. This is termed a **cortina**, the feature for which the genus *Cortinarius* is named. When a cortina tears during cap expansion, it may detach from either the cap margin or the stalk, perhaps leaving behind some dangling threads. Those on the stalk might be invisible but for the dusting of spores they tend to acquire.

Partial veils range from relatively tough to flimsy and rapidly disappearing tissue. When the latter is in question, check young specimens or inspect stalks for the presence of a circular zone where the surface texture suddenly changes. Mycologists refer to this as a **ring zone**.

Odor and Taste

Mushroom field guides list data about smell and taste. With practice, you'll learn to associate specific aromas with the terms used in descriptions and identification keys. Crush and sniff a bit of cap. Mycologists say that some milk mushrooms have an odor of **maple syrup** or **burnt sugar**. People who don't get that impression may instead detect a mildly **acrid** smell. What is acrid? Sharp, irritating, disagreeable, like something burning that shouldn't be. One version of acrid in myco-speak is "coal tar"; it reeks like a steam locomotive. If you're too young to remember coal-fired steam trains, imagine the pungent smell of burning rubber or plastic. **Farinaceous** is an odor variously compared to watermelon rind, cucumber, meal, bread dough, or farina (think Cream of Wheat). Other common terms for mushroom smells include green corn, spermatic, fruity, garlic, and floral.

Use caution when taste testing unknown mushrooms. You don't want to accidentally nibble *and swallow* a potentially deadly species. For a taste test, chew a sliver of cap in the front part of your mouth. Latent bitterness may take a minute or two to manifest. Then, regardless of taste, spit the bite out. Rinse your mouth with water and spit again. To taste the milk of milk mushrooms, put a drop on your tongue. If the latex isn't instantly hotter than Hades, spread it around your mouth, alert for other flavors before spitting and rinsing.

CHEMICAL REACTIONS

The cap or other tissues of a mushroom might reliably change color when exposed to a particular chemical. Three solutions commonly used for color testing are easily obtained. Store them in sturdy, tightly sealed plastic bottles.

To chemically test a mushroom, cut off the piece you'll use and keep it away from anything you might later taste or cook—don't accidentally eat your chemistry experiments. Dip a clean cotton swab into the test solution, then gently dab or swipe it on your test piece. Get in the habit of applying chemicals in the same order and location, relative to each other. Observe and write down the results.

Although most chemical reactions consist of a single color change, this isn't always true, especially when it comes to ammonia, NH_4OH. Watch carefully for a fleeting **color flash** that quickly morphs to a different color. The difference between one bolete species and another may come down to the presence or absence of that flash.

Chemical tests can be fickle, depending on the age of your solutions and the age or condition of your mushroom. For the most reliable results, use fresh chemicals on a fresh, healthy specimen at room temperature. Parasitized, filthy, or waterlogged fungi may respond differently. If a mushroom was refrigerated, warm it to room temperature before testing. Due to the vagaries of chemical testing, our

Ammonium hydroxide (NH$_4$OH): ordinary household ammonia, without added scents, soaps, etc. Ammonia is also used as a mounting medium for microscopic work. It is ideal for dried mushrooms that have been rehydrated in a 70–95% solution of ethyl alcohol, such as 151-proof or 190-proof Everclear liquor.

Potassium hydroxide (KOH): 5–14% solution in distilled water. KOH is another mounting medium for microscopy with fresh or dried specimens. Spore colors reported in the microscopic features section of species descriptions are typically based on spores mounted in KOH. *This solution is caustic. If you get any on you, wash it off.* It slowly corrodes glass too; that's why it should be kept in a sturdy plastic bottle.

Iron salts (FeSO$_4$): 10% solution, by weight, of crystalline ferrous sulfate in distilled water. Mix only as much as you'll need for a few weeks. It will oxidize and lose potency in a month or two.

species descriptions only note reactions of major diagnostic importance.

MICROSCOPIC INFORMATION

Most mushrooms can be identified using characteristics visible to the unaided eye. Although we emphasize these features, species descriptions also include microscopic findings useful to people with access to a microscope equipped with an oil immersion lens and micrometer scale. Microscopic features within a species are consistent. You'll see information on spore size, shape, presence or absence of textural ornamentation, and color. Occasionally we provide details of cellular structure as well. Mushrooms with a very similar appearance often distinguish themselves under high magnification.

The mushrooms included in this book belong to two subdivisions of true fungi. Most of the species we describe produce spores on the exterior of microscopic club-shaped cells called **basidia** and are classified as **Basidiomycetes**. The remaining species produce their spores inside microscopic saclike cells called **asci** and are classified as **Ascomycetes**.

While it is possible to study spores taken directly from fresh or dried mushrooms, it's better to examine those produced by a spore print; those will be mature. Since spores are so tiny, they're measured in thousandths of a millimeter, **micrometers**, abbreviated as **μm**. If the spores of species X are listed as 6-10 μm long and 3-4 μm wide, those numbers reflect the size range of a representative sample of mature spores—usually a minimum of twenty.

Spore shape is significant, as is the surface texture. Colorless spores are referred to as **hyaline**. Spores are said to be **amyloid** when they appear blue-black in Melzer's reagent, a federally controlled chemical unavailable to laypeople. Spores that turn reddish-brown in Melzer's are **dextrinoid**. If no color change occurs, the spores are **inamyloid** or **not amyloid**.

HABITAT AND ECOLOGY

Fungi are as choosy as other creatures about where and how they carry on their lives. A mushroomer who notes the neighborhood where an unknown species occurs has a leg up on identifying it. *Suillus spraguei*, the Painted Bolete, grows only in association with eastern white pine. Meadow Mushrooms, *Agaricus campestris*, those tasty wild cousins of supermarket agarics, are produced by mycelia that dine on decomposing grass. A similar-looking agaric found near a rotting hardwood stump in the woods is more likely to be *Agaricus silvicola*.

The dietary habits of terrestrial fungi can be hard to know with certainty. Many mycorrhizal species are less specialized than Painted Boletes, and the underground connections between tree roots and mycelia are inconspicuous in any case, best left for professionals with DNA sequencers to fuss over. Saprotrophic and parasitic fungi often reveal food sources more readily. Their mushrooms may be glued to it. Buried wood is a frequent source of confusion. Mushrooms that seem to grow in soil may instead be attached to woody roots or dead and buried branches.

The Deer Mushroom, *Pluteus cervinus*, is an edible brown species fruiting on wood, which may be buried; it has free gills, no partial veil, and pink spores. Some *Entolomas*—inedible or poisonous brown species with nearly free gills, no partial veil, and pink spores—grow in soil, which may be *near* dead wood. Failure to prove an attachment to buried wood invites misidentification and a remorseful bellyache.

HOW TO USE THIS BOOK

This field guide helps users identify mushrooms by employing a mix of tactics. Nearly 650 species are a lot to look through, so we begin by narrowing things down with an illustrated Color Key followed, in some instances, by a secondary key to subgroups. After that, you'll browse mugshots of candidate species, searching for a visual match. But this, by itself, is dangerously inadequate. Looks are often deceiving. That's why written descriptions accompany the photographs. If your mushroom looks right but doesn't closely match the species description, it's probably something else. Try again.

IDENTIFICATION KEYS

The identification keys are comprised of sets of paired, either/or questions known as **couplets**. You'll be asked to choose between two alternatives. The answer you select will direct you to another couplet or a species name. Couplets share the same number in the key and are individualized by a letter designation. The first couplet of each key is labeled 1a and 1b. If your mushroom fits the statement in 1a, you'll be directed to a certain place. But if 1b fits instead, you'll jump ahead to a different place. Imagine it as a board game where you get to skip over couplets instead of spaces. The only couplets you should answer are the first one and those resulting from your responses thereafter.

To identify an unknown mushroom:

1. Compare it with the images and information provided in the Color Key. Determine which of the 20 major groups it belongs to.
2. Turn to the page listed for that group. Double-check yourself by reading the group header. If there is a key to subgroups, answer the first question

couplet, select the alternative best fitting your mushroom, then proceed as your answer directs. Attend to qualifiers; *usually, sometimes, frequently, typically, when young, at maturity*, and so forth are not absolutes. Don't force your mushroom to "fit" when neither choice in a couplet seems right. You may have an atypical specimen or a mushroom not discussed in the book, or perhaps you were led astray higher up in the key. If there is no key to subgroups, proceed to step 3.

3. Compare your mushroom with the photos of species in the candidate group. When something looks promising, read and consider all the information provided about that species, including Comments. Your mushroom might be noted in a comment but not fully described and illustrated. If this occurs, you'll be asked to search for the mentioned species online. As a search term, use the scientific name in quotes— "Agaricus bisporus," for example.
4. When you find a species photo and description fitting your mushroom, you have a prospective identification. As best you're able, double-check it with other field guides, online resources, and veteran mushroomers in your area.

FRUSTRATION

No amount of blood, sweat, tears, digging, or cursing may be enough to secure a solid ID. Perhaps you'll get as far as genus; sometimes not. Don't take it personally. The next time you encounter that species, the specimen in hand could be younger or older. Maybe experience will have taught you a little more. It's a wonder how many mysteries evaporate with repeated exposure.

SPECIES DESCRIPTION FORMAT

Scientific Name: Current genus and species epithet. It might be different than the name given elsewhere. When an older name is in frequent use, the Comments section may note it.

Author Citation: The name(s) of the person(s) credited for naming the mushroom immediately follows the scientific name.

Common Name: Provided when available.

Description: The observable characteristics of fresh specimens.

Spore Print: The color of a spore print.

Occurrence: Where the species is commonly found, its growth habit, and typical fruiting season(s).

Edibility: This may be fallible and/or incomplete. *A rating of edible does not necessarily mean edible for you.* See "Can You Eat It?" on p. 6.

Microscopic Features: Spore details and cellular information useful to identifiers with the necessary equipment.

Comments: May include alternate names and information on look-alikes or similar species not covered in the text. Some chemical test results are also provided.

The temptation to cram a mushroom into an ill-fitting species description can be overwhelming. Resist it. Especially when skillets are involved, the sackcloth and ashes of uncertainty can beat the heck out of the consequences of an identification error.

COLOR KEY TO THE MAJOR GROUPS OF FUNGI

GILLED MUSHROOMS

Cap undersurface with gills that radiate from the stalk, or point of attachment on stalkless species, to the margin of the cap. If the "gills" are particularly thick or stiff and you don't find your species here, also check the polypores group. If your species is reddish-orange and has blunt gills with crossveins, also check out the chanterelles.

Amanita porphyria
Cap with gray warts; gray partial veil and gray ring; p. 46.

Lepiota felina
Cap with erect, dark brown scales and dark disc; grows in conifer woods; p. 89.

Marasmius nigrodiscus
Cap brownish to creamy white with a persistent brown umbo and vertically lined white stalk; p. 133.

Panellus serotinus
Cap brown but tinged greenish to purplish; stalk short, stubby; in groups on decaying wood during fall or early winter; p. 105.

CHANTERELLES AND SIMILAR FUNGI

Cap undersurface has false gills that may fork or be connected by crossveins. False gills are usually thicker, shorter, and more triangular in cross section than true gills. The undersurface of some species may be smooth or nearly so.

Cantharellus cinnabarinus
Cap cinnabar red to reddish-orange, decurrent gills; p. 190.

Cantharellus phasmatis
Cap yellow, gill ridges white to cream, then yellowing at maturity; p. 192.

Craterellus cinereus
Cap solitary or in clusters; fertile surface decurrent, with veinlike ridges; odorless; p. 193.

Craterellus odoratus
Caps densely clustered, trumpet- to funnel-shaped; p. 194.

BOLETES

Fleshy mushrooms with a cap and stalk that usually grow on the ground, rarely on wood. The cap undersurface consists of a spongy layer of vertically arranged tubes terminating as pores. This tube layer usually separates easily from the cap tissue. Almost all boletes form mycorrhizal relationships with particular species of trees.

Aureoboletus roxanae
Cap 3-9 cm wide; stalk typically has a dull orange zone at the apex; no part stains blue; p. 200.

Leccinellum albellum
Cap white to grayish or brownish, often pitted; stalk has whitish to brownish scabers; p. 205.

POLYPORES

Tough and leathery to woody, often clamshell-shaped with tubes and pores on the underside of the cap; the tube layer does not easily separate from the cap tissue. They usually grow on wood, sometimes on the ground, and may be stalked or stalkless. Polypores grow singly, arranged in shelflike groups, or sometimes in complex overlapping clusters. Polypores with eroded tube layers can be confused for tooth fungi. Lumpish polypores without distinct caps may resemble crust fungi or carbon and cushion fungi. Close inspection with a hand lens may be necessary to visualize the tube-and-pore structure that separates polypores from these other groups. The pore surface of one species, *Inonotus obliquus*, is hidden under tree bark; it appears as a blackened cinder erupting through the bark of birch trees or, rarely, ironwood, elm, or beech.

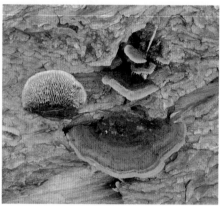

Gloeophyllum sepiarium
Cap stalkless; pore surface gill-like to mazelike; grows on conifer wood; p. 251.

Laetiporus cincinnatus
Cap bright orange to pinkish-orange; pore surface white; p. 268.

Trametes hirsuta
Cap stalkless, covered with coarse hairs, white to gray; margin often brownish; pore surface gray in age; pores minute; p. 274.

Trametes versicolor
Cap color highly variable, concentrically zoned; pore surface white to grayish; pores small; p. 274.

CRUST AND PARCHMENT FUNGI AND FIBER FANS

Crust and parchment fungi form tough and thin fruitbodies that are typically hard and crustlike to leathery or papery. They form somewhat flattened sheets that spread across the wood to which they are attached. Fiber fans and one species of parchment grow on the ground in rosettes or flaring trumpet shapes. The fertile surfaces of species in this group can be bumpy or wrinkled but not sandpapery rough, as in flat species of carbon and cushion fungi. They lack tubes and pores.

Chondrostereum purpureum
Fruitbody forming bright pink-violet to brown-violet wrinkled patches on dead hardwood; margin slightly fringed; p. 288.

Phlebia tremellosa
Fruitbody a spreading crust with a hairy whitish, upper surface and a yellowish to pinkish-orange lower surface; on logs; p. 284.

Thelephora terrestris
Circular to fan-shaped rosettes in clusters; margins coarsely torn; lower surface wrinkled and warted; p. 288.

Xylobolus frustulatus
Fruitbody a crustlike layer of numerous many-sided plates resembling broken pieces of dull ceramic tile; p. 289.

TOOTH FUNGI

Fleshy, leathery, or tough species with a fertile surface composed of uniformly shaped teeth or soft spines that hang downward. These teeth usually occur on the underside of a cap, but in the genus *Hericium*, the entire fruitbody is covered with them. Some species grow on the ground, others appear on wood, and one occurs on fallen pinecones. If the teeth appear irregular in shape or length, also consult the polypores section. If the toothed fungus has a gelatinous consistency, consider *Pseudohydnum gelatinosum* (p. 314).

Hydnellum ferrugineum
Fruitbody very similar to *Hydnellum spongiosipes* (p. 296), but its stalk base is smaller, and it grows under conifers.

Sarcodon joeides
Flesh dark violet; odor farinaceous; taste acrid to bitter; stalk base blackish-green; grows with oaks; p. 299.

CLUSTERED CORALS AND CAULIFLOWERS

Clustered corals are fleshy, solid, finger-shaped or repeatedly branched, flexible or brittle fruitbodies that are sometimes crowned with multiple upward-oriented points. They grow on the ground or on wood. Cauliflowers are large, rounded, flexible, cauliflower-shaped or leafy lettucelike stalked fruitbodies that resemble ribbon candy. They grow on the ground at the base of trees. If your unknown grows on wood and resembles a sparse growth of bright yellow grass less than an inch tall, see *Calocera cornea* (p. 311). If the stems of your fungus don't branch and you find no match here, check the earth tongues and earth clubs, the carbon and cushion fungi, and the *Cordyceps*, *Tolypocladium*, and similar fungi groups.

Ramaria spinulosa
Fruitbody up to 15 cm high and wide; branches creamy white to tan; base massive; on ground in mixed woods; p. 304.

Sparassis americana
Fruitbody a lettucelike cluster of fanlike branches; on the ground with conifers; p. 308.

JELLY FUNGI

Fruitbodies are distinctly gelatinous and can be soft or rubbery. They have highly variable shapes and colors. Some grow on the ground, others on wood. If your specimen doesn't key out here, consider the clustered corals, the earth clubs and earth tongues, and the cup fungi groups.

Auricularia angiospermarum
Fruitbody stalkless, ear-shaped to irregularly cup-shaped, rubbery-gelatinous; p. 310.

Ductifera pululahuana
Fruitbody a stalkless, whitish, convoluted, brainlike mass on barkless, decaying hardwood; p. 314.

STINKHORNS

Fruitbodies are egg-shaped when young, typically becoming pear-shaped, erect and phallic, squidlike, or ornately latticed as they mature. Mature specimens are partially coated with a foul-smelling, slimy spore mass that attracts a variety of flies and other organisms. Stinkhorns grow on the ground, in mulch, on wood chips, or on decaying wood.

Clathrus columnatus
Fruitbody consisting of orange to red columns fused at the tips, and a volva; spore mass fetid; p. 318.

Phallus ravenelii
Fruitbody consisting of a head, stalk, and volva; head has a white apical opening; spore mass fetid; p. 320.

Fruitbodies of this group are pear-shaped to irregularly rounded or star-shaped, with a thin or thick rindlike spore case that surrounds a soft, powdery interior when mature. Most species are stalkless or have a rudimentary stalk; a few are distinctly stalked. They usually grow on the ground or sometimes underground or on wood.

If you cut the specimen in half vertically and see what appears to be a baby gilled mushroom or stinkhorn inside, you have an "egg" from one of those groups. If your mushroom grows underground or partially so, consider species in the truffle section. If the interior is hard, it may be a member of the carbon and cushion fungi group.

Geastrum arenarium
Fruitbody a small earthstar about 1 cm wide, with 5-10 rays; pore mouth darker than the spore case; in sand; p. 323.

Lycoperdon americanum
Puffball 2.5-5 cm wide, covered with white spines with fused tips that become brown in age; p. 327.

Lycoperdon subincarnatum
Puffball is 1-3 cm wide, has reddish to purplish-brown spines, and grows on mossy hardwood logs and stumps; p. 328.

Rhizopogon roseolus
Fruitbody 1-2.5 cm wide, smooth, white when very young, soon reddish-brown, staining reddish when bruised; p. 330.

BIRD'S-NEST FUNGI AND THE SPHERE THROWER

Bird's-nest fungi are very small, cup- to vase-shaped fruitbodies that contain tiny egglike packets of spores called **peridioles**. Bird's-nests grow on wood, leaves, or other decaying matter. The sphere thrower has a tiny spore case that splits open at maturity to form a miniature star-shaped structure that surrounds a single peridiole. It grows on wood, dung, and other decaying matter.

Cyathus stercoreus
Cup brownish, exterior shaggy-hairy, interior not vertically lined; peridioles dark gray to black; p. 335.

Cyathus striatus
Cup brownish, exterior hairy, interior vertically lined; peridioles gray; p. 335.

CUP FUNGI

Species in this group have fruitbodies shaped like a cup, a saucer, or an animal ear. They may be stalked or stalkless and have flesh that is typically thin and brittle or, sometimes, rubbery. They lack gills, tubes, pores, or teeth and grow on the ground, on dung, or on decaying wood.

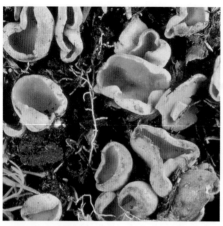

Caloscypha fulgens
Cup 1-5 cm wide, irregularly cup-shaped, often split on one side, margin stained dark bluish-green; p. 338.

Jafnea semitosta
Cup 2-5 cm wide, 2-7 cm high, interior whitish to creamy yellow, exterior pale yellowish-brown; p. 341.

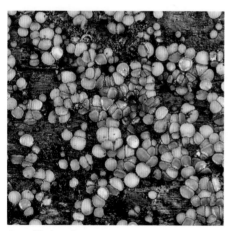

Scutellinia erinaceus
Cup 1.5-5 mm wide, interior pale to dull orange; exterior dull brownish-orange with long, stiff, brown hairs; p. 344.

Urnula craterium
Cup 2-7 cm wide, 4.5-11 cm high, dark brown to black; grows on wood in early spring; p. 345.

MORELS, FALSE MORELS, AND SIMILAR MUSHROOMS

Most members of this group have fruitbodies with a fertile head and a stalk that is at least partially hollow. The fertile surface is often conical to bell-shaped with pits and ridges, or saddle-shaped, wrinkled and brainlike, irregularly lobed, or sometimes nearly smooth. Members of this group grow on the ground or on decaying wood.

Helvella crispa
Cap saddle-shaped to irregularly lobed, creamy white to pale buff; stalk heavily ribbed and pitted; p. 349.

Helvella sulcata
Cap saddle-shaped to irregularly lobed, pale to dark gray; stalk heavily ribbed and pitted; p. 349.

Morchella americana
Fruitbody a busy network of randomly arranged ridges and pits on a whitish, granular, hollow stalk; p. 350.

Verpa conica
Fruitbody thimble- to bell-shaped, attached to the top of the stalk; hardwood or mixed woods, early spring; p. 352.

EARTH TONGUES AND EARTH CLUBS

This group includes ground-, wood-, or water-dwelling fungi shaped like vertical clubs, twigs, or stalks with odd-looking heads. Many species resemble spoons or spatulas or thick-headed nails. The heads may be smooth, finely textured, or minutely hairy, but are not roughened like sandpaper. They are mostly gelatinous to rubbery, but a few are woody. Unbranched coral fungi typically grow in clusters. If your specimen has a head with a rough texture, look at the carbon and cushion fungi and the *Cordyceps*, *Tolypocladium*, and similar fungi groups.

Microglossum rufum
Fruitbody consisting of a stalk and fertile head; growing on the ground, among mosses, or on wood; p. 356.

Trichoglossum farlowii
Fruitbody consisting of a stalk and fertile head; growing on the ground, among mosses, or on wood; p. 358.

CARBON AND CUSHION FUNGI

Species in this group have fruitbodies with highly variable shapes. Some are club-shaped to antlerlike, round to cushion-shaped, erect and cylindrical to club-shaped or highly irregular. Others are flat and somewhat circular or resemble thin spreading crusts. One species has a stalk and a head with a crown of tentacles. Many are soft and brightly colored; others are hard and blackish. They all have a roughened, sandpaper-like surface and usually grow on decaying wood or leaves. If you don't find a good match for your fungus here, also try the clustered corals, the earth clubs and earth tongues, and the *Cordyceps*, *Tolypocladium*, and similar fungi groups.

Diatrype stigma
Fruitbody a thin, blackish, smooth, or finely cracked, spreading crust on decaying hardwood; p. 362.

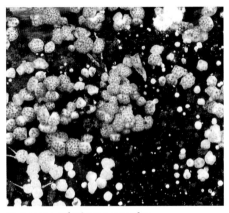

Hypocrea gelatinosa complex
Fruitbody 1-3 mm wide, cushion-shaped, yellow with green dots, or dark green; on decaying hardwood; p. 363.

Rhytisma americanum
Fruitbody circular, slightly raised, tarlike; only on red, silver, or sugar maple; p. 362.

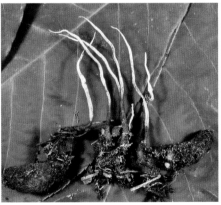

Xylaria oxyacanthae
Fruitbody 5-10 cm high, slender, filamentous, whitish or blackish; on hickory or pecan nuts or hawthorn fruits; p. 364.

CORDYCEPS, TOLYPOCLADIUM, AND SIMILAR FUNGI

Most of the representatives of this group have a head and stalk and are parasitic. Some invade living insects, others attack plants, and some grow on truffles. Their fertile surfaces are roughened like sandpaper. The presence of the parasitized host is a strong indicator of membership in this group. But in some species the host is easily disconnected or lost in the process of excavation.

Cordyceps militaris
Fruitbody consisting of a stalk and fertile head; on larvae and pupae of moths and butterflies; p. 367.

Purpureocillium atypicola
Fruitbody 1.5-3 cm high, cylindrical to spindle-shaped, scurfy; on buried woodland spiders; p. 367.

HYPOMYCES

These are parasitic fungi that cover and distort host mushrooms and use the host surface for production of spores. Commonly infected hosts include gilled mushrooms, boletes, polypores, and earth clubs. The fertile surface of the infected host may be powdery, moldy, or feathery and is often roughened like sandpaper.

Hypomyces chrysospermus
A mold that attacks boletes and gilled mushrooms, at first white, then yellow, and finally reddish-brown; p. 370.

Hypomyces completus
A mold that attacks boletes, especially *Suillus spraguei*, white at first, eventually yellow-brown to blackish; p. 370.

OTHER PLANT PATHOGENS

Fungi in this group are a mixed bag of agriculturally or horticulturally significant plant parasites likely to attract the attention of mushroom hunters. *Claviceps purpurea* forms hard, curved to spindle-shaped, purple to brownish-black fruitbodies on the seed heads of grasses. *Cryphonectria parasitica* (search online) forms bark-splitting cankers on the wood of American chestnut trees, a disease called chestnut blight. *Gymnosporangium juniperi-virginianae* produces swellings with orange to brown, jellylike horns on the branches and needles of cedar trees. *Ustilago maydis* makes whitish to silvery-gray, tumorlike growths on young ears of corn. Azalea, bilberry, blueberry, huckleberry, and other members of the heath family, as well as common sweetleaf, are parasitized by *Exobasidium* species that form a moldy white coating and later white or green galls on flowers, leaves, and shoots. *Uromyces ari-triphylli* (search online) and *Pucciniastrum potentillae* species attack jack-in-the-pulpits and cinquefoils, respectively, producing yellow or rusty orange patches on the leaves and stems of their host plants. *Taphrina alni* (search online) causes alder tongue gall, which resembles a long tongue protruding from a female alder catkin.

Exobasidium rhododendri
Greenish or white, irregular gall-like swellings on leaves of *Rhododendron* species; p. 374.

Exobasidium symploci
Greenish, gall-like swellings that become brown in age, on leaf buds and flowers of Common Sweetleaf; p. 375.

TRUFFLES AND OTHER UNDERGROUND FUNGI

Truffles and their relatives are usually round, or nearly so, and may have a smooth or conspicuously warted surface. They are not commonly collected because they are underground fungi and must be excavated. Partial or intact specimens are sometimes unearthed by squirrels or other animals that are attracted to the odor of the fruitbodies. Species in this group resemble earthballs or puffballs, but their interior is typically chambered, channeled, marbled, or somewhat hollow. If the fungus is found at ground level, consider the possibility that it belongs to the puffball group or is an "egg" of a gilled mushroom or stinkhorn.

Elaphomyces americanum
Fruitbody up to 2.7 cm wide, a stalkless, often warted spore case; spore mass marbled with white veins; p. 379.

Elaphomyces granulatus complex
Fruitbody up to 3.5 cm wide, a stalkless, often warted spore case; spore mass homogeneous, not marbled; p. 379.

Pachyphlodes species-20
Fruitbody 1-2 cm wide, a stalkless spore case ornamented by polygonal warts; spore mass marbled; p. 379.

Tuber canaliculatum
Fruitbody up to 7 cm wide, a stalkless spore case ornamented with low polygonal warts; spore mass marbled; p. 380.

SPECIES

DESCRIPTIONS

AND

ILLUSTRATIONS

GILLED MUSHROOMS

Several hundred species of gilled mushrooms are at home in the Carolinas. Only a fraction can be described here. We have emphasized species that attract attention due to their human importance or an eye-catching presentation. Still, the number is quite high. The key below simplifies identification somewhat by dividing the group into subgroups based on the color of the spore print. **Caution: gill color may be quite different than the color of the spore print.** See p. 11 for instructions on how to produce a spore print. Odor can be important in distinguishing many species of gilled mushrooms. Although many of the odors are easy to describe and recognize, "**farinaceous**" is especially difficult. Farinaceous is an odor variously compared to sliced watermelon rind, cucumber, meal, bread dough, or farina (think Cream of Wheat).

Use the following key to narrow down the gilled mushrooms suspect list.

KEY TO GILLED MUSHROOMS AND SIMILAR FUNGI

1a Mushroom with a stalk; cap some shade of red or brown; gills yellow or pale to dark olive-buff, decurrent, sometimes porelike, variably elongated and radially arranged..*Phylloporus* (p. 202-3)

1b Mushroom not entirely as above 2

2a Mushroom a stalkless cap growing on wood; "gills" woody or stiff like cardboard .... Polypores (p. 246)

2b Mushroom not as above, but may lack a stalk 3

3a Mushroom reddish-orange; cap typically less than 4 cm wide; "gills" thick, soft, and forking, lacking short gills .... *Cantharellus cinnabarinus* (p. 190)

3b Mushroom not entirely as above 4

4a Spore print green or greenish-gray; cap 7-30 cm wide, white, covered with pinkish-brown patches when young; gills initially white, becoming gray-green at maturity .... *Chlorophyllum molybdites* (p. 86)

4b Spore print some other color; mushroom not as above...5

5a Spore print white, cream, yellow, lavender, or faintly pinkish 6

5b Spore print some other color, including pink 12

6a Mushroom with a volva at the stalk base or typically with warts or patches on the cap .... *Amanita* (p. 43)

6b Mushroom lacking a volva, warts, or patches, but cap may have scales or other features 7

7a Mushroom growing on soil; gills typically exude latex (milk or variously colored liquid) when injured...Milk Mushrooms (p. 59)

7b Mushroom not as above 8

8a Mushroom growing on soil; stalk usually thicker than 3 mm, brittle or crumbly; can be dense but not tough or fibrous ....*Russula* (p. 77)

8b Mushroom not as above 9

9a Mushroom with a partial veil or ring zone at least in youth .... Group A (p. 84); see also *Pleurotus dryinus* (p. 107) and *Tricholoma* (p. 112)

9b Mushroom not as above 10

10a Mushroom lacking a stalk, or with a rudimentary stalk, or with a well-developed stalk *and* gills that are at least slightly decurrent ....Group B (p. 94); see also *Hygrocybe* (p. 127), *Lyophyllum decastes* (p. 130), *Mycena semivestipes* (p. 136), and *Tetrapyrgos nigripes* (p. 138)

10b Mushroom not entirely as above 11

11a Mushroom medium-sized or large, commonly with a stalk diameter of 7 mm or more, growing on the ground but not densely clustered from a single base; gills not thickened, waxy, slimy, or a shade of pink or purple in youth............... Group C (p. 111)

11b Mushroom with a thinner stalk and gills that are free or attached to the stalk but not notably decurrent... Group D (p. 120); see also *Armillaria tabescens* (p. 85), *Clitocybe odora* (p. 96), *Laccaria* (p. 101), *Leucopaxillus albissimus* (p. 104), *Tricholomopsis* (p. 118), and *Xeromphalina tenuipes* (p. 110)

12a Spore print distinctly pink, salmon, or pinkish-tan ....Pink-spored species (p. 139)

12b Spore print some other color... 13

13a Spore print olive-yellow, yellowish-brown, rusty orange, or brown to dark brown .... Brown-spored species (p. 150)

13b Spore print sooty gray, purplish, brownish-black, or black 14

14a Mature gills liquefying and forming a black inky fluid...
.... Dark-spored species with liquefying gills (p. 178)

14b Mature gills not liquefying...................... Dark-spored species with nonliquefying gills (p. 182); see also *Coprinellus disseminatus* (p. 179)

PALE- OR GREEN-SPORED SPECIES

This is a large, mixed group. Mushrooms described here differ from one another in ways that may be great or small. Read the descriptions carefully and match all characteristics to the mushroom in question. The color and other details of physical appearance are only part of the story. Is the center of the cap raised in an **umbo** or sunken, perhaps even **umbilicate** (like a navel)? Is the cap **hygrophanous** (drastically fading in color as it dries)? Are the gills so attached to the stalk that they are **decurrent** (running down the stalk)? If there is or was a partial veil, was it **membranous** (solid tissue), **cortinaceous** (spider-webby), or **fibrous** (somewhere in between)? Did it merely leave a circular **ring zone** around the stalk? You may need to smell or taste the specimen—being sure to spit and rinse, not swallow, the chewed pulp. The particulars of habit and habitat may be crucial information. Was the mushroom growing singly or as part of a clump? To what, if anything, was it attached? Many of these species are recyclers. While not always the case, the base of the mushroom may be attached to a species-specific food source, either by mycelium or thickened cords called **rhizomorphs**. For species apparently growing in soil, excavate carefully if there is any question of a hidden connection to buried wood or roots. If the spore print of your mushroom is an awkward shade of pale orange, pink, or tan and no species in this section matches the specimen, consider the possibility that it might be described in the pink-spored group.

Odor can be important in distinguishing many species of gilled mushrooms. Although many of the odors are easy to describe and recognize, "**farinaceous**" is especially difficult. Farinaceous is an odor variously compared to sliced watermelon rind, cucumber, meal, bread dough, or farina (think Cream of Wheat).

Some pale-spored mushrooms are good edibles but may require very thorough cooking (honey mushrooms) to prevent gastrointestinal distress. Honey mushrooms parasitized by *Entoloma abortivum* become the visually disgusting but delicious pale gray blobs mistakenly termed "Aborted Entolomas." Two poisonous pale-spored species are frequently confused for edibles. *Chlorophyllum molybdites* usually wins the coveted Porcelain Toadstool Award for most reported cases of mushroom poisoning in the United States. The Jack O'Lantern, *Omphalotus illudens*, a species sometimes mistaken for chanterelles, is another frequent offender in the Carolinas.

Genus *Amanita*

David Arora's classic tome *Mushrooms Demystified* begins its discussion of Amanitas by urging mushroomers to make an overriding priority of learning to recognize the genus. He's right. These mushrooms are conspicuous and often colorful. Many are dangerously toxic when ingested, some fatally so. The Destroying Angel, very common in the Carolinas, is among the world's deadliest. While certain Amanitas are rated "edible," none are recommended in this book. It is too easy to make mistakes with look-alikes or species that have yet to be formally recognized, let alone studied in terms of edibility. The 28 species described and illustrated here represent less than a fifth of the Amanitas thought to occur in the Carolinas.

Fortunately, it is possible to distinguish Amanitas from other mushrooms by combinations of readily observable characteristics. Members of this genus are ground-dwellers. Caps are sticky or slimy when young, later drying out. They are often decorated with **warts**, **patches**, **fluff**, or **powder** that may wash off after rains. Some have a central hump, the **umbo**. Cap margins may feature grooved **radial lines** or be **shaggy** with dangling fragments of veil tissue. Gills are white or pale in color, free of the stalk or slightly attached to it. Spore prints are white.

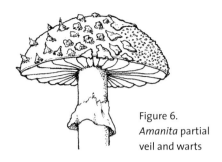

Figure 6.
Amanita partial veil and warts

Amanita mushrooms begin as rounded "eggs" forming at or just below the soil surface. The "eggshell," known as the universal veil or **volva**, ruptures when the mushroom "hatches." The character and disposition of volval remnants is species specific. It might remain largely intact, as a basal sack. (Other types of mushrooms growing from a saclike volva have pink or brown spores.) In other *Amanita* species the volva fragments into patches, warts, fluff, or powders that at least initially adhere to the sticky cap. (It may be necessary to look closely to distinguish warts from the cap scales often found in other genera. Scales are sections of cap surface that partially tear loose and may appear to overlap like feathers or shingles.)

Many Amanitas also have a **partial veil** protecting the gills from premature exposure. In mature mushrooms it may persist as a skirt that is often, but not always, located high on the stalk. In some species, threads or soft chunks of it hang from the cap margin. The fate and characteristics of the partial veil are also species specific.

The base of the stalk is diagnostic as well. It may rise out of a saclike volva, mimic a root vegetable, or be decorated with rings or scales. The entire base of the stalk should be collected, including any flakes of loose mushroom material or a rooting base.

Odor can be important in distinguishing Amanitas. Although many of the odors present in *Amanita* species are easy to

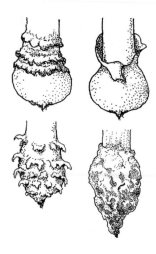

Figure 7. Various *Amanita* bases

describe and recognize, "**farinaceous**" is especially difficult. Farinaceous is an odor variously compared to sliced watermelon rind, cucumber, meal, bread dough, or farina (think Cream of Wheat). We do not advise tasting and spitting out the flesh, let alone consuming any member of the genus. Painful gastrointestinal symptoms are the mildest toxic consequence of a mistake. Depending on species, other possibilities include unpleasant neurological syndromes, kidney failure, and death from liver failure. Don't risk your life for a mushroom dinner.

Amanita abrupta Peck
AMERICAN ABRUPT-BULBED LEPIDELLA

Description: Cap 3.5-10 cm wide, spherical as a button, then convex and flattening with age, white, covered with spiky white warts that may wash off. Cap margin shaggy, not lined. Gills are free and closely spaced, white. The partial veil is persistent and dangling, white, with radial lines on the upper surface. Stalks are 4.5-9 cm long, up to 1 cm thick, white. The abrupt basal bulb is often topped by concentric ridges. Flesh white, no distinct odor.

Spore Print: White.

Occurrence: Conifer or hardwood forests. Summer-fall.

Edibility: Unknown.

Microscopic Features:
Spores 7-9 × 6-7.5 µm, subglobose to ellipsoid, smooth. Hyaline, amyloid.

Comments: The combination of the rounded basal bulb, spiky warts, and lack of a pronounced odor separate this species from most others. But see the larger *Amanita polypyramis*.

Amanita banningiana Tulloss, nom. prov.
YELLOW CAESAR

Description: Cap 4-11.5 cm wide, convex but flattening with age, bronze at the umbo, fading to yellow at a strongly lined cap margin. No warts. Gills are free or slightly attached, pale yellow, close to crowded. The partial veil is pale yellow or whitish, persistent and dangling. Stalk is 8-22 cm long and up to 1.5 cm thick, pale yellow. It arises from a sturdy, white, saclike volva. No distinct smell.

Spore Print: White.

Occurrence: Solitary or scattered under hardwoods or in mixed forests. Summer.

Edibility: Unknown.

Microscopic Features:
Spores 8.5-12 × 6-8 µm, elliptical, smooth. Hyaline, inamyloid.

Comments: This species was tentatively named by Dr. Rod Tulloss. The brownish center of the cap distinguishes it from *Amanita jacksonii* and *A. parcivolvata*. The latter lacks a skirt. *Amanita spreta* has a grayish to dirty brown cap and a volval sack that may flare away from the stalk.

Amanita bisporigera G. F. Atk.
DESTROYING ANGEL

Description: Cap 5-12 cm wide, convex then flattening, white but may darken toward the center. Cap margin not lined. Gills are free or slightly attached, close, white. The dangling partial veil is persistent and white. Stalk is 8-20 cm long, up to 2 cm thick, white. The base is a rounded saclike volva with a free margin that may cling to the stalk. Flesh white. Odor usually not distinctive.

Spore Print: White.

Occurrence: Scattered or in groups under hardwoods or conifers, near trees in lawns or parks. Early summer-fall.

Edibility: Deadly poisonous. One cap can kill an adult.

Microscopic Features:
Spores 7-10 × 6.5-9 µm, globose to broadly elliptical, smooth. Hyaline, amyloid.

Comments: This deadly species is as common as it is beautiful. Learning it is a critical priority for all mushroomers. *Leucoagaricus leucothites* (search online), formerly *L. naucinus*, has a lumpy cap in the button stage and lacks the saclike volva.

Amanita brunnescens G. F. Atk.
CLEFT-FOOT AMANITA
Description: Cap 3-15 cm wide, convex but flattening, usually some streaky shade of brown, sometimes mottled with white or reddish-brown stains. The few gray or tan warts easily wash off. Cap margin may be faintly lined. Gills free from the stalk, close, white, often with reddish stains. The dangling partial veil is thin and white. Stalk is 5-15 cm long, up to 2 cm thick, white, bruising reddish-brown. The abrupt bulb usually sports a wide vertical cleft. Flesh white, bruising red or brown. Odor of raw potato.
Spore Print: White.
Occurrence: Scattered or in groups in hardwoods or mixed woods. Summer-fall.
Edibility: Unknown.
Microscopic Features: Spores 8-9 × 7-8.5 µm, nearly globose, smooth. Hyaline, amyloid.
Comments: A white mushroom with otherwise similar features is variously treated as a variety of *Amanita brunnescens* or *A. aestivalis*, but see also *A. mutabilis*. The red-bruising *Amanita rubescens* is stouter and has a differently shaped bulb.

Amanita ceciliae complex
(Berk. & Broome) Bas
SNAKESKIN GRISETTE
Description: Cap 5.5-12 cm wide, convex then flat at maturity, brown, darkest centrally, adorned with gray-brown patches and warts. The cap margin is radially lined. Gills are free and close, white turning grayish. No partial veil. Stalk 7-16 cm long and up to 2 cm thick, pale gray, often with brown, flattened, hairlike fibrils. The base is not swollen. Volva consists of broken grayish patches around the base. Flesh white. Odor not distinctive.
Spore Print: White.
Occurrence: Scattered or in groups in hardwood and mixed forests. Summer.
Edibility: Unknown.
Microscopic Features: Spores 10.5-15 × 9.5-14.5 µm, globose, smooth. Hyaline, inamyloid.
Comments: *Amanita ceciliae* is a European name probably used for several American species. *Amanita brunnescens* has a white skirt. The skirt of *A. porphyria* is gray, and the cap may be tinged purple (see photo on p. 19). See also *Amanita onusta* and *A. vaginata*.

Amanita cokeri
E.-J. Gilbert & Kühner ex E.-J. Gilbert
COKER'S LEPIDELLA
Description: Cap 8-14 cm wide, oval, then flattening at maturity, white, covered with pointed white to brownish warts. The cap margin is shaggy, not radially lined. Gills are free or slightly attached, close, white. Partial veil is a thick, dangling skirt, lined on top, shaggy beneath, white. Stalk 11-20 cm long and 1-2.3 cm wide, white. The bulbous base is shallowly rooting and crowned by rings of cream to brown recurved scales. Flesh white. Odor not distinctive.
Spore Print: White.
Occurrence: Scattered or in groups in mixed woods. Summer-fall.
Edibility: Unknown.
Microscopic Features:
Spores 11-13 × 6.5-8.5 µm, elliptical, smooth. Hyaline, amyloid.
Comments: This mushroom was named in honor of North Carolina mycologist William Chambers Coker (1872-1953). The typical lack of odor, together with the circles of hooked basal scales and shallowly rooting bulb, separate this species from other large *Lepidellas*.

Amanita daucipes (Sacc.) Lloyd
TURNIP-FOOTED LEPIDELLA
Description: Cap 6-29 cm wide, convex expanding to nearly flat, white, covered with soft chunky warts that are white in the button, salmon-pink in youth, and gray in age. The cap margin is shaggy, not radially lined. Gills are free or slightly attached, close, pale yellow. Partial veil is a dangling skirt with orangish particles on the underside; it is often lost. Stalk 14.5-19 cm long (excluding bulb) and 1-3.3 cm thick, white with a sprinkling of colored particles. The massive rooting base is 6-15 by 3-6 cm, turnip- or carrot-shaped. Flesh white, unchanging when bruised, but old wounds redden. Odor of hambone or chlorine.
Spore Print: White.
Occurrence: Scattered or in groups with oak or in mixed woods. Summer-fall.
Edibility: Unknown.
Microscopic Features:
Spores 8-11.5 × 5-8 µm, elliptical, smooth. Hyaline, amyloid.
Comments: Also called the Carrot-foot. The combination of size, hambone odor, color, and rooting base dimensions are distinctive identification features.

Amanita farinosa Schwein.
POWDER-CAP AMANITA
Description: Cap 2.5-6.5 cm wide, convex then flat at maturity, brownish-gray, darkest at the center. Cap margin is strongly lined. Cap and upper surface of the basal bulb dusted with fine brownish-gray powder. Gills are free and close, white. No partial veil. Stalk 3-6.5 cm long and up to 1 cm thick, white to pale gray. The base is swollen and powdered with the same material as the cap. Flesh white. Odor not distinctive.
Spore Print: White.
Occurrence: Scattered or in groups under hardwood and mixed forests, especially along the margins. Also found in grass near trees. Summer-fall.
Edibility: Unknown.
Microscopic Features:
Spores 6.5-9 × 5.5-7 µm, subglobose to elliptical, smooth. Hyaline, inamyloid.
Comments: If the powder washes off the cap, this small species could be mistaken for a miniature *Amanita vaginata*. The cap of *Amanita cinereoconia* (search online) usually sports patches of fluffy gray powder and smells like chlorine.

Amanita flavoconia G. F. Atk.
YELLOW PATCHES
Description: Cap 3-9 cm wide, convex then flattening, orange to brownish-yellow, decorated with flat patches of yellow volva material that easily wash off. Cap margin is usually unlined. Gills are free or slightly attached, close, white. The dangling partial veil is pale yellow to yellow. Stalk is 5-10 cm long, up to 1.5 cm thick, pale yellow or yellow, smoothly transitioning to a small basal bulb. Yellow fragments of volva are found in soil around the bulb. Flesh white. No distinct smell.
Spore Print: White.
Occurrence: Scattered or in groups under hardwoods or in mixed woods. Summer-fall.
Edibility: Unknown.
Microscopic Features:
Spores 7-9 × 5-7 µm, elliptical, smooth. Hyaline, amyloid.
Comments: The cap margin of *Amanita parcivolvata* is strongly lined. *Amanita frostiana* (search online) has a lined cap margin, collared bulb, and inamyloid spores. The cap of *Amanita lavendula* has a greenish tinge in youth and off-white to lavender warts.

Amanita franchetii (Boud.) Fayod
FRANCHET'S AMANITA
Description: Cap 3-8.5 cm wide, convex
but flattening, golden- to grayish-
brown, the margin not lined, covered
with yellowish warts or patches that
may wash off. Gills are barely attached,
crowded, white. Partial veil a white
to yellowish dangling skirt. Stalk 6-12
cm long, up to 2 cm thick, expanding
downward to a slightly enlarged
bulb, white to yellowish. Remnants
of the volva may appear as yellow
flakes around the base. Flesh white,
not bruising when injured. Odor not
distinctive.
Spore Print: White.
Occurrence: Scattered or in groups
under hardwoods or in mixed woods.
Summer-fall.
Edibility: Unknown.
Microscopic Features:
Spores 7.5-9 × 5.5-6.5 µm, subglobose
to broadly elliptic, smooth. Hyaline,
amyloid.
Comments: According to Dr. Rod Tulloss,
Amanita franchetii is a European
species. He refers to the North
American version as *Amanita sp-36*.
The lack of red-staining flesh separates
it from *Amanita rubescens*. *Amanita
russuloides* has paler colors and a
different base.

Amanita fulva Fr.
TAWNY GRISETTE
Description: Cap 4-10 cm wide, convex
but flattening, brown over the umbo,
lightening to tawny at the strongly
lined margin. No warts. Gills are free
or barely attached, crowded, white. No
partial veil. Stalk 7-16 cm long, up to
1.5 cm thick, hollow, white to pale tan.
The base is not swollen. Volva is a thin
white sack collapsed around the base,
darkening in age. Flesh white. Odor not
distinctive.
Spore Print: White.
Occurrence: Scattered or in groups under
hardwoods and conifers. Summer-fall.
Edibility: Edible, not recommended.
Microscopic Features:
Spores 9-12 × 9-11 µm, globose
to subglobose, smooth. Hyaline,
inamyloid.
Comments: *Amanita fulva* is a European
species. Dr. Rod Tulloss has proposed
Amanita amerifulva for the North
American variety. Compare with
Amanita banningiana, *A. brunnescens*,
and *A. vaginata*. An Orange Grisette,
tentatively named *Amanita
pseudocrocea* (search online) by Dr.
Tulloss, might occur in North Carolina.

Amanita hesleri Bas
HESLER'S LEPIDELLA

Description: Cap 3-10 cm wide, convex then flattening, with or without a low umbo or central depression, white to pale, covered with brown to grayish-brown warts, margin shaggy and faintly lined or unlined. Gills attached, initially white, sometimes pinkening in age, crowded. Partial veil flimsy, leaving remnants on the cap margin but seldom on the stalk. Stalk 4-14 cm long including the bulb, up to 1.5 cm thick, white, covered with soft whitish fibrils or scales; the bulb is club-shaped or simply swollen. The volva is either obscure or present as a few dark scales or warts atop the bulb. Odor not distinctive.

Spore Print: White.

Occurrence: Scattered or in groups in mixed woods with oaks, occasionally under pines. Summer-fall.

Edibility: Unknown.

Microscopic Features:
Spores 9.5-12.5 × 5-6.5 μm, elliptical, smooth. Hyaline, amyloid.

Comments: Also known as *Aspidella hesleri*. The typically smaller *Amanita onusta* has a more evident volva and odor of chlorine or rotting meat.

Amanita jacksonii Pomerl.
AMERICAN CAESAR

Description: cap 7-14 cm wide, hot orange to bright red at the umbo, yellowing toward a strongly lined margin. No warts. Gills are free of the stalk, yellow to orange-yellow, close to crowded. The partial veil is a yellow-orange skirt, radially lined on top. Stalks are 9-15 cm long and up to 1.5 cm thick, yellow, decorated with orange fibrils or scales. The volva is a sturdy white sack. No distinct smell.

Spore Print: White.

Occurrence: Solitary or scattered under oaks or pines. Summer-fall.

Edibility: Edible, not recommended.

Microscopic Features:
Spores 8-10 × 6-7.5 μm, elliptical, smooth. Hyaline, inamyloid.

Comments: The gorgeous American Caesar is larger than *Amanita parcivolva*, which lacks a skirt and, at least initially, has warts. *Amanita banningiana* has a bronze umbo. *Amanita arkansana* (search online) is larger and has a white skirt.

Amanita lavendula (Coker) Tulloss, K. W. Hughes, Rodrig. Cayc. & Kudzma complex
COKER'S LAVENDER-STAINING AMANITA
Description: Cap 5-12 cm wide, convex then flattening, pale greenish-yellow fading at maturity to whitish, flecked with off-white to pale lavender warts that easily wash off. Cap margin unlined to slightly lined. Gills free or slightly attached, close, white. The dangling partial veil is pale yellow. Stalk 6-13 cm long, up to 2 cm wide, white. The basal bulb is abrupt, sometimes vertically split, and often topped by a rim of off-white volva material. Flesh white. Odor of raw potato.
Spore Print: White.
Occurrence: Solitary or scattered under hardwoods or in mixed woods. Late summer-fall.
Edibility: Likely poisonous.
Microscopic Features:
Spores 5.5-9 µm, globose, smooth. Hyaline, amyloid.
Comments: *Amanita citrina* f. *lavendula* (Coker) Veselý is a synonym. *Amanita citrina* Pers. is a European species not found in North America. The deadly *Amanita phalloides* (search online) has a greenish-tinged cap and might occur in the Carolinas.

Amanita longipes
Bas ex Tulloss & D. T. Jenkins
DOG-LEGGED LEPIDELLA
Description: Cap 2-10 cm wide, hemispheric becoming broadly convex, pale gray or grayish-brown over the center, fading to white at the margin, covered with fluffy white to pale gray powder. Cap margin is inrolled at first, shaggy, not radially lined. Gills are attached, close, white. No partial veil on the stalk of an open cap. Stalk 2.5-15 cm long and 0.5-2 cm thick, white. The rooting base is elongated and flattened or bent, often topped with white, fluffy powder. Flesh white. Odor not distinctive or weakly of disinfectant.
Spore Print: White.
Occurrence: Solitary or scattered in mixed woods. Summer-fall. Occasional.
Edibility: Unknown.
Microscopic Features:
Spores 10-14 × 4.5-6 µm, elliptical to cylindrical, smooth. Hyaline, amyloid.
Comments: *Amanita chlorinosma* (search online) is larger and smells of chlorine or old ham. The provisionally named *Amanita tephrea* (search online) is pale gray in maturity and has no distinct smell.

GILLED MUSHROOMS

Amanita multisquamosa Peck
SMALL FUNNEL-VEIL AMANITA
Description: Cap 3-11 cm wide, convex and flattening at maturity, whitish overall, sometimes with a darker center, covered with numerous pale warts that often wash off. Cap margin is faintly lined. Gills free or narrowly attached to the stalk, crowded, white. The partial veil is white, often pulled up into a funnel shape. Stalk is 3.5-15 cm long, to 1.5 cm thick, white. The expanded bulb is topped by a rolled collar of volva tissue. Flesh white. No distinct smell.
Spore Print: White.
Occurrence: Solitary or scattered in hardwoods or mixed woods. Summer-fall.
Edibility: Poisonous.
Microscopic Features:
Spores 7-11 × 5.5-8.5 μm, subglobose to elliptical, smooth. Hyaline, inamyloid.
Comments: *Amanita cothurnata* was a previous name. *Amanita lavendula* and *A. russuloides* have yellower caps. *Amanita velatipes* is larger and has a more highly colored cap. *Amanita aestivalis* (search online) slowly bruises brown and lacks the rolled bulb collar.

Amanita muscaria var. *guessowii* Veselý
YELLOW FLY AGARIC
Description: Cap 5-20 cm wide, convex and then flattening, pale yellow to orange, darkest at center. Numerous cream-colored warts darken with age but may wash off. Margin often weakly lined at maturity. Gills free or narrowly attached, crowded, white. The dangling partial veil is thin but persistent, white. Stalk is 6-15 cm long, up to 3 cm thick, white to cream-colored, the lower portion with multiple partial or complete rings of volva tissue. The stalk base is slightly bulbed. Flesh white. No distinct smell.
Spore Print: White.
Occurrence: Solitary or scattered with conifers or hardwoods. Summer-fall. Common in the Southern Appalachians.
Edibility: Poisonous.
Microscopic Features:
Spores 9-12 × 6.5-8 μm, elliptical, smooth. Hyaline, inamyloid.
Comments: *Amanita persicina* occurs at lower elevations. Compare with *Amanita velatipes* and the smaller *A. frostiana* (search online), which has a roll of volva tissue at the neck of the bulb.

Amanita mutabilis Beardslee

Description: Cap 4.5-11 cm wide, cushion-shaped then flattening, white to tan, often partly covered by a thin, white volval patch. Cap margin may be slightly shaggy, not lined. Gills free or narrowly attached to the stalk, close, pale cream. The dangling partial veil is thin, white. Stalk is 6-11 cm long, up to 2 cm thick. The round to oval bulb typically is topped by a free fringe of volva material. Flesh white. All parts quickly bruise/stain raspberry red. Odor frequently of anise.

Spore Print: White.

Occurrence: Often found in groups under low country hardwoods or mixed woods. Summer.

Edibility: Unknown.

Microscopic Features:
Spores 10-14.5 × 6-8 μm, elliptical to elongate, smooth. Hyaline, amyloid.

Comments: The smell of anise distinguishes this member of the *Lepidella* section from other red-staining Amanitas. Compare with *Amanita volvata*, *A. peckiana* (search online), and other poorly differentiated species in *Amanita* section *Amidella*, all of which have a saclike volva.

Amanita onusta (Howe) Sacc.
GUNPOWDER LEPIDELLA

Description: Cap 3-8 cm wide, convex, flattening, grayish, with concentric circles of brownish-gray warts; margin shaggy, not radially lined. Gills free or nearly so, loosely spaced to close, white, soon waterlogged and yellow. Shreds of white partial veil usually hang from the upper stalk and cap margin. Stalk up to 15 cm long, 1.5 cm thick, white at the apex, graying below, elongated into a rooting base ringed on top by gray warts or recurved scales. Flesh white. Odor of chlorine or rotting meat.

Spore Print: White.

Occurrence: Solitary or scattered in oak or mixed forests. Late spring-fall.

Edibility: Unknown.

Microscopic Features:
Spores 8-11 × 5.5-7 μm, elliptical, smooth. Hyaline, amyloid.

Comments: The warts of the larger *Amanita atkinsoniana* (search online) usually have a reddish tinge. The Gray Rags Lepidella, *Amanita cinereopannosa* (search online), has a larger, white, sticky cap, pale gray partial veil remnants, and a farinaceous odor. Also compare with *Amanita hesleri*.

GILLED MUSHROOMS

Amanita parcivolvata (Peck) E.-J. Gilbert
RINGLESS FALSE FLY AGARIC
Description: Cap 3-12 cm wide, convex and flattening with age, hot orange to scarlet with a few pale yellow warts that easily wash off. The cap margin is strongly lined. Gills are free and close, white to cream-colored. No partial veil. Stalk 3-10 cm long, up to 1.5 cm thick, pale yellow to white. The base is often slightly swollen, may be topped by yellow flakes or a concentric ridge of volva tissue. Flesh white. Odor mildly unpleasant or not indistinctive.
Spore Print: White.
Occurrence: Solitary or scattered with oaks or pines. Late spring–fall.
Edibility: Unknown.
Microscopic Features:
   Spores 9-11.5 × 6.5-8 µm, elliptical, smooth. Hyaline, inamyloid.
Comments: This species resembles a miniature red Fly Agaric. A cap washed free of warts could also be confused for *Amanita jacksonii*, but that species has a partial veil and saclike volva.

Amanita persicina
(Dav. T. Jenkins) Tulloss & Geml
PEACH-COLORED FLY AGARIC
Description: Cap 4-20 cm wide, convex and then flattening, pale orange to melon orange, darkest centrally. Numerous yellow warts may wash off. Margin often weakly lined at maturity. Gills free or narrowly attached, crowded, cream-colored, may have a pinkish tinge. The dangling partial veil is thin, white. Stalk 8-25 cm long, up to 3 cm thick, white, the lower portion with scattered fragments of volva tissue. The stalk base is slightly expanded. Flesh white. No distinct smell.
Spore Print: White.
Occurrence: Solitary or scattered near conifers or in mixed woods. Summer–fall. Common in the Piedmont and low country.
Edibility: Poisonous.
Microscopic Features:
   Spores 7-13 × 6-8.5 µm, elliptical, smooth. Hyaline, inamyloid.
Comments: *Amanita muscaria* var. *persicina* Dav. T. Jenkins is a synonym. The classic red Fly Agaric is a western species. See comments under *Amanita muscaria* var. *guessowii*. Compare with *Amanita flavoconia* and *A. parcivolvata*.

Amanita polypyramis
(Berk. & M. A. Curtis) Sacc.
PLATE FULL OF PYRAMIDS LEPIDELLA
Description: Cap 7.5-20 cm wide, convex before flattening, white, covered with soft, pyramidal, white warts that disintegrate with age. Cap margin shaggy, not radially lined. Gills are free and close to crowded, white to cream. The partial veil is flimsy and soon lost. Stalks are 9-20 cm long and 2-3.5 cm thick, white. The rounded basal bulb, to 5 cm wide, expands smoothly from the stalk, may elongate with age, and is sprinkled with fluffy white powder. Flesh white, odor of chlorine or spoiled meat.

Spore Print: White.

Occurrence: Solitary or scattered, associated with oak and pines. Summer-fall.

Edibility: Probably poisonous.

Microscopic Features:
Spores 9-13 × 6-7.5 μm, elliptical, smooth. Hyaline, amyloid.

Comments: Compare the smooth upper surface of the bulb with *Amanita cokeri* and the smaller *A. abrupta*. The rooting bulb of other large *Lepidellas* typically has a different shape. *Amanita chlorinosma* (search online) is smaller.

Amanita ravenelii (Berk. & Broome) Sacc.
PINECONE LEPIDELLA
Description: Cap 8-20 cm wide, convex then flattening, white, covered with pinecone-like rings of yellowish to brown warts that resemble scales anchored by stretched fibrils; margin shaggy, unlined. Gills free or attached, crowded, cream-colored. The thick partial veil tends to fall off. Stalk (excluding bulb) 9-12 cm long by 1-3 cm, white, may show rings of volva material above the rooting bulb. Bulb 7-20 cm long, 3-6 cm thick, often showing long cracks or rusty stains and a dog-leg bend. Flesh white. Odor of chlorine or old ham.

Spore Print: White.

Occurrence: Solitary or scattered in hardwood or mixed forests. Late summer-fall.

Edibility: Unknown.

Microscopic Features:
Spores 8-12 × 5-7.5 μm, elliptic, smooth. Hyaline, amyloid.

Comments: This species honors South Carolina mycologist Henry William Ravenel (1814-87). *Amanita daucipes* has different warts and usually a shorter bulb. *Amanita rhopalopus* (search online) has a narrower bulb and randomly arranged warts lacking marginal fibrils.

Amanita rubescens Pers.

BLUSHER

Description: Cap 5-14 cm wide, convex, flattening at maturity, tan- to reddish-brown, often with red stains, initially covered with yellow warts that fade to pinkish-tan and easily wash off. Margin not lined. Gills free or narrowly attached, close, white, discoloring reddish. The dangling partial veil is persistent, white. Stalk is 5-18 cm long, up to 3 cm thick, white, with a smooth transition to a slightly enlarged bulb. Flesh white, staining reddish. No distinct smell.

Spore Print: White.

Occurrence: In groups under hardwoods or in mixed woods. Summer-fall.

Edibility: Edible, but not recommended.

Microscopic Features:
Spores 7.5-9.5 × 6-7 μm, broadly elliptical, smooth. Hyaline, amyloid.

Comments: This has tentatively been renamed *Amanita amerirubescens* by Dr. Rod Tulloss. *Amanita rubescens* var. *alba* is a white form. The Yellow Blusher, *Amanita flavorubens* (search online), has a persistently yellow cap and warts. *Amanita velatipes* and *A. muscaria* var. *guessowii* do not stain reddish when bruised.

Amanita russuloides complex (Peck) Sacc.

Description: Cap 2.5-12 cm wide, convex and flattening with age, pale yellow, dotted with a few white warts that often wash off. The cap margin is weakly lined. Gills are free or narrowly attached, crowded, white to cream-colored. Partial veil absent or present, often at midstalk. Stalk 3.5-12 cm long and 0.5-2 cm thick, white to pale yellow. The base is a small bulb, usually topped by a roll of free tissue. Flesh white. No distinctive odor.

Spore Print: White.

Occurrence: Solitary or scattered in hardwoods, mixed woods, or grassy areas near trees. Late spring-fall.

Edibility: Unknown.

Microscopic Features:
Spores 8.5-10 × 6.5-7 μm, elliptical, smooth. Hyaline, inamyloid.

Comments: This species complex was previously lumped with the Western *Amanita gemmata*. Specimens in the Carolinas are usually smallish and may lack a partial veil. Compare with *Amanita lavendula*, *A. multisquamosa*, and the larger *A. velatipes*.

Amanita spreta (Peck) Sacc.

HATED CAESAR

Description: Cap 5-15 cm wide, broadly convex to flat, brown or grayish-brown, smooth or showing a patch or two of white volva material. The margin is lined. Gills are free or slightly attached, close to crowded, white. The partial veil is a white dangling skirt. Stalks are 5-19 cm long and up to 2 cm thick, enlarging slightly downward, white, nearly smooth, hollow in age. The volva is a thin white sac that often flares away from the base. Odor not distinctive.

Spore Print: White.

Occurrence: Solitary or scattered under hardwoods or conifers. Summer-fall.

Edibility: Poisonous.

Microscopic Features: Spores 10-13 × 6-8 µm, elliptical to elongate, smooth. Hyaline, inamyloid.

Comments: This mousy-colored Caesar mushroom tends to be larger than *Amanita brunnescens*, which has a bulbous, vertically cleft base and lacks the saclike volva.

Amanita vaginata complex (Bull.) Lam.

GRISETTE

Description: Cap 3-10 cm wide, convex but flattening, dark brown over the umbo, lightening toward the strongly lined cap margin. A white wart or two is occasionally present. Gills are free or barely attached, close to crowded, white. No partial veil. Stalk 7-16 cm long, 0.5-2 cm thick, white. The base is not swollen. Volva is saclike and white, discoloring in age. Flesh white. Odor not distinctive.

Spore Print: White.

Occurrence: Solitary or scattered under hardwoods and conifers, in parks and other disturbed areas. Summer-fall.

Edibility: Edible, but not recommended.

Microscopic Features: Spores 7-14 × 7-13 µm, globose, smooth. Hyaline, inamyloid.

Comments: A white form of grisette is known as variety *alba* (beware confusion with the deadly *Amanita bisporigera*). *Amanita fulva* is tawny. *Amanita brunnescens* and *A. porphyria* have skirts and lack the volval sack.

Amanita velatipes G. F. Atk.
FUNNEL-VEIL AMANITA
Description: Cap 5-18 cm wide, convex and flattening at maturity, yellow-cream to tan, covered with concentric circles of pale warts that may wash off. The cap margin is lined. Gills free or narrowly attached, crowded, white. The partial veil at midstalk is white, often pulled up into a funnel shape. Stalk is 8-20 cm long, up to 2 cm thick, white. The expanded bulb is topped by a rolled collar and possibly also scaly bands of volva tissue. Flesh white. No distinct smell.

Spore Print: White.

Occurrence: Often in groups in mixed woods, parks, or lawns with nearby trees. Late spring-fall.

Edibility: Poisonous.

Microscopic Features:
Spores 8-13 × 6.5-8 µm, elliptical, smooth. Hyaline, inamyloid.

Comments: This eastern "Panther" is larger than *Amanita russuloides* and *A. multisquamosa*. *Amanita muscaria* var. *guessowii* has a more brightly colored cap.

Amanita volvata complex (Peck) Lloyd
AMERICAN AMIDELLA
Description: Cap 3.5-10 cm wide, convex then flattening, whitish, decorated with soft white volval patches that age brownish. Cap margin shaggy, may be slightly lined. Gills are free or narrowly attached, close to crowded, white to pale cream. No partial veil. Stalk is 4-10 cm long, up to 1.5 cm thick, white but develops pink to brown areas with age or bruising. Stalk rises from a thick, white, volval sack. Flesh white, not staining when exposed. No distinct smell.

Spore Print: White.

Occurrence: Solitary or scattered under hardwoods or conifers. Summer-fall.

Edibility: Unknown.

Microscopic Features:
Spores 7-10 × 4.5-7 µm, elliptical, smooth. Hyaline, amyloid.

Comments: The *Amidella* section of *Amanita* is poorly understood. Multiple species may go under the name *Amanita volvata*. Another species, *Amanita peckiana* (search online), has pink volval patches on the cap, and its flesh slowly stains brown. The deadly *Amanita bisporigera* has a partial veil.

Milk Mushrooms

Milk mushrooms are supposed to exude a clear or colored juice, **latex**, when injured. But this trait may not be obvious in dry weather or when you're dealing with a stingy species or old specimen.

In youth, the cap margins of some milk mushrooms are **inrolled**, rolled under. In maturity, the cap is usually flat or upturned. It may be dry or sticky with bits of litter stuck to it. It may have a central bump or **umbo**. Caps in many species are **zoned** with concentric circles of color. Absence of zones is termed **azonate**. Standard color terminology in these mushrooms strays from that found on crayon boxes; **vinaceous** is the color of a red wine stain. Milk mushroom gills are usually **decurrent** (running down the stalk) or attached at a right angle. The stalks of some species are **scurfy** (finely flaky) or pocked with sunken **pits** of a different color shade. Spore prints are white or pale.

Identifying a milk mushroom to species is apt to be a multisensory enterprise. You'll get a little messy. After noting the general appearance of an unknown specimen, cut some gills and observe the latex that begins to bead. Note the original color and be aware that it may change within a minute, up to several hours later, or not at all. It might stain nearby mushroom tissues or your skin. Taste a drop of the liquid. Is it milky sweet? Spicy hot and **acrid**? Does it start mild and become acrid within a minute or two? Whatever the outcome, spit out the latex and rinse your mouth when you're satisfied that you have a good answer. (Tasting the latex or chewing the flesh of a mushroom poses no risk of toxicity unless the material is swallowed.)

Crush a small piece of cap and sniff the flesh. Many species have a distinctive odor. This can range from dead fish to coconut suntan lotion or a sharp fragrance reminding some people of maple syrup.

Figure 8. Cap zonation

But smell is notoriously subjective; one person's "maple syrup" is another person's "industrial chemical." When possible, seek the guidance of experienced mushroom hunters to calibrate your mycological catalog of fragrances.

These mushrooms, like those of their *Russula* cousins, are relatively brittle or crumbly. Milk mushrooms occur on the ground and participate in mycorrhizal

Figure 9. Stalk pits

relationships with trees. Knowledge of whether a mushroom was found among conifers or deciduous trees is sometimes important.

Three species of milk mushroom are popular table fare in the Carolinas. A few others are edible as well. Some species are rendered inedible by an atrocious flavor. Moderately poisonous species also occur in our region.

Lactarius argillaceifolius Hesler & A. H. Sm.

Description: Cap 4-18 cm wide, convex with a depressed center, bald, slimy and sticky when wet, lilac-brown fading to pale lilac-gray or tan. Gills attached to slightly decurrent, broad, close, creamy, becoming dull brownish-orange. Stalk 6-9 cm long, 1.5-3.5 cm thick, whitish, spotted and stained brownish in age. Flesh firm, white to buff. Odor not distinctive. Taste mild to slowly slightly acrid. Latex creamy on exposure, staining gills brown.

Spore Print: Pinkish-buff.

Occurrence: Scattered or in groups under hardwoods. Summer-fall.

Edibility: Unknown.

Microscopic Features:
Spores 7-11 × 7-8 μm, subglobose to elliptic, with warts and ridges, sometimes forming a partial reticulum. Hyaline, amyloid.

Comments: *Argillaceifolius* means "clay-colored gills," a reference to the color of the mature gills. *Lactarius fumeacolor* (search online) is very similar, but it has narrow, white to buff gills that don't become brownish-orange at maturity.

Lactarius atroviridis Peck

Description: Cap 6-15 cm wide, convex
with a depressed center, scurfy, pitted,
dry, olive-green, typically zoned
with concentrically arranged dark
green spots. Gills attached to slightly
decurrent, close, creamy to pinkish,
sometimes forked; edges usually
greenish to olive-brown. Stalk 2-8 cm
long, 1-3 cm thick, dry, colored like
the cap, pitted. Flesh white to pinkish.
Odor not distinctive. Taste acrid. Latex
white on exposure, very slowly turning
greenish, staining gills grayish-green to
brown.

Spore Print: Cream to buff.

Occurrence: Solitary to scattered under
conifers or hardwoods. Summer-fall.

Edibility: Unknown.

Microscopic Features:
Spores 7-10 × 6-9 μm, subglobose to
elliptic with warts and ridges that form
a partial reticulum. Hyaline, amyloid.

Comments: The green colors of the cap and
stalk and darker green spots are good
field identification features. *Atroviridis*
means "dark green." *Lactarius turpis*
(search online) has an olive-brown cap
and a pitted olive-brown stalk.

Lactarius camphoratus (Bull.) Fr.
**AROMATIC MILKY,
SPICY MILK CAP**

Description: Cap 1.5-5 cm wide, broadly
conic to convex and depressed, often
with a pointed umbo, bald, moist or
dry, dark red-brown fading to pale
vinaceous-pink. Gills attached to
slightly decurrent, close to crowded,
pale pinkish-cinnamon. Stalk 1.5-6 cm
long, 3-15 mm thick, colored like the
cap, base with stiff hairs. Flesh pale
vinaceous-pink. Odor fragrant, like
maple sugar. Taste disagreeable to
bitter. Latex white on exposure, soon
becoming wheylike, unchanging and
not staining tissues.

Spore Print: White to yellowish.

Occurrence: Scattered or in groups under
conifers or hardwoods. Summer-fall.

Edibility: Unknown.

Microscopic Features:
Spores 7-8.5 × 6-7.5 μm, globose to
broadly ellipsoid, with isolated spines
and ridges. Hyaline, amyloid.

Comments: Addition of KOH to the
cap surface produces an olive color
reaction. *Lactarius oculatus* (search
online) has a more orange-brown cap
and stalk, a darker umbo; its flesh tastes
very slowly faintly acrid, and it lacks a
distinctive odor.

Lactarius chelidonium
var. *chelidonium* Peck
CELANDINE LACTARIUS
Description: Cap 3-8 cm wide, convex with a depressed center, smooth, slightly sticky, grayish-green to grayish-yellow or brownish, developing bluish-green tints in age. Gills attached to slightly decurrent, narrow, close, forked, grayish-yellow. Stalk 2.5-6 cm long, up to 2.5 cm thick, dry, colored like the cap. Flesh yellow at first, becoming blue overall. Odor and taste not distinctive. Latex scant, yellow on exposure, changing to dingy brownish-yellow or brownish, staining gills green.

Spore Print: Yellowish.

Occurrence: Scattered or in groups under pines. Summer-fall.

Edibility: Edible.

Microscopic Features:
Spores 8-10 × 6-7 μm, ellipsoid, with warts and ridges that form a partial reticulum. Hyaline, amyloid.

Comments: *Chelidonium* means "brown with a reddish-orange tinge." *Lactarius paradoxus* has scant, dark vinaceous-brown latex that stains tissues green.

Lactarius chrysorrheus Fr.
GOLD DROP MILK CAP
Description: Cap 3-9 cm wide, convex, becoming broadly funnel-shaped, with a whitish bloom, azonate or with watery spots arranged in zones, whitish to pale yellowish-cinnamon. Gills attached to subdecurrent, narrow, close, sometimes forked, whitish to pale orange-buff. Stalk 3-8 cm long, 1-2 cm thick, moist or dry, whitish or flushed orange-buff, sometimes with stiff hairs at the base. Flesh whitish, soon yellow when cut. Odor not distinctive. Taste slowly, distinctly acrid. Latex white on exposure, quickly turning yellow, not staining the gills.

Spore Print: Pale yellow.

Occurrence: Solitary, scattered, or in groups under hardwoods. Summer-fall.

Edibility: Unknown.

Microscopic Features:
Spores 6-9 × 5.5-6.5 μm, broadly ellipsoid, with warts and ridges that sometimes form a partial reticulum. Hyaline, amyloid.

Comments: *Chrysorrheus* means "flowing golden," a reference to the latex. *Lactarius vinaceorufescens* has a pinkish-cinnamon cap and white latex on exposure that rapidly changes to bright sulfur yellow; it grows under pines.

Lactarius croceus Burl.

Description: Cap 5-10 cm wide, convex with a depressed center, margin downy when young, surface slimy when wet, shiny when dry, bright orange to saffron yellow, fading to yellowish-tan in age, azonate or distinctly zoned with darker orange bands. Gills attached to slightly decurrent, close, buff to pale yellow-tan. Stalk 3-6 cm long, 1-2 cm thick, bald, colored like the cap, sometimes pitted or spotted brownish. Flesh whitish. Odor not distinctive. Taste bitter or acrid. Latex white on exposure, soon changing to sulfur yellow, staining gills and flesh sulfur yellow.

Spore Print: Yellowish.

Occurrence: Solitary or scattered under hardwoods. Summer-fall.

Edibility: Unknown.

Microscopic Features:
Spores 7.5-10 × 5.5-7.5 μm, elliptic, with warts and ridges that form a partial reticulum. Hyaline, amyloid.

Comments: *Croceus* means "saffron-colored," a reference to the color of its cap and stalk. This species is notorious in the mountains for not producing any milk. It could be confused for a large chanterelle.

Lactarius gerardii var. *gerardii* Peck
GERARD'S MILKY

Description: Cap 3-13 cm wide, convex, becoming broadly convex with a depressed center, wrinkled, with or without an umbo, dry, velvety, azonate, tan to yellow-brown or brown. Gills attached to decurrent, broad, nearly distant to distant, crossveined, whitish to cream. Stalk 3.5-8 cm long, 8-20 mm thick, dry, velvety, dark brown to yellow-brown, paler and often with vertical ridges at the apex. Flesh firm, white. Odor not distinctive. Taste mild, then slightly acrid. Latex white on exposure, unchanging, not staining tissues.

Spore Print: White.

Occurrence: Scattered or in groups under hardwoods or conifers. Summer-fall.

Edibility: Edible.

Microscopic Features:
Spores 7-10 × 7.5-9 μm, globose to broadly ellipsoid, with warts and ridges that form a reticulum. Hyaline, amyloid.

Comments: *Lactarius gerardii* var. *subrubescens* (search online) has white flesh that stains vinaceous-pink when exposed.

Lactarius imperceptus Beardslee & Burl.

Description: Cap 3-9 cm wide, broadly convex, bald, azonate, dry to slightly sticky, pale reddish-brown, slightly pitted or spotted with darker pinkish-cinnamon. Gills attached to subdecurrent, close, whitish to pinkish-white, usually staining brownish. Stalk 3-9 cm long, 3-20 mm thick, bald, pinkish-white, darkening with age. Flesh whitish, sometimes staining yellow when exposed. Odor not distinctive. Taste acrid, sometimes slowly. Latex white to cream on exposure, sometimes slowly darkening to yellowish, not staining tissues.

Spore Print: White to pale cream.

Occurrence: Scattered or in groups under conifers or hardwoods. Summer-fall.

Edibility: Unknown.

Microscopic Features:
Spores 8-11 × 7-8.5 μm, broadly ellipsoid, ornamented with warts and ridges that do not form a reticulum. Hyaline, amyloid.

Comments: *Lactarius fumosus* (search online) has a pale dingy yellow-brown to smoky tinged whitish cap; white, unchanging latex that stains tissues reddish; mild-tasting white flesh that slowly becomes faintly acrid; and a pinkish-buff spore print.

Lactarius indigo (Schwein.) Fr.

INDIGO MILKY

Description: Cap 5-16 cm wide, convex to convex-depressed, becoming broadly funnel-shaped, sticky, smooth, blue with darker blue concentric zones, fading to grayish with a silvery luster, often with dark green areas in age. Gills attached to subdecurrent, close, dark blue then paler blue at maturity. Stalk 2-8 cm long, 1-2.5 cm thick, sticky or dry, dark blue, paler when older, often pitted. Flesh whitish, rapidly staining dark blue on exposure. Odor not distinctive. Taste not distinctive, rarely slightly bitter or acrid. Latex scant, dark blue on exposure, slowly becoming dark green, staining gills green.

Spore Print: Creamy white.

Occurrence: Solitary, scattered, or in groups under conifers or hardwoods. Summer-fall.

Edibility: Edible.

Microscopic Features:
Spores 7-9 × 5.5-7.5 μm, broadly elliptical to subglobose, ornamented with ridges that form a partial reticulum. Hyaline, amyloid.

Comments: The cap of *Lactarius paradoxus* has grayish-blue, grayish-purple, and green concentric zones and scant, dark vinaceous-brown latex.

Lactarius lignyotus Fr.
CHOCOLATE MILKY
Description: Cap 2-10 cm wide, convex
with a small pointed umbo, margin
grooved, surface dry, velvety, usually
wrinkled, azonate, blackish-brown
becoming dingy yellow-brown. Gills
attached to decurrent, close to nearly
distant, white to pale yellowish.
Stalk 5-11 cm long, 5-13 mm thick,
with vertical ridges at the apex, dry,
velvety, blackish-brown to pale yellow-
brown, base white. Flesh white,
staining pinkish. Odor not distinctive.
Taste not distinctive or slightly bitter.
Latex abundant, white on exposure,
unchanging, staining gills reddish.
Spore Print: Bright brownish-yellow.
Occurrence: Scattered or in groups under
conifers or hardwoods. Summer-fall.
Edibility: Unknown.
Microscopic Features:
Spores 9-11 × 9-10 μm, nearly globose,
ornamented with ridges that form a
partial reticulum. Hyaline, amyloid.
Comments: *Lactarius lignyotellus* (search
online) has a depressed, dark brown,
sometimes wrinkled cap with a small
umbo, whitish gills with brown edges, a
pale brown stalk, white flesh, and white
unchanging latex that tastes mild. It
associates with spruce.

Lactarius maculatipes Burl.
Description: Cap 5-9 cm wide, broadly
convex to nearly flat with a depressed
center, margin incurved then uplifted,
surface bald, sticky when fresh, whitish
to cream overall, becoming tawny on
the disc in age, with pale yellow zones
and spots that darken with age. Gills
decurrent, crowded, sometimes forked,
whitish to buff, staining yellowish
when bruised. Stalk 3-8 cm long,
1-2.5 cm thick, tapered downward,
sticky, colored like the cap, pitted.
Flesh white, slowly staining yellowish.
Odor not distinctive. Taste slowly acrid.
Latex white on exposure, unchanging,
staining gills yellowish.
Spore Print: Pinkish-buff to yellowish.
Occurrence: Scattered or in groups under
oaks. Summer-fall.
Edibility: Unknown.
Microscopic Features:
Spores 6.5-8 × 6-7.5 μm, subglobose
to broadly ellipsoid, ornamented with
warts and ridges that sometimes form
a partial reticulum. Hyaline, amyloid.
Comments: *Maculatipes* means having
spots on the stalk. *Lactarius carolinensis*
(search online) has a tan cap with darker
yellowish-brown zones, white flesh,
and a white spore print.

GILLED MUSHROOMS

Lactarius paradoxus Beardslee & Burl.
SILVER-BLUE MILKY
Description: Cap 5-8 cm wide, broadly convex with a depressed center, often funnel-shaped in age, bald, slimy to sticky when wet, with a silvery sheen when young, zoned with bands of grayish-blue, grayish-purple, green, and blue, bruising green. Gills attached to subdecurrent, close, sometimes forked, pinkish-orange, bruising blue-green. Stalk 2-3 cm long, 1-1.5 cm thick, hollow, dry, colored like the cap, staining blue-green. Flesh whitish with greenish or bluish tints, slowly staining greenish. Odor not distinctive. Taste not distinctive or slightly acrid. Latex scant, dark vinaceous-brown, staining tissues green.

Spore Print: Cream to yellow.

Occurrence: Solitary, scattered, or in groups under pines, oaks, or palmetto palms. Summer-early winter.

Edibility: Edible.

Microscopic Features:
Spores 7-9 × 5.5-6.5 µm, broadly ellipsoid, ornamented with warts and ridges that form a partial reticulum. Hyaline, amyloid.

Comments: *Lactarius chelidonium* var. *chelidonium* has a grayish-green cap with blue and yellow tints, and yellow latex.

Lactarius peckii var. *peckii* Burl.
PECK'S MILKY
Description: Cap 5-15.5 cm wide, broadly convex with a depressed center, margin incurved, velvety to scurfy, brick red to reddish- or brownish-orange, often paler near the margin, usually zoned with darker bands. Gills decurrent, close, pale cinnamon-buff initially, darkening to cinnamon, staining rusty brown. Stalk 2-6 cm long, 1-2.5 cm thick, colored like the cap or paler, often spotted with brown or orange but not pitted. Flesh pale vinaceous-brown, not staining. Odor not distinctive. Taste acrid. Latex copious, white, unchanging, not staining tissues.

Spore Print: White.

Occurrence: Scattered or in groups in oak woods. Summer-fall.

Edibility: Unknown.

Microscopic Features:
Spores 6-7.5 µm, globose to subglobose, ornamented with warts and ridges that form a partial to complete reticulum. Hyaline, amyloid.

Comments: *Lactarius peckii* var. *glaucescens* (search online) has white latex that dries pale bluish-green. *Lactarius peckii* var. *lactolutescens* (search online) has very acrid white latex that quickly changes to ivory-yellow on exposure and dries pale yellowish-green.

Lactarius psammicola A. H. Sm.

Description: Cap 4-15 cm wide, broadly convex and depressed to funnel-shaped, margin inrolled, coated with stiff hairs when young, matted or bald at maturity, surface sticky, smooth, or coated with slimy fibers, zoned, yellowish-buff to dull brown. Gills decurrent, close, sometimes forked, whitish to cinnamon-buff becoming pale yellow to brownish, staining dull brown or pinkish-lilac. Stalk 1-5 cm long, 1-3 cm thick, tapered downward, whitish to grayish, often pitted. Flesh thick, pale, sometimes staining pinkish-lilac. Odor not distinctive. Taste acrid to strongly acrid. Latex copious, white, slowly staining tissues pinkish-cinnamon.

Spore Print: Buff to yellowish.

Occurrence: Scattered or in groups in hardwoods or mixed woods, usually with oak. Summer-fall.

Edibility: Unknown.

Microscopic Features:
Spores 7.5-9 × 6-7.5 µm, broadly ellipsoid, ornamented with warts and ridges that sometimes form a partial reticulum. Hyaline, amyloid.

Comments: *Lactarius proximellus* (search online) is similar, but the cap margin lacks stiff hairs; the yellowish stalk bruises pale blue-green and lacks pits.

Lactarius quietus var. *incanus* Hesler & A. H. Sm.

Description: Cap 3-11 cm wide, convex to nearly flat with a depressed center, nearly bald, sometimes with water spots, typically zoned, dark purplish-brown or purplish-gray when young, becoming red-brown at the center and pinkish-brown toward the margin. Gills attached to subdecurrent, close, often forked, whitish with pink tints, becoming cinnamon and staining orange-cinnamon. Stalk 4-14 cm long, to 1 cm thick, colored like the cap and darkening progressively toward the apex with age. Flesh pinkish-buff. Odor like burnt sugar. Taste mild, becoming weakly acrid. Latex white or watery, unchanging, not staining tissues.

Spore Print: Pinkish-buff.

Occurrence: Scattered or in groups under oaks. Summer-fall.

Edibility: Unknown.

Microscopic Features:
Spores 6.5-9 × 5-7.5 µm, elliptic, ornamented with warts and ridges that sometimes form a partial reticulum. Hyaline, amyloid.

Comments: *Lactarius camphoratus* has a smaller dark red-brown cap usually with a small pointed umbo, and flesh that is disagreeable to bitter, but not acrid.

Lactarius salmoneus Peck

Description: Cap 2.5-8 cm wide, nearly flat with a depressed center, margin inrolled to incurved at first, becoming decurved as it ages, surface dry, azonate, white overall at first, becoming orange as the white layer wears away in age, staining orange when bruised. Gills attached to decurrent, close, orange to pale orange, bruising dark orange. Stalk 1.2-2.5 cm long, 6-13 mm thick, white at first, becoming light orange overall as the white layer wears away, typically lacking spots. Flesh light orange. Odor not distinctive. Taste slightly peppery. Latex scant, dark orange, staining gills dark orange.

Spore Print: Creamy white.

Occurrence: Solitary, scattered, or in groups under pines or in mixed oak and pine woods. Summer-fall.

Edibility: Unknown.

Microscopic Features:
Spores 7.5-9 × 5-6 μm, ellipsoid, with warts and ridges that form a partial reticulum. Hyaline, amyloid.

Comments: *Lactarius salmonicolor* (search online) has a sticky, salmon-orange to peach-colored and faintly zonate cap; the stalk is pitted and orange.

Lactarius speciosus Burl.

Description: Cap 3-10 cm wide, broadly convex with a depressed center, becoming broadly funnel-shaped, margin inrolled and bearded with coarse hairs when young, uplifted and bald in age, surface initially sticky then dry, pale cinnamon or orange-brown, conspicuously zoned with bands of pinkish-tan and cinnamon-brown. Gills attached to slightly decurrent, close, cream to pinkish-buff. Stalk 3-5 cm long, 1-2.5 cm thick, whitish, pitted, with reddish-brown or yellowish spots. Flesh whitish. Odor not distinctive. Taste not distinctive to slightly bitter or acrid. Latex white, unchanging, staining tissues dull lilac.

Spore Print: White.

Occurrence: Scattered or in groups in hardwoods or mixed woods. Summer-fall.

Edibility: Unknown.

Microscopic Features:
Spores 10-13.5 × 9-11 μm, broadly ellipsoid, with warts and ridges that form a partial reticulum. Hyaline, amyloid.

Comments: *Lactarius dispersus* (search online) is very similar but has darker cap fibrils, more conspicuous and darker zones, a yellowish spore print, and smaller, less reticulate spores that measure 7.5-10 × 6-7.5 μm.

Lactarius subplinthogalus Coker
Description: Cap 3-5 cm wide, nearly
flat to broadly funnel-shaped, margin
pleated like pie crust, dry, smooth
or slightly wrinkled, yellowish-buff
to brownish-yellow. Gills attached to
subdecurrent, distant, colored like the
cap, bruising pink. Stalk 3-8 cm long,
7-15 mm thick, solid or hollow, bald,
dry, cream, sometimes with orange-
brown stains. Flesh whitish, staining
pink. Odor not distinctive. Taste acrid.
Latex white, unchanging, staining
tissues pink.
Spore Print: Pinkish- to cinnamon-buff.
Occurrence: Scattered or in groups under
oaks or in mixed oak and pine woods.
Summer-fall.
Edibility: Unknown.
Microscopic Features:
Spores 7.5-9.5 × 7-8 μm, subglobose
to broadly ellipsoid, ornamented with
warts and ridges that do not form a
reticulum. Hyaline, amyloid.
Comments: *Lactarius sumstinei* (search
online) has a whitish to pinkish-
cinnamon cap with a pleated margin
and mild-tasting flesh that does not
stain tissues. *Lactarius subvernalis* var.
cokeri has crowded gills and lacks the
pleated cap margin.

Lactarius subvernalis var. *cokeri*
Hesler & A. H. Sm.
Description: Cap 2-6 cm wide, broadly
convex to shallowly depressed, may
have an umbo, margin lobed or wavy,
surface dry, bald or slightly wrinkled,
sometimes zoned near the margin,
whitish to buff or pale smoky brownish.
Gills attached to subdecurrent, forked
near the stalk. Stalk 5-7 cm long,
8-15 mm thick, solid or hollow, dry,
whitish, staining pink when bruised.
Flesh white, staining pink. Odor not
distinctive. Taste acrid. Latex white,
unchanging, staining tissues pink.
Spore Print: Yellow.
Occurrence: Scattered or in groups under
hardwoods. Late spring-fall.
Edibility: Unknown.
Microscopic Features:
Spores 7-9 × 7-9 μm, globose,
ornamented with warts and ridges that
form a complete reticulum. Hyaline,
amyloid.
Comments: *Subvernalis* means "near
springtime," a reference to when this
mushroom begins to appear, and *cokeri*
honors Carolina mycologist William
Chambers Coker (1872-1953). *Lactarius
subplinthogalus* has distant gills and a
pleated cap margin.

Lactarius vinaceorufescens A. H. Sm.

YELLOW-LATEX MILKY, YELLOW-STAINING MILK CAP

Description: Cap 4-12 cm wide, convex to broadly convex, bald, pale pinkish-cinnamon with pinkish-buff at the margin when young, becoming darker pinkish- to orange-cinnamon, often faintly zoned. Gills attached to subdecurrent, close, often forked, whitish to pinkish-buff, soon spotted vinaceous to reddish-brown. Stalk 4-7 cm long, 1-2.5 cm thick, hollow, nearly bald, pinkish-white, with stiff white or brown hairs at the base. Flesh white to pinkish. Odor not distinctive. Taste acrid. Latex white, rapidly changing to sulfur yellow.

Spore Print: White to yellowish.

Occurrence: Scattered or in groups under pines. Summer-fall.

Edibility: Poisonous.

Microscopic Features:
Spores 6.5-9 × 6-7 µm, subglobose to broadly ellipsoid, ornamented with warts and ridges that may form a partial reticulum. Hyaline, amyloid.

Comments: *Lactarius chrysorrheus* has a whitish to pale yellowish-cinnamon cap and whitish to pale orange-buff gills that do not discolor or spot vinaceous or brown; it grows under hardwoods, especially oak.

Lactarius yazooensis Hesler and A. H. Sm.

Description: Cap 5-15.5 cm wide, broadly convex with a depressed center, becoming broadly funnel-shaped, margin inrolled at first, surface sticky, smooth, zoned with shades of orange and red-orange, becoming paler with cinnamon-buff and pale brownish-yellow zones in age. Gills attached to decurrent, crowded, whitish to pale vinaceous-cinnamon, slowly staining brownish. Stalk 2-6 cm long, 1-2.5 cm thick, dry, bald, whitish. Flesh whitish. Odor not distinctive. Taste excruciatingly acrid. Latex copious, white, unchanging, not staining tissues.

Spore Print: Buff-yellow.

Occurrence: Scattered or in groups in grassy areas under hardwoods, especially oak. Summer-fall.

Edibility: Unknown.

Microscopic Features:
Spores 7-9 × 6-7.5 µm, subglobose to broadly ellipsoid, ornamented with warts and ridges that do not form a reticulum. Hyaline, amyloid.

Comments: *Lactarius psammicola* has a similarly colored cap, but it has close gills that sometimes stain pinkish-lilac, a pitted stalk, and white latex that slowly changes to dingy pinkish-lilac.

Lactifluus allardii (Coker) De Crop

Description: Cap 6-15 cm wide, broadly convex with a depressed center, margin incurved, surface dry, somewhat velvety, azonate, whitish when very young, becoming pinkish-cinnamon then dull brick red, usually spotted and streaked white especially on the margin. Gills attached to decurrent, nearly distant, white to ivory. Stalk 2-5 cm long, 1-3 cm thick, hollow, colored like the cap or paler. Flesh white, slowly staining pink then olive. Odor not distinctive. Taste acrid. Latex white, slowly becoming greenish, staining gills dull green then slowly brown.

Spore Print: White to cream.

Occurrence: Scattered or in groups under hardwoods or in mixed woods. Summer-fall.

Edibility: Unknown.

Microscopic Features:
Spores 8-11 × 5-8 μm, ellipsoid to subglobose, ornamented with warts and ridges that do not form a reticulum. Hyaline, amyloid.

Comments: *Lactarius allardii* is a synonym. The flesh rapidly stains vinaceous-red with FeSO$_4$. Portions of the cap of this mushroom remain pale when covered by fallen leaves.

Lactifluus corrugis (Peck) Kuntze

CORRUGATED-CAP MILKY

Description: Cap 4-20 cm wide, convex to flat with a depressed center, velvety, dry, azonate, distinctly wrinkled to finely corrugated, reddish-brown. Gills attached, close, occasionally forked, pale cinnamon to pale golden-brown. Stalk 5-11 cm long, 1.5-3 cm thick, dry, velvety, pale grayish-cinnamon or pinkish-cinnamon. Flesh whitish. Odor slightly or strongly fishy. Taste not distinctive. Latex copious, white on exposure, unchanging, staining gills and flesh tawny brown.

Spore Print: White.

Occurrence: Solitary or scattered under hardwoods. Summer-fall.

Edibility: Edible.

Microscopic Features:
Spores 9-12 × 8.5-12 μm, subglobose, with warts and ridges that form a partial reticulum. Hyaline, amyloid.

Comments: *Corrugis* means "wrinkled." *Lactarius corrugis* is a synonym. *Lactifluus volemus* has a less wrinkled, dark orange-brown cap. *Lactifluus volemus* var. *flavus* (search online) has a yellow to orange-yellow cap and a cream to pale yellow stalk.

Lactifluus deceptivus (Peck) Kuntze
DECEPTIVE MILK CAP
Description: Cap 7.5-25.5 cm wide, convex, becoming broadly funnel-shaped, margin distinctly cottony and inrolled when young, surface dry, bald, whitish, with yellowish or brownish stains when young, becoming scaly and brownish-yellow in age. Gills attached, close or almost distant, white, then cream to pale brownish-yellow. Stalk 4-10 cm long, up to 3 cm thick, dry, scurfy or bald, white. Flesh white. Odor pungent or not distinctive. Taste strongly acrid. Latex white on exposure, unchanging, staining tissues brownish.
Spore Print: White.
Occurrence: Solitary or in groups under conifers or hardwoods. Summer-fall.
Edibility: Edible when thoroughly cooked.
Microscopic Features:
Spores 9-13 × 7-9 μm, broadly ellipsoid, with warts and ridges, not forming a partial reticulum. Hyaline, amyloid.
Comments: *Deceptivus* means "deceiving," a reference to the strongly acrid taste. *Lactarius deceptivus* is a synonym.

Lactifluus glaucescens (Crossl.) Verbeken
Description: Cap 4-12 cm wide, broadly convex with a depressed center, margin inrolled to incurved, surface dry, bald, smooth or somewhat finely cracked, white to cream at first, becoming yellow-brown especially over the center in age. Gills decurrent, crowded, often forked, whitish, bruising brown. Stalk 3-9 cm long, 1-3 cm thick, dry, solid, whitish. Flesh hard, pale cream, unchanging or very slowly staining pale blue-green. Odor not distinctive. Taste acrid. Latex white, drying pale blue-green, not staining tissues.
Spore Print: White to yellowish.
Occurrence: Scattered or in groups under hardwoods, especially oak. Summer-fall.
Edibility: Poisonous.
Microscopic Features:
Spores 6.5-9 × 5-7 μm, broadly ellipsoid, ornamented with warts and ridges that do not form a reticulum. Hyaline, amyloid.
Comments: *Lactarius glaucescens* is a synonym. The latex stains yellow to orange with KOH. *Lactifluus piperatus* is very similar, but its white latex dries yellow.

Lactifluus hygrophoroides
(Berk. & M. A. Curtis) Kuntze
HYGROPHORUS MILKY
Description: Cap 3-10 cm wide, broadly
convex with a depressed center or
sometimes broadly funnel-shaped in
age, dry, bald, dull orange to orange-
brown. Gills attached to slightly
decurrent, broad, distant at maturity,
crossveined, white to yellowish-buff.
Stalk 3-5 cm long, 5-15 mm thick,
dry, pale orange-brown to orange-
yellow. Flesh white. Odor and taste not
distinctive. Latex white on exposure,
unchanging, not staining tissues.
Spore Print: White.
Occurrence: Scattered or in groups under
hardwoods. Summer-fall.
Edibility: Edible.
Microscopic Features:
Spores 7.5-10.5 × 6-7.5 μm, elliptic,
ornamented with warts and ridges
that do not form a reticulum. Hyaline,
amyloid.
Comments: *Hygrophoroides* means
"resembling the genus *Hygrophorus*."
Lactarius hygrophoroides is a synonym.
Lactifluus rugatus (search online)
has conspicuous concentric wrinkles
near the cap margin and grows under
hardwoods, especially oaks.

Lactifluus luteolus (Peck) Verbeken
BUFF FISHY MILKY
Description: Cap 2.5-8 cm wide, broadly
convex, sometimes shallowly
depressed, dry, slightly velvety,
azonate, whitish to buff with a white
bloom, becoming brownish in age.
Gills attached to slightly decurrent,
close, white to cream. Stalk 2.5-6 cm
long, 6-20 mm thick, solid, dry, slightly
velvety, whitish to buff. Flesh white.
Odor distinctly fishy, unpleasant,
resembling spoiled crab. Taste not
distinctive. Latex copious, sticky,
watery white to white, unchanging,
staining tissues brown.
Spore Print: White to cream.
Occurrence: Scattered or in groups under
hardwoods or in mixed woods. Late
spring-fall.
Edibility: Edible.
Microscopic Features:
Spores 7-9 × 5.5-7 μm, elliptic,
ornamented with warts and ridges that
sometimes form a partial reticulum.
Hyaline, amyloid.
Comments: *Lactarius luteolus* is a
synonym. *Russula compacta* is very
similar and its flesh also has a fishy
odor, but it does not produce latex
when cut.

GILLED MUSHROOMS

Lactifluus petersenii
(Hesler & A. H. Sm.) Stubbe

Description: Cap 3-5 cm wide, broadly convex with a depressed center, margin typically uplifted at maturity, surface dry, minutely velvety, finely wrinkled, smoky yellowish-brown. Gills attached to decurrent, close, white to cream. Stalk 3-4 cm long, 6-10 mm thick, dry, hollow in age, minutely velvety, colored like the cap. Flesh white. Odor and taste not distinctive. Latex dingy brownish to pale pinkish-brown, unchanging, staining gills brown.

Spore Print: White.

Occurrence: Scattered or in groups under hemlock or in mixed woods with hemlock present. Late spring-fall.

Edibility: Unknown.

Microscopic Features:
Spores 7.5-10 × 6-8 μm, ellipsoid to broadly ellipsoid, ornamented with warts and ridges that form an obscure reticulum. Hyaline, amyloid.

Comments: *Lactarius petersenii* is a synonym. This species was named in honor of mycologist Ron Petersen, who first collected it in Cades Cove, Tennessee.

Lactifluus piperatus (L.) Roussel
PEPPERY MILKY,
PEPPERY WHITE MILK CAP

Description: Cap 3-15.5 cm wide, convex, becoming funnel-shaped, margin bent downward or uplifted, surface dry, bald or slightly wrinkled, azonate, white when young, becoming creamy white with pale brownish-yellow to dingy tan stains in age. Gills attached to decurrent, very crowded, often forked, white to cream, sometimes staining yellowish. Stalk 2-8 cm long, 1-2.5 cm thick, solid, firm, dry, appearing finely powdered, white. Flesh white, unchanging, sometimes slowly staining yellowish. Odor not distinctive. Taste quickly and strongly acrid. Latex white, unchanging, sometimes slowly staining gills yellowish, drying yellow.

Spore Print: White.

Occurrence: Scattered or in groups under conifers or hardwoods. Summer-fall.

Edibility: Edible.

Microscopic Features:
Spores 4.5-7 × 5-5.5 μm, ellipsoid, ornamented with fine lines and isolated warts that do not form a reticulum. Hyaline, amyloid.

Comments: *Lactarius piperatus* is a synonym. *Lactifluus glaucescens* is nearly identical, but the whitish latex dries pale blue-green.

Lactifluus subvellereus (Peck) Nuytinck
Description: Cap 5-15 cm wide, broadly convex with a depressed center, becoming broadly funnel-shaped, margin incurved and sometimes pleated, dry, somewhat velvety, azonate, white with yellowish tinges in age. Gills attached to subdecurrent, close when young, becoming nearly distant, white to yellowish, sometimes with droplets of clear liquid. Stalk 2-5 cm long, 1-2.5 cm thick, dry, velvety, white with brownish tinges. Flesh compact, hard, white. Odor not distinctive. Taste acrid. Latex white, changing to dull yellow, staining gills brown.
Spore Print: White.
Occurrence: Scattered or in groups in mixed woods. Summer-fall.
Edibility: Edible.
Microscopic Features:
Spores 7.5-9 × 5-7 μm, ellipsoid to broadly ellipsoid, ornamented with warts and ridges that do not form a reticulum. Hyaline, amyloid.
Comments: *Lactarius subvellereus* and *L. subvellereus* var. *subdistans* are synonyms. The flesh stains reddish-cinnamon with FeSO$_4$ and orange with KOH. *Lactifluus piperatus* and *L. glaucescens* both have crowded gills with white latex that does not change to dull yellow.

Lactifluus volemus (Fr.) Kuntze
LEATHERBACK, BRADLEY, VOLUMINOUS-LATEX MILKY
Description: Cap 5-10 cm wide, broadly convex with a depressed center, becoming funnel-shaped, dry, velvety initially, bald to finely wrinkled in age, orange- to cinnamon-brown at the center, paler toward the margin, fading at maturity. Gills attached to subdecurrent, close, often forked, pale. Stalk 5-12 cm long, to 2 cm thick, smooth, orange-brown to dull orange. Flesh white. Odor fishy or not distinctive. Taste not distinctive. Latex copious, sticky, white, darkening and staining tissues, clothing, and fingers brown.
Spore Print: White.
Occurrence: Scattered or in groups under hardwoods or in mixed woods. Late spring-fall.
Edibility: Edible.
Microscopic Features:
Spores 7.5-10 × 7.5-9 μm, ornamented with warts and ridges that form a reticulum. Hyaline, amyloid.
Comments: *Lactarius volemus* is a synonym. *Lactifluus volemus* var. *flavus* (search online) has a yellow to orange-yellow cap and a cream to pale-yellow stalk. *Lactarius subvelutinus* (search online) has an orange to orange-brown cap and lacks the fishy odor.

Multifurca furcata
(Coker) Buyck & V. Hofst.

Description: Cap 6-10 cm wide, broadly convex, becoming funnel-shaped at maturity, somewhat sticky, finely velvety, zoned, yellowish to brownish-yellow. Gills decurrent, crowded, repeatedly forked, brownish-yellow with a salmon tint. Stalk 2-3 cm long, 8-15 mm thick, solid, firm, tough, sticky, yellowish, pitted, spots brownish-orange. Flesh white with brownish-yellow zones. Odor not distinctive. Taste acrid. Latex white, slowly changing to blue-green, not staining tissues.

Spore Print: Pinkish-yellow.

Occurrence: Scattered or in groups in mixed woods. Late spring-fall.

Edibility: Unknown.

Microscopic Features:
Spores 3.5-5 × 3.5-4 μm, ellipsoid to subglobose, ornamented with a few bands and occasional fine lines. Hyaline, amyloid.

Comments: *Lactarius furcatus* is a synonym. *Lactarius lanuginosus* (search online) reported only from North Carolina is similar, but the gills are not repeatedly forked, and the latex is white and unchanging.

Genus *Russula*

Russula is a very common genus of ground-dwelling, pale-spored mushrooms with a generally stocky build. The frequently colorful caps of mature Russulas tend to be flat or upturned. Gills are white to pale in color, attached to the stalk, and often close or crowded together. As with their cousins the milk mushrooms, *Russula* flesh is crumbly and can be very dense in some species; stalks often snap like pieces of chalk. Russulas don't exude latex, and the caps are not zoned as they are in many milk mushrooms.

Common diagnostic features include observing whether the mushroom cap is sticky and possibly decorated with bits of adherent litter, or dry. In some Russulas the skin layer, **cuticle**, of the cap peels easily from the underlying flesh. The edge of the cap may show a diagnostically important pattern of **radial lines**. Close inspection may be required to determine whether and how frequently the gills fork. The flesh of a few species bruises a different color after a few minutes and may change to a third color over a longer period of time. Smell and taste are significant clues as well. While most species have no distinct smell, others smell like overripe fruit or seafood. Tastes range from not distinctive to fiery hot. As always when tasting mushrooms in the field, spit and rinse after making your determination; never swallow.

Although Russulas may be the most common genus in the woods, they typically get little respect from mushroomers. Part of this has to do with the difficulty in telling species apart. There are probably dozens of species with pink or red tops and white to pink stalks. Also, while there are some edible varieties, none are culinary stars. Some Russulas induce vomiting and other gastrointestinal symptoms. We describe only a few relatively distinctive species.

Russula aeruginea Lindblad ex Fr.
TACKY GREEN RUSSULA
Description: Cap 4-12 cm wide, convex, becoming nearly flat and depressed in age with an uplifted margin, slimy when moist, silky when dry, grayish-green, darker centrally, whitish toward the margin, often with reddish-brown to rusty spots, cuticle peeling halfway to center. Gills attached to slightly decurrent, forking near the stalk, white when young, pale to dark yellow when mature. Stalk 5-7 cm long, 1.2-2 cm thick, equal, sometimes thickened in the middle or tapered downward, longitudinally lined, white, developing brownish spots toward the base. Flesh white. Odor not distinctive. Taste initially mild, then slowly acrid.
Spore Print: Cream to pale yellow.
Occurrence: In groups in mixed woods. Summer-fall.
Edibility: Edible.
Microscopic Features:
Spores 6.5-9 × 5.5-7 μm, elliptic, surface ornamented with warts and ridges. Hyaline, amyloid.
Comments: The cap of *Russula virescens* (search online) has quiltlike patches. *Russula variata* has more gill forks.

Russula atropurpurea Peck
BLACKISH-RED RUSSULA
Description: Cap 4-12 cm wide, convex becoming flat with a depressed center, sticky when moist, smooth, bald, various shades of dark purple to wine red, dark purplish-black over the center, paler toward the margin, sometimes mottled with paler areas, cuticle peeling one-half to two-thirds to center. Gills attached, close to subdistant, forking at the stalk, white becoming pale yellow to straw yellow. Stalk 3.5-6 cm long, 1-2 cm thick, equal or enlarged downward, smooth, sometimes longitudinally lined, solid, white, darkening to grayish in age. Flesh white. Odor sweet, fruity, or not distinctive. Taste acrid or not distinctive.
Spore Print: Cream to pale yellow.
Occurrence: Scattered in hardwoods or mixed woods, especially with oak and beech. Spring-fall.
Edibility: Inedible.
Microscopic Features:
Spores 6.5-9 × 5.5-7 μm, elliptic, surface ornamented with warts and ridges. Hyaline, amyloid.
Comments: *Russula krombholzii* and *R. vinacea* are synonyms. *Russula fragilis* (search online) is smaller and grows with conifers or in mixed woods.

Russula brevipes Peck
SHORT-STALKED
WHITE RUSSULA
Description: Cap 6-20 cm wide, convex
with a depressed center, margin inrolled
well into maturity, dry, felty, white,
bruising yellowish to brown, cuticle
peeling up to one-third to center. Gills
attached to slightly decurrent, crowded,
white, bruising like the cap. Stalk 2.5-
7.5 cm long, 2.5-4 cm thick, smooth,
dry, white, bruising brown. Odor
disagreeable or not distinctive. Taste
mild at first, then slowly acrid.
Spore Print: White to cream.
Occurrence: Solitary or scattered in mixed
woods. Summer-fall.
Edibility: Inedible.
Microscopic Features:
Spores 8-11 × 6.5-10 μm, elliptical,
surface ornamented with warts and
ridges. Hyaline, amyloid.
Comments: *Russula brevipes* var. *acrior*
was formerly considered a distinct
variety; that name was used for
specimens with bluish-green tints on
the gills and stalk apex. *Russula brevipes*
is often parasitized by *Hypomyces
lactifluorum*, transforming it into the
sought-after edible lobster mushroom.
Lactifluus deceptivus is similarly colored
but exudes a white, very acrid latex.

Russula compacta Frost
FIRM RUSSULA
Description: Cap 6.5-18 cm wide, convex
with an inrolled margin initially,
flattening in age, sometimes depressed
in the center, sticky when moist,
often developing cracks, whitish to
buff, becoming darker reddish-tan to
cinnamon, bruising brownish, cuticle
peels halfway to center. Gills attached,
crowded to close or nearly distant with
several tiers of short gills, whitish to
buff, bruising reddish-brown. Stalk
4-10 cm long, 1-3.5 cm thick, equal,
smooth, white or colored and bruising
like the cap. Flesh white, firm, bruising
yellowish to brownish. Odor fishy,
unpleasant, especially in old specimens.
Taste disagreeable to not distinctive.
Spore Print: White.
Occurrence: Solitary or in groups with
hardwoods and in mixed woods.
Summer-fall.
Edibility: Reportedly edible.
Microscopic Features:
Spores 7-10 × 6-8 μm, broadly elliptic,
surface ornamented with warts and
ridges. Hyaline, amyloid.
Comments: *Russula ballouii* (search online)
has the same coloration but lacks the
fishy odor. *Russula nigricans* has white
flesh that bruises red, then blackish.

Russula crustosa Peck
GREEN QUILT RUSSULA
Description: Cap 5-15 cm wide, convex becoming nearly flat, often with a depressed center and an uplifted and radially lined margin, dry, becoming cracked overall into quiltlike or mosaic-like patches, buff, blue- or yellowish-green, sometimes brownish-yellow, may have lilac tints along the margin, cuticle peeling halfway to center. Gills attached, close with some forking, white to cream. Stalk 3.5-8.5 cm long, 1.5-3 cm thick, dry, smooth, white. Flesh white. Odor not distinctive. Taste slightly acrid or not distinctive.
Spore Print: Pale buff to pale yellow.
Occurrence: Scattered or in groups with hardwoods, especially oaks. Summer-fall.
Edibility: Edible.
Microscopic Features:
Spores 6-10 × 4.5-8 μm, ellipsoid to subglobose, surface ornamented with warts and ridges. Hyaline, amyloid.
Comments: *Russula virescens* (search online) is similar but has a white spore print. The cap of *Russula aeruginea* is smooth and does not break up into patches.

Russula earlei Peck
BEESWAX RUSSULA
Description: Cap 4-11 cm wide, convex to broadly convex, often with a depressed center, with a wavy and irregular margin in age, sometimes faintly lined at maturity, roughened and irregularly pitted, dry and waxy, sticky when moist, straw to honey yellow, cuticle not peeling. Gills white to pale yellow, attached, distant, thick and appearing waxy. Stalk 2-5 cm long, 5-25 mm wide, equal or enlarged downward, slightly roughened, dry, waxy, white to pale yellow, occasionally with reddish-brown stains near the base, basal mycelium white. Flesh whitish to pale yellow. Odor not distinctive. Taste slightly bitter or acrid or not distinctive.
Spore Print: White.
Occurrence: Solitary or in groups on the ground in hardwoods, especially beech and oak. Summer-fall.
Edibility: Unknown.
Microscopic Features:
Spores 5.5-7 × 3.5-5.5 μm, subglobose, minutely warted. Hyaline, amyloid.
Comments: The overall waxy appearance and distant gills are distinctive features. Peck named this species to honor American mycologist Franklin S. Earle (1856-1929).

Russula emetica (Schaeff.) Pers.
EMETIC RUSSULA
Description: Cap 4-10 cm wide, convex with an incurved, slightly radially grooved margin, becoming flat with a depressed center, shiny, slimy, or sticky when moist, smooth, sometimes finely cracked, scarlet, cherry red, sometimes with paler areas, cuticle peeling one-third to entirely to center. Gills white to cream, attached, close, with some forking. Stalk 4-9 cm long, 7-20 mm thick, equal or slightly enlarged downward, finely longitudinally lined, solid, white. Flesh white. Odor fruity. Taste very acrid.

Spore Print: White to cream.

Occurrence: Scattered or in groups among sphagnum mosses in bogs and wet woodlands. Summer-fall.

Edibility: Poisonous.

Microscopic Features:
Spores 8-11 × 7-8.5 μm, oval to subglobose, surface ornamented with warts and ridges. Hyaline, amyloid.

Comments: Several species of red-capped Russulas grow in a variety of habitats. Some can only be differentiated microscopically or by DNA sequencing. A key identification feature of *Russula emetica* is that it grows among sphagnum mosses.

Russula grata Britzelm.
ALMOND-SCENTED RUSSULA
Description: Cap 4-11.5 cm wide, convex becoming nearly flat, often depressed in the center, sticky when moist, smooth, margin with radially arranged tiny bumps, yellowish to brownish-yellow, cuticle peeling three-quarters to center. Gills attached, close, creamy white to yellowish, usually staining brown in age. Stalk 2.5-10 cm long, 1-3 cm thick, equal or somewhat thickened in the middle, smooth or slightly wrinkled, white to pale yellow, usually bruising brown. Flesh brittle, white to yellowish. Odor like bitter almonds or marzipan. Taste acrid or not distinctive.

Spore Print: Creamy white to yellowish.

Occurrence: Scattered or in groups mostly with hardwoods, sometimes in mixed woods. Summer-fall.

Edibility: Inedible.

Microscopic Features:
Spores 7-10.5 × 7-9 μm, subglobose, surface ornamented with warts and ridges. Hyaline, amyloid.

Comments: *Russula laurocerasi* is a synonym. *Russula pectinatoides* (search online) is similar but has smaller spores: 5.5-9 × 4.5-6 μm. *Russula fragrantissima* (search online) is larger and has a fragrant, then rancid, odor.

GILLED MUSHROOMS

Russula nigricans Fr.
BLACKENING RUSSULA
Description: Cap 4.5-20 cm wide, convex becoming flat with a depressed center, margin incurved, slippery and shiny when moist, whitish to cream, becoming grayish-brown to blackish, darker at the center and paler toward the margin, cuticle peeling three-quarters to the center. Gills attached, thick, distant with some forking, whitish, aging to yellowish. Stalk 3-8 cm long, 1-4 cm thick, equal, sometimes tapered downward, finely powdery, solid, white, bruising red and then black. Flesh white, bruising reddish and then black. Odor somewhat unpleasant, fruity. Taste slowly acrid or not distinctive.
Spore Print: Whitish to yellowish.
Occurrence: In groups in hardwood and conifer forests. Summer-fall.
Edibility: Inedible.
Microscopic Features:
Spores 6-8 × 5-7 µm, ovoid to subglobose, surface ornamented with warts and ridges. Hyaline, amyloid.
Comments: Nearly identical *Russula dissimulans* (search online) has close to nearly distant gills and larger spores. *Russula densifolia* (search online) has close to crowded gills, acrid-tasting flesh, and larger spores.

Russula perlactea Murrill
Description: Cap 3-8 cm wide, convex becoming flat with a depressed center in age, dry, smooth, white, yellowish over the center, cuticle peeling three-quarters of the way to the center. Gills attached, close or nearly distant, white. Stalk 2.5-8 cm long, 1-1.5 cm thick, equal, smooth, white. Flesh white. Odor not distinctive. Taste quickly and intensely acrid.
Spore Print: White.
Occurrence: Scattered or in groups in mixed woods. Summer-fall.
Edibility: Inedible.
Microscopic Features:
Spores 9-10 × 7-8.5 µm, ovoid, surface ornamented with warts and ridges. Hyaline, amyloid.
Comments: *Russula brevipes* has a larger cap that bruises yellowish to brown, a shorter stalk, and flesh that tastes mild at first and then slowly acrid.

Russula redolens Burl.
PARSLEY-SCENTED RUSSULA
Description: Cap 4-8 cm wide, broadly convex to nearly flat, centrally depressed, smooth to slightly wrinkled, sticky when moist, margin radially lined, grayish blue-green to grayish-green, sometimes with purplish tints, cuticle peeling two-thirds of the way to the center. Gills attached, crowded, forked near the stalk, white. Stalk 4-7 cm wide, 6-25 mm wide, equal or tapered downward, dry, smooth or slightly wrinkled, white to grayish. Flesh brittle, whitish. Odor unpleasant, fishy or resembling parsley when mature. Taste disagreeable with an aftertaste of parsley or not distinctive.
Spore Print: White to cream.
Occurrence: Solitary, scattered, or in groups on the ground in hardwoods or mixed woods. Summer-fall.
Edibility: Unknown.
Microscopic Features:
Spores 6-8 × 4.5-6 µm, elliptical, ornamented with warts and ridges. Hyaline, amyloid.
Comments: *Redolens* means "emitting a scent." The odor distinguishes this species from greenish look-alikes such as *Russula aeruginea* and *R. modesta* (search online).

Russula variata Banning
VARIABLE RUSSULA
Description: Cap 5-12.5 cm wide, convex becoming flat with a depressed center, sticky when moist, smooth, sometimes radially wrinkled or cracked along the margin, various mixtures of green, olive, violet, or reddish-purple, cuticle peeling halfway to the center. Gills attached to somewhat decurrent, crowded and repeatedly forked, white, aging to yellowish. Stalk 2.5-10 cm long, 1-3 cm thick, equal or tapered downward, smooth, at times longitudinally wrinkled, white. Flesh white, brittle. Odor not distinctive. Taste acrid, sometimes slowly.
Spore Print: White.
Occurrence: Scattered or in groups with hardwoods, especially oak, and in mixed woods. Summer-fall.
Edibility: Edible.
Microscopic Features:
Spores 7-11 × 5.5-9 µm, ovoid to subglobose, surface ornamented with warts and ridges. Hyaline, amyloid.
Comments: *Russula aeruginea* has a green to yellowish-green cap and a cream-colored spore print. The cap of *Russula virescens* (search online) has green quiltlike patches.

Pale-Spored Group A: Mushrooms with a partial veil or ring zone

Armillaria gallica Marxm. & Romagn.

Description: Cap 2-6 cm wide, convex then broadly convex, sticky or dry, tan to pinkish- or reddish-brown with erect yellowish or brownish hairs that wash off in the rain. Cap margin may show white remnants of partial veil. Gills slightly decurrent, nearly distant, whitish, may discolor pinkish-brown. The stalk is 5-10 cm long, up to 1 cm thick, enlarging downward to a club-shaped base, white, sometimes staining yellow at the base, attached to black rhizomorphs. Partial veil cortinaceous, leaving a yellowish ring zone on the stalk. Flesh white. Odor fragrant. Taste not distinctive.

Spore Print: White.

Occurrence: Usually solitary or in small groups on the ground (from buried roots) or the base of dead hardwoods. Summer-fall.

Edibility: Edible if thoroughly cooked.

Microscopic Features:
  Spores 7-9.5 × 4.5-6 µm, elliptic, smooth. Hyaline, inamyloid.

Comments: The small size, thin partial veil, and sparse fruitings from dead wood help distinguish this common species from other honey mushrooms.

Armillaria mellea (Vahl) P. Kumm.

HONEY MUSHROOM

Description: Cap 3-15 cm wide, convex then flattening, sticky or dry, honey-colored and smooth or with a few dark hairs at the center of the cap. Gills attached or slightly decurrent, nearly distant, whitish. The stalk is 5-15 cm long, up to 2 cm or more thick, tapering downward, whitish near the apex, browner below, usually hairy or scaly below the partial veil. Partial veil a thick, membranous skirt. Flesh white. Odor and taste not distinctive.

Spore Print: White.

Occurrence: A virulent parasite, usually of hardwoods, growing in dense clusters on or around infected trees. Spring (less common) or fall.

Edibility: Edible if thoroughly cooked.

Microscopic Features:
  Spores 7-9 × 5.5-6.5 µm, elliptic, smooth. Hyaline, inamyloid.

Comments: Rhizomorphs under the loosening bark of a dying tree are a telltale sign of *Armillaria* infection. Stump removal reduces but does not eliminate the fungus in the soil.

Armillaria ostoyae (Romagn.) Herink

Description: Cap 3-20 cm wide, convex then flattening, dry, yellowish- to reddish-brown, covered with tan to dark brown scales. Gills attached or slightly decurrent, close, white, sometimes developing reddish-brown discolorations. The stalk is 5-21 cm long, up to 3 cm thick, nearly equal, tapering at the base, whitish near the apex, blackening below, hairy, basal mycelium yellow, rhizomorphs often present. Partial veil a thick, membranous skirt, white with a brown margin. Flesh white. Odor and taste not distinctive.

Spore Print: White.

Occurrence: A devastating parasite typically found in dense clusters on or around infected conifers. Summer-fall.

Edibility: Edible if thoroughly cooked.

Microscopic Features:
Spores 8-11 × 5.5-7 μm, broadly elliptic, smooth. Hyaline, inamyloid.

Comments: *Armillaria gemina* (search online) is a nearly identical decomposer of dead hardwoods. *Armillaria sinapina* (search online) occurs sparsely on hardwoods, has a yellow partial veil, and is initially covered by a universal veil that leaves yellow patches on the cap and stalk.

Armillaria tabescens (Scop.) Emel
RINGLESS HONEY MUSHROOM

Description: Cap 1-10 cm wide, convex then broadly convex with a low umbo, dry, yellowish- to cinnamon-brown, covered with small dark scales. Gills slightly decurrent, nearly distant, white, often bruising pinkish-brown. The stalk is 7.5-20 cm long, up to 1.5 cm thick, tapering at the base, white at the apex, darkening to yellow-brown below, hairy toward the base. Partial veil absent. Flesh white to brownish. Odor not distinctive. Taste bitter or not distinctive.

Spore Print: White to cream.

Occurrence: A parasite and decomposer found in clusters at the base of trees or on buried roots. Summer-fall.

Edibility: Edible if thoroughly cooked.

Microscopic Features:
Spores 8-10 × 5-7 μm, elliptic, smooth. Hyaline, inamyloid.

Comments: *Lyophyllum decastes* has a smooth cap, its gills lack brownish discolorations, and it grows on soil. Also compare with the dark-spored *Hypholoma lateritium* and the deadly brown-spored *Galerina marginata*.

GILLED MUSHROOMS

85

Chlorophyllum molybdites (G. Mey.) Massee
GREEN-SPORED PARASOL
Description: Cap 7-40 cm wide, rounded, then convex and flattening with age, typically with a broad umbo, dry, white, covered with pinkish-brown to cinnamon patches radiating from the center of the cap and breaking up into scales. Gills free, close, initially white, turning gray-green and staining yellowish when bruised. Stalks are 5-25 cm long, to 2.5 cm thick, equal or with a swollen base, white, smooth. Partial veil thick, white, double-edged at the margin, may slide on the stalk. Flesh white, not staining or staining pinkish to reddish-brown at the base. Odor and taste not distinctive.
Spore Print: Gray-green.
Occurrence: Grassy areas, often in groups or fairy rings. Summer-fall.
Edibility: Poisonous.
Microscopic Features:
Spores 9-13 × 6-9 μm, broadly elliptic, smooth, with an apical pore. Hyaline, dextrinoid.
Comments: The greenish spore color distinguishes this common source of mushroom poisoning from the edible *Macrolepiota procera* and *Chlorophyllum rhacodes*.

Chlorophyllum rhacodes (Vittad.) Vellinga
SHAGGY PARASOL
Description: Cap 5-20 cm wide, rounded, then convex and flattening with age, dry, brown at first but breaking up into large brown scales over a white background. Gills free, close, initially white, eventually may develop brown stains. Stalks 9-20 cm long, 1-3 cm thick, equal above a bulbous base that may have an upper rim, smooth, white, bruising yellow or brown. Partial veil thick, white, double-edged at the margin, moveable on the stalk. Flesh white, staining orange-yellow to reddish-brown. Odor and taste not distinctive.
Spore Print: White.
Occurrence: Often in groups or fairy rings on grassy areas, compost, wood chips, or needle duff. Fall.
Edibility: Edible, with caution.
Microscopic Features:
Spores 6-13 × 5-9 μm, elliptic, smooth, with an apical pore. Hyaline, dextrinoid.
Comments: Similar to poisonous species such as *Chlorophyllum molybdites* and *Agaricus pocillator*. *Leucoagaricus americanus* has finer scales, a different base, and an immobile ring.

Cystoderma amianthinum (Scop.) Fayod
PUNGENT CYSTODERMA
Description: Cap 2-5 cm wide, broadly
conical becoming convex, often
with a low umbo, dry, granular to
nearly smooth, with or without radial
wrinkles, yellow to reddish-brown, the
margin hung with toothlike fragments
of partial veil. Gills are attached, close or
crowded, white to pale yellow. The stalk
is 3-7.5 cm long, 3-8 mm thick, equal
or enlarging downward, dry, coarsely
granular below the partial veil, smooth
above; stalk apex white, colored like the
cap below the partial veil. Partial veil
briefly leaves a ring around the stalk.
Flesh white. Odor variously described
as like corn silk or geraniums. Taste not
distinctive.
Spore Print: White.
Occurrence: Solitary or scattered in moss
or needle duff under conifers. Summer-
winter.
Edibility: Unknown.
Microscopic Features:
Spores 5-6 × 3-4 μm, elliptic, smooth.
Hyaline, amyloid.
Comments: The white spore print
immediately distinguishes this species
from *Pholiota flammans*. *Leucocoprinus
birnbaumii* is more commonly found in
flowerpots.

Cystodermella granulosa (Batsch) Harmaja
Description: Cap 1-5 cm wide, convex
then flattening, dry, covered with
granules or scales, tawny brown to brick
red, occasionally orange-brown, the
margin initially inrolled and hung with
tags of partial veil. Gills are attached,
close, white to pale yellow. The stalk is
2-6 cm long, 3-10 mm thick, equal or
enlarging downward, dry, smooth, and
white or pale orange above the partial
veil, sheathed below with granules/
scales colored like the cap. Partial veil
fibrous, leaving a flaring skirt around
the stalk. Flesh white. Odor and taste
not distinctive.
Spore Print: White.
Occurrence: Solitary or scattered on the
ground, well-rotted bits of wood, or
woodland mosses. Summer-winter.
Edibility: Unknown.
Microscopic Features:
Spores 3.5-5 × 2.5-3 μm, elliptic,
smooth. Hyaline, inamyloid.
Comments: *Cystoderma amianthinum* has
a pungent odor and different spores.
Leucopholiota decorosa grows on logs
or stumps. *Cystodermella cinnabarina*
(search online) is generally larger
and reddish-orange. *Flammulaster
erinaceellus* (search online) has a brown
spore print.

GILLED MUSHROOMS

Echinoderma asperum (Pers.) Bon
SHARP-SCALED LEPIOTA
Description: Cap 3-11 cm wide, convex but flattening with maturity, dry, at first brown to cinnamon-brown and covered with soft hairs that later clump into pointy brown scales over a white background. The scales don't wash off. Gills are free, crowded, white. The stalk is 5-11 cm long, up to 1.5 cm thick, equal, dry, hairy but not shaggy, whitish, may be slightly bulbed. Partial veil flimsy but somewhat persistent, white, may have brown scales on the underside. Flesh white. Odor fragrant or not distinctive. Taste not distinctive.
Spore Print: White.
Occurrence: Solitary or scattered on humus-rich woodland soil or rotted hardwood. Summer-fall.
Edibility: Edible, with caution.
Microscopic Features:
Spores 6.5-11 × 2-3.5 μm, smooth, long-elliptic. Dextrinoid.
Comments: Also known as *Lepiota aspera* and *L. acutosquamosa*. It is easily confused with poisonous species such as *Lepiota clypeolaria* or Amanitas. *Leucoagaricus americanus* and *L. brunnescens* (search online) bruise reddish-brown. See also *Armillaria gallica*.

Lentinula edodes (Berk.) Pegler
SHIITAKE
Description: Cap 5-11 cm wide (occasionally larger), convex then flattening, occasionally with a low umbo, dry, variably scaly, sometimes cracked, dark brown at first, lightening with age and toward the margin; the margin inrolled and tagged with white patches and fibrils of partial veil. Gills attached but often free themselves, crowded, edges smooth at first but soon serrated, white, bruising brown when injured. Stalk 3-4 cm long and 8-13 mm thick, equal or enlarging downward, solid, pale brown to reddish-brown, sheathed in shaggy fibers or scales. Partial veil fibrous, seldom leaving a ring on the stalk. Flesh fibrous, whitish bruising brown. Odor and taste not distinctive.
Spore Print: White.
Occurrence: In groups on hardwood logs or debris. Season limits in the wild uncertain.
Edibility: Edible, choice.
Microscopic Features:
Spores 5-6.5 × 3-3.5 μm, ovoid to elliptic. Hyaline, inamyloid.
Comments: This commercially grown species is beginning to escape into natural settings.

Lepiota clypeolaria complex
(Bull.) P. Kumm.
SHAGGY-STALKED LEPIOTA
Description: Cap 2.5-7 cm wide, bell-shaped then broadly convex or flattening, usually with an umbo, dry, whitish under orange-brown scales that are densest centrally, the margin hung with rags of partial veil. Gills free, close, whitish. The stalk is 4-11.5 cm long, up to 1 cm thick, equal or enlarging downward, whitish near the apex shading to yellow-brown at the base, smooth above the ring zone and shaggy/scaly below. Partial veil fibrous, white, fleeting on the stalk. Flesh white, not bruising reddish. Odor and taste not distinctive or unpleasant.
Spore Print: White.
Occurrence: Solitary or scattered on the ground in the woods. Summer-fall.
Edibility: Poisonous.
Microscopic Features:
  Spores 14-20 × 4-6 μm, spindle-shaped, smooth. Hyaline, dextrinoid.
Comments: Sorting this group with certainty relies on microscopy and/or DNA analysis, but *Lepiota magnispora* (search online) and MushroomExpert's *Lepiota sp. 1* (search online) have darker, more contrasting cap centers and differently shaped spores.

Lepiota cristata (Bolton) P. Kumm.
STINKING PARASOL
Description: Cap 1-7 cm wide, convex then flattening, often with an umbo, dry, initially smooth and reddish-brown, breaking up into rings of flat, reddish-brown scales over a white background. Gills free or nearly so, close, whitish, smooth-edged or serrated. The stalk is 2-8 cm long and 2-6 mm thick, equal or with a bulbous base, smooth, whitish, frequently brown at the base. Partial veil a white, membranous skirt. Flesh white. Odor and taste foul, fragrant, or not distinctive.
Spore Print: White.
Occurrence: Solitary or scattered on the ground in woodland or grassy areas. Summer-fall.
Edibility: Unknown.
Microscopic Features:
  Spores 5-8 × 3-5 μm, wedge-shaped with a small corner spur, smooth. Hyaline, dextrinoid.
Comments: Other small Lepiotas with distinctive scaly caps include *Lepiota atrodisca* (search online), which has flat, dark gray scales, and *L. felina*, with erect, dark brown scales (see photo on p. 19). The larger *Echinoderma aspera* (search online) also has erect brown scales.

GILLED MUSHROOMS

89

Leucoagaricus americanus (Peck) Vellinga
REDDENING LEPIOTA
Description: Cap 3-15 cm wide, convex then flattening, usually with an umbo, dry, reddish-brown at first, cracking into rings of medium-sized scales over a pale background that ages or bruises reddish-brown; the margin is finely lined, often tattered at maturity. Gills free, close, whitish, aging or bruising reddish-brown. Stalk 5-14 cm long, up to 2.5 cm thick, sometimes swollen above the base, smooth, whitish, bruising yellow then reddish-brown. Partial veil membranous, white, leaving a fixed, double-edged collar high on the stalk. Flesh white, bruising reddish. Odor and taste not distinctive.
Spore Print: White.
Occurrence: Solitary or scattered in lawns, wood chips, or compost piles or near stumps. Summer-fall.
Edibility: Edible, with caution.
Microscopic Features:
Spores 8-14 × 5-10 µm, elliptic, smooth with an apical pore. Hyaline, dextrinoid.
Comments: *Leucoagaricus brunnescens* (search online) is a smaller, woodland species. Also consider *Chlorophyllum rhacodes*, *Macrolepiota procera*, and the poisonous, green-spored *Chlorophyllum molybdites*.

Leucocoprinus birnbaumii (Corda) Singer
LEMON YELLOW LEPIOTA
Description: Cap 2-6 cm wide, conic or bell-shaped, usually with a knobby umbo, dry, powdery or finely scaled, some shade of yellow fading toward whitish in age, the margin strongly lined all the way to the umbo. Gills free, crowded, pale yellow or yellow. The stalk is 3-12 cm long and 1.5 to 6 mm thick, equal or enlarging downward, powdery or smooth, colored like the cap. Partial veil a thin yellow skirt that is sometimes lost. Flesh pale yellow. Odor and taste not distinctive.
Spore Print: White.
Occurrence: Commonly found in flowerpots, also in rich soils or wood chips. Summer-fall.
Edibility: Poisonous.
Microscopic Features:
Spores 8-13 × 5-8 µm, elliptic, smooth, thick-walled. Hyaline, dextrinoid.
Comments: Formerly known as *Lepiota lutea*. *Leucocoprinus cepistipes* is predominantly white. Small Lepiotas— see *L. cristata*—lack the strongly lined cap. *Pholiota flammans* is shaggier and brown-spored; it grows on conifer wood.

Leucocoprinus cepistipes (Sowerby) Pat.
ONION-STALK LEPIOTA
Description: Cap 2-8 cm wide, bell-shaped to broadly convex with an often knobby umbo, dry, powdery or finely scaled, whitish except for the yellow-brown umbo, sometimes yellowing overall at maturity, the margin strongly lined. Gills free, crowded, whitish. Stalk 4-14 cm long and 3-6 mm thick, equal or enlarging downward, smooth to powdery, whitish, bruising yellowish. Partial veil a thin white skirt. Flesh white. Odor not distinctive. Taste bitter or not distinctive.

Spore Print: White.

Occurrence: Grouped or clustered in rich soils, straw, or wood chips, sometimes in flowerpots. Summer.

Edibility: Unknown; may be poisonous. Caution advised.

Microscopic Features:
Spores 7-10 × 6-8 μm, elliptic, thick-walled, smooth with a small pore. Hyaline, weakly dextrinoid.

Comments: Also known as *Lepiota cepistipes*. *Leucocoprinus cretaceus* (search online) is nearly identical, but the umbo is white in youth and cap scales are microscopically different. The cap margin of *Lepiota cristata* is unlined.

Leucocoprinus fragilissimus (Ravenel ex Berk. & M. A. Curtis) Pat.
FRAGILE LEUCOCOPRINUS
Description: Cap 1-4.5 cm wide, bell-shaped becoming nearly flat with a small umbo, moist or dry, minutely scaly, translucent, pale yellow fading toward white, with a darker umbo, the margin strongly grooved/lined all the way to the umbo. Gills attached or free, distant, pale yellow. Stalk 4-15.5 cm long and 1 to 3 mm thick, equal above a small bulb, minutely scaly, dry, hollow, colored like the cap. Partial veil a fragile yellow skirt. Flesh very fragile, whitish. Odor and taste not distinctive.

Spore Print: White.

Occurrence: Solitary, scattered, or in groups on the ground in woodlands. Summer-fall.

Edibility: Unknown.

Microscopic Features:
Spores 9-13 × 7-8 μm, broadly elliptic, smooth with an apical pore. Hyaline, dextrinoid.

Comments: The fragility of this beautiful little mushroom makes it difficult to collect intact. *Leucocoprinus birnbaumii* isn't as leggy and is typically found in the woods.

GILLED MUSHROOMS

91

Leucopholiota decorosa
(Peck) O. K. Mill., T. J. Volk & Bessette
DECORATED PHOLIOTA
Description: Cap 2-7 cm wide, convex
with an inrolled margin, expanding to
nearly flat, dry, bright yellow or orange-
yellow, densely covered with recurved,
rusty brown scales, the margin hairy
with fibers from the partial veil. Gills
attached, close, white. Stalk 2.5-8 cm
long, up to 1.5 cm thick, dry, equal or
enlarging downward, often curved,
smooth and whitish above the ring
zone, covered with rusty scales below.
Partial veil consists of upward flaring
fibers that leave a ring zone marked
by textural change. Flesh white. Odor
not distinctive. Taste bitter or not
distinctive.
Spore Print: White.
Occurrence: Solitary to clustered on
decaying logs or stumps. Late summer–
fall.
Edibility: Unknown.
Microscopic Features:
Spores 5.5-7 × 3.5-4 µm, elliptic,
smooth. Hyaline, amyloid.
Comments: The white spore print rules
out similar-appearing Pholiotas,
Gymnopilus penetrans, and the smaller
Flammulaster erinaceellus (search
online).

Macrolepiota procera (Scop.) Singer
PARASOL
Description: Cap 7-25 cm wide, oval at
first, becoming broadly convex with a
conspicuous umbo, dry, pinkish-brown
to brown and nearly smooth when
young, breaking into coarse brown to
grayish-brown scales and patches over
a whitish ground color when mature.
Gills free, close, white to pale tan. Stalk
15-25 cm long, 1-1.5 cm thick, enlarged
downward to a bulbous base, dry, coated
with tiny brownish scales on a white
ground color. Partial veil thick, double-
layered, white, leaving a movable ring
on the stalk. Flesh white, unchanging.
Odor and taste not distinctive.
Spore Print: White.
Occurrence: Scattered or in groups in
woodlands or grassy areas. Summer–
fall.
Edibility: Edible.
Microscopic Features:
Spores 12-18 × 8-12 µm, broadly elliptic,
smooth. Hyaline, dextrinoid.
Comments: *Chlorophyllum rhacodes* (p. 86)
is more robust with coarser, reddish-
brown cap scales, a thicker stalk, and
flesh that bruises pinkish-orange then
brownish. *Leucoagaricus americanus*
also has a thicker stalk and reddish-
bruising flesh.

Neolentinus lepideus (Fr.) Redhead & Ginns
TRAIN WRECKER
Description: Cap 5-20 cm wide, convex or
almost flat, with brownish scales over a
whitish to yellowish ground color. Gills
attached or decurrent, nearly distant,
broad, smooth-edged at first, serrated
in age, white to yellowish. Stalk 2.5-
8 cm long, 1-2.5 cm thick, sometimes
off-center, equal, dry, whitish with
brownish hairs or scales. Partial veil
membranous, whitish, leaving a ring
on the stalk that may disappear. Flesh
thick, tough, white. Odor fragrant or not
distinctive. Taste not distinctive.
Spore Print: White.
Occurrence: Solitary or in groups or
clusters on decaying coniferous wood,
fence posts, and railroad ties. Rarely on
hardwood. Late spring-fall.
Edibility: Edible when young and tender.
Microscopic Features:
Spores 9-12 × 4-5 μm, cylindric,
smooth. Hyaline, inamyloid.
Comments: *Lentinus tigrinus* is smaller and
has a cobwebby veil that leaves only
a faint ring zone. The cap of *Lentinus
crinitus* is smaller and densely covered
with brown hairs.

GILLED MUSHROOMS

Ampulloclitocybe clavipes (Pers.) Redhead, Lutzoni, Moncalvo & Vilgalys
CLUB-FOOTED CLITOCYBE

Description: Cap 2-9 cm wide, shaped like an inverted cone, often with a depressed center in age, moist or dry, smooth, color varies from pinkish- to grayish- to olive-brown. Gills are decurrent, close to nearly distant, whitish to creamy at maturity. The stalk is 3.5-6 cm long, 4-12 mm thick, enlarging downward to a club-shaped base, stuffed with spongy material, covered with tiny brownish fibers; basal mycelium is white. Partial veil absent. Flesh white. Odor fragrant or almondlike. Taste not distinctive.

Spore Print: White.

Occurrence: Under conifers or occasionally deciduous trees. Summer-fall.

Edibility: Edible, but adverse reactions have occurred when combined with alcohol.

Microscopic Features:
Spores 6-10 × 3.5-5 µm, ovoid to irregularly elliptic, smooth. Hyaline, inamyloid.

Comments: Also known as *Clitocybe clavipes*. Similarly colored milk mushrooms exude colored latex when injured. *Clitocybe squamulosa* (search online) is more cinnamon in color and lacks the notably inflated base.

Cantharellula umbonata (J. F. Gmel.) Singer
GRAYLING

Description: Cap 1-5 cm wide, convex at first with an inrolled margin, later becoming flat or with a depressed center, moist or dry, smooth or nearly so, gray to grayish-brown, often with white blotches. Gills decurrent, crowded, highly forked, whitish, typically developing yellowish or reddish spots with age. Stalk is 2.5-12.5 cm long, 3-7 mm thick, equal, smooth to silky, stuffed, white or gray; bound to moss by white mycelium. Partial veil absent. Flesh white. Odor and taste not distinctive.

Spore Print: White.

Occurrence: Gregarious, sometimes in fairy rings, on haircap (*Polytrichum spp.*) moss. Late summer-fall.

Edibility: Edible and good when young.

Microscopic Features:
Spores 8-11 × 3-4.5 µm, spindle-shaped, smooth. Hyaline, amyloid.

Comments: The inedible *Pseudoclitocybe cyathiformis* (search online) is similar but has a dark gray-brown cap and is found in grass or woodland situations other than moss. The typical mossy substrate also helps distinguish it from funnel caps such as *Ampulloclitocybe clavipes*.

Chromosera cyanophylla
(Fr.) Redhead, Ammirati & Norvell

Description: Cap 6-25 mm wide, broadly convex, becoming centrally depressed, smooth, sticky, lavender in youth, becoming dull yellow with a translucent and lined margin. Gills slightly decurrent, close to nearly distant with two tiers of short gills, initially lavender, fading to cream. Stalks 1-3.5 cm long, 1 mm thick, equal, smooth, slimy, colored like the cap, basal mycelium lilac. Partial veil absent. Flesh pale yellow. Odor and taste not distinctive.

Spore Print: White.

Occurrence: In groups on decaying conifer wood. Spring-fall.

Edibility: Unknown.

Microscopic Features:
Spores 6-7 × 3-4 µm, elliptic, smooth. Hyaline, inamyloid.

Comments: This little cutie was once known as *Mycena lilacifolia*. The slightly decurrent gills distinguish it from colorful ex-relatives among the mycenas. *Xeromphalina campanella* (search online) grows on conifer wood but isn't slimy. Waxcaps such as *Gloioxanthomyces nitidus* (search online) can be slimy and yellow but usually at least appear to be growing on the ground.

Clitocybe gibba (Pers.) P. Kumm.
COMMON FUNNEL CAP

Description: Cap 3-9 cm wide, flat to centrally depressed in youth, funnel-shaped at maturity, moist or dry, smooth, tan to pinkish-cinnamon. Gills are decurrent, close or crowded, sometimes forked, whitish. The stalk is 3-8 cm long, 3-12 mm thick, dry, smooth, equal or enlarging at the base, hollow in age, whitish, with white basal mycelium. Partial veil absent. Flesh white. Odor and taste not distinctive.

Spore Print: White.

Occurrence: Solitary, scattered, or grouped under hardwoods or in mixed woods. Summer-fall.

Edibility: Edible.

Microscopic Features:
Spores 5-9 × 3.5-6 µm, elliptic, smooth. Hyaline, inamyloid.

Comments: Also known as *Infundibulicybe gibba*. A related species, *Clitocybe squamulosa* (search online), grows under conifers; the stalk is colored like the cap. *Ampuloclitocybe clavipes* is usually found under conifers and has a more inflated or club-shaped base.

GILLED MUSHROOMS

Clitocybe odora (Bull.) P. Kumm.
ANISE-SCENTED CLITOCYBE
Description: Cap 2-11 cm wide, convex
with an inrolled margin at first, then
flattening and typically centrally
depressed, moist or dry, radially
streaked with tiny fibers, greenish
to blue-green, often fading in age,
especially centrally. Gills are attached
or slightly decurrent, close, whitish.
The stalk is 1.5-9 cm long, up to 1.5 cm
thick, moist or dry, finely hairy, equal
or enlarging at the base, hollow in age,
whitish, with white basal mycelium.
Partial veil absent. Flesh whitish. Odor
and taste of anise (licorice).
Spore Print: Cream or, when heavy, pale
pink.
Occurrence: Solitary, scattered, or grouped
under hardwoods or in mixed woods.
Summer-early fall.
Edibility: Edible.
Microscopic Features:
Spores 5-9 × 3.5-5 µm, elliptic, smooth.
Hyaline, inamyloid.
Comments: The odor and taste of anise is
often quite strong, suggesting culinary
use as a seasoning. *Clitocybe aeruginosa*
(search online) is very similar but has a
white spore print and no distinct odor.

Cuphophyllus colemannianus
(A. Bloxam) Bon
Description: Cap 1-5 cm wide, hemi-
spherical becoming broadly convex
or flat, usually with an umbo, moist
or greasy, smooth, some shade of
orangish-, reddish-, or date brown,
translucently lined when moist,
hygrophanous when dry. Gills
decurrent, close or nearly distant,
forking, whitish to pale brown, connecting veins prominent. The stalk is
2-8 cm long, up to 3-7 mm thick, equal
or tapering downward, dry, smooth or
with scant fibers on the surface, whitish
to pale brown. Partial veil absent. Flesh
thick, brittle, paler brown than the cap.
Odor and taste not distinctive.
Spore Print: White.
Occurrence: Scattered or grouped under
hardwoods or in mixed woods. Late
summer-fall.
Edibility: Unknown.
Microscopic Features:
Spores 6-9 × 4.5-7 µm, elliptic or
broadly elliptic, smooth. Hyaline,
inamyloid.
Comments: *Hygrocybe colemanniana* and
Hygrophorus colemannianus are synonyms. This species resembles the more
common *Cuphophyllus pratensis*, which
has a cap predominantly orange rather
than brown.

Cuphophyllus lacmus (Schumach.) Bon
Description: Cap 2-6 cm wide, broadly
conical then flattening, usually with a
low umbo at first, but the center may be
depressed at maturity, greasy or sticky,
smooth, bluish- to violet-gray with
central brownish shades at maturity,
translucently lined when moist,
hygrophanous when dry. Gills are
decurrent, distant, sometimes forking,
pale gray to gray-violet, connecting
veins present. Stalk is 3-7 cm long,
up to 12 mm thick, equal or tapering
downward, dry, smooth, whitish overall
but possibly grayish at the apex. Partial
veil absent. Flesh thick, colored like the
cap or paler. Odor unpleasant or not
distinctive. Taste bitter or acrid.
Spore Print: White.
Occurrence: Scattered or grouped in grassy
areas or damp woods, often under
conifers. Summer-fall.
Edibility: Unknown.
Microscopic Features:
Spores 6-8.5 × 4-7 µm, broadly elliptic
or subglobose, smooth. Hyaline,
inamyloid.
Comments: Also known as *Hygrocybe
lacmus* and *H. subviolacea*. The gills of
Cantharellula umbonata are pale and
crowded.

Cuphophyllus pratensis (Fr.) Bon
SALMON WAXY CAP
Description: Cap 2-7 cm wide, convex
becoming broadly convex, usually with
a low umbo, moist or dry, smooth but
may have cracks on the disc in age,
some shade of orange, eventually fading
toward tan. Gills are slightly decurrent,
distant, short gills and connecting veins
present, creamy with a hint of orange.
The stalk is 3-8 cm long, up to 2 cm
thick, equal or tapering downward, dry,
smooth, whitish to pale salmon-buff.
Partial veil absent. Flesh thick, brittle,
white to pale cinnamon. Odor and taste
not distinctive.
Spore Print: White.
Occurrence: Scattered or grouped in grassy
areas or woodland humus. Late spring-
fall.
Edibility: Edible.
Microscopic Features:
Spores 5-8 × 3-5 µm, elliptic to
subglobose, smooth. Hyaline,
inamyloid.
Comments: Formerly named *Hygrocybe
pratensis*. The brittleness and generally
unwaxy feel of this species might easily
mislead identifiers. *Russula earlei*
(p. 80) lacks the umbo and crossveins
between gills; its spores are warted, not
smooth.

Cuphophyllus virgineus (Wulfen) Kovalenko
SNOWY WAXCAP
Description: Cap 1-7 cm wide, hemispheric at first, opening to nearly flat, often with a low umbo or central depression, the margin initially incurved, moist or greasy, smooth, whitish and translucent, showing lines halfway to the center when fresh. Gills are decurrent, nearly distant, sometimes forked, white. The stalk is 2-12 cm long, up to 1 cm thick, nearly equal or tapering downward, round or flattened in cross section, dry, smooth, white. Partial veil absent. Flesh thick or thin, white. Odor and taste not distinctive.
Spore Print: White.
Occurrence: Solitary or scattered in grassy areas, in moss beds, or on the ground in woods. Summer-fall.
Edibility: Edible.
Microscopic Features:
Spores 6-9 × 4-6 µm, elliptic, smooth. Hyaline, inamyloid.
Comments: Also known as *Hygrocybe virginea*. Another greasy to sticky white waxcap, *Hygrophorus occidentalis* (search online) appears similar in youth, but the cap browns with maturity.

Gerronema strombodes
(Berk. & Mont.) Singer
Description: Cap 2-10 cm wide, broadly convex at first, developing a depressed center or funnel shape with a wavy margin, slightly sticky or dry, smooth, greenish-yellow to gray-brown with darker radial steaks. Gills decurrent, sometimes forked, close to nearly distant, whitish to yellow. The stalk is 2.5-6.5 cm long, up to 8 mm thick, equal, dry, very finely hairy, hollow, whitish or colored like the cap. Partial veil absent. Flesh thin, whitish, not staining when injured. Odor not distinctive. Taste bitter or not distinctive.
Spore Print: White.
Occurrence: Often clustered, usually on rotting hardwood. Late spring-fall.
Edibility: Unknown.
Microscopic Features:
Spores 7-9 × 3-6 µm, elliptic, smooth. Hyaline, inamyloid.
Comments: Despite the shape, this is not related to chanterelles. A similar species, *Pseudoarmillariella ectypoides*, has tiny scales rather than radiating fibers on the cap and prefers conifer wood. The stalk of another conifer specialist, *Chrysomphalina chrysophylla* (search online), doesn't stain brown.

Hohenbuehelia mastrucata (Fr.) Singer
**WOOLY OYSTER,
SHEEPSKIN MUSHROOM**
Description: Cap 2-7 cm wide, shaped like a clamshell with an inrolled margin, moist, covered with coarse gelatinous ridges or spines, bluish- to brownish-gray, paler in age. Gills close or nearly distant, arising from the point of attachment to the host, whitish or pale gray. Stalk absent. Partial veil absent. Flesh rubbery, colored like the cap and gills. Odor farinaceous or not distinctive. Taste mildly unpleasant or not distinctive.
Spore Print: White.
Occurrence: Grouped on the wood of dead maples or other hardwoods. Summer-fall.
Edibility: Unknown.
Microscopic Features:
Spores 6-9 × 5-6 μm, elliptic, smooth. Hyaline, inamyloid.
Comments: *Hohenbuehelia atrocaerulea* (search online) is similar but has a finely hairy cap. The cap of *Lentinellus ursinus* has brown hairs; gill edges are serrated. *Hohenbuehelia angustata* (search online) has a smooth, whitish to brownish cap and a doughy smell. Caps of *Pleurotus ostreatus* are also smooth.

Hygrophoropsis aurantiaca (Wulfen) Maire
FALSE CHANTERELLE
Description: Cap 2-10 cm wide, convex at first with an inrolled margin, becoming flat or centrally depressed, dry, minutely velvety, yellow-orange to orangish-brown, darkest in the center. Gills decurrent, close or crowded, repeatedly forked, some shade of orange. The stalk is 2-10 cm long, up to 2 cm thick, sometimes off-center, equal, dry, minutely velvety, orange. Partial veil absent. Flesh tough and orangish. Odor and taste not distinctive.
Spore Print: White.
Occurrence: Scattered under conifers or on rotted conifer humus. Late summer-fall.
Edibility: Debatable, with reports of possible digestive upset; poor at best.
Microscopic Features:
Spores 5.5-8 × 2.5-4.5 μm, elliptic to subglobose, smooth. Hyaline, mostly dextrinoid.
Comments: True chanterelles have thickened pseudo-gills rather than crowded true gills. *Gymnopilus* species have brown spore prints. *Lactarius croceus* is larger, grows under hardwoods, and usually produces latex when injured. *Omphalotus illudens*, also larger, grows in clusters on hardwoods.

Hygrophorus russula
(Schaeff. ex Fr.) Kauffman
RUSSULA-LIKE WAXCAP
Description: Cap 5-12 cm wide, convex
with a cottony inrolled margin at first,
opening to flat or centrally depressed,
sticky or dry, minutely scaly to smooth,
streaked or mottled with pinks and
purplish-reds, sometimes bruising
yellow near the margin. Gills are
attached and decurrent at maturity,
close or crowded, becoming spotted
or flushed with purplish-red. The stalk
is 3-8 cm long, up to 3.5 cm thick,
nearly equal, dry, solid, powdery at
the apex and smooth below, initially
white, then colored like the cap. Partial
veil absent. Flesh firm, white or pink-
tinged, sometimes bruising yellow.
Odor not distinctive. Taste bitter or not
distinctive.
Spore Print: White.
Occurrence: Solitary or scattered, usually
under oaks. Summer-fall.
Edibility: Edible, but often bitter.
Microscopic Features:
Spores 6-8 × 3-5 μm, elliptic, smooth.
Hyaline, inamyloid.
Comments: The firm flesh helps
distinguish this mushroom from
crumbly Russulas such as *Russula
emetica*.

Hygrophorus sordidus Peck
SORDID WAXCAP
Description: Cap 5-20 cm wide, convex
with an inrolled margin, becoming
broadly convex and sometimes
centrally depressed, sticky becoming
dry, smooth, white, then often dirty
yellow in the center. Gills attached and
usually slightly decurrent at maturity,
nearly distant, white to dingy yellow
in age. The stalk is 5-10 cm long,
up to 3 cm thick, equal or enlarging
downward above a narrowing base, dry,
solid, smooth or finely hairy, whitish.
Partial veil absent. Flesh firm and white.
Odor not distinctive. Taste mildly bitter
or not distinctive.
Spore Print: White.
Occurrence: Solitary or scattered, usually
under oaks. Summer-fall.
Edibility: Edible, may be slightly bitter.
Microscopic Features:
Spores 6-8 × 4-5.5 μm, elliptic, smooth.
Hyaline, inamyloid.
Comments: Encrusted debris often
makes cleaning this mushroom a
challenge. The Dirty Southern Waxcap,
Hygrophorus subsordidus (search online)
is smaller and has narrower spores: 5.5-
8 × 3-4 μm. *Russula earlei* (p. 80) is also
smaller, is consistently yellowish, and
has warted spores.

Laccaria amethystina Cooke
AMETHYST LACCARIA
Description: Cap 0.5-5 cm wide, convex
to flat or centrally dimpled, the margin
inrolled at first, usually displaying
radial lines, dry, granular to finely scaly,
grayish-purple soon fading toward buff.
Gills attached or slightly decurrent,
more or less distant, thick, purplish. The
stalk is 1-7.5 cm long and 1-7 mm thick,
equal or with a swollen base, finely
hairy or scaly, colored like the cap, basal
mycelium white or pale violet. Partial
veil absent. Flesh colored like the cap or
paler. Odor and taste not distinctive.
Spore Print: White to faintly lilac.
Occurrence: Scattered or grouped, usually
under oaks or beech. Spring-summer.
Edibility: Caps edible; stalks stringy.
Microscopic Features:
Spores 7-10 μm, globose excluding
spines that are 1.5-3 μm long and up
to 1 μm thick at the base. Hyaline,
inamyloid.
Comments: *Baeospora myriadophylla* and
Mycena haematopus grow on rotting
wood. *Mycena pura* smells and tastes
like radish.

Laccaria laccata complex (Scop.) Cooke
COMMON LACCARIA
Description: Cap 1-6 cm wide, convex
then flattening, often with a wavy
uplifted margin and central dimple or
perforation, dry, finely scaly to smooth,
orange-brown fading toward buff, the
margin not strongly lined. Gills attached
or slightly decurrent, close or nearly
distant, thin or thickened, pinkish,
sometimes tinged with purple. Stalk
1.5-10 cm long, 3-10 mm thick, equal
or with a swollen base, finely hairy or
smooth, sometimes twisted, flattened,
or longitudinally striped, hollowing,
colored like the cap, basal mycelium
white. Partial veil absent. Flesh thin,
colored like the cap. Odor and taste not
distinctive.
Spore Print: White.
Occurrence: Scattered to grouped in
dirt, duff, grassy areas, or woodlands.
Spring-fall.
Edibility: Edible.
Microscopic Features:
Spores 6-13 μm, globose excluding
spines that are 1-2.5 μm long and up
to 1 μm thick at the base. Hyaline,
inamyloid.
Comments: A commonly encountered
but confusing species complex. For
the average mushroomer, "*Laccaria
laccata*" is close enough.

GILLED MUSHROOMS

Laccaria ochropurpurea (Berk.) Peck
PURPLE-GILLED LACCARIA

Description: Cap 3.5-12.5 cm wide, broadly convex with an inrolled margin, then flattening and often centrally depressed, dry, smooth or finely scaly, pale purplish-brown fading toward whitish, the margin not lined. Gills attached or slightly decurrent, close or nearly distant, thick, purple to grayish-violet. The stalk is 4.5-19 cm long and up to 3.5 cm thick, equal or enlarging downward, hairy or scaly, solid, colored like the cap or with reddish-brown discolorations, basal mycelium pale violet. Partial veil absent. Flesh thick, colored like the cap. Odor and taste not distinctive.

Spore Print: White to pale violet.

Occurrence: Scattered to grouped in mixed woods. Summer-fall.

Edibility: Edible.

Microscopic Features: Spores 7-9 µm, globose excluding spines that are 1-2 µm long and up to 1.5 µm thick at the base. Hyaline, inamyloid.

Comments: Take care to distinguish this edible from potentially poisonous brown-spored corts such as *Cortinarius alboviolaceus*.

Laccaria trullisata (Ellis) Peck
SANDY LACCARIA

Description: Cap 2-7.5 cm wide, convex with an inrolled margin, then flattening and often centrally depressed, dry, finely hairy or scaly, initially grayish-purple fading through reddish-brown toward buff; the margin is not radially lined. Gills attached or slightly decurrent, close or nearly distant, thick, purple to grayish-purple, becoming reddish-violet. The stalk is 4-9 cm long and up to 2.5 cm thick, enlarging downward, hairy, often longitudinally striped, solid, colored like the cap and partially covered with sand, basal mycelium pale violet. Partial veil absent. Flesh thick, colored like the cap. Odor and taste not distinctive.

Spore Print: White.

Occurrence: Solitary, scattered, or in groups in sand dunes or very sandy soil. Summer-winter.

Edibility: Edible, but usually too sandy.

Microscopic Features: Spores 14-21 × 5.5-8 µm, broadly fusiform to elliptic, smooth or finely roughened. Hyaline, inamyloid.

Comments: Frequently found buried up to the cap in sand. The habitat and spores are quite different for *Laccaria ochropurpurea*.

Lentinellus ursinus (Fr.) Kühner
BEAR LENTINUS
Description: Cap 2.5-10 cm wide, shell-shaped from a narrow point of attachment, convex to flat or centrally depressed, dry, with brown hair at least near the attachment, reddish-brown to buff overall, lighter toward the initially inrolled margin. Gills radiate from the point of attachment, close or nearly distant, edges serrated, whitish or pale pinkish-brown. Stalk absent. Partial veil absent. Flesh firm, whitish. Odor mildly fruity or not distinctive. Taste acrid.
Spore Print: White to slightly creamy.
Occurrence: In groups on decaying hardwoods, rarely on conifers. Summer-fall.
Edibility: Inedible.
Microscopic Features:
Spores 3-4.5 × 2-3.5 µm, subglobose, minutely spiny. Hyaline, amyloid.
Comments: The Bitter Oyster, *Panellus stipticus*, is much smaller and has a stubby stalk. Members of the *Pleurotus ostreatus* complex have smooth caps. *Crepidotus mollis* has watery flesh and brown spores.

Lentinus crinitus (L.) Fr.
Description: Cap 2.5-7.5 cm wide, convex with a dimpled center or funnel-shaped, dry, densely covered with yellowish- to reddish-brown hairs, the ground color pale tan or pale purplish. Gills are strongly decurrent, crowded, edges finely serrated (use hand lens), whitish to cream. Stalk 2-4 cm long and 2-6 mm thick, dry, solid, finely flaky, colored like the cap or paler. Partial veil absent. Flesh fibrous and tough, whitish. Odor and taste not distinctive.
Spore Print: White.
Occurrence: In groups or clusters on decaying hardwoods. Summer-fall.
Edibility: Inedible.
Microscopic Features:
Spores 5.5-8 × 2-3 µm, elliptic, smooth. Hyaline, inamyloid.
Comments: *Panus neostrigosus* is similar but has little to no stalk; it also lacks the gill serrations. *Lentinula edodes* is scaly rather than hairy and has a fibrous partial veil leaving a ring zone on the stalk.

GILLED MUSHROOMS

Lentinus tigrinus (Bull.) Fr.

Description: Cap 1-10 cm wide, convex to broadly convex with a dimpled center, dry, covered at least centrally by small brown scales over a paler ground color. The gills are decurrent, crowded, edges serrated, buff or faintly pinkish. Stalk 2-8 cm long and 4-8 mm thick, dry, equal, brown, scaly to densely hairy near the base, the base often rooting in the rotting wood of the host. Partial veil cobwebby, white, leaving a faint ring zone on the stalk. Flesh fibrous and tough, white. Odor pleasantly resinous. Taste not distinctive.

Spore Print: White.

Occurrence: Solitary to densely clustered from a rooting base on decaying hardwoods. Spring-fall.

Edibility: Inedible.

Microscopic Features:
Spores 6.5-12 × 2.5-3.5 µm, narrowly elliptic, smooth. Hyaline, inamyloid.

Comments: The similar *Lentinellus micheneri* (search online) has a smooth cap, more distantly spaced gills, and a peppery taste.

Leucopaxillus albissimus (Peck) Singer
WHITE LEUCOPAX

Description: Cap 2.5-20 cm wide, convex then flattening, margin inrolled at first, surface dry, smooth, finely cracked in age, whitish, often yellowing toward the center, the margin sometimes radially lined. Gills attached or decurrent, close or crowded with several tiers of short gills, occasionally forking, whitish, gill layer peelable from the cap as a unit. The stalk 3-8 cm long, up to 3 cm thick, enlarging downward, dry, smooth or finely hairy, colored like the cap, the base attached to a heavy, white mycelial mat. Partial veil absent. Flesh thick, tough, white. Odor fragrant or not distinctive. Taste bitter or farinaceous.

Spore Print: White.

Occurrence: Scattered, in groups, clusters, or fairy rings in conifer debris. Late summer-fall.

Edibility: Unknown.

Microscopic Features:
Spores 5-8.5 × 3.5-5 µm, elliptic with prominent, amyloid warts. Hyaline.

Comments: The rubbery toughness separates this and its hardwood-decomposing cousin, *Leucopaxillus laterarius* (search online), from other whitish species with decurrent gills.

Omphalotus illudens
(Schwein.) Bresinsky & Besl
JACK O'LANTERN

Description: Cap 7-20 cm wide, convex
then flattening or centrally depressed,
but may retain a small umbo, dry,
smooth, bright orange, stained reddish-
brown in age, the margin incurved and
wavy. Gills decurrent, close, narrow
(vertically), bright orange to yellow-
orange. Stalk 5-20 cm long, 1-2 cm
thick, equal or tapered downward, dry,
smooth, solid, yellow-orange. Flesh
pale orange. Odor unpleasant or not
distinctive. Taste not distinctive.

Spore Print: Whitish to pale yellow.

Occurrence: Clustered at the base of
hardwood trees and stumps, especially
oak. Late spring-early winter.

Edibility: Poisonous, causing
gastrointestinal upset.

Microscopic Features:
Spores 3-5 μm, globose, smooth.
Hyaline, inamyloid.

Comments: The gills of fresh Jack
O'Lanterns often glow green in the
dark. The cap stains green with
the application of KOH or NH₄OH.
Often mistaken for smaller, edible
chanterelles, which have yellower
caps and low, forking, gill-like ridges,
and don't grow on wood or in dense
clusters.

Panellus stipticus (Bull.) P. Karst.
BITTER OYSTER,
LUMINESCENT PANELLUS

Description: Cap 1-3 cm wide, convex,
semicircular to kidney-shaped, dry,
velvety to hairy, sometimes cracked
or scaly, whitish to brownish, margin
incurved. Gills attached to slightly
decurrent, close or crowded, often
forked and crossveined, narrow
(vertically), pale brown. Stalk 3-8 mm
long, 2-5 mm thick, lateral, finely
velvety, whitish to brownish. Flesh
thin, whitish to brownish. Odor not
distinctive. Taste somewhat bitter or
not distinctive.

Spore Print: White.

Occurrence: In groups or clusters on
decaying hardwood branches and logs.
Year-round.

Edibility: Inedible.

Microscopic Features:
Spores 3-6 × 2-3 μm, oblong to
allantoid, smooth. Hyaline, amyloid.

Comments: The gills of fresh caps glow
faintly green in the dark. So does the
radially arranged pore surface of *Panellus
pusillus* (search online), which has a
whitish to pinkish-buff cap. The Late Fall
Oyster Mushroom, *Panellus serotinus*
(see photo on p. 19), has a greenish to
purplish cap and yellowish gills; it grows
on hardwoods or sometimes conifers.

Panus conchatus (Bull.) Fr.
SMOOTH PANUS
Description: Cap 4-15 cm wide, convex
with a depressed center to broadly
funnel-shaped, dry, smooth, becoming
cracked and finely scaly in age, violet
at first, fading to reddish-brown or
tan; the inrolled or incurved margin
may be lobed or wavy. Gills decurrent,
nearly distant, narrow (vertically),
often forked, violet-tinted, fading to
tan or buff. Stalk 2-5 cm long, up to
3 cm thick, centrally to laterally placed,
usually tapered downward, dry, covered
with fine hairs at least near the base,
solid, colored like the cap or paler.
Flesh tough, white. Odor and taste not
distinctive.
Spore Print: White.
Occurrence: Solitary, grouped, or clustered
on hardwood logs and stumps. Spring-
fall.
Edibility: Edible, but tough.
Microscopic Features:
Spores 5-7 × 2.5-3.5 µm, elliptical,
smooth. Hyaline, inamyloid.
Comments: *Conchatus* means "shell-
shaped." *Panus torulosus* is a synonym.
The cap of *Panus neostrigosus* is hairy.
Lentinus crinitus has finely serrated gills
(use a hand lens).

Panus neostrigosus
Drechsler-Santos & Wartchow
HAIRY PANUS, RUDDY PANUS
Description: Cap 2-10 cm wide, fan- to
kidney- or broadly funnel-shaped, dry,
densely hairy, purplish when young,
becoming reddish-brown to pinkish-
tan, the margin inrolled or incurved
and sometimes lobed. Gills decurrent,
close or crowded, narrow (vertically),
purplish at first, then whitish to pale
tan. Stalk rudimentary or up to 1-4 cm
long and 1 cm thick, eccentric to lateral,
densely hairy, dry, solid, colored like
the cap or paler. Flesh tough, white.
Odor not distinctive. Taste slightly
bitter or not distinctive.
Spore Print: White.
Occurrence: Solitary, grouped, or clustered
on decaying hardwood logs and stumps.
Year-round.
Edibility: Inedible.
Microscopic Features:
Spores 4.5-7 × 2-4 µm, elliptical,
smooth. Hyaline, inamyloid.
Comments: *Panus rudis* and *Lentinus
rudis* are synonyms. The cap of *Panus
conchatus* may be smooth, cracked, or
scaly, but not hairy. Another look-alike,
Lentinus crinitus, has finely serrated
gills (use a hand lens).

Pleurocybella porrigens (Per.) Singer
ANGEL'S WINGS
Description: Cap 3-10 cm wide, shell- to fan-shaped, typically depressed at the center, sometimes funnel-like, flexible, smooth, white, the margin incurved at first and often lobed or wavy. Gills decurrent, crowded, narrow (vertically), white. Stalk rudimentary or absent. Flesh very thin, white. Odor and taste not distinctive.

Spore Print: White.

Occurrence: Solitary or in groups or clusters on decaying conifer wood. Summer-fall.

Edibility: Edible, with caution. See comments below.

Microscopic Features:
Spores 6-7 × 5-6 μm, oval to subglobose, smooth. Hyaline, inamyloid.

Comments: *Porrigens* means "projecting horizontally." *Pleurotus porrigens* is a synonym. In Japan, deaths from eating large quantities of this mushroom have been reported among people with kidney problems. Moderation is advised. *Pleurotus ostreatus* and *Pleurotus pulmonarius* (search online) are usually off-white or brownish, have much thicker flesh, and don't grow on conifer wood. *Crepidotus applanatus* is white at first but has a brown spore print.

Pleurotus dryinus (Pers.) P. Kumm.
VEILED OYSTER
Description: Cap 5-13 cm wide, broadly convex, dry, covered with matted, grayish fibrils over a whitish ground color when young, becoming fairly smooth and whitish to yellowish-tan in age, margin incurved, often tufted with white remnants of partial veil. Gills decurrent, close or nearly distant, occasionally forked or crossveined, white to yellowish. Stalk 4-12 cm long, 1-3 cm thick, off-centered or central, equal or tapering downward, often scurfy and occasionally with a white ring on the upper portion, solid, whitish. Partial veil membranous, white, soon disappearing. Flesh tough, white. Odor fragrant or slightly pungent. Taste not distinctive.

Spore Print: White.

Occurrence: Solitary, in groups, or in small clusters on hardwood. Summer-fall.

Edibility: Edible.

Microscopic Features:
Spores 9-14 × 3-5 μm, elliptic, smooth. Hyaline, inamyloid.

Comments: The stalk base of the very similar *Lentinus levis* (search online) is densely covered with white hairs, and the odor resembles grapefruit. *Neolentinus lepideus* has serrated gills.

Pleurotus ostreatus (Jacq.) P. Kumm.

OYSTER MUSHROOM

Description: Cap 5-20 cm wide, convex to flat, fan-shaped or semicircular with an incurved and often wavy margin, smooth, white to creamy white, brownish, or grayish. Gills decurrent, close or crowded, whitish, yellowing with age. Stalk short, typically off-center or lateral, white, usually showing tiny hairs at the base. Flesh whitish. Odor pleasant, resembling anise, almond, or fresh seafood. Taste not distinctive.

Spore Print: White to pale lilac.

Occurrence: Solitary, in groups, or in overlapping clusters on logs, trunks, and stumps of hardwoods, sometimes on conifers. Year-round.

Edibility: Edible.

Microscopic Features: Spores 8-11 × 3-4 μm, cylindric, smooth. Hyaline.

Comments: *Ostreatus* means "oyster-shaped." *Pleurotus pulmonarius* (search online) is very similar, but the cap margin has short radial lines. The Elm Oyster, *Hypsizygus tessulatus* = *H. ulmarius* (search online), has a more circular, convex to slightly depressed, whitish to tan or pinkish-tinged cap with distinct grayish "water spots."

Pseudoarmillariella ectypoides (Peck) Singer

WOOD CLITOCYBE

Description: Cap 2-6 cm wide, flattish with a depressed center when young, becoming funnel-shaped at maturity, coated with minute blackish- to reddish-brown scales that often disappear in age, the margin incurved and remaining so well into maturity. Gills strongly decurrent, nearly distant, often developing reddish-brown stains. Stalk 2-7 cm long, 3-9 mm thick, enlarging downward, smooth or slightly scurfy, solid, pale yellow, staining brownish when bruised. Flesh yellowish. Odor and taste not distinctive.

Spore Print: White.

Occurrence: Scattered or in groups on decaying conifer wood. Late spring-fall.

Edibility: Unknown.

Microscopic Features: Spores 6-8 × 3-5 μm, elliptic, smooth. Hyaline, amyloid.

Comments: *Omphalina ectypoides* and *Clitocybe ectypoides* are synonyms. The stalk of a conifer look-alike, *Chrysomphalina chrysophylla* (search online), doesn't stain brown when bruised. Compare both with the larger *Gerronema strombodes*, which is often greenish-yellow, has dark radial fibers on the cap, grows mainly on hardwood, and has inamyloid spores.

Schizophyllum commune Fr.
COMMON SPLIT GILL
Description: Cap 1-4.5 cm wide, fan- to shell-shaped, densely covered with tiny hairs, dry, white to grayish-white, the margin incurved to inrolled when young, often wavy and torn in age. Gills nearly distant, split lengthwise along the free edge, usually serrated or torn, white to pinkish-gray. Stalk absent or rudimentary. Flesh thin, flexible, whitish to grayish, sometimes with brownish tinges. Odor and taste not distinctive.

Spore Print: White.

Occurrence: Solitary, scattered, or in overlapping clusters on decaying hardwood. Year-round.

Edibility: Inedible.

Microscopic Features:
Spores 5-7.5 × 2-3 µm, cylindric, smooth. Hyaline.

Comments: *Schizophyllum commune* means "split gills growing in groups." This global citizen occurs on all continents except Antarctica. It is a rare cause of fungal sinusitis or lung disease. The Crimped Gill, *Plicaturopsis crispa* (search online), which also grows on hardwood, has a fan- to shell-shaped cap zoned with shades of yellow-orange to reddish-brown. The gills are veinlike, crinkled, and often forked.

Xeromphalina kauffmanii A. H. Sm.
CROSSVEINED TROOP MUSHROOM
Description: Cap 5-25 mm wide, convex to broadly convex with a depressed or dimpled center, smooth, moist, yellowish-orange to orange-brown, the margin radially lined. Gills decurrent, more or less distant with conspicuous crossveins, pale yellow to pale orange. Stalk 1-5 cm long, 0.5-2 mm thick, dry, yellow at the apex and dark reddish-brown below, with a dense tuft of long orangish hairs at the base. Flesh yellowish to brownish-yellow. Odor and taste not distinctive.

Spore Print: Pale buff.

Occurrence: In groups or dense clusters on decaying hardwood. Spring-fall.

Edibility: Unknown.

Microscopic Features:
Spores 5-7 × 3-4 µm, elliptic to cylindric, smooth. Hyaline, amyloid.

Comments: *Kauffmanii* honors University of Michigan mycologist Calvin Henry Kauffman (1869-1931). *Xeromphalina campanella* (search online) looks the same but grows on decaying conifer wood.

Xeromphalina tenuipes
(Schwein.) A. H. Sm.

Description: Cap 2.5-7 cm wide, convex to broadly convex, usually with a low, broad umbo, dry, velvety, finely wrinkled, orange-brown at the center, brownish-orange toward the margin, sometimes with olive tints, the margin radially lined. Gills attached, close or nearly distant, often forked, white when young, becoming pale yellow. Stalk 5-9 cm long, 2-8 mm thick, more or less equal, sometimes compressed lengthwise, velvety to hairy, tough, hollow, colored like the cap or darker brown. Flesh brownish. Odor not distinctive. Taste bitter or not distinctive.

Spore Print: White.

Occurrence: Solitary, scattered, or in groups on decaying hardwood or surrounding litter. Spring-summer.

Edibility: Unknown.

Microscopic Features:
Spores 7-9 × 3.5-5 µm, allantoid, smooth. Hyaline, amyloid.

Comments: *Tenuipes* means "having a slender stalk." *Flammulina velutipes* also has a velvety brown stalk, but the cap is smooth and slimy or sticky. It typically fruits in wintry months. *Simocybe centunculus* has brown spores.

Hymenopellis furfuracea
(Peck) R. H. Petersen
ROOTED COLLYBIA
Description: Cap 2-10 cm wide, convex to
flat, often with an umbo, greasy or dry,
usually radially wrinkled, some shade
of light to dark brown. Gills are attached
but often detach, nearly distant, white.
The stalk above ground is 7-20 cm
long, up to 2 cm thick, equal, tough and
straight, white but decorated below the
apex with a pattern of grayish-brown
scales. The base is a brown "taproot."
Partial veil absent. Flesh white. Odor
and taste not distinctive.
Spore Print: White.
Occurrence: Solitary or grouped under
hardwoods or on well-rotted logs.
Spring-fall.
Edibility: Caps edible; fried stalks make
good toothpicks.
Microscopic Features:
Spores 14-17 × 9.5-12 μm, elliptic to
oval, smooth. Hyaline, inamyloid.
Comments: *Xerula furfuracea*
and *Oudemansiella furfuracea*
are synonyms. *Hymenopellis
rubrobrunnescens* (search online) lacks
the stalk scales and bruises reddish-
brown. *Hymenopellis megalospora*
(search online) also lacks the scales; its
white gills turn orange when dry.

Megacollybia rodmanii
R. H. Petersen, K. W. Hughes & Lickey
PLATTERFUL MUSHROOM
Description: Cap 4-20 cm wide, convex
to flat, often with a low, broad umbo,
dry, radially streaked, dark brown to
grayish-brown, usually darker over the
center. Gills attached, nearly distant,
very broad (vertically), often split,
white. Stalk 5-12 cm long, 1-2.5 cm
thick, equal or enlarged downward,
hollow when mature, base often with
thick, white mycelial cords. Flesh thin,
whitish. Odor not distinctive. Taste
bitter or not distinctive.
Spore Print: White.
Occurrence: Solitary or in groups on
decaying hardwood logs and stumps, or
on buried wood. Spring-summer.
Edibility: Edible, but has caused
gastrointestinal upset. It must be
thoroughly cooked.
Microscopic Features:
Spores 6-10 × 5-8 μm, ellipsoid,
smooth. Hyaline, inamyloid.
Comments: Previously misidentified
as *Megacollybia platyphylla* =
Tricholomopsis platyphylla, a European
species not found in North America.
Entoloma strictius and *Pluteus cervinus*
may appear similar, but they have pink
spore prints.

GILLED MUSHROOMS

Tricholoma aestuans (Fr.) Gillet

Description: Cap 3.5-9 cm wide, convex to broadly convex, usually with a low rounded umbo, dry, dingy yellow to yellow-green, browner centrally, radially streaked with grayish fibrils. Gills attached, close, golden- to greenish-yellow, bruising pale brownish-gray. Stalk 3-7 cm long, 1-2 cm thick, silky, hollow, white tinged with yellow or green. Flesh whitish to grayish-green. Odor not distinctive. Taste initially mild or bitter, turning very acrid after a minute.

Spore Print: White.

Occurrence: Scattered or in groups usually under pine, but also with oak or beech. Fall-winter.

Edibility: Unknown.

Microscopic Features:
Spores 6.5-8 × 4-5.2 μm, elliptic, smooth. Hyaline.

Comments: The persistently mild-tasting *Tricholoma equestre* has a slightly sticky cap that lacks green tints. The cap of *Tricholoma sejunctum* is sticky at first; its gills are mainly white but often tinged with yellow. *Tricholoma palustre* (search online) doesn't grow under pine, lacks an umbo, and has a darker, often blackish, cap center.

Tricholoma caligatum (Viv.) Ricken

BROWN MATSUTAKE

Description: Cap 6-12 cm wide, broadly convex, dry, developing flattened, coarse, reddish, grayish, or brownish scales over a paler ground color, margin inrolled and cottony when young, fringed with white remnants of partial veil. Gills attached to nearly free, close, white, usually developing brownish stains. Stalk 4-10 cm long, 1.5-3 cm thick, equal, dry, solid, covered with a membranous sheath that leaves a white, flaring, cottony ring on the upper portion, white above the ring, colored like the cap below, the sheath eventually breaking into patches. Flesh white to cream. Odor farinaceous, unpleasant, or not distinctive. Taste bitter or not distinctive.

Spore Print: White.

Occurrence: Scattered or in groups with conifers or hardwoods. Fall-winter.

Edibility: Edible, if not bitter.

Microscopic Features:
Spores 6-8 × 4.5-5.5 μm, elliptic, smooth. Hyaline.

Comments: The Matsutake, *Tricholoma magnivelare* (search online), is paler, more robust, and smells spicy-sweet. *Catathelasma ventricosum* (search online) has decurrent gills and a tapering or rooting stalk.

Tricholoma equestre (L.) P. Kumm.

CANARY TRICH

Description: Cap 5-10 cm wide, convex to broadly convex, sticky and smooth when fresh, becoming dry, usually developing small central scales, pale to sulfur yellow, often golden-brown over the center. Gills attached to nearly free, close, pale yellow to bright sulfur yellow. Stalk 3-15 cm long, 1-3 cm thick, equal or enlarged at the base, dry, solid, whitish, pale yellow, or sulfur yellow. Flesh white. Odor farinaceous. Taste farinaceous or not distinctive.

Spore Print: White.

Occurrence: Scattered or in groups with conifers or in mixed woods. Fall-winter.

Edibility: No longer considered a safe edible; varieties of this species have caused fatal poisonings in Europe.

Microscopic Features:
Spores 6-7 × 4-5 µm, elliptic, smooth. Hyaline.

Comments: *Tricholoma flavovirens* is a synonym in North America. *Tricholoma sejunctum* has a golden- to greenish-yellow cap with brownish to blackish radiating fibrils. *Tricholoma intermedium* and *T.subluteum* are also similar but have white gills.

Tricholoma focale (Fr.) Ricken

Description: Cap 5-14 cm wide, convex to flat, sometimes with a broad umbo, sticky initially, becoming dry, covered with radiating fibrils or scales, yellow-orange to olive-green or shades of tans and browns. Gills attached, close or crowded, whitish, then darkening and staining rusty orange or brown. Stalk 4.5-11 cm long, 1.5-3 cm thick, equal, often tapered to a pointed base, covered with a membranous sheath that leaves a cottony, ragged ring on the upper portion; whitish and silky to powdery above the ring, staining orange-brown; matted and shaggy below the ring, colored like the cap over a whitish ground color. Flesh solid, white. Odor farinaceous. Taste farinaceous/bitter.

Spore Print: White.

Occurrence: Scattered or in groups with conifers. Fall-winter.

Edibility: Inedible.

Microscopic Features:
Spores 5-6 × 3-4 µm, elliptic, smooth. Hyaline.

Comments: *Tricholoma aurantium* (search online) lacks a ring. *Tricholoma caligatum* lacks orange and green tints. *Tricholoma magnivelare* (search online) has spicy-sweet-smelling flesh.

GILLED MUSHROOMS

113

Tricholoma intermedium Peck

Description: Cap 4-10 cm wide, convex to flat, sometimes with a broad umbo, smooth and sticky when fresh, then dry with tiny yellowish- or reddish-brown flat scales and short fibrils over a yellow ground color, the margin inrolled well into maturity. Gills attached, close, white to whitish, with several tiers of short gills, the edges usually eroded in age. Stalk 3-9 cm long, 1-2.5 cm thick, equal, scurfy, solid becoming hollow, white to whitish, bruising brown especially at the base. Flesh white. Odor farinaceous. Taste farinaceous or not distinctive.

Spore Print: White.

Occurrence: Scattered or in groups with conifers. Fall-winter.

Edibility: Reportedly edible.

Microscopic Features:
Spores 5-7 × 3.7-4.8 μm, elliptic, smooth. Hyaline.

Comments: *Tricholoma leucophyllum* is a synonym. *Tricholoma equestre* has yellow gills. The cap of *Tricholoma subluteum* is dull orange to yellow with long, radiating, yellowish fibrils.

Tricholoma portentosum (Fr.) Quél.

STICKY GRAY TRICH

Description: Cap 6-12 cm wide, broadly conic then flattening, smooth, sticky to slimy, gray, olive- to gray-brown, or blackish, sometimes with faint yellow or purple tones, often streaky with radial, dark gray fibrils. Gills attached to nearly free, close, usually white and yellowing near the margin, sometimes yellowish or gray overall. Stalk 5-10 cm long, 1-2 cm thick, equal, covered with tiny fibrils, solid at first, hollowing in age, whitish or slightly yellow. Flesh white, sometimes yellowish near the stalk base. Odor and taste farinaceous or not distinctive.

Spore Print: White.

Occurrence: Hiding in pine duff, often in groups or clusters. Fall-winter.

Edibility: Edible.

Microscopic Features:
Spores 5.5-7.6 × 3-5 μm, elliptic to oval, smooth. Hyaline.

Comments: Deer love this species. Their scratchings are a clue to its presence. The sticky gray cap of *Tricholoma niveipes* (search online) lacks yellow tints. *Tricholoma luteomaculosum* (search online) has a dry gray cap.

Tricholoma saponaceum complex
(Fr.) P. Kumm.

SOAP-SCENTED TRICH

Description: Cap 2.5-16 cm wide, convex
to flat, usually with a broad umbo,
slippery/moist, smooth but often
developing cracks over the center,
various dingy shades of greenish-
yellow, gray-green, blue-gray, or gray-
brown. Gills attached or almost free,
nearly distant, white to yellowish with
a green tinge, sometimes staining
pinkish-brown or orange. Stalk 3.5-11
cm long, 1-4 cm thick, equal to club-
shaped or with a slightly bulbous
base, dry, smooth, solid, white to pale
greenish, usually with some pink or
orange near the base. Flesh white to
pale green, typically with pinkish-
brown or orange at the stalk base.
Odor like soap, farinaceous, or not
distinctive. Taste mildly soapy.

Spore Print: White.

Occurrence: Scattered or in groups with
conifers or hardwoods. Year-round.

Edibility: Inedible.

Microscopic Features:
Spores 5-7.6 × 3.5-5 µm, elliptic,
smooth. Hyaline.

Comments: The extremely variable cap
color makes this mushroom hard to
identify by sight, but the soapy taste is
unique.

Tricholoma sejunctum (Sowerby) Quél.

Description: Cap 4-9 cm wide, conical
becoming broadly convex with an
umbo, sticky at first, becoming dry,
brownish to blackish fibers radiate
from a dark center, ground color
yellow to golden-yellow. Gills attached,
fairly close, white, sometimes tinged
yellowish. Stalk 5-9 cm long, 1-2 cm
thick, equal or enlarged at the base, dry,
smooth, solid, white to yellowish. Flesh
white to yellowish. Odor farinaceous or
not distinctive. Taste usually bitter or
astringent.

Spore Print: White.

Occurrence: Scattered or in groups with
conifers or in mixed woods. Fall-winter.

Edibility: Inedible.

Microscopic Features:
Spores 5-7 × 3-5 µm, elliptic to
subglobose, smooth. Hyaline.

Comments: *Tricholoma equestre* has a
yellower cap and gills. The yellow colors
of *Tricholoma davisiae* (search online)
are tinged with green; the gill edges
often develop pinkish-orange stains;
the flesh usually tastes farinaceous. The
cap of *Tricholoma subluteum* lacks the
dark center.

Tricholoma subluteum Peck

Description: Cap 4-11 cm wide, conic then broadly convex with a low umbo, slightly sticky when moist, often cracked when dry, dull orange to golden-yellow at first, typically maturing to pale yellow, the margin decorated with yellowish radiating fibrils. Gills attached or nearly free, close, white. Stalk 7.5-12 cm long, 1-2 cm thick, equal or enlarged downward, dry, solid when young, hollow in age, usually yellow on the upper portion and white toward the base but sometimes white or yellow overall. Flesh white. Odor and taste farinaceous.

Spore Print: White.

Occurrence: Scattered or in groups with conifers or in mixed woods. Fall-winter.

Edibility: Unknown.

Microscopic Features:
Spores 5.7-7.5 × 4.8-6 μm, broadly elliptic to subglobose, smooth. Hyaline.

Comments: The cap of *Tricholoma intermedium* does not show yellowish radiating fibrils. *Tricholoma sejunctum* has a stickier cap with a dark center, brown or black radiating fibrils, and bitter flesh.

Tricholoma subresplendens (Murrill) Murrill

Description: Cap 2-11 cm wide, convex to nearly flat, sometimes with a low umbo, sticky when moist, smooth, usually silky, white to cream, developing yellowish to tan or pale pinkish-cinnamon tints or spots especially over the center, at times discoloring blue-green. Gills attached to nearly free, close or nearly distant with several tiers of short gills, white to whitish, the edges uneven or finely scalloped. Stalk 5-10 cm long, 1-2.5 cm thick, equal or tapered toward the base, dry, silky smooth or slightly scurfy, whitish, usually with yellow to brownish stains overall, may bruise blue-green near the base. Flesh white. Odor and taste farinaceous or not distinctive.

Spore Print: White.

Occurrence: Scattered or in groups with hardwoods or in mixed woods. Fall-winter.

Edibility: Unknown.

Microscopic Features:
Spores 5.6-7 × 4-5 μm, elliptic, smooth. Hyaline.

Comments: The frequent blue-green bruising reaction is distinctive. *Tricholoma sulphurescens* has flesh smelling of coal tar or burnt rubber.

Tricholoma sulphurescens Bres.

Description: Cap 5-12 cm wide, convex to broadly convex, sometimes with a low umbo, dry, smooth, white to creamy, bruising yellow or brownish when handled or in age. Gills attached, close with several tiers of short gills, white to creamy white, aging yellowish to buff. Stalk 3-10 cm long, 1-3 cm thick, equal or enlarged downward, dry, nearly smooth, colored and staining like the cap. Flesh white. Odor like coal tar or burnt rubber. Taste acrid or not distinctive.

Spore Print: White.

Occurrence: Scattered or in groups under hardwoods, often beech or oak, or in mixed woods. Fall-winter.

Edibility: Unknown.

Microscopic Features:
Spores 5-7 × 4-5 µm, broadly elliptic to subglobose, smooth. Hyaline.

Comments: The following three species share the coal tar odor: *Tricholoma inamoenum* (search online) is white but smaller, grows with conifers, and has more distant gills; *T. odorum* (search online) is yellower overall, including yellow gills; *T. sulphureum* has more distant gills and sulfur yellow flesh.

Tricholoma sulphureum (Bull.) P. Kumm.
SULFUR TRICH

Description: Cap 2-7.5 cm wide, conic to broadly convex, dry, smooth, pale to dark sulfur yellow, sometimes streaked or spotted with reddish-brown, margin incurved often well into maturity. Gills attached, nearly distant, with several tiers of short gills, yellow. Stalk 2.5-7.5 cm long, 7-20 mm thick, equal or enlarged downward, dry, solid, colored like the cap overall, the base covered with fine, white, matted hairs. Flesh sulfur yellow. Odor like coal tar or burnt rubber, or strongly floral like hyacinths. Taste unpleasant or not distinctive.

Spore Print: White.

Occurrence: Scattered or in groups with both hardwoods and conifers. Fall-winter.

Edibility: Suspected to be poisonous.

Microscopic Features:
Spores 8.5-11 × 5-7 µm, broadly elliptic to almond-shaped, smooth. Hyaline.

Comments: *Tricholoma sulphurescens* has white flesh and a white to creamy white cap that bruises yellow to brownish. *Tricholoma inamoenum* (search online) has white flesh, and *T. odorum* (search online) has close gills and whitish to pale yellow flesh.

GILLED MUSHROOMS

Tricholoma transmutans (Peck) Sacc.

Description: Cap 2.5-11 cm wide, conic to nearly flat, usually with a low umbo, slightly sticky, becoming dry, the center densely covered with matted fibrils, reddish- to dark brown, the margin paler, radially lined, and incurved well into maturity. Gills attached or nearly free, close, yellowish-white to buff at first, the faces eventually spotted reddish, the edges becoming entirely reddish. Stalk 4-15 cm long, 7-20 mm thick, equal or club-shaped, dry, powdery at the apex with tiny matted fibers below, sometimes slightly rooting, solid or hollow, yellowish-buff to grayish-orange, the base reddish-brown in age. Flesh white to buff. Odor and taste farinaceous.

Spore Print: White.

Occurrence: Scattered or in groups with conifers or in mixed woods. Fall-winter.

Edibility: Unknown.

Microscopic Features:
Spores 5-8.6 × 3.4-6.2 µm, elliptic to broadly elliptic, smooth. Hyaline.

Comments: *Tricholoma pessundatum* (search online) lacks yellowish tints in the cap or stalk and has white flesh that bruises reddish.

Tricholomopsis decora (Fr.) Singer
DECORATED MOP

Description: Cap 2.5-6 cm wide, convex to broadly convex, sometimes slightly depressed at the center, dry, with tiny blackish fibers and scales over a golden- to greenish-yellow ground color. Gills attached, crowded, yellow. Stalk 2-6 cm long, 3-10 mm thick, equal, sometimes curved, dry, yellow with tiny blackish scales. Flesh yellowish. Odor and taste not distinctive.

Spore Print: White.

Occurrence: Solitary, scattered, or in groups on decaying conifer wood. Summer-late fall.

Edibility: Unknown.

Microscopic Features:
Spores 6-7.5 × 4-5.5 µm, elliptic, smooth. Hyaline, inamyloid.

Comments: *Decora* means "beautiful." The cap of *Tricholomopsis sulphureoides* (search online) is more brownish-yellow, with yellowish, not blackish, fibers and scales. *Tricholomopsis formosa* is browner overall; it has whitish gills and flesh and often has a foul odor. *Gymnopilus sapineus* (search online) and *G. penetrans* have rusty brown spores.

Tricholomopsis formosa (Murrill) Singer

Description: Cap 3-10 cm wide, convex to broadly convex with an incurved and sometimes wavy margin, dry, covered with rusty brown to tawny fibers and scales over a cinnamon-buff to dull yellow ground color. Gills attached, close or crowded, whitish to pinkish-cream. Stalk 4-8 cm long, 5-10 mm thick, equal or tapering downward, dry, covered with tiny fibers and scales, colored like the cap. Flesh whitish. Odor and taste disagreeable or not distinctive.

Spore Print: White.

Occurrence: Solitary, scattered, or in groups on decaying conifer wood.

Edibility: Unknown.

Microscopic Features: Spores 5-7 × 5-6 μm, ovoid, smooth. Hyaline, inamyloid.

Comments: *Formosa* means "beautiful or lovely." The cap and stalk of *Tricholomopsis rutilans* have red to purplish-red fibers and tiny scales over a yellowish ground color. *Tricholomopsis decora* has a yellowish to greenish-yellow cap with blackish fibers and scales.

Tricholomopsis rutilans (Schaeff.) Singer

PLUMS AND CUSTARD

Description: Cap 5-12 cm wide, convex to broadly convex with an incurved margin, dry, covered with red to purplish-red fibers and tiny scales over a yellowish ground color. Gills attached, close with several tiers of short gills, yellow. Stalk 5-12 cm long, 1-2 cm thick, equal, often curved, dry, densely or sparingly coated with red to purplish-red fibers and tiny scales over a yellowish ground color. Flesh pale yellow. Odor fragrant or not distinctive. Taste somewhat radish-like or not distinctive.

Spore Print: White.

Occurrence: Solitary, scattered, or in groups on decaying conifer wood, chips, sawdust, or the surrounding litter. Spring-fall.

Edibility: Edible.

Microscopic Features: Spores 5-7 × 3-5 μm, elliptic, smooth. Hyaline, inamyloid.

Comments: *Rutilans* means "reddish," a reference to the color of the fibers and scales. *Tricholomopsis formosa* has a browner cap, whitish gills, and typically an unpleasant odor.

GILLED MUSHROOMS

119

Asterophora lycoperdoides (Bull.) Ditmar
STAR-BEARING POWDER CAP
Description: Cap 1-2 cm wide, rounded to convex, dry, cottony at first, then thickly covered with brown powder. Gills attached, thick and malformed, distant, often forked, white to pale gray or beige. The stalk is 2-5 cm long, 3-10 mm thick, equal, smooth or silky, white to pale brownish, stuffed, becoming hollow in age. Partial veil absent. Flesh white. Odor and taste farinaceous.
Spore Print: White, if you can get one.
Occurrence: In clusters on rotting mushrooms, especially *Russula* and *Lactarius* species. Summer-fall.
Edibility: Unknown.
Microscopic Features:
  Basidiospores 5-6 × 3-4 µm, elliptic, smooth; hyaline, inamyloid. Clamydo-spores (asexual) 13-20 × 10-20 µm excluding spines or warts; pale brown, inamyloid.
Comments: The asexual clamydospores resemble microscopic stars. *Asterophora parasitica* (search online) parasitizes the same hosts; it has browner, less deformed gills and a cap that does not become powdery at maturity.

Baeospora myosura (Fr.) Singer
CONIFER-CONE CAP
Description: Cap 5-20 mm wide, convex then flattening, moist, smooth, tan to pinkish-brown; the margin is initially inrolled and faintly radially lined if at all. Gills attached, crowded, white. The stalk is 1-5 cm long, 1-2 mm thick, equal, whitish to pinkish-brown, finely hairy with coarse basal hairs attaching it to the conifer cone, hollow. Partial veil absent. Flesh insubstantial. Odor and taste not distinctive.
Spore Print: White.
Occurrence: In groups on the cones of conifer trees. Summer-fall.
Edibility: Unknown.
Microscopic Features:
  Spores 3-4.5 × 1-2.5 µm, elliptic, smooth. Hyaline, amyloid.
Comments: *Strobilurus conigenoides* is similar but has inamyloid spores and grows on magnolia cones and sweetgum fruits.

Baeospora myriadophylla (Peck) Singer
LAVENDER BAEOSPORA
Description: Cap 1-4 cm wide, convex then flattening, sometimes with a depressed center, moist, smooth, lavender at first, fading toward tan in age, lavender colors remaining longest at the margin. Gills attached or nearly free, crowded, lavender. The stalk is 2-5 cm long, 1-3 mm thick, equal, smooth, eventually hollow, colored like the cap; long hairs are present at the base. Partial veil absent. Flesh grayish and insubstantial. Odor and taste not distinctive.
Spore Print: White.
Occurrence: In small groups on decaying conifers or hardwoods, especially hemlocks. Spring-fall.
Edibility: Unknown.
Microscopic Features:
Spores 3.5-4.5 × 2-3 μm, elliptic, smooth. Hyaline, amyloid.
Comments: This species could be confused with pink mycenas, such as *Mycena haematopus*, which initially has white gills, and *M. pura*, which grows on humus/soil rather than wood. *Laccaria amethystina* also grows on soil but has thicker gills.

Clitocybula familia (Peck) Singer
FAMILY CLITOCYBE
Description: Cap 1-4 cm wide, bell-shaped with an inrolled margin at first, then flattening, usually *not* centrally depressed, moist, smooth, creamy to tan, the margin uplifted in age, sometimes torn or faintly lined. Gills are nearly free, crowded, whitish. The stalk is 4-8 cm long, 1.5-3 mm thick, moist or dry, smooth, grayish-white with white hairs at the base. Partial veil absent. Flesh whitish. Odor and taste of anise (licorice).
Spore Print: White.
Occurrence: Clustered, usually on conifer wood, occasionally on hardwood. Summer-fall.
Edibility: Edible.
Microscopic Features:
Spores 3.5-4.5 μm, globose, smooth. Hyaline, amyloid.
Comments: Formerly known as *Collybia familia*. *Clitocybula abundans* (search online) has a centrally depressed cap and spores measuring 4.5-6.5 × 3.5-5 μm. *Clitocybula lacerata* (search online) has a streaky, brownish-gray cap that fades toward tan; spores measure 6-8 × 4.5-6 μm.

GILLED MUSHROOMS

121

Connopus acervatus (Fr.) K. W. Hughes, Mather & R. H. Petersen
CLUSTERED COLLYBIA
Description: Cap 1-5 cm wide, convex then flattening, moist or dry, smooth, reddish- to chestnut brown, lighter toward the margin, hygrophanous, usually retaining the paler margin. Gills attached, crowded, white or pink-tinged. Stalk 2-12 cm long, 2-6 mm thick, equal, dry, smooth, hollow and brittle, brown or yellowish-, reddish-, or purplish-brown, with white basal hairs. Partial veil absent. Flesh whitish. Odor and taste not distinctive.
Spore Print: White to cream.
Occurrence: Usually densely clustered on conifer wood, which may be buried. Also reported among sphagnum mosses in bogs. Summer-fall.
Edibility: Unknown.
Microscopic Features:
Spores 5.5-7 × 2.5-3 μm, elliptic, smooth. Hyaline, inamyloid.
Comments: Synonyms include *Collybia acervata* and *Gymnopus acervatus*. The darker colors separate it from *Clitocybula familia*. Conifer preference and dense clustering distinguish the Clustered Collybia from *Flammulina velutipes* and brown Mycenas. *Hypholoma capnoides* (search online) has purplish-black spores.

Flammulina velutipes (Curtis) Singer
VELVET FOOT
Description: Cap 1-7 cm wide, convex then flattening, slimy or sticky, smooth, yellowish- to orangish-brown, the margin radially lined and initially incurved. Gills are attached, close, pale yellow. The stalk is 2-11 cm long, 3-5 mm thick, equal or enlarging downward, possibly with a long "taproot," tough, dry, smooth and yellowish at the apex, transitioning to dark reddish-brown and fuzzy toward the base. Partial veil absent. Flesh watery, yellowish. Odor and taste not distinctive.
Spore Print: White.
Occurrence: Clustered on dead hardwood. Early spring, late fall, and winter warm spells.
Edibility: Cap edible; the stalks are tough.
Microscopic Features:
Spores 7-9 × 3-6 μm, elliptic, smooth. Hyaline, inamyloid.
Comments: When grown commercially in conditions of chilly darkness and high levels of carbon dioxide, this mushroom is white, has a tiny cap, and a long, skinny stalk. Trade names include Enotake and Enoki. Beware confusing the wild form with the Deadly Galerina.

Gliophorus psittacinus (Schaeff.) Herink
PARROT WAXCAP
Description: Cap 1-3 cm wide, broadly conical at first, then convex to nearly flat, sometimes with a broad umbo, sticky/slimy when moist, smooth, initially with a translucent margin that appears radially lined. Color starts green but changes into some combination of blue-green, olive-green, orange, yellow, and even pink. Gills attached, nearly distant, waxy, yellowish, greenish, or reddish. The stalk is 3-7 cm long, 2-5 mm thick, nearly equal, smooth, slimy, usually green at least at the apex, with whitish, pale yellow, or pinkish shades below. Partial veil absent. Flesh thin, colored like the cap. Odor and taste not distinctive.
Spore Print: White.
Occurrence: Hiding on the ground in groups or clusters in woods or grassy areas. Summer-winter.
Edibility: Edible.
Microscopic Features:
Spores 6.5-10 × 4-6 μm, elliptic, smooth. Hyaline, inamyloid.
Comments: Also known as *Hygrocybe psittacina* and *Hygrophorus psittacinus*. The sticky slime makes a pristine collection difficult.

Gymnopus confluens
(Pers.) Antonín, Halling & Noordel
TUFTED COLLYBIA
Description: Cap 1-6 cm wide, convex then flattening, moist or dry, smooth, reddish-brown at first, fading through pinkish-cinnamon toward white. Gills narrowly attached or free, close to crowded, white to pinkish-buff. The stalk is 2.5-13 cm long, 1.5-9 mm thick, nearly equal, dry, color similar to the cap, coated top to base with fine white to grayish hairs, basal mycelium white. Partial veil absent. Flesh thin, white. Odor and taste not distinctive.
Spore Print: White.
Occurrence: Growing clustered or in groups on leaf litter or humus. Summer-fall.
Edibility: Edible.
Microscopic Features:
Spores 7-11 × 3-5 μm, shape lacrimoid to elliptic or fusiform, smooth. Hyaline, inamyloid.
Comments: Previously termed *Collybia confluens*. The completely hairy stalk separates it from *Gymnopus subnudus* (search online) which has a bald upper stalk. *Gymnopus polyphyllus* (search online) smells like garlic or rotting cabbage. *Lyophyllum decastes* is a much larger, stouter species with a smooth stalk.

Gymnopus dichrous
(Berk. & M. A. Curtis) Halling

Description: Cap 1-5 cm wide, convex then flattening or with an uplifted margin, moist to dry, radially lined or wrinkled, translucent toward the margins when wet, reddish-brown or dark brown at the center and paler toward the margin, fading with age. Gills narrowly attached or free, close to nearly distant, crossveined, whitish, sometimes with rusty spots. The stalk is 1-5 cm long, 1-5 mm thick, nearly equal above a slightly bulbous base, dry, finely hairy, hollow, whitish above and reddish-brown below with white hairs/fuzz at the base. Partial veil absent. Flesh thin, white. Odor and taste not distinctive.

Spore Print: White to cream.

Occurrence: Growing clustered or in groups on hardwood sticks, logs, and stumps. Summer-fall.

Edibility: Unknown.

Microscopic Features:
Spores 10-12 × 3-4.5 μm, lacrimoid to elliptic, smooth. Hyaline, inamyloid.

Comments: Also known as *Collybia dichrous*. The similar *Gymnopus subnudus* (search online) grows on fallen leaves.

Gymnopus dryophilus (Bull.) Murrill
OAK-LOVING COLLYBIA

Description: Cap 1-7 cm wide, convex then flattening, moist when fresh, smooth, reddish-brown fading toward yellowish-tan with the center of the cap remaining darker, hygrophanous. Gills narrowly attached or free, crowded, white. The stalk is 1-10 cm long, 2-8 mm thick, nearly equal or enlarging downward, dry, smooth, hollow, tough, whitish above and pale yellowish below, basal mycelium white. Partial veil absent. Flesh thin, white. Odor and taste not distinctive.

Spore Print: White to cream.

Occurrence: Solitary or in loose troupes on fallen twigs or woodland leaf litter. Late spring-fall.

Edibility: Uncertain; authorities disagree.

Microscopic Features:
Spores 5-7 × 3-3.5 μm, lacrimoid to elliptic, smooth. Hyaline, inamyloid.

Comments: Formerly called *Collybia dryophila*. The springtime *Gymnopus subsulphureus* is yellower overall, with pinkish basal rhizomorphs. *Rhodocollybia butyracea* grows under pines and often has serrated gills. *Marasmius strictipes* has creamy to yellowish gills and larger spores and is not hygrophanous.

Gymnopus iocephalus
(Berk. & M. A. Curtis) Halling
VIOLET COLLYBIA
Description: Cap 1-3 cm wide, convex with an incurved margin, then flattening with the edge upturned and wavy, moist or dry, radially wrinkled or lined, violet but fading with age. Gills narrowly attached or free, close to nearly distant, violet. The stalk is 2.5-5 cm long, up to 3 mm thick, nearly equal, minutely hairy, whitish or purplish above and discoloring below. Partial veil absent. Flesh thin, colored like the cap. Odor not distinctive or resembling radish or gunpowder. Taste not distinctive or unpleasant.
Spore Print: White.
Occurrence: Growing scattered or grouped on dead leaves. Late summer-fall.
Edibility: Unknown.
Microscopic Features:
Spores 6.5-8.5 × 3-4.5 μm, lacrimoid to elliptic, smooth. Hyaline, inamyloid.
Comments: A drop of KOH turns the cap green or blue. Similar species include the thick-gilled *Laccaria amethystina* and *Mycena pura*, which tend to be larger. *Inocybe geophylla* var. *lilacina* (search online) has brown spores.

Gymnopus luxurians (Peck) Murrill
Description: Cap 2-12 cm wide, convex with an incurved margin, then flattening, moist or dry, smooth, reddish-brown centrally, lighter toward the margins, fading to tan overall. Gills attached, close to crowded, white to pinkish-buff. Stalk 3-12 cm long, 2-13 mm thick, nearly equal or tapering downward, usually with spiraling ridges, dry, covered with easily dislodged hairs, color pale at the apex and yellowish-brown below, basal mycelium and rhizomorphs white. Partial veil absent. Flesh white or pale pinkish-tan. Odor not distinctive. Taste not distinctive or slightly acrid.
Spore Print: Cream.
Occurrence: Clustered or in groups on wood chips or lawns containing buried wood or dead tree roots. Summer-fall.
Edibility: Unknown.
Microscopic Features:
Spores 6-10 × 3-6 μm, lacrimoid, smooth. Hyaline, inamyloid.
Comments: Previously known as *Collybia luxurians*. Stalk details help differentiate this from other *Gymnopus* species. *Entoloma strictius* also has a twisted stalk, but the spore print is pink.

GILLED MUSHROOMS

Gymnopus spongiosus
(Berk. & M. A. Curtis) Halling
HAIRY-STALKED COLLYBIA
Description: Cap 1-4 cm wide, convex
then flattening, greasy to dry, smooth,
reddish-brown at first, fading toward
pinkish-buff with a white margin. Gills
narrowly attached or free, close to
crowded, white to creamy. The stalk
is 2-6 cm long, the apex up to 4 mm
thick, enlarging downward to a spongy
base, dry, whitish above, transitioning
to reddish-brown below, covered with
matted or erect reddish-brown hairs.
Partial veil absent. Flesh thin, white.
Odor and taste not distinctive.
Spore Print: White.
Occurrence: Clustered or in groups on leaf
or needle litter or other woody debris.
Summer-fall.
Edibility: Edible.
Microscopic Features:
Spores 6-8.5 × 3.5-4 µm, lacrimoid to
elliptic, smooth. Hyaline, inamyloid.
Comments: Formerly *Collybia spongiosa*.
The combination of reddish hairs on
the stalk and a green cap reaction to
ammonia or KOH are diagnostically
important. Only the lower third of
the stalk in spring-fruiting *Gymnopus
semihirtipes* (search online) is hairy.

Gymnopus subsulphureus (Peck) Murrill
Description: Cap 1-6 cm wide, convex then
flattening, moist when fresh, smooth,
yellowish, often with a tan center,
hygrophanous fading toward whitish
from the center out. Gills narrowly
attached, crowded, pale yellow but
sometimes whitish at first. The stalk
is 2-12 cm long, 2-7 mm thick, nearly
equal above a small bulb, dry, smooth,
hollow, tough, yellowish, with pink
basal rhizomorphs. Partial veil absent.
Flesh thin, yellowish. Odor and taste
not distinctive.
Spore Print: White to cream.
Occurrence: Solitary or in loose troupes
under hardwoods. Spring.
Edibility: Unknown.
Microscopic Features:
Spores 5-6.5 × 2.5-3.5 µm, elliptic,
smooth. Hyaline, inamyloid.
Comments: This springtime cousin of
Gymnopus dryophilus is yellower
overall, fruits earlier in the season, and
has pink rhizomorphs rather than white
mycelium at the base. *Rhodocollybia
butyracea* grows under pines.
Marasmius strictipes fruits later, has
larger spores, and is not hygrophanous.

Humidicutis marginata var. *marginata* (Peck) Singer

ORANGE-GILLED WAXCAP

Description: Cap 1-5 cm wide, broadly conical at first with an incurved margin, becoming convex or nearly flat, greasy, smooth, orange or yellow-orange, hygrophanous (fading to pale yellow); the margin may show faint radial lines. Gills attached, nearly distant, connected by crossveins, bright orange and remaining so after the cap fades. Stalk 4-10 cm long, 3-6 mm thick, nearly equal, smooth, moist or dry but not sticky, hollow, orange-yellow. Partial veil absent. Flesh colored like the cap. Odor and taste not distinctive.

Spore Print: White.

Occurrence: Solitary or scattered in mixed woodlands or on humus. Summer-fall.

Edibility: Edible.

Microscopic Features:
Spores 7-10 × 4-6 μm, elliptic or suboblong, smooth. Hyaline, inamyloid.

Comments: The differential fading of cap and gills separates this from other orange waxcaps, including *Humidicutis marginata* var. *concolor* (search online) with its yellow-orange gills. The cap of *Humidicutis marginata* var. *olivacea* (search online) has olive tones mixed in with the orange.

Hygrocybe acutoconica (Clem.) Singer

Description: Cap 2-10 cm wide, sharply to broadly conical at first, then bell-shaped with an umbo, sticky or slimy, smooth, dull orange to bright red-orange; the margin sometimes uplifted and split at maturity. Gills attached or free in age, close or nearly distant, yellow, the edges sometimes ragged. Stalk 6-12 cm long, 3-12 mm thick, nearly equal or enlarging downward, smooth, greasy, often twisted, colored like the cap or paler with a whitish base. Partial veil absent. Flesh soft, yellow, not blackening when bruised. Odor and taste not distinctive.

Spore Print: White.

Occurrence: Scattered or grouped on the ground among field grasses, along roadsides, or in mixed woods. Spring-early winter.

Edibility: Edible.

Microscopic Features:
Spores 9-15 × 5-9 μm, elliptic, smooth. Hyaline, inamyloid.

Comments: The very similar *Hygrocybe cuspidata* (search online) is bright red. *Hygrocybe flavescens* is yellower and has a flattening cap. *Hygrocybe conica* bruises black when injured.

GILLED MUSHROOMS

Hygrocybe cantharellus (Schwein.) Murrill
CHANTERELLE WAXCAP

Description: Cap 1-3.5 cm wide, convex, then flat or centrally depressed, dry, finely hairy to scaly in the center, orange to scarlet, fading with age, the margin often wavy. Gills decurrent, distant or nearly so, paler than the cap or whitish, short gills present. Stalk 3-9 cm long, 2-5 mm thick, nearly equal, smooth, dry, stuffed or hollow, colored like the cap or paler. Partial veil absent. Flesh yellowish. Odor of potato or not distinctive. Taste not distinctive.

Spore Print: White.

Occurrence: Grouped in rich woodland soil, in mosses, or on decaying wood. Summer-early winter.

Edibility: Edible.

Microscopic Features: Spores 7-12 × 4-8 µm, elliptic to oval, smooth. Hyaline, inamyloid.

Comments: Can be confused with *Cantharellus cinnabarinus*, which has forking false gills rather than separate long and short gills (use hand lens) and a cinnabar red to orange-red cap. The gills of *Hygrocybe miniata* are not consistently decurrent.

Hygrocybe conica (Schaeff.) P. Kumm.
WITCH'S HAT

Description: Cap 2-9 cm wide, sharply conical to bell-shaped, usually with an umbo, slightly sticky or dry, smooth, commonly red-orange to red but sometimes yellowish, especially toward the margin, or tinged green, blackening when bruised. Gills free from the stalk, close, yellow to greenish-orange, blackening when bruised. Stalk 2-10 cm long, 3-10 mm thick, nearly equal, smooth, moist or dry, often twisted, hollow, yellowish, bruising black. Partial veil absent. Flesh colored like the cap. Odor and taste not distinctive.

Spore Print: White.

Occurrence: Solitary, scattered, or grouped on the ground in various types of woodlands or edge areas. Summer-early winter.

Edibility: Not recommended; cases of poisoning have been reported.

Microscopic Features: Spores 8-10 × 5-5.5 µm, elliptic, smooth. Hyaline, inamyloid.

Comments: The blackening reaction of all parts is distinctive. If blackening reactions are not present, compare with *Hygrocybe acutoconica*.

Hygrocybe flavescens (Kauffman) Singer
GOLDEN ORANGE WAXCAP
Description: Cap 2.5-7 cm wide, broadly convex then flattening or shallowly depressed, sticky when fresh, later dry and shiny, smooth, typically orange to yellow-orange, fading toward yellow in age, rarely white, the margin incurved at first and radially lined. Gills attached, close or nearly distant, yellow. Stalk 4-7 cm long, 5-16 mm thick, nearly equal or narrowed at the base, often flattened and grooved on one side, smooth, greasy to dry, not sticky, hollow, yellow-orange with a whitish base. Partial veil absent. Flesh yellowish. Odor and taste not distinctive.
Spore Print: White.
Occurrence: Scattered to grouped on the ground in woodlands or grassy edges. Summer-fall.
Edibility: Not recommended; cases of poisoning have been reported.
Microscopic Features:
Spores 7-9 × 4-5 µm, elliptic, smooth. Hyaline, inamyloid.
Comments: *Gloioxanthomyces nitidus* (search online) is a sticky yellow relative with a dimpled, not simply depressed, cap. The smaller *Mycena leaiana* grows in clusters on rotting wood.

Hygrocybe miniata (Fr.) P. Kumm.
FADING SCARLET WAXCAP
Description: Cap 2-4 cm wide, broadly convex then flattening or shallowly depressed, moist at first then dry, smooth and bright scarlet when moist; when dry it develops fibrils and fades toward yellow. Gills attached to slightly decurrent, close or nearly distant, colored like the cap and fading with it. Stalk 2.5-5 cm long, 3-6 mm thick, nearly equal, sometimes laterally compressed, smooth, dry, stuffed, colored like the cap and fading with it. Partial veil absent. Flesh colored like the cap. Odor and taste not distinctive.
Spore Print: White.
Occurrence: Scattered or grouped on the ground or banks of moss in woodlands. Summer-early winter.
Edibility: Edible.
Microscopic Features:
Spores 6-8 × 4-6 µm, elliptic, often constricted in the middle and widened at the base, smooth. Hyaline, inamyloid.
Comments: *Gliophorus perplexus* (search online) is reddish- to brownish-orange and has a sticky/slimy cap and stalk. *Hygrocybe cantharellus* has notably decurrent gills.

Hygrocybe punicea (Fr.) P. Kumm.
CRIMSON WAXCAP
Description: Cap 2-12 cm wide, bluntly or broadly conical at first, then flattening with an umbo and upturned margin that often splits, sticky or slimy, smooth, deep red, fading to dull orange, yellow, or buff. Gills barely attached, nearly distant, yellow to yellow-orange with smooth yellow edges. Stalk 2-12 cm long, 5-15 mm thick, nearly equal, often laterally compressed, dry, fragile, stringy and hairy in age, colored like the cap or paler with a whitish base. Partial veil absent. Flesh yellow to reddish-orange. Odor and taste not distinctive.

Spore Print: White.

Occurrence: Scattered or in groups on the ground in grassy areas or woodlands. Summer-fall.

Edibility: Edible.

Microscopic Features:
Spores 7-12 × 3.5-6 μm, oblong to elliptic, often constricted in the middle, smooth. Hyaline, inamyloid.

Comments: *Hygrocybe coccinea* (search online) is slightly smaller, has a greasy but not sticky/slimy cap, broadly attached gills, and a stalk that doesn't become stringy.

Lyophyllum decastes (Fr.) Singer
FRIED CHICKEN MUSHROOM
Description: Cap 4-12 cm wide, convex with an inrolled margin, becoming broadly convex to nearly flat, smooth, moist, slippery, brownish to dark brown before fading to pale grayish-brown. Gills attached to slightly decurrent, close, whitish. Stalk 5-10 cm long, 5-25 mm thick, equal, often curved, solid, smooth, dry, white, becoming brownish near the base. Flesh firm, whitish. Odor and taste not distinctive.

Spore Print: White.

Occurrence: Typically in large clusters on the ground in various habitats, especially grassy areas and disturbed places; usually not found in woodlands. Summer-fall.

Edibility: Considered edible, but gastrointestinal upset has been reported.

Microscopic Features:
Spores 4-6 μm, globose to subglobose, smooth. Hyaline, inamyloid.

Comments: *Decastes* means "by the tens," a reference to its growth habit. *Clitocybe multiceps* and *Tricholoma aggregatum* are synonyms. *Lepista subconnexa* also fruits in clusters but has a satiny white cap and a pale pinkish-buff spore print; it grows in the woods.

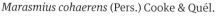

Marasmius cohaerens (Pers.) Cooke & Quél.
FUSED MARASMIUS
Description: Cap 1-4 cm wide, convex to broadly convex, bald, yellow- to reddish-brown, fading to pale tan. Gills attached or nearly free, almost distant, whitish to pale brown, edges sometimes darker. Stalk 3-8 cm long, 1.5-3 mm thick, equal, dry, hollow, smooth, whitish, becoming dark reddish-brown from the base upward. Flesh thin, white. Odor unpleasant or not distinctive. Taste bitter or not distinctive.

Spore Print: White.

Occurrence: Solitary or in groups or clusters on decaying hardwood leaves and woody debris. Spring-fall.

Edibility: Inedible.

Microscopic Features:
Spores 7-10 × 3-5.5 µm, ellipsoid, smooth. Hyaline, inamyloid.

Comments: *Marasmius sullivantii* (search online) is similar but has a smaller, reddish-orange cap and thinner stalk. *Marasmius delectans* (search online) also grows on hardwood leaf litter; it has a wrinkly whitish cap and a thinner stalk, white near the apex and dark brown below. The larger *Gymnopus confluens* has close gills and a hairy stalk.

Marasmius fulvoferrugineus Gilliam
TAWNY PINWHEEL
Description: Cap 2-4.5 cm wide, convex to bell-shaped, dry, strongly pleated, tawny brown to rusty brown. Gills attached to free, distant, whitish to yellowish. Stalk 2.5-6.5 cm long, up to 1.5 mm thick, smooth, wiry, whitish to yellowish near the apex, brown to blackish-brown below, with white basal mycelium. Flesh thin, whitish. Odor and taste mildly farinaceous or not distinctive.

Spore Print: White.

Occurrence: Scattered or in groups on decaying leaves, conifer needles, twigs, or other woody debris. Summer-fall.

Edibility: Unknown.

Microscopic Features:
Spores 15-18 × 3-4.5 µm, oblanceolate or fusoid-clavate, smooth. Hyaline.

Comments: *Fulvoferrugineus* means "reddish-yellow and rusty." *Marasmius siccus* is smaller and has a more orange cap. *Marasmius pulcherripes* (search online) is smaller and more delicate and has a pink to pinkish-brown cap. The Fire Cap, *Rhizomarasmius pyrrhocephalus* (search online), has a smaller, 1-2.5 cm wide, orange-yellow to orange-brown cap and a scurfy, blackish-brown stalk with a pale yellow apex.

Marasmius rotula (Scop.) Fr.

PINWHEEL MARASMIUS

Description: Cap 3-20 mm wide, convex, centrally depressed, pleated, bald, dry, white with a brownish center. Gills attached to a collar surrounding the stalk, distant, white. Stalk 1-8 cm long, up to 1.5 mm thick, wiry, blackish-brown, the apex whitish. Flesh whitish. Odor not distinctive. Taste slightly bitter or not distinctive.

Spore Print: White.

Occurrence: In groups or clusters on decaying hardwood. Year-round.

Edibility: Inedible.

Microscopic Features:
Spores 6-10 × 3-5 μm, lacrimoid, smooth. Hyaline, inamyloid.

Comments: The very similar *Marasmius capillaris* (search online) grows on hardwood leaf litter, while *M. felix* (search online) grows exclusively on decaying sycamore leaves. *Mycetinis opacus* (search online) has attached gills and often has flyaway rhizomorph "hairs" distant from the stalk base. The brown cap of *Marasmiellus praeacutus* (search online) fades to whitish. Gills are attached to a brown stalk that ends in a pointed, white base rising from decaying leaves or wood.

Marasmius siccus (Schwein.) Fr.

ORANGE PINWHEEL

Description: Cap 2-25 mm wide, convex to bell-shaped, strongly pleated, dry, orange to reddish-orange. Gills attached or free, distant, whitish to yellowish. Stalk 2-7 cm long, up to 1 mm thick, equal, wiry, smooth, yellowish near the apex, dark brown below, basal mycelium white. Flesh thin, whitish. Odor not distinctive. Taste bitter or not distinctive.

Spore Print: White.

Occurrence: Scattered or in groups on decaying leaves, woody debris, twigs or needles with hardwoods or conifers. Summer-fall.

Edibility: Unknown.

Microscopic Features:
Spores 15-22 × 3-5 μm, subfusiform, smooth. Hyaline.

Comments: *Siccus* means "dry." *Marasmius fulvoferrugineus* is larger and has a tawny to rusty brown cap. *Marasmius pulcherripes* (search online) is smaller and more delicate and has a pink to pinkish-brown cap. The orange to reddish-brown cap of *Marasmius graminum* (search online) is smaller yet: 3-10 mm wide. Its threadlike stalk is attached to a decaying blade of grass.

Marasmius strictipes (Peck) Singer
ORANGE-YELLOW MARASMIUS
Description: Cap 2-6.5 cm wide, convex or almost flat with a low, broad umbo, bald, orange- to dull yellow, the margin faintly lined. Gills attached to free, close or crowded, sometimes forked, with several tiers of short gills, whitish to yellowish or pale orange-yellow. Stalk 2-8.5 cm long, 3-10 mm thick, equal, dry, hollow, whitish to pale yellow, basal mycelium white. Flesh thin, whitish. Odor not distinctive. Taste radish-like or not distinctive.
Spore Print: White.
Occurrence: Scattered or in groups on hardwood leaf litter. Summer-fall.
Edibility: Inedible.
Microscopic Features:
Spores 6-11 × 3-4.5 μm, elliptic to lacrimoid, smooth. Hyaline, inamyloid.
Comments: *Marasmius nigrodiscus* (see photo on p. 19) has a brownish cap fading to creamy white, a persistently brown umbo, and a whitish, vertically grooved stalk. The cap and stalk of *Marasmius oreades* (search online) are pale tan to buff; the pale gills are nearly distant, and it grows in grassy areas. See also *Gymnopus dryophilus*.

Mycena epipterygia var. *viscosa*
(Secr. ex Maire) Ricken
Description: Cap 1-2 cm wide, broadly conical, smooth, sticky, dingy yellowish, becoming brownish with reddish stains in age, powdery at first. Gills attached, nearly distant, yellowish, with reddish stains in age. Stalk 5-8 cm long, 1-2 mm thick, equal, sticky, yellowish, reddish near the base, sometimes powdery. Flesh thin, whitish. Odor farinaceous. Taste farinaceous and unpleasant.
Spore Print: White.
Occurrence: In groups or clusters, often at the base of conifer trees. Fall-winter.
Edibility: Unknown.
Microscopic Features:
Spores 8-11 × 5-8 μm, lacrymoid to elliptic, smooth. Hyaline, amyloid.
Comments: Two other varieties occur in conifer woods and have a farinaceous odor. Variety *lignicola* (search online) has a yellow-green cap. Variety *epipterygia* (search online) has a dingy yellowish to grayish-green cap. *Mycena epipterygioides* (search online) has a dark olive-gray cap and grows on the ground with oak and pine. *Mycena griseoviridis* (search online) has a grayish-brown cap and grows on the ground with conifers.

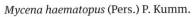

Mycena haematopus (Pers.) P. Kumm.

BLEEDING MYCENA

Description: Cap 1-5 cm wide, convex to broadly convex, usually with an umbo, moist, smooth, with translucent radial lines, dark reddish-brown over the center, fading toward the margin. Gills attached, close or nearly distant with numerous short gills, whitish or grayish at first, aging to reddish-brown. Stalk 2.5-10 cm long, 1-3 mm thick, reddish-brown, hollow, exuding a dark, blood-red or brown latex when cut, base hairy. Flesh thin, also "bleeding" when cut. Odor not distinctive. Taste bitter or not distinctive.

Spore Print: White.

Occurrence: In groups or clusters on decaying wood. Spring-fall.

Edibility: Edible.

Microscopic Features:
Spores 8-11 × 5-7 µm, oval to elliptic, smooth. Hyaline, amyloid.

Comments: Another "bleeder," *Mycena sanguinolenta* (search online), has dark reddish-purple gill edges and grows on the ground. *Mycena atkinsoniana* (search online) exudes yellow-orange latex when cut, has yellow gills with maroon edges, and grows on decaying beech or oak leaves.

Mycena inclinata (Fr.) Quél.

Description: Cap 1-6 cm wide, broadly conical with a broad umbo, radially lined or grooved, smooth, sticky, brownish centrally and pale toward the margin, fading to whitish, the margin finely serrated when young and sometimes split in age. Gills attached, close or nearly distant, whitish to yellowish. Stalk 5-10 cm long, 1.5-4 mm thick, equal, hollow, smooth, whitish near the apex, yellowish in the mid-portion, and reddish-brown below. Flesh whitish. Odor farinaceous or unpleasant. Taste farinaceous.

Spore Print: White.

Occurrence: In groups or clusters on decaying hardwood. Spring-fall.

Edibility: Unknown.

Microscopic Features:
Spores 7-10 × 5-7 µm, broadly ellipsoid, smooth. Hyaline, amyloid.

Comments: *Mycena niveipes* (search online) also grows on decaying hardwood but is grayer at first and smells of bleach. The cap of *Mycena galericulata* (search online) is brownish with a darker umbo and lacks the serrated margin. The lower stalk lacks red tones. Odor and taste mildly farinaceous or not distinctive.

Mycena leaiana (Berk.) Sacc.
ORANGE MYCENA
Description: Cap 1-5 cm wide, convex, smooth, sticky, bright orange at first, fading to yellowish-orange or whitish, the margin translucent and radially lined when young and moist. Gills attached, close with several tiers of short gills, orange and bruising yellowish-orange, the edges a darker shade of brilliant reddish-orange. Stalk 2-7 cm long, 1.5-4 mm thick, equal, tough, smooth, hollow, orange, base covered with whitish to orange hairs. Flesh white to orangish. Odor and taste not distinctive.

Spore Print: White.

Occurrence: In clusters on hardwood. Spring-fall.

Edibility: Unknown.

Microscopic Features:
Spores 7-10 × 5-6 µm, elliptic, smooth. Hyaline, amyloid.

Comments: *Mycena luteopallens* (search online) has a similar cap, but the yellowish gills have white edges. It fruits on decaying walnut or hickory nut hulls. The small (up to 1.5 cm wide) orange cap of *Rickenella fibula* (search online) is also radially lined. Gills are decurrent though, and it grows in moss.

Mycena pura (Pers.) P. Kumm.
PINK MYCENA, LILAC MYCENA
Description: Cap 2-7 cm wide, convex to broadly convex, smooth, moist, some shade of pink, red, purple, or grayish lilac, the margin radially lined. Gills attached, close or nearly distant with several tiers of short gills, crossveined, whitish to grayish, gill edges whitish. Stalk 3-10 cm long, 2-6 mm thick, enlarged downward, often compressed or twisted, tough, hollow, colored like the cap or paler. Flesh whitish to purplish. Odor and taste strongly radish-like.

Spore Print: White.

Occurrence: Scattered or in groups on humus in conifer or hardwood forests. Spring-fall.

Edibility: Reportedly edible.

Microscopic Features:
Spores 6-10 × 3-4 µm, narrowly elliptic, smooth. Hyaline, amyloid.

Comments: *Mycena rutilantiformis* (search online) also smells like radish, but the gill edges are reddish to purple and it has a yellow stalk apex. *Inocybe geophylla = I. lilacina* (search online) has a brown spore print and spermatic odor.

GILLED MUSHROOMS

Mycena semivestipes (Peck) A. H. Sm.

Description: Cap 1-3.5 cm wide, convex to broadly convex, smooth, sticky, dark brown fading to brown or grayish with a darker center, the margin radially lined. Gills attached or slightly decurrent, close, white, sometimes with a pinkish tinge. Stalk 2-6 cm long, 1-3 mm thick, equal, tough, whitish at the apex, brown to dark brown and covered with tiny soft hairs near the base. Flesh thin, whitish or brownish. Odor bleachlike. Taste unpleasant or slightly bitter.

Spore Print: White.

Occurrence: In clusters on decaying hardwood trunks, logs, or stumps. Spring-fall.

Edibility: Unknown.

Microscopic Features:

Spores 4-5 × 2-3 μm, ellipsoid, smooth. Hyaline.

Comments: *Semivestipes* means "somewhat decorated stalk," referring to the basal hairs. Look-alikes smelling of bleach include *Mycena leptocephala* (search online), which has a similar cap but more distant gills and grows on conifer debris, and *M. niveipes* (search online); it grows on decaying hardwood but has a paler gray cap fading toward white.

Neohygrocybe subovina
(Hesler & A. H. Sm.) Lodge & Padamsee
BROWN SUGAR WAXCAP

Description: Cap 2-5 cm wide, convex to broadly convex, dry, almost smooth or with tiny fibers or scales over the center, dark gray-brown to blackish-brown. Gills attached, distant, broad, whitish to grayish-brown, bruising reddish. Stalk 3-6 cm long, 4-9 mm thick, equal, dry, hollow, more or less colored like the cap. Flesh brittle, grayish-brown, not staining when bruised. Odor resembling brown sugar. Taste unpleasant or not distinctive.

Spore Print: White.

Occurrence: Scattered or in groups with hardwoods, especially oak. Summer-fall.

Edibility: Unknown.

Microscopic Features:

Spores 5-6 × 5-5.7 μm, globose to subglobose, smooth. Hyaline, inamyloid.

Comments: *Hygrocybe subovina* and *Hygrophorus subovinus* are synonyms. *Hygrocybe ovina* (search online) has a paler brown cap, whitish gills, and flesh that bruises reddish. *Hygrocybe nitrata* (search online) has a paler brown cap, whitish gills, flesh that does not bruise reddish, and a strong nitrous or ammonia odor.

Rhodocollybia butyracea (Bull.) Lennox
BUTTERY COLLYBIA
Description: Cap 2-11 cm wide, convex
then flattening, often with a broad
umbo, smooth, slippery when fresh
and moist, reddish-brown, fading to
pale brown or tan, the margin incurved
at first and usually radially lined.
Gills attached or nearly free, close or
crowded, often finely serrated in age,
white to slightly pinkish. Stalk 4-10
cm long, 3-10 mm thick, enlarging
downward, longitudinally lined,
sometimes twisted, hollow in age,
pinkish-buff to pale reddish-brown,
often with white basal mycelium. Flesh
white to grayish. Odor and taste not
distinctive.
Spore Print: Whitish with a pinkish tinge.
Occurrence: Scattered or in groups
among needle litter in conifer woods,
especially pine. Summer-fall.
Edibility: Edible.
Microscopic Features:
  Spores 6-11 × 3.5-5 µm, lacrimoid to
  ellipsoid, smooth. Hyaline.
Comments: *Butyracea* means "buttery," a
  reference to the slippery cap. *Gymnopus
  dryophilus* grows in conifer or hardwood
  forests, gill edges are smooth, and the
  spore print is white to cream.

Rhodocollybia maculata
(Alb. & Schwein.) Singer
SPOTTED COLLYBIA
Description: Cap 3-10 cm wide, convex
then flattening, sometimes with a low,
broad umbo, smooth, pinkish-buff
when young, whiter in age, spotted and
streaked with rusty-brown, especially
toward the center. Gills attached, close
or crowded, whitish to buff, developing
rusty brown spots. Stalk 5-12 cm long,
1-1.3 cm thick, equal, longitudinally
lined, dry, hollow, whitish with rusty
brown spots in age. Flesh white. Odor
unpleasant or not distinctive. Taste
bitter.
Spore Print: Whitish to pinkish-buff.
Occurrence: Solitary, scattered, or in
groups on the ground under conifers or
in mixed woods. Summer-fall.
Edibility: Inedible because of the bitter
taste.
Microscopic Features:
  Spores 5.5-7 × 5-6 µm, globose to
  subglobose, smooth. Hyaline, often
  dextrinoid.
Comments: *Maculata* means "stained
  or spotted." *Collybia maculata* is a
  synonym. *Rhodocollybia maculata* var.
  scorzonerea (search online) differs by
  having distinctly yellow gills and a
  yellow or white stalk.

GILLED MUSHROOMS

137

Strobilurus conigenoides (Ellis) Singer
MAGNOLIA-CONE MUSHROOM
Description: Cap 5-20 mm wide, convex to nearly flat, dry, covered with a dense layer of minute hairs, white, the margin incurved when young. Gills attached, close or crowded, white. Stalk 2-5 cm long, 0.75-2 mm thick, equal, dry, densely covered with minute hairs, white at the apex, often tan below. Flesh thin, whitish. Odor and taste not distinctive.
Spore Print: White.
Occurrence: In groups on magnolia cones or sweetgum balls. Summer-early winter.
Edibility: Unknown.
Microscopic Features:
Spores 6-7 × 3-3.5 μm, elliptic, smooth. Hyaline, inamyloid.
Comments: The growth on magnolia or sweetgum fruits is a strong diagnostic indicator. The similar Conifer-cone Baeospora, *Baeospora myosura*, has a cinnamon to pale tan cap and distinctly crowded gills. *Marasmius rotula* and other white-capped *Marasmius* species typically have darker stalks and fruit on different types of forest litter.

Tetrapyrgos nigripes (Fr.) E. Horak
BLACK-FOOTED MARASMIUS
Description: Cap 1-2 cm wide, convex then flattening, finely dusted with white powder or bald, often becoming wrinkled, white. Gills attached or slightly decurrent, nearly distant, crossveined and sometimes forked, white, occasionally staining reddish. Stalk 2-5 cm long, 1-1.5 mm thick, equal or tapering downward, tough, dry, coated with minute white hairs, white at first but blackening as it ages. Flesh thin, rubbery, white. Odor and taste not distinctive.
Spore Print: White.
Occurrence: Solitary or in groups on leaves, twigs, hickory nuts, and other woodland debris. Summer-fall.
Edibility: Unknown.
Microscopic Features:
Spores 8-9 × 8-9 μm, triangular to jack-shaped, smooth. Hyaline.
Comments: *Marasmiellus nigripes* is a synonym. *Marasmius capillaris* (search online) also has a white cap and a black stalk and grows on debris, but the cap is pleated and has a depressed center. The cap of *Marasmius rotula* is also pleated with a depressed center. It grows on decaying hardwood.

PINK-SPORED SPECIES

The mushrooms in this group share little in common other than the presence of gills and a spore print that mycologists describe as "pink." It would be great if pink always meant pink in the common sense of the term, but this isn't the case. Mycological shades of pink range from nearly white through pink-pink and salmon-pink to the sort of blushing tan one might find in a face powder for Caucasian women. If the spore print of the mushroom you're trying to identify falls near an end of this spectrum and you don't find a good match here, try the section for spore prints of the adjacent color range.

Pink-spored mushrooms demonstrate the range of shape possibilities for the center of a cap. They range from a nipplelike **umbo** (central bump) to a sunken navel. Pay close attention to other descriptive details as well. The general appearance of edible and poisonous species can be very similar. The culinary star of the group, the Blewit, *Lepista nuda*, is a case in point. Spore color and the absence of easily overlooked rusty threads often present on the stalks of inedible or poisonous species of silver-violet *Cortinarius* make all the difference.

Odor can be important in distinguishing many species of gilled mushrooms. Although many of the odors are easy to describe and recognize, "**farinaceous**" is especially difficult. Farinaceous is an odor variously compared to sliced watermelon rind, cucumber, meal, bread dough, or farina (think Cream of Wheat).

Clitocella mundula (Lasch) Kluting, T. J. Baroni & Bergemann

CRACKED-CAP RHODOCYBE

Description: Cap 2.5-7.5 cm wide, convex to flat, often with a depressed center, dry, smooth but developing a concentric pattern of shallow cracks, dirty grayish-white. Gills are decurrent, crowded, pale gray and pinkening at maturity. The stalk is 2.5-6.5 cm long, up to 7 mm thick, nearly equal, dry and finely flaky-hairy, off-white, often with white mycelium at the base. Partial veil absent. Flesh white. Odor farinaceous. Taste bitter.

Spore Print: Salmon-pink.

Occurrence: Scattered or in groups in mixed woods. Summer-fall.

Edibility: Unknown.

Microscopic Features:
Spores 4-6 × 4-5 µm, globose to subglobose, smooth or slightly bumpy, ends angular. Hyaline, inamyloid.

Comments: Formerly known as *Rhodocybe mundula*. The distinctive cracked cap pattern is reminiscent of a potter's cracked glaze technique.

Clitopilus prunulus (Scop.) P. Kumm.

SWEETBREAD MUSHROOM, THE MILLER

Description: Cap 3-12 cm wide, convex to flat or sunken in the center, wavy and often irregularly shaped with an inrolled margin, dry, white or grayish-with a feltlike texture. Gills are decurrent, close, initially white but pinkening. The stalk is 2.5-8 cm long, 3-15 mm thick, often somewhat off-center, equal, smooth, colored like the cap. Partial veil absent. Flesh white, firm. Odor and taste farinaceous.

Spore Print: Salmon-pink.

Occurrence: Scattered or in groups on the ground in open woods or grassy verges. Summer.

Edibility: Edible with caution.

Microscopic Features:
Spores 9-12 × 4-7 µm, elliptic with longitudinal ridges and angular ends. Inamyloid.

Comments: Many medium-sized white mushrooms inhabit the woods. Some, including *Entoloma rhodopolium*, are poisonous. Before eating, be certain of the farinaceous odor, decurrent gills, uncracked cap, and spore print color. Better yet, have your identification confirmed by someone experienced with this species.

Entoloma abortivum
(Berk. & M. A. Curtis) Donk
**ABORTIVE ENTOLOMA,
SHRIMP OF THE WOODS**
Description: Cap 3-10 cm wide, convex, dry, somewhat fibrous to almost smooth, pale gray or grayish-brown, the margin inrolled and occasionally irregular at maturity. Gills are decurrent, close, grayish then pinkening. The stalk is 2.5-10 cm long, up to 2 cm thick, enlarging downward, smooth or finely flaky-hairy, white to grayish. Partial veil absent. Flesh white, firm. Odor and taste farinaceous.
Spore Print: Salmon-pink.
Occurrence: Typically grouped or clustered around woodland stumps or debris. Summer-fall.
Edibility: Edible.
Microscopic Features:
Spores 8-10 × 5-6.5 μm, elliptic and angular, 6-sided. Hyaline, inamyloid.
Comments: This species parasitizes honey mushrooms, turning them into misshapen whitish-gray lumps with pink-streaked interiors and a farinaceous odor. Although these aborted honey mushrooms look like something better left untouched, they are tastier than the Abortive Entoloma mushroom, which has the further drawback of resembling poisonous species and shouldn't be eaten unless found alongside the aborted honeys.

Entoloma incanum (Fr.) Hesler
GREEN LEPTONIA
Description: Cap 1-5 cm wide, convex with a depressed central navel, dry, silky to smooth, olive-yellow to blue-green, darkest centrally, fading to yellowish-brown; the margin usually is radially lined. Gills are attached, distant, pale before pinkening, bruising blue-green. The stalk is 2-7 cm long, up to 4 mm thick, equal and hollow, smooth, colored like the cap, bruising blue-green, the base covered with white mycelium. Partial veil absent. Flesh yellowish, bruising blue-green. Odor of mice. Taste not distinctive.
Spore Print: Salmon-pink.
Occurrence: Scattered or in groups on soil or in woodland leaf mold, also grassy verges and disturbed soil. Spring-fall.
Edibility: Possibly poisonous.
Microscopic Features:
Spores 8.5-13 × 7-9.5 μm, elliptic and angular, 6-7 sides. Hyaline, inamyloid.
Comments: Also known as *Leptonia incana*. The blue staining in this species does not indicate psychoactive potential. *Gliophorus psittacinus* is slimy and has a white spore print.

Entoloma nodosporum (G. F. Atk.) Noordel.
HAIRY-STALKED ENTOLOMA
Description: Cap 1-5 cm wide, convex, with or without an umbo, dry, covered with dense, erect fibers or scales, some shade of brown; the initially incurved margin is radially lined. Gills are attached, nearly distant, gray at first, then dark brown with a pinkish tinge. The stalk is 2-10 cm long, 2-7 mm thick, enlarging upward, colored like the cap, hairy with especially stiff hairs at the base. Partial veil absent. Flesh whitish. Odor and taste not distinctive.
Spore Print: Pink to cinnamon-brown.
Occurrence: Scattered or in groups on leaf mold or rotten wood. Summer-fall.
Edibility: Inedible.
Microscopic Features:
Spores 12-19 × 7-9 µm, elliptic and angular, 7-9 sides. Hyaline, inamyloid.
Comments: *Pouzarella nodospora* is a synonym. This shaggy *Entoloma* can be confused with shaggy species of *Inocybe*, such as *I. calamistrata*, which is blue-green at the base of the stalk. *Inocybe* spore prints lack pinkish or reddish tones.

Entoloma quadratum
(Berk. & M. A. Curtis) E. Horak
SALMON UNICORN ENTOLOMA
Description: Cap 1-5 cm wide, conical or bell-shaped with a pointed umbo, sticky when moist, silky smooth, salmon-orange, fading somewhat with age. Gills are attached, nearly distant, salmon-orange. The stalk is 5-10 cm long, 2-6 mm thick, equal, colored like the cap, sometimes developing a green tinge; the basal mycelium is white. Partial veil absent. Flesh orange, fragile. Odor and taste not distinctive.
Spore Print: Salmon-pink.
Occurrence: Solitary or scattered on the ground in woods, particularly damp areas. Summer-fall.
Edibility: Unknown.
Microscopic Features:
Spores 10-12 µm, angular, 4 sided. Hyaline, inamyloid.
Comments: Other names for this species include *Entoloma salmoneum, Nolanea salmonea,* and *N. quadrata. Inocephalus murrayii* is bright yellow. *Entoloma luteum* (search online) is brownish-yellow and may also have greenish tinges.

Entoloma rhodopolium complex (Fr.) P. Kumm.
WOOD PINKGILL
Description: Cap 3-12 cm wide, convex to nearly flat, umbo often present but the center may be depressed in age. The cap is sticky when moist, smooth, ranging from nearly white to tan or yellowish- or grayish-brown in color; the margin is radially lined at maturity. Gills are attached, close to nearly distant, initially white, then pinkening. The stalk is 4-10 cm long, 5-12 mm thick, equal, dry, white, smooth, hollowing with age. Partial veil absent. Flesh thin and whitish. Odor and taste slightly farinaceous or not distinctive.
Spore Print: Salmon-pink.
Occurrence: Scattered or in groups under deciduous trees in the woods. Summer-fall.
Edibility: Poisonous.
Microscopic Features:
Spores 6.5-11 × 7-9 μm, elliptic and angular, 5-8 sides. Hyaline, inamyloid.
Comments: Several stout American species of *Entoloma* may share this European name. Take care not to mistake pale examples for the edible *Clitopilus prunulus*, which has decurrent gills. See also *Entoloma sinuatum*.

Entoloma serrulatum (Fr.) Hesler
BLUE-TOOTHED ENTOLOMA
Description: Cap 1-4 cm wide, convex to nearly flat, dry, developing a depressed center with fine scales or fibrils, smooth toward the margin, colors range from blue velvet to almost black. Gills are attached, close, pale blue-gray, then pinkening, the edges notably darker than the faces and serrated (use hand lens). The stalk is 4-7.5 cm long, up to 3 mm thick, equal, dry, flaky, colored like the cap but whiter at the base. Partial veil absent. Flesh thin and pale blue. Odor and taste not distinctive.
Spore Print: Salmon-pink.
Occurrence: Solitary or scattered, usually on humus, moss, or rotten wood. Summer.
Edibility: Unknown.
Microscopic Features:
Spores 9-12 × 6-8 μm, elliptic and angular, 5-7 sides. Hyaline, inamyloid.
Comments: Also known as *Leptonia serrulata*. Intensely blue specimens can be visually stunning. The serrated and dark (marginate) gill edges distinguish it from several blue-black *Entoloma* cousins that are hard to separate from one another.

Entoloma sinuatum (Bull.) P. Kumm.
LEAD POISONER
Description: Cap 7-15 cm wide, convex
  then flattening, often retaining a low
  umbo, dry, satiny smooth with radial
  fibers, perhaps showing concentric
  ripples, lead gray to dirty brown, the
  unlined margin inrolled at first and
  wavy at maturity. Gills attached, close
  or nearly distant, white or yellowish
  before pinkening. Stalks 4-12 cm long
  and 1-2.5 cm thick, equal or enlarging
  downward, with longitudinal fibers and
  perhaps a twisted appearance, hollow,
  white to pale gray. Partial veil absent.
  Flesh white or brown-tinged. Odor and
  taste farinaceous.
Spore Print: Salmon-pink.
Occurrence: Solitary or in loose groups
  under hardwoods, especially oaks.
  Summer-fall.
Edibility: Poisonous.
Microscopic Features:
  Spores 7-10 × 7-9 µm, globose and
  angular. Hyaline.
Comments: *Lepista nuda* and *Cortinarius
  argentatus* have purple gills in youth
  and a different smell. The cap of
  Entoloma rhodopolium is sticky when
  fresh and lined at maturity. *Clitopilus
  prunulus* has decurrent gills.

Entoloma strictius (Peck) Sacc.
STRAIGHT-STALKED ENTOLOMA
Description: Cap 2-7.5 cm wide, conical to
  convex with an umbo, moist, smooth,
  pale pinkish-, yellowish-, or grayish-
  brown, the margin radially lined. Gills
  are attached, close, whitish, then
  pinkening. The stalk is 5-10 cm long,
  3-10 mm thick, equal, straight, white,
  decorated with spiraling longitudinal
  grooves and white basal mycelium.
  Partial veil absent. Flesh white or pale.
  Odor and taste farinaceous or not
  distinctive.
Spore Print: Salmon-pink.
Occurrence: Solitary or scattered on the
  ground or rotten wood, often in damp
  areas. Late spring-fall.
Edibility: Unknown; opinions vary from
  inedible to poisonous.
Microscopic Features:
  Spores 10-13 × 7-9 µm, elliptic and
  angular, 5-6 sides. Hyaline or pale pink,
  inamyloid.
Comments: Also known as *Nolanea strictia*.
  Entoloma vernum has fairly straight
  longitudinal grooves that sometimes
  spiral near the apex, and smaller
  spores. The stalk of the comparatively
  squat *Entoloma bicolor* (search online)
  enlarges downward and is often curved.

Entoloma vernum S. Lundell
SPRINGTIME ENTOLOMA
Description: Cap 2.5-6.5 cm wide, conical to bell-shaped with a pointed umbo, moist to dry, smooth or satiny, often streaked or slightly wrinkled, grayish-brown to dark brown, fading notably as it dries, the margin incurved at first, wavy or upturned in age. Gills are attached, close, whitish, then pinkening. The stalk is 2.5-10 cm long, up to 1 cm thick, nearly equal, grayish or brownish-gray, with fairly straight longitudinal grooves that sometimes spiral near the apex, and white basal mycelium. Partial veil absent. Flesh watery brown. Odor and taste farinaceous or not distinctive.
Spore Print: Salmon-pink.
Occurrence: Scattered in wooded areas, along roadsides, or in disturbed soil. Spring.
Edibility: Poisonous.
Microscopic Features:
Spores 8-11 × 7-8 μm, elliptic and angular, 5-7 sides. Hyaline, inamyloid.
Comments: Also called *Nolanea verna*. It fruits about the same time as morels. So does *Psathyrella pseudovernalis*, which lacks an umbo and has a dark brown spore print.

Inocephalus murrayi
(Berk. & M. A. Curtis) Rutter & Watling
YELLOW UNICORN ENTOLOMA
Description: Cap 1-3 cm wide, conical or bell-shaped with a nipplelike umbo, moist, silky smooth, bright yellow fading slightly over time. Gills are attached, nearly distant, yellow, developing pink tinges. The stalk is 5-10 cm long, 2-5 mm thick, equal, yellow, sometimes showing white mycelium at the base. Partial veil absent. Flesh yellow, fragile. Odor and taste not distinctive.
Spore Print: Salmon-pink.
Occurrence: Scattered on the ground in woods, particularly damp areas. Summer-fall.
Edibility: Unknown.
Microscopic Features:
Spores 9-12 × 8-10 μm, elliptic and angular, 4 sides. Hyaline, inamyloid.
Comments: Also called *Nolanea murrayi* and *Entoloma murrayi*. *Entoloma salmoneum* is bright orange. A brownish-yellow relative, *Entoloma luteum* (search online), is comparatively drab. It has a blunt umbo and may show green tinges.

Lepista nuda (Bull.) Cooke
BLEWIT
Description: Cap 4-20 cm wide, convex with an inrolled margin when young, later flattening with a wavy or uplifted margin, sticky when moist, smooth or with small central cracks, dirty pinkish to lilac-gray or violet, fading toward tan. Gills slightly attached, crowded, violet, later tan. Stalk 3-10 cm long, to 3 cm thick, equal or with a bulbous base, dry, slightly hairy or flaky, off-white to lavender, bruising dark lavender and aging to tan. Partial veil absent. Flesh lavender to tan. Odor fragrant. Taste not distinctive or bitter.
Spore Print: Pinkish-buff.
Occurrence: Scattered or grouped in rich woodland soil, landscape areas, lawns, and compost piles. Fall.
Edibility: Edible.
Microscopic Features:
Spores 5.5-8 × 3.5-5 μm, elliptic, smooth or roughened. Hyaline, inamyloid.
Comments: *Clitocybe nuda* is a synonym. Avoid confusion with potentially toxic look-alikes including *Cortinarius argentatus* and *C. obliquus* by making a spore print.

Lepista subconnexa (Murrill) Harmaja
Description: Cap 2.5-9 cm wide, convex with an inrolled margin at first, then flattening, often with a wavy margin, dry, smooth, satiny white eventually darkening toward buff. Gills attached or slightly decurrent, close to crowded, occasionally forked, whitish to pinkish-buff. Stalk 2-8 cm long, to 2 cm thick, equal or with a bulbous base, dry, smooth or satiny hairy, buff, basal mycelium white. Partial veil absent. Flesh whitish, brittle. Odor fragrant or not distinctive. Taste not distinctive or bitter in age.
Spore Print: Pale pinkish-buff.
Occurrence: Clustered on the ground in woods. Summer-fall.
Edibility: Edible when young.
Microscopic Features:
Spores 4.5-6 × 3-3.5 μm, elliptic, minutely roughened. Hyaline, inamyloid.
Comments: *Clitocybe subconnexa* is a synonym. *Lyophyllum decastes* has a white spore print and brownish cap that pales in age. *Hygrophorus sordidus* is sticky slimy; it grows gregariously but not in clumps from a shared base.

Phyllotopsis nidulans (Pers.) Singer
ORANGE MOCK OYSTER
Description: Cap 2-8 cm wide, fan-shaped and broadly convex with an inrolled margin in youth, dry, densely fuzzy, bright orange or yellow-orange with a whitish bloom at first, fading toward yellow or brownish-yellow. Gills close or crowded, orange. Stalk absent. Partial veil absent. Flesh orange, tender. Odor frequently of rotting cabbage, but may not be distinctive. Taste disagreeable or not distinctive.
Spore Print: Pale pink (a thick spore print may be necessary to distinguish from white).
Occurrence: Solitary or clustered on fallen logs. Summer-winter.
Edibility: Inedible.
Microscopic Features:
Spores 6-8 × 3-4 μm, allantoid, smooth. Hyaline, inamyloid.
Comments: The orange hairiness of this stalkless mushroom makes it hard to confuse with others. The variation in smell and taste might come down to the species of the substrate log.

Pluteus cervinus
(Schaeff.) P. Kumm. complex
DEER MUSHROOM
Description: Cap 3-15 cm wide, convex and flattening in age, possibly wrinkled in youth but later smooth, moist or dry, some shade of cinnamon-, grayish-, or dull brown, often radially streaked. Gills free, close or crowded, white then pinkening. Stalk 5-13 cm long, to 2.5 cm thick, nearly equal, dry, white, sometimes with brownish fibers. Partial veil absent. Flesh white. Odor and taste of radish or not distinctive.
Spore Print: Pink.
Occurrence: On decaying wood, which may be buried, or sawdust piles. Spring-fall.
Edibility: Edible.
Microscopic Features:
Spores 5.5-7 × 4-6 μm, elliptic, smooth. Hyaline.
Comments: This name most likely covers a variety of species. Be careful not to confuse the Deer Mushroom with similarly colored *Entoloma* species or the deadly *Galerina marginata*. The cap of *Pluteus granularis* (search online) has dark brown granules and sometimes becomes wrinkled or veined. *Pluteus chrysophlebius* (search online) has a yellow cap and stalk.

Pluteus flavofuligineus G. F. Atk.
SMOKY YELLOW PLUTEUS
Description: Cap 2-8 cm wide, bell-shaped then flattening, dry, velvety and typically wrinkled in the center, initially golden-yellow with a sooty brown to olive-brown center, duller yellow but retaining the brownish center at maturity, the margin not lined. Gills are free, crowded, white or pale yellow before pinkening. The stalk is 4-8 cm long, up to 8 mm thick, equal, smooth or longitudinally twisted, white to pinkish and yellowing in age. Partial veil absent. Flesh whitish. Odor and taste not distinctive.
Spore Print: Salmon-pink.
Occurrence: Solitary or loosely grouped on decaying deciduous wood. Spring-fall.
Edibility: Unknown.
Microscopic Features:
Spores 6-8 × 5.5-6.5 μm, smooth, ovoid. Inamyloid.
Comments: Often lumped with *Pluteus leoninus* (search online), which classically has a lined cap margin and clear white stalk. *Pluteus chrysophlebius*, aka *P. admirabilis* (search online), is smaller with a yellower cap and stalk. *Pluteus mammillatus* (search online) is also similar but has a white partial veil.

Pluteus longistriatus (Peck) Peck
PLEATED PLUTEUS
Description: Cap 1-5 cm wide, convex then expanding toward flat, with or without a central depression or umbo, slightly scaly over the center and radially streaked, grayish- to reddish-brown. Gills free, close, white then pinkening. Stalk 2-5 cm long, to 3 mm thick, nearly equal, whitish, smooth to slightly flaky; longitudinal lines may be present. Partial veil absent. Flesh flimsy and white. Odor and taste not distinctive.
Spore Print: Pink.
Occurrence: On decaying hardwood and woody debris. Summer-early fall.
Edibility: Edible.
Microscopic Features:
Spores 6-7.5 × 5-5.5 μm, subglobose, smooth. Hyaline, inamyloid.
Comments: The pink spore print distinguishes this species from many other small wood-dwellers, including *Mycena inclinata*.

Pluteus pellitus (Pers.) P. Kumm.

Description: Cap 3-8 cm wide, convex then flattening, moist, smooth with radiating fibrils, dull white or yellow-tinged in age. Gills are free, close or crowded, white before pinkening. The stalk is 4-10 cm long, up to 8 mm thick, equal, white, smooth at the apex, becoming hairy below, with a scaly and sometimes bulbous base. Partial veil absent. Flesh white, firm. Odor and taste slightly radishy or not distinctive.

Spore Print: Salmon-pink.

Occurrence: Solitary or in loose groups on deciduous logs or stumps. Summer-fall.

Edibility: Edible.

Microscopic Features:
Spores 7-9 × 4.5-5.5 µm, broadly elliptic, smooth, clamp connections absent. Hyaline.

Comments: Some call this *Pluteus nothopellitus*, reserving *P. pellitus* for specimens with smaller spores and clamp connections. *Pluteus petasatus* (search online) is a closely related pale species with a brownish, hairy or scaly cap center. *Pluteus tomentosulus* (search online) is also white. It has a slightly wooly cap and usually prefers conifer wood.

Volvariella bombycina (Schaeff.) Singer
SILKY ROSEGILL

Description: Cap 5-20 cm wide, oval then expanding toward flat, dry, silky with fine hairs, white to yellowish-white in age. Gills free, crowded, white then pinkening. Stalk 6-20 cm long, 1-2 cm thick, enlarging downward, white, smooth, arising from a sturdy saclike volva that is white to brown in color. Partial veil absent. Flesh white. Odor and taste not distinctive.

Spore Print: Pink.

Occurrence: On hardwood trees, stumps, and logs. Summer-early fall.

Edibility: Edible.

Microscopic Features:
Spores 6.5-10.5 × 4.5-6.5 µm, elliptic, smooth. Hyaline.

Comments: This is the American flagship species of *Volvariella*, a genus characterized by a pink spore print and "hatching" from a sac. Other Carolina *Volvariellas* are typically smaller and mousy in color. One such is the terrestrial *Volvariella nigrodisca* (search online); it is gray with a hairy, radially lined cap, darkest in the center. Amanitas may have a saclike volva but are exclusively terrestrial and pale-spored.

BROWN-SPORED SPECIES

Spore prints treated in this section are shades of brown ranging from yellowish- to rusty to dark brown. If you don't find your mushroom here and its spore print falls at one end of the color spectrum, try the section for the adjacent color range.

Brown-spored mushrooms are a huge category that can only be sparingly sampled. We emphasize edibles and species with distinctive characteristics. Here is found the rusty-spored genus *Cortinarius*, a group of terrestrial mushrooms that forms mycorrhizal partnerships with trees. Most corts are not identifiable to species, at least by amateurs. The situation is no better for the mixed bag that mushroomers call LBMs or little brown mushrooms, but try them anyway. Sometimes you do score.

Pay attention to details, including cap shape—is there, for instance, a central bump (**umbo**)? What about cap texture and feel? Is the cap **hygrophanous** (the color fading in a dramatic and patchy manner as the cap begins to dry)?

Partial veils, when present, are of special diagnostic interest. Membranous partial veils vary from vanishingly thin to thick, double-layered sheets with a **cogwheel** design on the undersurface. In genus *Cortinarius* and a few others the partial veil is typically composed of cobwebby fibrils spanning the gap between stalk and cap margin. This type of veil is called a **cortina**. It ruptures as the cap expands, hopefully leaving a few threads stuck to the stalk, where they become visible as rusty threads when spores fall and adhere to them. If you don't see a partial veil on a mature specimen but are wondering if it had one in youth, inspect the upper section of stalk for an abrupt change in texture, a **ring zone**.

In this group of mushrooms, textural features of the cap or stalk may be crucial as well. The difference between a **scaly** stalk and the flakiness mycologists refer to as **scurfy** is illustrated in figs. 12 and 13.

Does your unknown mushroom live on the ground? What types of trees, if any, were nearby? If the mushroom grew from wood, was it from a deciduous tree or a conifer?

Figure 10. Cogwheel partial veil

Figure 11. Cortina

Figure 12. Scaly stalk

GILLED MUSHROOMS

Figure 13. Scurfy stalk

almond or fennel flavor to dishes—which might not be what you're looking for on a hamburger. But be careful; poisonous *Agraricus* species are out there too, along with the deadly white *Amanita bisporigera* and dozens of other button mushroom look-alikes. We describe one edible *Cortinarius* species. Except for the edible *Agaricus* species and *Cortinarius caperatus*, don't eat any other brown-spored mushrooms described in this guide. Many are poisonous. The Deadly Galerina is, well, potentially lethal.

Odor can be important in distinguishing many species of gilled mushrooms. Although many of the odors are easy to describe and recognize, "**farinaceous**" is especially difficult. Farinaceous is an odor variously compared to sliced watermelon rind, cucumber, meal, bread dough, or farina (think Cream of Wheat).

Edible wild members of genus *Agaricus* are at least as tasty as their supermarket relatives: the buttons, cremini, and portobellos. Some wild species add an

Key to Brown-Spored Gilled Species

1a Mushroom growing on a log, stump, or other substantial piece of wood ....
.... Brown-Spored Species Growing on Wood (p. 152)
1b Mushroom growing on soil or in grass, mulch, sawdust, dung, or other debris..............
...................................Brown-Spored Species Growing on Soil, Grass, Mulch, Dung, or
Debris (p. 160); see also *Agrocybe* (p. 152), *Gymnopilus* (p. 154), and *Pholiota* (p. 156)

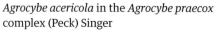

Agrocybe acericola in the *Agrocybe praecox* complex (Peck) Singer
MAPLE AGROCYBE
Description: Cap 2.5-10 cm wide, convex then flattening, possibly with a low umbo, moist or dry, smooth or centrally wrinkled, some shade of yellow-brown. May have white fragments of partial veil at the margin. Gills attached, close, pale becoming gray-brown. Stalk 4-12.5 cm long, to 2 cm thick, smooth, white, browning from the base upward. Partial veil membranous, white at first. Flesh white. Odor farinaceous. Taste farinaceous to bitter.

Spore Print: Dark brown.

Occurrence: Solitary to clumped on deciduous logs or stumps, commonly maples. Spring-summer.

Edibility: Not recommended.

Microscopic Features:
Spores 8-11 × 5-6.5 µm, elliptic with an apical pore, smooth. Pale brown.

Comments: Other members of the *Agrocybe praecox* complex (search online) grow on grass or in mulch. Compare grass-dwelling suspects with *Agaricus auricolor*. The edible and often cultivated Black Poplar Mushroom, *Cyclocybe aegerita* (search online), has a different taste and smell.

Crepidotus applanatus (Pers.) P. Kumm.
FLAT CREP
Description: Cap 1-4 cm broad, shell- or fan-shaped, relatively thin in profile, moist, smooth, sometimes finely hairy near the point of attachment, the margin often radially lined, white in youth, aging to pale brown, hygrophanous. Gills attached, close or crowded, narrow, radiating from the attachment point, colored like the cap. Stalkless, attached to wood at a single point. Flesh thin and watery. Odor and taste not distinctive.

Spore Print: Brown.

Occurrence: In groups, often overlapping clusters, on decaying hardwood, rarely reported on conifers. Summer-early fall.

Edibility: Unknown.

Microscopic Features:
Spores 4-5.5 µm, globose, finely punctate. Pale brown.

Comments: This common species has been mistaken for small caps of *Pleurotus ostreatus*, which has white or lilac spores and a different smell. It could also be confused with the conifer-dwelling *Pleurocybella porrigens*. That larger species retains its white color at maturity and also has a white spore print.

Crepidotus cinnabarinus Peck
CINNABAR OYSTERLING

Description: Cap 5-15 mm broad, shell- to fan- or kidney-shaped, convex and flattening at maturity, dry, usually hairy but may be smooth, bright red. Gills attached, fairly distant and broad, radiating from a narrow attachment point; gill edges red, faces yellow to red, browning with age. Stalkless. Flesh thin, pale. Odor and taste not distinctive.

Spore Print: Brown.

Occurrence: Solitary or in small groups on decaying hardwood. Summer-early fall.

Edibility: Unknown.

Microscopic Features:
Spores 6-10 × 5-6 μm, ovate, punctate or finely warted. Pale brown.

Comments: The bright red (cinnabar) color of this tiny "oyster" rescues it from obscurity. The more common *Phyllotopsis nidulans* is much larger and has a pale pink to pinkish-brown spore print.

Crepidotus mollis (Schaeff.) Staude
PEELING OYSTERLING

Description: Cap 1-8 cm broad, to 2.5 cm wide, typically kidney-shaped, broadly convex to flat, moist or dry, with ocher- to orange-brown fibers or scales over a paler gelatinous cuticle that can be peeled away, hygrophanous. Gills variably close, narrow, radiating from the attachment point, white at first, then browning. Stalk rudimentary or absent. Flesh thin, watery. Odor not distinctive. Taste not distinctive or bitter.

Spore Print: Brown.

Occurrence: In groups that may overlap, on decaying hardwood or, less commonly, conifer wood. Spring-early fall.

Edibility: Unknown.

Microscopic Features:
Spores 7-10 × 4.5-6 μm, elliptical with a double wall, smooth. Pale brown.

Comments: This can be mistaken for edible oyster mushrooms of the *Pleurotus ostreatus* complex, but they have white or lilac spore prints and firmer flesh. *Crepidotus crocophyllus* (search online) has orange gills in youth. *Hohenbuehelia mastrucata* is grayer and hairier and has white spores.

GILLED MUSHROOMS

153

Galerina marginata (Batsch) Kühner
DEADLY GALERINA
Description: Cap 1-6.5 cm wide, convex then flattening, may retain a low umbo, smooth, sticky and radially lined at the margin when moist, brown, hygrophanous. Gills attached or slightly decurrent, close, yellowish then rusty. Stalk 2-10 cm long, 3-8 mm thick, nearly equal, dry, hollow, pale brown at the apex, darkening below, often shaggy below the ring zone, base usually covered with white mycelium. Partial veil a thin white skirt that collapses as a brown band around the stalk. Flesh brown and watery. Odor not distinctive or slightly farinaceous. Taste not distinctive.
Spore Print: Rusty brown.
Occurrence: Solitary or in small groups and clusters on logs or stumps. Spring-fall.
Edibility: Deadly poisonous.
Microscopic Features:
Spores 8-11 × 5-6.5 μm, elliptic, roughened. Pale brown.
Comments: Also known as *Galerina autumnalis*. This may grow on the same logs as the edible *Hypholoma lateritium* or *Armillaria gallica*. See also *Simocybe centunculus* and *Xeromphalina tenuipes*.

Gymnopilus luteofolius (Peck) Singer
YELLOW-GILLED GYMNOPILUS
Description: Cap 2-8 cm wide, convex then broadly convex, dry, covered with small purplish-red scales. Cap purplish- or brick red fading toward dingy yellow by maturity, may stain blue-green when bruised. Gills attached or slightly decurrent, close, yellowish then rusty. Stalk 3-9.5 cm long, 3-12 mm thick, equal or enlarging downward, dry, hairy, longitudinally striped, purplish-pink above and browning below, instantly bruising pinkish-red. Partial veil a cortina, usually leaving a thin ring of fibers around the stalk. Flesh stains reddish when cut. Odor not distinctive. Taste bitter.
Spore Print: Rusty orange.
Occurrence: Often in clusters on conifer chips, sawdust, or wood. Occasionally on hardwood logs. Summer-fall.
Edibility: Bitter, mildly hallucinogenic.
Microscopic Features:
Spores 5.5-8.5 × 3.5-4.5 μm, elliptic, warted, dextrinoid. Orange-brown in KOH.
Comments: Michael Kuo also reports this growing on treated lumber. KOH stains the cap surface black. *Tricholomopsis rutilans* has a white spore print and lacks the staining reactions.

Gymnopilus penetrans (Fr.) Murrill
LITTLE GYM
Description: Cap 2-5 cm wide, convex then broadly convex, moist to dry, smooth or finely hairy, yellow or yellow-orange to reddish-brown. Gills attached, close, pale yellow, developing rusty spots. Stalk 2.5-6 cm long, 3-7 mm thick, equal or enlarging downward, dry, smooth, pale yellow with white fuzz at the base, instantly bruising pinkish-red. Partial veil a cortina seldom leaving evidence on the stalk. Flesh white. Odor not distinctive. Taste bitter.
Spore Print: Rusty brown.
Occurrence: Solitary to clumped, mainly on conifer wood, chips, or sawdust, occasionally on hardwoods. Summer-fall.
Edibility: Unknown.
Microscopic Features:
Spores 6.5-10 × 4-5.5 μm, elliptic, warted, dextrinoid. Pale orange-yellow.
Comments: There might or might not be a genetic difference between this species and *Gymnopilus sapineus* (search online), which has tiny scales on the cap. Most of us can safely choose not to concern ourselves with this ambiguity.

Gymnopilus validipes (Peck) Hesler
Description: Cap 7.5-15 cm wide, convex then broadly convex, dry, finely hairy or with yellowish-brown scales, cap pale yellow to orange-yellow, may very slowly bruise blue or green. Gills attached to decurrent, close, pale yellow, turning rusty in age. Stalk 10-13 cm long, 2.5-5 cm thick, roughly equal or swollen at midlevel, solid, hairy, color and bruising reaction similar to the cap. Partial veil thin, but usually leaves a ring zone on the stalk. Flesh white. Odor and taste not distinctive.
Spore Print: Rusty brown.
Occurrence: Several to clumped on hardwood stumps or logs. Fall.
Edibility: Weakly psychoactive.
Microscopic Features:
Spores 7.5-10 × 4-5.5 μm, elliptic, warted, dextrinoid. Pale orange-yellow in KOH.
Comments: The nearly identical *Gymnopilus luteus* (search online) has a bitter taste. *Gymnopilus junonius* = *G. spectabilis* (search online) is also similar but has a pungent smell in addition to the bitter taste.

Pholiota flammans (Batsch) P. Kumm.

YELLOW PHOLIOTA

Description: Cap 3-10 cm wide, convex to nearly flat, sticky to slimy, bright yellow or orange-yellow, covered with curved, yellow, fibrous scales. The colors soon turn dull. Gills attached but sharply notched at the stalk, close, yellow, staining brown when injured. Stalk 5-12 cm long, up to 1 cm thick, dry, equal, yellow and relatively smooth above the ring zone, covered with yellow scales below. Partial veil thinly fibrous or cobwebby, usually leaving at least some evidence on the stalk. Flesh yellow. Odor and taste not distinctive.

Spore Print: Rusty brown.

Occurrence: Solitary or grouped on coniferous logs or stumps. Late summer-fall.

Edibility: Inedible.

Microscopic Features:
Spores 4-5 × 2.5-3 μm, elliptic, smooth, lacking an apical pore. Brownish.

Comments: The Yellow Pholiota is a rapidly fading flower, seldom found at its peak. The combination of stickiness, prominent scales, and occurrence on conifers helps distinguish it from other species.

Pholiota malicola (Kauffman) A. H. Sm.

Description: Cap 3-8 (rarely 15) cm wide, convex then flattening, smooth, slimy at first but soon drying, yellow to yellow-orange, sometimes with a greenish tinge. Gills attached, close, yellow becoming rusty brown, may bruise orange. Stalk 4-18 cm long, up to 2.5 cm thick, equal, dry, whitish or pale yellow at the apex, browning from the base upward, showing longitudinal fibers but no scales. Partial veil composed of fibers that may leave a ring zone. Flesh pale yellow. Odor faintly fragrant. Taste not distinctive.

Spore Print: Brown.

Occurrence: Found in clumps at the base of stumps, on logs, or on woody debris. Late summer-fall.

Edibility: Unknown.

Microscopic Features:
Spores 7.5-11 × 4.5-5.5 μm, elliptic, smooth, showing an apical pore. Pale brown.

Comments: The similar *Pholiota alnicola* (search online) tastes bitter. *Kuehneromyces* (formerly *Pholiota*) *mutabilis* (search online) has scales below the ring zone. *Pholiota lenta* (search online) has a whitish to grayish cap with pinkish tinges and smaller spores.

Pholiota polychroa
(Berk.) A. H. Sm. & H. J. Brodie
VARIABLE PHOLIOTA

Description: Cap 2-10 cm wide, convex then flattening, slimy, covered at first with wine-colored scales that often wash off. Cap also wine-colored, or multicolored with olive and/or, especially centrally, shades of yellow or orange. The margin is often hung with triangular veil fragments. Gills attached, close to crowded, creamy or pale lilac before darkening toward purplish-brown. Stalk 2-6 cm long, up to 1 cm thick, equal, often scaly below the ring zone, the apex yellow to blue-green, the base becoming reddish-brown. Partial veil thin, leaving a ring that often disappears. Flesh white to greenish. Odor and taste not distinctive.

Spore Print: Brown to purplish-brown.

Occurrence: Solitary or in groups, usually on decaying hardwood or sawdust, rarely on conifers. Summer-fall.

Edibility: Unknown.

Microscopic Features:
Spores 6-7.5 × 3.5-4.5 μm, elliptic or bean-shaped, smooth, with a tiny apical pore. Brownish.

Comments: A photogenic *Pholiota*. Pale specimens with whitish flesh may be *Pholiota lenta* (search online).

Pholiota squarrosoides (Peck) Sacc.
SCALY PHOLIOTA

Description: Cap 3-11 cm wide, convex; under the dry, erect brown scales the surface is sticky when moist, pale at first, darkening toward cinnamon-buff. Gills attached or slightly decurrent, close, white becoming rusty brown without an intermediate greenish phase. Stalk 5-10 cm long, up to 1.5 cm thick, equal, pale, smooth above the ring zone, scaly brown below. Partial veil whitish, fibrous or membranous, often disappearing. Flesh white. Odor and taste not distinctive.

Spore Print: Brown.

Occurrence: In clumps on hardwood logs or stumps. Late summer-fall.

Edibility: Not recommended; may cause gastrointestinal distress.

Microscopic Features:
Spores 4-6 × 2.5-3.5 μm, elliptic, smooth, no apical pore. Pale brown.

Comments: The very similar *Pholiota squarrosa* (search online) has a dry, scaly cap, gills that pass through a greenish phase, and a garlic-like odor. Microscopy may be required to distinguish these species with certainty. *Pholiota limonella* (search online) has a slimy yellow cap.

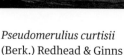

Pseudomerulius curtisii
(Berk.) Redhead & Ginns

Description: Cap 2-5 cm wide, fan- or shell-shaped with an inrolled margin at first, dry, fuzzy to smooth, brownish- to olive-yellow, sometimes with reddish-brown stains. Gills radiate from a narrowed point of attachment, close, thick, crinkled, freely forking and fusing, with crossveins present, not easily peelable from the cap as a layer, yellow-orange, staining darker orange. Stalk absent or rudimentary. Partial veil absent. Flesh tough, yellowish. Odor strong and sickly sweet to some, not distinctive to others. Taste bitter or not distinctive.

Spore Print: Olive-yellow to yellowish-brown.

Occurrence: Solitary or in clusters on decaying conifer wood. Summer-fall.

Edibility: Unknown.

Microscopic Features:
  Spores 3-3.5 × 1.5-2 μm, broadly elliptic, smooth. Pale yellow, dextrinoid.

Comments: Other names include *Paxillus corrugatus*, *P. curtisii*, *Meiorganum curtisii*, and *Tapinella corrugata*. Some people smell this odd little species before they see it. *Tapinella panuoides* has straighter gills that are peelable from the cap as a layer.

Simocybe centunculus (Fr.) P. Karst.
AMERICAN SIMOCYBE

Description: Cap 1-3 cm wide, convex then flattening, dry, initially velvety or silky with a translucent radially lined margin, smoothing in age, olive-brown to olive but fading, leaving the center darker than the margin. Gills attached, close, pale at first, darkening to a yellowish- or grayish-brown; the white edges appear fringed or frayed (use hand lens). Stalk 1-4 cm long, 2-4 mm thick, equal, hollow, initially whitish, then browning, faintly powdery or scurfy at the apex in youth. White mycelium is often visible at the base. No partial veil. Flesh brown. Odor and taste not distinctive.

Spore Print: Brown.

Occurrence: Scattered on the decaying wood of deciduous trees. Summer-fall. Occasionally in spring as well.

Edibility: Unknown.

Microscopic Features:
  Spores 6-7.5 × 4-5 μm, elliptic or bean-shaped, smooth. Pale brown.

Comments: The frayed/fringed gill edges rescue this mushroom from obscurity in the legion of little brown mushrooms that grow on wood.

Tapinella atrotomentosa (Batsch) Šutara
VELVET-FOOTED PAX
Description: Cap 4-15 cm wide, convex
with an inrolled margin at first,
becoming flat or centrally depressed,
finely hairy, dry, yellowish- to reddish-
brown, darkening with age. Gills
decurrent, close or crowded, forking or
crossveined near the stem, whitish to
pale tan, separable as a layer. Stalk 2-12
cm long, up to 3 cm thick, equal, off-
center to lateral, pale and smooth at the
apex, with dark brown wooliness below.
No partial veil. Flesh whitish or pale
yellow, tough, not staining. Odor and
taste not distinctive.
Spore Print: Pale yellow to yellowish-
brown.
Occurrence: Solitary or in clusters on
conifer stumps or logs. Summer-fall.
Edibility: Unknown.
Microscopic Features:
  Spores 5-7 × 3-4 µm, elliptic, smooth.
  Hyaline or pale brown, dextrinoid.
Comments: Previously known as *Paxillus
atrotomentosus*. It is used to dye woolen
fiber and silk shades of gray, green, and
purple.

Tapinella panuoides (Fr.) E.-J. Gilbert
STALKLESS PAXILLUS
Description: Cap 3-11 cm wide, fan- or
shell-shaped with an inrolled margin
at first, dry, smooth or feltlike,
yellowish- to orangish-brown. Gills
radiate from the point of attachment,
typically straight, occasionally crinkled,
forking, sometimes fusing or with
crossveining, peelable from the cap as
a layer, pale yellow to yellow-orange.
Stalk absent or rudimentary. Partial
veil absent. Flesh tough, nearly white.
Odor not distinctive. Taste bitter or not
distinctive.
Spore Print: Yellowish-brown to brown.
Occurrence: Solitary or in groups on
decaying conifer wood. Late spring-fall.
Edibility: Unknown.
Microscopic Features:
  Spores 4-6 × 3-4 µm, elliptic, smooth.
  Weakly amyloid.
Comments: Previously known as *Paxillus
panuoides*. A related conifer lover,
Pseudomerulius curtisii, has thicker,
conspicuously crinkled gills that don't
peel easily as a layer. *Phyllotopsis
nidulans* is fuzzier and orange and has a
paler spore print. *Panellus stipticus* has a
stubby stalk and a white spore print and
grows on decaying hardwood.

GILLED MUSHROOMS

159

Agaricus abruptibulbus Peck

ABRUPTLY BULBOUS AGARICUS

Description: Cap to 15 cm wide, dry, convex, flattening with age, whitish, bald or with a few flattened fibrils, bruises pale yellow. Gills free of stalk, pale at button stage, then pink, becoming dark brown. Stalk slender, 5-15.5 cm long and 1-1.5 cm thick, white, ending in an abrupt basal bulb. Mushroom stains pale yellow when bruised but stalk base does not stain bright yellow when cut. Partial veil thick, with a cogwheel underside, persistent. Odor of almond extract or anise when young. Taste not distinctive.

Spore Print: Dark brown.

Occurrence: In rich woodland soil, often near rotting stumps or logs. Summer-fall.

Edibility: Edible and good, but avoid any with an unpleasant rather than an almond or anise smell.

Microscopic Features:
Spores 6-8 × 4-5 µm, elliptic, smooth. Purple-brown.

Comments: *Agaricus silvicola* (search online) is similar but lacks the basal bulb. See also the poisonous *Agaricus pocillator* and *A. xanthodermus*.

Agaricus auricolor L. Krieg.

Description: Cap to 7 cm wide, dry, convex, flattening, with a scattering of small scales. Cap center and scales are cadmium yellow in youth, fading to whitish at the margin. Cap browns in age. Gills free of stalk, initially pale, then pink, then dark brown. Stalk to 7 cm long, relatively thick, widening before possibly tapering to a point, white to pale yellow. Base not staining yellow when cut. Partial veil thin, flaring. Odor strongly of almond extract.

Spore Print: Dark brown.

Occurrence: Scattered or in groups in grassy woodland trails, lawns, hardwoods. Summer.

Edibility: Edible, flavor of almond extract.

Microscopic Features:
Spores 4.5-6 × 3.8-4.5 µm, oval. Brown.

Comments: This species resembles a yellow *Agaricus campestris*, but the smell is diagnostic. *Agaricus xanthodermus* smells different, and the flesh at the base of the stalk stains yellow when cut. Some *Amanitas* have yellowish caps, but gills and spore prints remain pale.

Agaricus campestris L.
MEADOW MUSHROOM, PINK BOTTOM
Description: Cap 3-11 cm wide, dry, convex, flattening with age, often with a scattering of fibrils or small scales. Color of cap and scales initially white, tinging brown at maturity. Gills free of stalk, initially pale, becoming pink, then dark brown. Stalk thick, 2.5-6 cm long, white, may bruise pink. Base not staining yellow when cut. Partial veil thin, dangling and may disappear. Odor and taste not distinctive.

Spore Print: Dark brown.

Occurrence: Scattered, in groups, or in fairy rings in grassy areas. Spring and fall.

Edibility: Choice. Caution: Match spore color and all other mushroom characteristics before firing up the sauté pan!

Microscopic Features: Spores 6-9 × 4-6 µm, elliptic, smooth. Pale brown.

Comments: The poisonous *Agaricus xanthodermus* typically has an unpleasant smell and bruises yellow, and the flesh in the base of the stalk usually stains bright yellow. *Agrocybe molesta* (search online) has a longer stalk; the gills and spore print are lighter brown.

Agaricus diminutivus Peck

Description: Cap 1-4 cm wide, dry, white, convex then flattening, covered with hairy brown scales. Gills free of stalk, pink then dark brown. Stalk slender, 3-6 cm long and 3-6 mm wide, white to pale pink, may expand at base and taper to a point. Stalk may bruise pale yellow but base not staining bright yellow when cut. Partial veil relatively thin, dangling, persistent. Odor and taste not distinctive.

Spore Print: Dark brown.

Occurrence: Solitary or scattered under hardwoods. Summer.

Edibility: Unknown.

Microscopic Features: Spores 4.5-5.5 × 3.5-5 µm, oval. Brown.

Comments: This tiny agaric could be confused with a *Lepiota*, but they have white gills and white spore prints. Some *Inocybe* species have shaggy caps and brown spore prints but lack the persistent partial veil and usually have a strong spermatic or green corn odor. Other brown-spored look-alikes with shaggy caps also lack the prominent partial veil.

Agaricus pocillator Murrill

Description: Cap 3-10 cm wide, dry, convex, flattening with age, dark brown at the center, with radiating pattern of brown scales over white to the margin, darkening with age. Gills free of stalk, pale, then pink, becoming dark brown. Stalk slender, 4-9 cm long and 6-12 mm thick, white, ending in an abrupt basal bulb. Stalk base typically stains bright yellow when cut. Partial veil thick, with a cogwheel underside, persistent. Crushed flesh often smells unpleasant or like library paste but may not be distinctive. Taste unpleasant or not distinctive.

Spore Print: Dark brown.

Occurrence: Solitary or scattered in hardwoods, mixed woods, or grassy areas with trees. Late spring-early fall.

Edibility: Poisonous.

Microscopic Features:
Spores 4.5-6 × 3-4 µm, oval, smooth. Pale brown.

Comments: A burlier northern cousin, the poisonous *Agaricus placomyces* (search online), is also found in the Carolinas. It shares the unpleasant smell and yellow-staining stem base, but the base is not abruptly bulbous.

Agaricus xanthodermus Genev.
YELLOW STAINER

Description: Cap 5-20 cm wide, dry, convex, whitish, flattening and tanning with age, bald or with a few pale fibrils, bruises yellow then brown. Gills free of stalk, pale, then pink, finally dark brown. Stalk thick in youth but becoming slender, 5-18 cm long, white, bruising yellow then brown; base may be enlarged but is not abruptly bulbous. Stalk base typically stains bright yellow when cut. Partial veil thick, flaring, with a cogwheel underside. Crushed flesh usually has an unpleasant or library paste odor but may not be distinctive. Taste unpleasant or not distinctive.

Spore Print: Dark brown.

Occurrence: Solitary or in groups, usually in grassy or disturbed areas, occasionally in woods. Summer-early fall.

Edibility: Poisonous.

Microscopic Features:
Spores 4.5-6 × 3-4.5 µm, oval, smooth. Brown.

Comments: *Agaricus campestris* does not bruise or stain yellow, and its odor is not distinctive. Also compare with *Agaricus pocillator* and *A. abruptibulbous*.

Agrocybe pediades (Fr.) Fayod
HEMISPHERIC AGROCYBE
Description: Cap 1-5 cm wide, initially
hemispheric in shape, then broadly
convex, smooth, sticky or dry and
shiny, pale yellowish to pale reddish-
brown; the margin sometimes retains
white fragments of partial veil. Gills
are attached, close to almost distant,
pale brown at first, darkening to
orange-brown. Stalk 2-7 cm long, to
12 mm thick, possibly slightly bulbous
at the base, colored like the cap, no
evident ring zone. Partial veil white,
soon disappearing. Flesh thin, white
or pale yellow. Odor farinaceous. Taste
farinaceous or bitter and unpleasant.
Spore Print: Dark tobacco brown.
Occurrence: Solitary or several in grass,
mulch, or manured sawdust. Spring-
fall.
Edibility: Edible, but poor.
Microscopic Features:
Spores 10-14 × 7-10 µm, elliptic with an
apical pore, smooth. Pale brown.
Comments: See comments under *Agrocybe
acericola* for a larger wood-dwelling
relative. *Conocybe apala* has a cone-
shaped cap with a lined margin.

Bolbitius titubans (Bull.) Fr.
YELLOW BOLBITIUS
Description: Cap 1-7 cm wide, conical at
first, nearly flat in age, often with a
broad umbo, slimy, radially lined, egg-
yolk to greenish-yellow but fading, the
margin strongly lined at maturity. Gills
free or narrowly attached, initially pale
yellow then browning, may become
gelatinous. Stalk 3-12 cm long, up to
1 cm thick, equal, hollow and fragile,
slightly sticky, scurfy, pale yellow.
Partial veil absent. Flesh thin, pale.
Odor and taste not distinctive.
Spore Print: Rusty brown.
Occurrence: Solitary or scattered on dung,
grass, compost, or wood chips. Look for
it in the morning; it's gone by evening.
Late spring-late fall.
Edibility: Edible, but of no culinary
interest.
Microscopic Features:
Spores 11-15 × 6-8 µm, elliptic with an
apical pore, smooth. Brownish-yellow.
Comments: Conocybes have dry caps.
Hygrocybe flavescens and *Mycena
leaiana* are woodland species and have
pale spore prints.

Conocybe apala (Fr.) Arnolds
WHITE DUNCE CAP

Description: Cap 1-3 cm wide, conical, becoming bell-shaped, often with an upturned edge at maturity, dry, radially lined, white to pale tan or slightly darker at the center. Gills are almost free of the stalk, close, white at first, then browning. Stalk 4-10 cm long, 1-3 mm thick, equal, often with a slight bulb, whitish, hollow and fragile. Partial veil absent. Flesh thin, white. Odor and taste not distinctive.

Spore Print: Reddish-brown.

Occurrence: Often in groups in lawns or fields. Late spring–summer.

Edibility: Edible, but of no culinary interest.

Microscopic Features: Spores 10-14 × 6-9 μm, elliptic with an apical pore, smooth. Pale brown.

Comments: Other names include *Conocybe lactea* and *C. albipes*. Look for this species in the morning. They're often gone by afternoon. *Agrocybe pediades* has a thicker stalk and a rounder cap. *Agrocybe molesta* (search online) is larger and initially has a partial veil.

Conocybe tenera complex (Schaeff.) Fayod
BROWN DUNCE CAP

Description: Cap 1-3 cm wide, conical, becoming bell-shaped, dry, radially lined, yellowish- to reddish-brown when fresh, paling markedly when dry. Gills barely attached, close to nearly distant, white at first then turning rusty. Stalk 3-9 cm long, occasionally up to 7 mm thick, equal, faintly powdery, often with fine vertical lines, color ranges from whitish to brown. Partial veil absent. Flesh reddish-brown. Odor and taste are not distinctive.

Spore Print: Reddish-brown.

Occurrence: Solitary or scattered in woods, grassy areas, and gardens with rich or fertilized soil. Late spring and early fall.

Edibility: Unknown.

Microscopic Features: Spores 10-14 × 5-6 μm, elliptic with an apical pore, smooth. Pale brown.

Comments: Several species probably pass under this name. *Conocybe apala* is lighter in color and more ephemeral.

Cortinarius albidus Peck

Description: Cap 5-11 cm wide, convex, then broadly convex, sticky when fresh, shiny when dry, smooth texture, white to creamy tan. Gills attached, close, initially white, becoming rusty brown. Stalk 4-8 cm long, up to 2 cm thick at the apex, with an obliquely flattened and somewhat rimmed basal bulb to 3 cm wide, whitish. Partial veil a white cortina, which may disappear. Flesh white, unchanging when exposed. Odor not distinctive. Taste sweet.

Spore Print: Rusty brown.

Occurrence: Solitary to scattered under hardwoods. Late summer-fall.

Edibility: Unknown; not recommended.

Microscopic Features:

Spores 9-12 × 5.5-7 µm, elliptic, warted. Pale brown.

Comments: The pale colors of this mushroom might cause it to be mistaken for any number of white, pale-spored species. Another pale cort with a rimmed bulb, *Cortinarius scaurotraganoides* (search online), smells strongly of pears.

Cortinarius alboviolaceus (Pers.) Fr.

SILVERY-VIOLET CORT

Description: Cap 3-9.5 cm wide, bell-shaped then broadly convex, sometimes with a low umbo, dry, silky silver-violet in youth, developing brown tints. Gills attached, close, initially purple, turning rusty brown. Stalk 4-8 cm long, 5-10 mm thick at the apex, equal or enlarging downward, pale violet, sheathed at first with cobwebby material below the thin fibrous ring zone. Partial veil a white cortina, the threads becoming rusty. Flesh pale violet, not changing when exposed. Odor and taste not distinctive.

Spore Print: Rusty brown.

Occurrence: Solitary to clumped under hardwoods. Summer-fall.

Edibility: Reportedly edible; not recommended.

Microscopic Features:

Spores 7-10 × 4-6 µm, elliptic, slightly roughened. Pale brown.

Comments: Stalk details separate this species from *Cortinarius argentatus* and *C. obliquus*. *Cortinarius camphoratus* (search online) prefers conifers and has a disagreeable odor. Another strong-smelling conifer lover, *Cortinarius traganus* (search online), has yellowish flesh.

GILLED MUSHROOMS

Cortinarius argentatus (Pers.) Fr.

Description: Cap 5-9 cm wide, bell-shaped then broadly convex, dry, silky silver-violet, with brown tints in age. Gills attached, close, initially purple, becoming rusty brown. Stalk 5-8 cm long, up to 1 cm thick at the apex, club-shaped with a fat basal bulb, pale violet, no cobwebby sheath below the ring zone. Partial veil a cortina, the whitish threads becoming rusty. Flesh white to pale violet, unchanging when exposed. Odor not distinctive or of radish. Taste not distinctive.

Spore Print: Rusty brown.

Occurrence: Solitary to scattered under hardwoods, often oaks, or in mixed woods. Summer-fall.

Edibility: Unknown.

Microscopic Features:

Spores 7-9.5 × 5-6 μm, elliptic, slightly roughened. Pale brown.

Comments: This squatty cort lacks the stalk sheath of a young *Cortinarius alboviolaceus*. The bulb is different than that of *Cortinarius obliquus*. The flesh of *Cortinarius cyanites* stains red. *Lepista nuda* lacks a cortina and has a pinkish-tan spore print.

Cortinarius armillatus (Fr.) Fr.
BRACELET CORT

Description: Cap 5-12 cm wide, bell-shaped then broadly convex, sometimes with a low umbo, moist to dry, nearly smooth but covered with fine radial fibers or scales, burnt orange to reddish-brown. Gills attached, close to almost distant, pale brown turning rusty. Stalk 5-15 cm long, 1-2.5 cm thick, typically enlarging downward to a bulb, off-white to brownish with multiple reddish bands below a rusty ring zone. Partial veil a white cortina. Flesh white to brownish, unchanging when bruised. Odor not distinctive or radishy. Taste not distinctive to slightly bitter.

Spore Print: Rusty brown.

Occurrence: Solitary to scattered, often with birch; also found in mixed woods. Summer-fall.

Edibility: Edible, but poor.

Microscopic Features:

Spores 7-12 × 5-7 μm, elliptic to almond-shaped, warted. Pale brown.

Comments: Of greater visual than culinary interest. The smaller *Cortinarius bolaris* also has a stalk with reddish bands or patches, but flesh in the base of the stalk bruises yellow-orange.

Cortinarius atkinsonianus Kauffman

Description: Cap 6-9 cm wide, convex then flattening, smooth, sticky, often yellow at first but developing a mottling of olive and/or tawny tones, eventually becoming reddish-brown. Gills attached, initially violet, possibly with greenish-yellow edges, soon turning rusty. Stalk is 6-8 cm long, 12-18 mm thick at the apex, enlarging downward to a bulb that may be flattened or rimmed. Stalk violet but may show yellowish fibrils as well, colors unchanging when bruised. Partial veil a greenish-yellow cortina. Flesh is violet, fading by maturity. Odor and taste not distinctive.

Spore Print: Rusty brown.

Occurrence: Solitary to scattered in hardwoods or mixed woods. Fall.

Edibility: Edible, but not recommended.

Microscopic Features:
Spores 13-15 × 7-8.5 µm, elliptic to almond-shaped, rough. Pale brown.

Comments: This species can present a riot of simultaneous colors. Eating it is not recommended due to the risk of confusion with other purplish corts. *Cortinarius collinitus* complex is slimier and lacks the basal bulb.

Cortinarius bolaris (Pers.) Fr.
SAFFRON-FOOTED CORT

Description: Cap 2.5-8 cm wide, convex then broadly convex to centrally depressed in age, dry, whitish under a pattern of red or reddish-brown scales. Gills attached, close, pale buff at first, becoming rusty. Stalk 4-6 cm long, up to 1.5 cm thick, equal or enlarging downward, whitish with multiple wide reddish bands or patches below a thin fibrous ring zone. Partial veil a white cortina that usually disappears. Flesh white to pale brown, bruising yellow-orange to reddish in the stalk base. Odor and taste not distinctive.

Spore Print: Rusty brown.

Occurrence: Solitary to scattered under hardwoods or in mixed woods, often damp areas. Late summer-fall.

Edibility: Poisonous.

Microscopic Features:
Spores 6-9 × 5-6 µm, ovoid to subglobose, warted. Pale brown.

Comments: These are often found in small groups at the beginning of autumn. *Cortinarius rubicundulus* (search online) has orange-brown cap scales and elliptical spores. *Cortinarius armillatus* is larger and lacks the "saffron" bruising reaction.

Cortinarius caperatus (Pers.) Fr.
GYPSY MUSHROOM
Description: Cap 5-15 cm wide, egg-shaped becoming broadly convex with a low umbo, moist or dry, usually slightly wrinkled, initially coated with a thin white frosting over a ground color of pale yellow to yellowish- or orange-brown. The white dust persists longest at the center of the cap. Gills attached, close, pale yellow then rusty. Stalk 5-13 cm long, to 2.5 cm thick, equal or enlarging downward, whitish to pale brown, scurfy above the partial veil. Partial veil membranous, white, leaving a thick white skirt. Flesh white to yellowish. Odor and taste not distinctive.

Spore Print: Rusty brown.

Occurrence: Scattered under conifers or hardwoods. Late summer-fall.

Edibility: Edible.

Microscopic Features:
Spores 9-14 × 7-9 μm, almond-shaped, slightly roughened. Pale brown.

Comments: Formerly known as *Rozites caperata*. The membranous partial veil is unusual in this genus, as is the white dusting on the cap. Match all features, including spore—not gill—color, before considering the Gypsy as food.

Cortinarius cinnamomeus (L.) Fr.
ORANGE-GILLED CORT
Description: Cap 1.5-6 cm wide, initially convex but eventually uplifted at the margin, often with a low umbo, dry, covered with fine radial fibers, yellow to olive-yellow at first, gradually turning orange- to olive-brown. Gills are attached, close, pale yellow to olive-yellow, soon becoming orange, then rusty. Stalk 2.5-10 cm long, 3-10 mm thick, equal, yellow to yellow-brown, ringed with tawny fibers or scales below the partial veil. Partial veil a yellow or olive-yellow cortina, often disappearing. Flesh yellowish to olive-yellow. Odor radishy; taste bitter or like radish.

Spore Print: Rusty brown.

Occurrence: Scattered under birch or conifers. Spring and fall.

Edibility: Unknown.

Microscopic Features:
Spores 6-9.5 × 4-5 μm, elliptic, minutely roughened. Pale brown.

Comments: Dyers prize this species for its orange colors. *Cortinarius semisanguineus* appears similar but has blood red gills in youth. *Cortinarius hesleri* (search online) is orange all over. See also *Cortinarius luteus*.

Cortinarius collinitus complex (Pers.) Fr.
SLIMY-BANDED CORT
Description: Cap 3-10 cm wide, bell-shaped, eventually becoming uplifted with a depressed center, smooth or faintly lined at the margin under a thick slime coat that dries shiny. Cap color yellowish- to purplish-brown. Gills attached, close, pale lilac transitioning in age to rusty brown. Stalk 6-12 cm long, 5-15 mm thick, equal or narrowing toward the base, white to pale violet, thickly slimy, the slime often forming violet patches or rings around the stalk. Partial veil a white cortina, usually leaving a rusty ring zone. Flesh white, unchanging when exposed. Odor and taste not distinctive.
Spore Print: Rusty brown.
Occurrence: Scattered under hardwoods or mixed woods. Summer-fall.
Edibility: Unknown.
Microscopic Features:
Spores 10-15 × 6-8 µm, elliptic to almond-shaped, minutely roughened. Pale brown.
Comments: With age and drying of the thick slime jacket, the violet colors on the stalk fade to off-white.

Cortinarius corrugatus Peck
WRINKLED CORT
Description: Cap 3-10 cm wide, initially bell-shaped but becoming broadly convex, usually with a low umbo, texture sticky and radially wrinkled, some shade of yellowish-, orange-, or reddish-brown. Gills are attached, close, pale lilac gray at first, then rusty. Stalk 5-12 cm long, up to 2 cm thick, whitish to yellowish or pale brown, often scurfy at the apex, equal above a small bulb that is often ringed with slime. Partial veil a cortina leaving little or no trace on the stalk. Flesh white, staining yellowish when exposed. Odor and taste not distinctive.
Spore Print: Rusty brown.
Occurrence: Scattered under hardwoods, often oak or beech, or in mixed woods. Summer-fall.
Edibility: Unknown.
Microscopic Features:
Spores 10-14 × 7-9 µm, almond-shaped, warted. Pale brown.
Comments: In dry weather, dampen the cap to check for stickiness. The similar-appearing *Psathyrella rugocephala* grows from wood. *Cortinarius squamulosus* has a scaly, not wrinkly, cap.

Cortinarius cyanites Fr.

BLUSHING VIOLET CORT

Description: Cap 5-15 cm wide, initially convex, developing a depressed center, tacky at first, then dry, textured with small scales or flattened fibers, color a mix of violet and reddish-browns, with browns predominating at the center. Gills attached, close, retaining violet tones well into maturity. Stalk 9-15 cm long, up to 3.5 cm thick, expanding downward to a basal bulb, vertically streaked in shades of violet. Partial veil a cortina leaving little or no trace on the stalk. Flesh is a marbled variety of violet shades that slowly turn red or wine-colored following exposure. Odor not distinctive. Taste not distinctive to slightly bitter.

Spore Print: Rusty brown.

Occurrence: Scattered under hardwoods or in mixed woods. Summer-fall.

Edibility: Unknown.

Microscopic Features: Spores 9-11.5 × 5-6.5 µm, elliptic, warted. Pale brown.

Comments: The red-staining flesh distinguishes this from other violet or silver-violet corts and from the edible Blewit, *Lepista nuda*.

Cortinarias distans Peck

DISTANT-GILLED CORT

Description: Cap 2-7 cm wide, initially bell-shaped expanding to broadly convex, often with a pointed umbo, moist, texture roughened by tiny grains or scales, cinnamon to purplish-brown when moist, drying golden-brown, the margin often whitish in youth and splitting in age. Gills are attached, distant, tawny yellow, then dark rusty brown. Stalk 4-8 cm long, up to 1.5 cm thick, equal or enlarging downward, colored like the cap, paler at the apex, silky. Partial veil a white cortina, leaving a white ring zone on the stalk. Flesh white at first, turning yellowish or brownish. Odor and taste radishy or not distinctive.

Spore Print: Rusty brown.

Occurrence: Scattered under hardwoods. Spring-fall.

Edibility: Unknown.

Microscopic Features: Spores 6-8 × 5-6 µm, oval, roughened. Pale brown.

Comments: Sometimes appears early in the spring and then again in late summer. *Cortinarius torvus* (search online) is similar, but lilac-tinged and sweet smelling. *Neohygrocybe subovina* has a white spore print.

Cortinarius iodes Berk. & M. A. Curtis
SPOTTED CORT
Description: Cap 2-6 cm wide, bell-shaped becoming broadly convex, texture smooth, sticky or slimy in wet weather, dark lilac to purple with yellowish spots or streaks. Gills are attached, close, initially lilac, becoming dingy cinnamon at maturity. Stalk 4-7 cm long, 5-15 mm thick, equal or enlarging downward, sticky, whitish to pale violet, with a thin, fibrous ring zone. Partial veil a pale violet cortina. Flesh pale violet, unchanging when exposed. Odor and taste not distinctive.
Spore Print: Rusty brown.
Occurrence: Scattered under hardwoods. Summer-fall.
Edibility: Reportedly edible; not recommended.
Microscopic Features:
Spores 8-10 × 5-6.5 μm, elliptic, slightly roughened. Pale brown.
Comments: *Cortinarius iodeoides* (search online) looks identical but has smaller spores (7-8 × 4-5 μm) and bitter cap slime. *Cortinarius collinitus* complex is slimier than either and has a brown cap.

Cortinarius luteus Peck
Description: Cap 2-5 cm wide, conical at first, becoming broadly convex or flat with a low umbo, dry and covered with flattened fibers or tiny scales, dull yellow, darker centrally. Gills are attached, almost distant, pale yellow, tinging toward cinnamon at maturity. Stalk 5-10 cm long, to 2 cm thick, equal, with yellow fibrils over a white background. Partial veil a yellow cortina that leaves a thin ring on the stalk. Flesh yellow. Odor and taste not distinctive.
Spore Print: Rusty brown.
Occurrence: Scattered in mixed woods, on the ground or in moss. Summer-early fall.
Edibility: Unknown.
Microscopic Features:
Spores 6-8 × 6-7 μm, subglobose to broadly elliptic, roughened. Pale brown.
Comments: *Agaricus auricolor* never has yellow gills. *Armillaria mellea* grows in clumps and has a white spore print.

Cortinarius marylandensis (Ammirati)
Ammirati, Niskanen & Liimat.

Description: Cap 1-6 cm wide, bell-shaped
becoming broadly convex or flat with a
low umbo, dry, silky smooth to finely
hairy, orange-red to brownish-red.
Gills attached, fairly distant, brownish-
red before turning rusty. Stalk 2-7 cm
long, to 1.5 cm thick, equal, colored
like the cap, with a thin, fibrous ring
zone. Partial veil is a red cortina. Flesh
yellowish, or pink in the cap and
reddening toward the base. Odor and
taste radishy or not distinctive.

Spore Print: Rusty brown.

Occurrence: Scattered under hardwoods.
Late summer-fall.

Edibility: Unknown.

Microscopic Features:
Spores 7-9 × 4-5 µm, elliptic, slightly
roughened. Pale brown.

Comments: One of several dyer's corts
found in the Carolinas. This species
produces shades of red. The very similar
Cortinarius sanguineus (search online)
is associated with conifers; its cap has a
red (rather than a rose turning purplish)
reaction to KOH. The cap of *Cortinarius
cinnabarinus* (search online) doesn't
change color with KOH.

Cortinarius obliquus Peck
OBLIQUE-BULBED CORT

Description: Cap 3-8 cm wide, convex
to broadly convex, dry, pale silver-
violet tinging brown in age. Gills
attached, close, initially purple, turning rusty brown. Stalk 3-8 cm long,
6-12 mm thick at the apex, equal above,
terminating in an abrupt, flattened,
and often rimmed bulb that is set at
an angle to the stalk, whitish to pale
violet. Partial veil a white cortina. Flesh
whitish to pale violet, not changing
when exposed. Odor not distinctive.
Taste not distinctive or slightly hot.

Spore Print: Rusty brown.

Occurrence: Scattered under hardwoods or
in mixed woods. Summer-fall.

Edibility: Unknown.

Microscopic Features:
Spores 7-9.5 × 4.5-5.5 µm, elliptic,
slightly roughened. Pale brown.

Comments: The squat build and flattened,
cockeyed bulb are characteristic of this
species. Stalk details of other silver-
violet corts are different. *Lepista nuda*
has a different base and a pinker spore
print and lacks a cortina.

Cortinarius semisanguineus (Fr.) Gillet
RED-GILLED CORT

Description: Cap 1.5-7 cm wide, convex then flattening, often with a low umbo, dry, covered with fine radial fibers, yellowish- to cinnamon-brown, darker at the center. Gills are attached, crowded, blood red, turning rusty at maturity. Stalk 2-10 cm long, to 1.5 cm thick, equal, pale yellowish, reddening toward the base. Partial veil is a yellow cortina that usually leaves a rusty ring zone. Flesh white to yellowish. Odor and taste radishy or not distinctive.

Spore Print: Rusty brown.

Occurrence: Scattered on soil or in moss under conifers or mixed conifer-birch woods. Late summer-fall.

Edibility: Unknown.

Microscopic Features:
Spores 5-8 × 3-5 μm, elliptic, roughened. Pale brown.

Comments: This little dyer's cort produces sought-after red, wine red, burgundy, red-brown, and purple-black colors. The combination of brownish cap and red gills is distinctive. The gills of *Cortinarius cinnamomeus* are orange rather than red.

Cortinarius squamulosus Peck
BULBOUS SCALY CORT

Description: Cap 3-10 cm wide, convex then flattening, dry, covered with dark scales, reddish- to purplish-brown at first, then dark brown. Gills are attached, close, initially purple, then dark brown. Stalk 6-15 cm long, up to 2 cm thick at the apex, with a basal bulb to 6 cm wide, smooth or slightly scaly, colored like the cap, usually with a fibrous ring zone at midstalk. Partial veil a white cortina. Flesh whitish or tinged pink or gray. Odor "spicy." Taste not distinctive.

Spore Print: Rusty brown.

Occurrence: Scattered under hardwoods, often in low, wet areas. Late summer-fall.

Edibility: Unknown.

Microscopic Features:
Spores 6-8 × 5-7 μm, subglobose, roughened. Pale brown.

Comments: Other scaly corts in the Carolinas include *Cortinarius violaceus*, *C. bolaris*, and *C. pholideus* (search online). All lack the outsized basal bulb.

GILLED MUSHROOMS

173

Cortinarius violaceus (L.) Gray
VIOLET CORT
Description: Cap 4-12 cm wide, broadly convex, dry, densely hairy to scaly, deep purple, discoloring to dark brown in age. Gills are attached, fairly distant, dark violet, gradually turning rusty brown. Stalk 6-16 cm long, up to 2.5 cm thick, enlarging downward, dark violet to purple, covered with tiny matted fibers; a thin, fibrous ring zone is present. Partial veil a violet cortina. Flesh violet to violet-gray, not changing when exposed. Odor mildly fragrant or not distinctive. Taste not distinctive.
Spore Print: Rusty brown.
Occurrence: Scattered on the ground or in moss under hardwoods or conifers. Late summer-fall.
Edibility: Edible; not recommended.
Microscopic Features:
   Spores 12-17 × 8-10 µm, elliptic or almond-shaped, roughened or warted. Pale brown.
Comments: Some authors distinguish *Cortinarius violaceus* (hardwood-associated, with almond-shaped spores) from *C. hercynicus*, which fruits under conifers and has elliptical spores. Compare with *Cortinarius squamulosus* and *C. cyanites*.

Hebeloma crustuliniforme (Bull.) Quél.
POISON PIE
Description: Cap 3-11 cm wide, convex with an inrolled margin at first, then flattening, smooth, sticky, white to dirty yellow-brown, darkest at the center. Gills attached, crowded, whitish, turning gray-brown, typically dotted with liquid that dries as brown spots. Gill edges white and fringed. Stalk 3-13 cm long, to 2 cm thick, equal or with a small bulb, scurfy at the apex, smooth below, white to buff. Veil or ring zone absent. Flesh white. Odor and taste radishy.
Spore Print: Brown.
Occurrence: Scattered or in groups under hardwoods or conifers, or in grassy areas near shrubs. Summer-fall.
Edibility: Poisonous.
Microscopic Features:
   Spores 9-13 × 5-7.5 µm, elliptic, slightly roughened, dextrinoid. Pale brown.
Comments: This species lacks the hanging cone of tissue and conspicuous stalk scales of *Hebeloma sinapizans*. A conifer-dwelling cousin, *Hebeloma mesophaeum* (search online) often shows a ring zone or veil fragments at the cap margin and may be tinged pink or orange.

Hebeloma sinapizans (Paulet) Gillet
SCALY-STALKED HEBELOMA
Description: Cap 4-15 cm wide, convex
then flattening, smooth and sticky,
pinkish-tan to reddish-brown, margin
cottony at first. Gills attached, close,
pale becoming pale brown, sometimes
with drops of liquid. Gill edges white,
minutely fringed. Stalk 4-12 cm long,
to 3 cm thick, equal above a small bulb,
with a powdery apex and scales or
bands of scales below, whitish. Stalk
hollows, leaving an internal hanging
tooth of tissue at the apex. Veil or ring
zone absent. Flesh white. Odor and
taste radishy.
Spore Print: Pinkish-brown or brown.
Occurrence: Scattered under hardwoods
or conifers, or in grassy woodland
margins; may produce fairy rings. Late
summer-fall.
Edibility: Poisonous.
Microscopic Features:
Spores 10-14 × 6-8 μm, broadly elliptic,
slightly roughened, dextrinoid. Pale
brown.
Comments: Sticky brown members of
genus *Cortinarius* have a rusty spore
print and often display remnants of
a cortina or a ring zone. *Hebeloma
crustuliniforme* lacks the hanging tooth
and conspicuous stalk scales.

Inocybe calamistrata (Fr.) Gillet
GREEN-FOOT INOCYBE
Description: Cap 1-4 cm wide, convex,
dry, covered with pointed or recurved
scales, cap dark brown or reddish-
brown. Gills attached, close, white at
first, turning cinnamon-brown. Gill
edges remain whitish. Stalk 3-9 cm
long, 2-6 mm thick, equal, solid, scaly,
pale brown at the apex, darkening
below but blue-green at the base.
Partial veil a flimsy cortina that soon
vanishes. Flesh white, staining red in
the upper half and blue-green in the
base when exposed. Odor mildly fishy
or spermatic. Taste not distinctive.
Spore Print: Dull yellowish-brown.
Occurrence: Scattered under hardwoods.
Summer-fall.
Edibility: Poisonous.
Microscopic Features:
Spores 9.5-13.5 × 5-6.5 μm, elliptic,
smooth, inamyloid. Brown.
Comments: The only scaly-capped *Inocybe*
in the Carolinas to have a green base.
Despite the bluing reaction, this species
is apparently not hallucinogenic.
Mycological toxicologist Dr. Michael
Beug reports that it, like other *Inocybes*,
contains muscarine. Poisoning
symptoms include intense salivation,
tearing, urination, and diarrhea.

Inocybe lacera (Fr.) P. Kumm.
TORN FIBER HEAD
Description: Cap 1-4 cm wide, convex then flattening, often with an umbo, dry, brown, covered with radiating matted hairs or scales, the margin often ragged or torn. Gills attached, close, white at first, turning grayish-brown, the edges remaining pale. Stalk 3-6 cm long, 3-6 mm thick, equal, solid, with or without a covering of longitudinal fibers, pale at the apex, darkening to brown below. Partial veil a flimsy cortina leaving little or no evidence on the stalk or cap margin. Flesh white to pale tan. Odor and taste not distinctive.
Spore Print: Brown.
Occurrence: Scattered under hardwoods or conifers. Summer-fall.
Edibility: Poisonous.
Microscopic Features: Spores 12-17 × 4.5-6 μm, elliptic to subcylindric, smooth. Pale brown.
Comments: This is one of several species having the same macroscopic description. Microscopy is required for a more certain identification.

Inocybe rimosa (Bull.) P. Kumm.
STRAW-COLORED FIBER HEAD
Description: Cap 2-9 cm wide, bell-shaped then flattening but retaining a pointed umbo, dry, silky and shiny, covered with integral radiating fibers, straw-colored, darker centrally, the margin often upturned and torn. Gills attached, close, white to yellowish at first, turning gray then brown, with edges remaining white. Stalk 3-9 cm long, 3-12 mm thick, more or less equal, solid, often showing silky longitudinal or spiral markings, white to pale yellow. Partial veil not evident. Flesh white. Odor not distinctive or spermatic. Taste not distinctive.
Spore Print: Brown.
Occurrence: Scattered under hardwoods or conifers or in woodland mosses. Summer-fall.
Edibility: Poisonous.
Microscopic Features: Spores 9-15 × 5-8 μm, elliptic, smooth. Pale brown.
Comments: Also known as *Inocybe fastigiata*. One of several yellowish *Inocybes*; diagnostic certainty requires microscopy. *Inocephalus murrayi* and waxcaps such as the yellow form of *Humidicutis marginata* have yellow gills and different spore prints.

Inocybe sororia Kauffman
PUNGENT FIBER HEAD
Description: Cap 2-7.5 cm wide, conical, becoming convex but retaining a peaked umbo, dry, silky, covered with integral radiating fibers, creamy to yellowish-brown, darker centrally, the margin often upturned and torn. Gills attached, close or crowded, white in youth, aging to yellowish-brown, the edges remaining white. Stalk 2.5-10 cm long, 2-6 mm thick, equal or with a slight bulb, solid, silky, sometimes scurfy at the apex, whitish before darkening to yellowish-brown. Partial veil not evident. Flesh white. Odor strongly of raw corn on the cob. Taste not distinctive.
Spore Print: Brown.
Occurrence: Scattered under hardwoods or conifers. Summer-fall.
Edibility: Poisonous.
Microscopic Features:
    Spores 9-17 × 5-8 µm, elliptic, smooth. Pale brown.
Comments: The distinctive odor sets this species apart from other *Inocybes* with smooth caps. *Panaeolina foenisecii* and *P. papilionaceus* have purple-brown to black spore prints.

Paxillus involutus (Batsch) Fr.
POISON PAX
Description: Cap 4-15 cm wide, convex to broadly convex or centrally depressed, the margin inrolled, smooth or slightly hairy, sticky when moist, dull brown, possibly tinged with yellow, red or olive tones. Gills decurrent, crowded, forking, some shade of tan, bruising reddish-brown and separable as a layer from the cap. Stalk 2-10 cm long, up to 2 cm thick, equal or enlarging downward, solid, usually central, smooth, yellowish-brown. No partial veil. Flesh tan, staining reddish. Odor and taste not distinctive.
Spore Print: Pale yellowish-brown to dark brown.
Occurrence: Scattered on the ground in a variety of woodland or city settings with trees. Summer-fall.
Edibility: Poisonous.
Microscopic Features:
    Spores 7-9 × 4-6 µm, elliptic, smooth. Pale brown.
Comments: The unusual combination of gill features separates this dangerous look-alike from the edible *Phylloporus leucomycelinus* and *Clitopilus prunulus*.

DARK-SPORED SPECIES WITH LIQUEFYING GILLS

An inky slurry of dissolving gills or gill and cap tissue may not be the most aesthetic way to launch the next generation, but it works for inkcap mushrooms. All but one species in the Carolinas do it. The exception, *Coprinellus disseminatus*, is also described here.

You might think that black, dissolving gills would be an indicator of close kinship. Until 1994 most professional mycologists agreed and lumped these species within genus *Coprinus*. But work partly conducted by Rytas Vilgalys and others at Duke University has dissolved that concept. *Coprinus comatus*, commonly known as Shaggy Mane, is genetically close to the brown-spored genus *Agaricus*, edible puffballs, and white-spored *Macrolepiota procera*. The remainder of the inkcaps are cousins to the dark-spored mushrooms of genus *Psathyrella*. It's easy to be annoyed by the relentless drizzle of scientific name changes in mushroom world, but the underlying research results can be downright fascinating.

The Shaggy Mane is a prized edible when collected and cooked before the cap begins to dissolve. After that, taste deteriorates as rapidly as the cap. We do not recommend eating other members of this group. Some contain compounds that cause physical reactions similar to the anti-drinking medication disulfiram when combined with alcohol.

Coprinellus disseminatus (Pers.) J. E. Lange
FAIRY INKCAP
Description: Cap 6-20 mm wide at
maturity, egg-shaped then bell-
shaped or convex, dry, finely hairy
or with shiny granules at first, later
smooth with deep radial grooves and
a scalloped margin; color ranges from
almost white with a yellowish-brown
center to gray-brown with a brown
center. Gills are free or attached, nearly
distant, pale in youth, then black but
not dissolving. Stalk 13-40 mm long,
1-2 mm thick, nearly equal, hollow,
white or gray, smooth; the base is
downy or shows stiff white hairs.
Partial veil absent. Flesh insubstantial.
Odor and taste not distinctive.
Spore Print: Black.
Occurrence: Clustered on dead wood or
around the base of stumps. Spring-fall.
Edibility: Edible, but insubstantial.
Microscopic Features:
Spores 7-10 × 4-5 μm, elliptical,
smooth, with an apical pore. Blackish.
Comments: Other inkcaps have dissolving
gills. *Mycena inclinata* and *Gymnopus
dichrous* have pale gills and white spore
prints.

Coprinellus micaceus
(Bull.) Vilgalys, Hopple & Jacq. Johnson
MICA CAP
Description: Cap 2-6 cm wide, egg-shaped
then bell-shaped or convex, dry,
sprinkled with shiny white granules at
first but later smooth, radially grooved,
tawny to honey-colored centrally, paler
toward the margins, which soon tatter
and begin to dissolve. Gills attached or
free, crowded, pale in youth, then black
and partially dissolving. Stalk 2-8 cm
long, 2-6 mm thick, equal, smooth or
finely granular, hollow, white. Partial
veil absent. Flesh thin and white. Odor
and taste not distinctive.
Spore Print: Black.
Occurrence: Clustered on dead wood,
which may be buried. Spring-fall.
Edibility: Edible.
Microscopic Features:
Spores 7-11 × 4-7 μm, elliptical, smooth,
with an apical pore. Blackish.
Comments: The sparkly flakes on young
Mica Caps are a fun find. *Coprinopsis
atramentaria* is larger and has a gray to
gray-brown cap.

GILLED MUSHROOMS

Coprinopsis atramentaria
(Bull.) Redhead, Vilgalys & Moncalvo
COMMON INKCAP, ALCOHOL INKCAP, TIPPLER'S BANE
Description: Cap 4-10 cm wide at maturity, initially egg-shaped and later convex, dry, smooth or finely scaly over the center of the cap, gray to brownish-gray, often weakly radially lined, cap margin typically curls or tatters as the gills dissolve. Gills are free, crowded, white before turning black and auto-digesting to black goo. Stalk 4-15 cm long, 6-20 mm thick, equal, smooth or finely hairy, hollow, white. Partial veil remnants may remain as a white ring at the stalk base. Flesh grayish-white. Odor and taste not distinctive.
Spore Print: Black.
Occurrence: In clusters on or around dead wood. Spring-fall.
Edibility: Edible, with caution.
Microscopic Features:
Spores 8-12 × 4.5-6 μm, elliptical, smooth, with an apical pore. Blackish.
Comments: Eating this species within two days before or after ingesting alcohol may cause symptoms including flushed skin, rapid breathing, severe headache, and vomiting. Yum!

Coprinopsis variegata
(Peck) Redhead, Vilgalys & Moncalvo
SCALY INKCAP
Description: Cap 4-7.5 cm wide at maturity, initially egg-shaped and later bell-shaped, dry, covered with white to dirty yellow scales; underneath them the cap is gray to brownish-gray; the usually unlined cap margin curls and tatters as the gills dissolve. Gills are free and crowded, white before blackening and dissolving in an inky mess. Stalk 4-12 cm long, 5-10 mm thick, equal, finely wooly, hollow, white. Partial veil remnants may remain as white bits at the base of the stalk. Flesh tan. Odor strong and unpleasant. Taste unpleasant or not distinctive.
Spore Print: Black.
Occurrence: In clusters on or around decaying hardwood. Summer-fall.
Edibility: Edible, with caution.
Microscopic Features:
Spores 7.5-10 × 4-5.5 μm, elliptical, smooth, with an apical pore. Blackish.
Comments: May cause poisoning symptoms similar to the Alcohol Inkcap. The smaller *Coprinopsis lagopus* (search online) is hairy rather than scaly.

Coprinus comatus (O. F. Müll.) Pers.
SHAGGY MANE
Description: Cap 3-15 cm wide (at maximum expansion), cylindrical and later flaring as the cap dissolves, dry, white with a brownish center, covered with shaggy white or pale reddish-brown scales. Gills are attached, becoming free, crowded, white, then pink, then blackening and dissolving. Stalk 5-30 cm long, up to 2.5 cm thick, enlarging downward, smooth or silky, hollow, white. Partial veil remains as a ring around the stalk. Flesh white. Odor and taste not distinctive.

Spore Print: Black.

Occurrence: Solitary or in groups in hard-packed dirt, in lawns, or on wood chips. Spring-fall.

Edibility: Choice when young.

Microscopic Features:
Spores 10-14 × 6-8.5 μm, elliptical, smooth, with an apical pore. Purplish-brown.

Comments: This striking species often fruits in poor soil. Think twice before consuming mushrooms collected in areas where pesticides or other chemicals are applied. Buttons of *Leucoagaricus americanus*, and the poisonous *Chlorophyllum molybdites*, could be confused with Shaggy Mane.

Parasola plicatilis (Curtis) Redhead, Vilgalys & Hopple
PLEATED INKCAP
Description: Cap 1-3.5 cm wide at maturity, egg-shaped before flattening or broadly inverting in age, dry, smooth and radially grooved, at first yellow-orange to orange-brown centrally and pale toward the margins, later gray or translucent. Gills are free, close or distant, pale in youth, then black and dissolving. Stalk 3.5-10 cm long, up to 3 mm thick, hollow, white, smooth and equal above a small bulb. Partial veil absent. Flesh insubstantial. Odor and taste not distinctive.

Spore Print: Black.

Occurrence: Scattered in grassy areas following rains. Spring-fall.

Edibility: Allegedly edible.

Microscopic Features:
Spores 10-15 × 8-10 μm, angular-ovoid, smooth, with an eccentric pore. Grayish-black.

Comments: This species and its browner cousin *Parasola auricoma* (search online) can be beautiful curiosities in their old age, resembling dark-veined glass flowers. Caps of *Parasola auricoma* are finely hairy under magnification, and the spores have an apical pore.

DARK-SPORED SPECIES WITH NONLIQUEFYING GILLS

No group of gilled species better makes the case for spore prints than dark-spored mushrooms. None have dark gills in youth; some remain deceptively colored even at maturity. Take a close look at gill details. The flat surfaces where spores are produced, known as **gill faces**, often become mottled. The free **edges** might characteristically remain light in color, be fringed or ragged, or display tiny liquid droplets. A hand lens is helpful in assessing these minute but critical features.

Caps of some species have a central bump or **umbo**. Partial veils, when present, may be fleeting. Some leave evidence on the cap margin, others on the stalk as a skirt or ring zone accentuated by a dusting of dark spores. The base of the stalk might connect to the mycelium below by rootlike threads called **rhizomorphs**.

Microscopy is sometimes needed to distinguish between look-alikes. In *Chroogomphus*, a definite species determination may hinge on the wall thickness of **cystidia**. Cystidia are the sterile cells that crowd around and prop up the spore-producing basidial cells on the gill faces.

Two members of the dark-spored group, the Wine Cap, *Stropharia rugosoannulata*, and the Brick Cap, *Hypholoma lateritium*, are cultivated for food. The latter can be common in the autumn woods, but take care to distinguish it from poisonous yellow-capped cousins and the Deadly Galerina. Multiple species might fruit on

Figure 14. Mottled gills

the same log at the same time. The Carolina low country lies within the northern range of the Magic Mushroom, *Psilocybe cubensis*. Possession of it is considered a felony.

Odor can be important in distinguishing many species of gilled mushrooms. Although many of the odors are easy to describe and recognize, "**farinaceous**" is especially difficult. Farinaceous is an odor variously compared to sliced watermelon rind, cucumber, meal, bread dough, or farina (think Cream of Wheat).

If your mushroom has a blackish- or purplish-brown spore print and you don't find it here, also consult the brown-spored section. If your mushroom is small, growing in clusters at the base of a dead tree or stump, and has a conical, white to brownish-gray cap, consider *Coprinellus disseminatus*.

Chroogomphus vinicolor (Peck) O. K. Mill.
WINE-CAP CHROOGOMPHUS
Description: Cap 2-10 cm wide, convex,
  sometimes with a small umbo,
  smooth, sticky when moist, in youth
  may be yellowish- or reddish-brown,
  usually purplish-red at maturity.
  Gills decurrent, distant, pale yellow-
  orange at first, darkening toward
  black. Stalk 3-15 cm long, up to 2 cm
  thick, narrowing downward, dry, pale
  yellowish to orangish, coloring like
  the cap in age. Partial veil fibrous, pale
  yellow, sometimes leaving a thin ring
  zone of fibers. Flesh pale orange. Odor
  and taste not distinctive.
Spore Print: Smoky-gray to black.
Occurrence: Scattered or in groups under
  conifers and pines. Late summer-fall.
Edibility: Edible.
Microscopic Features:
  Spores 17-23 × 4.5-7.5 µm, elliptic to
  spindle-shaped, smooth. Pale gray-
  brown; cystidial walls up to 7.5 µm thick
  at the midportion.
Comments: The thick-walled cystidia
  separate this species from wine-colored
  specimens of *Chroogomphus ochraceus*
  and *C. jamaicensis*. Information on both
  species is available online.

Hypholoma fasciculare (Huds.) P. Kumm.
SULPHUR TUFT
Description: Cap 2-8 cm wide, convex,
  becoming broadly convex to flat,
  occasionally with a low umbo, smooth,
  moist or dry, sulfur yellow to orangish-
  or greenish-yellow, darkest centrally;
  the margin may be hung with veil
  fragments. Gills attached, close, yellow
  to greenish-yellow, tinged purple in age.
  Stalk 5-12 cm long, up to 1 cm thick,
  equal or nearly so, pale and smooth at
  the apex, shading to rusty brown below,
  may show flattened hairs below the
  ring zone. Partial veil a whitish cortina,
  leaving a thin ring on the stalk. Flesh
  thin, yellow, bruises dirty brown. Odor
  not distinctive. Taste bitter.
Spore Print: Dark purplish-brown.
Occurrence: Clustered on logs or buried
  wood. Late spring-fall.
Edibility: Poisonous.
Microscopic Features:
  Spores 6.5-8 × 3.5-4 µm, elliptic,
  smooth, apical pore present. Pale
  purplish-brown.
Comments: Formerly known as
  Naematoloma fasciculare. Some authors
  distinguish a smaller but presumably
  still poisonous species, *Hypholoma
  subviride* (search online).

GILLED MUSHROOMS

183

Hypholoma lateritium (Schaeff.) P. Kumm.
BRICK CAP
Description: Cap 2-10 cm wide, convex, becoming broadly convex to flat, smooth with a few yellowish hairs, moist or dry, brick red centrally, paler at the margin. Gills attached, close, pale yellow to greenish-yellow at first, later tinged purple. Stalk 5-12 cm long, to 1.5 cm thick, equal, pale and smooth at the apex, dull brown and covered with reddish-brown fibers below the ring. Partial veil a whitish cortina, leaving a thin ring. Flesh thick, dull yellow, not staining. Odor not distinctive. Taste not distinctive or bitter.
Spore Print: Dark purplish-brown.
Occurrence: Clustered on deciduous logs. Summer-fall.
Edibility: Edible.
Microscopic Features:
Spores 6-7 × 3.5-4.5 µm, elliptic, smooth, apical pore present. Pale brown.
Comments: Formerly known as *Hypholoma sublateritium*. The Japanese name for this sometimes cultivated species is Kuritake. The edible *Hypholoma capnoides* (search online) grows on conifer wood. Beware confusion with the deadly *Galerina marginata*.

Lacrymaria lacrymabunda (Bull.) Pat.
WEEPING WIDOW,
VELVETY PSATHYRELLA
Description: Cap 2-12 cm wide, convex to broadly convex or flattish, sometimes with a small umbo, dry, covered with hairs that may aggregate into small scales or disappear in age, yellowish- to orangish- to reddish-brown, darkest centrally, the margin often hung with blackening veil fragments. Gills attached, close, initially pale, then mottled dark brown with a white edge, possibly beaded with tiny drops of liquid. Stalk 3-15 cm long, to 1.5 cm thick, equal, pale and smooth at the apex, yellowish-brown and covered with orange-brown fibers or scales below the ring. Partial veil fibrous and cottony, leaving a thin ring. Flesh yellowish-brown, not staining when bruised. Odor and taste not distinctive.
Spore Print: Blackish-brown.
Occurrence: Scattered in grassy areas or woody debris where hardwoods recently grew. Summer-fall.
Edibility: Edible.
Microscopic Features:
Spores 8-12 × 5-8 µm, elliptic, warted, with a protruding apical pore. Pale brown.
Comments: Also known as *Psathyrella velutina* and *Lacrymaria velutina*.

Panaeolina foenisecii (Pers.) Maire
LAWNMOWER'S MUSHROOM
Description: Cap 0.5-3 cm wide, bell-
shaped then convex, dry, smooth,
reddish- or grayish-brown, fading
to grayish-tan or showing bands of
grayish-tan as the cap dries, the fresh
margin slightly lined. Gills attached,
close, brown, darkening with age; the
gill faces may be mottled with paler
edges. Stalk 2.5-10 cm long, to 3 mm
thick, equal, smooth, white to pinkish-
brown. Partial veil absent. Flesh pale
brown, not staining when bruised. Odor
and taste not distinctive.
Spore Print: Dark brown or purplish-
brown.
Occurrence: Scattered in grassy areas
throughout the mowing season.
Edibility: May have slight hallucinogenic
properties.
Microscopic Features:
Spores 11-18 × 6-9 μm, elliptic,
roughened, apical pore present. Pale
purplish-brown.
Comments: Also known as *Panaeolus
foenisecii*. The hallucinogenic potential
of this species was apparently overrated
in older field guides. Compare with
Conocybe apala and *Agrocybe pediades*,
both of which have brown spore prints.

Panaeolus solidipes (Peck) Sacc.
SOLID-STEMMED PANAEOLUS
Description: Cap 4-10 cm wide,
hemispheric to broadly bell-shaped,
moist, smooth or wrinkled, the surface
often becoming scaly with age, white
to buff or dingy yellow. Gills attached,
close; the faces are pale at first and
mottled gray to black at maturity; the
edges remain pale. Stalks are 4-20
cm long, up to 1.5 cm thick, equal or
enlarging downward, smooth or with
spiraling grooves, colored like the cap or
dusty gray from spores, stalk apex often
beaded with liquid. Partial veil absent.
Flesh whitish, not staining when
bruised. Odor and taste not distinctive.
Spore Print: Black.
Occurrence: Scattered or in groups on
manure or rich compost. Late spring-
fall.
Edibility: Edible.
Microscopic Features:
Spores 14-22 × 9-14 μm, elliptic,
smooth. Dark brown.
Comments: Large for a *Panaeolus* species.
Panaeolus semiovatus (search online) is
also large and pale and grows on horse
dung. It has a partial veil and leaves a
fleeting ring on the stalk.

Psathyrella candolleana (Fr.) Maire
COMMON PSATHYRELLA
Description: Cap 3-11 cm wide, broadly
conical in youth, then flattening, with
or without a low umbo, dry, smooth or
slightly wrinkled, honey-colored but
fading to pale tan or white. The cap
margin is slightly lined and may display
veil fragments. Gills attached, close or
crowded, initially white, darkening to
gray-brown; the minutely scalloped
edges remain pale. Stalks are 4-13 cm
long, up to 1 cm thick, equal, hollow,
brittle, smooth or covered by tiny fibrils,
white. The partial veil is membranous
and thin, leaving a ring that soon
disappears. Flesh thin, pale yellow to
white. Odor and taste not distinctive.
Spore Print: Purplish-brown.
Occurrence: Scattered on the ground
around decaying hardwood or on lawns.
Late spring–summer.
Edibility: Edible.
Microscopic Features:
Spores 7-10 × 4-5 µm, elliptic, smooth,
with an apical pore. Pale brown.
Comments: *Agrocybe molesta* (search
online) is similar but has a tougher,
solid stalk and brown spores measuring
10-14 × 6.5-8 µm.

Psathyrella pseudovernalis A. H. Sm.
Description: Cap 2-4.5 cm wide,
broadly conical to convex in youth,
expanding toward flat, with or without
a low umbo, dry, smooth or slightly
wrinkled, a shade of rich brown but
hygrophanous, fading to buff as the
cap dries, the young margin hung
with sparse threads of veil material.
Gills attached, close, pale, darkening
to brown, edges may develop pinkish
tinges in age. Stalk 4-8 cm long, to
3 mm thick, equal, smooth, white,
hollow and fragile. Partial veil a thin,
white cortina, leaving little or no
evidence on the stalk. Flesh white.
Odor and taste not distinctive.
Spore Print: Blackish-brown.
Occurrence: In groups under hardwoods
or on grassy woodland verges. Early
spring.
Edibility: Unknown.
Microscopic Features:
Spores 7-10 × 4-5.5 µm, ovate to elliptic,
smooth, apical pore present. Brown.
Comments: The appearance is close to
Panaeolina foenisecii, which appears
in grass later in the season. *Gymnopus
dryophilus* has white spores.

Psathyrella rugocephala
(G. F. Atk.) A. H. Sm.
WRINKLED-CAP PSATHYRELLA
Description: Cap 3-10 cm wide, convex
then flattening, with or without a
low umbo, dry, radially wrinkled,
dark reddish-brown or brown before
fading toward tan. The cap margin is
often hung with veil fragments. Gills
attached, close or crowded, white in
youth, becoming rusty or purplish-
brown; the edges are fringed and may
remain white. Stalk 4-10 cm long, up
to 1.5 cm thick, enlarging downward,
hollow, smooth or silky, white but
darkening in age, the base fuzzy with
white mycelium. The partial veil is
membranous but fails to leave a ring.
Flesh watery brown. Odor and taste not
distinctive.
Spore Print: Purplish-brown.
Occurrence: Scattered on decaying
hardwood. Summer-early fall.
Edibility: Unknown.
Microscopic Features:
Spores 9-11 × 6-8 μm, elliptical, finely
warted, with a prominent apical pore.
Pale brown.
Comments: This species is separated from
Psathyrella delineata (search online)
by the latter's smaller, smooth spores
(6.5-9 × 4.5-5.5 μm).

Psilocybe cubensis (Earle) Singer
MAGIC MUSHROOM, GOLD CAPS
Description: Cap 1.5-9 cm wide, conical at
first, convex with an umbo at maturity,
sticky when moist, smooth, white to
cream-colored with a darker yellowish-
brown center, bruising blue with age
or injury. The cap margin is often
hung with white fragments of partial
veil. Gills attached, close or crowded,
gray then purplish-black; the edges
remain white. Stalk 4-15 cm long, up
to 14 mm thick, enlarging downward,
smooth or slightly grooved at the apex,
white, bluing if bruised. Partial veil
membranous, white, leaving a ring that
blackens from falling spores. Odor and
taste farinaceous.
Spore Print: Purplish-brown.
Occurrence: Scattered or in groups on cow
manure or in manure-enriched soil.
Year-round.
Edibility: Hallucinogenic.
Microscopic Features:
Spores 11-17 × 7-12 μm, elliptical,
smooth. Purplish-brown.
Comments: This illegally cultivated
species occurs naturally in subtropical
environments, including the low
country. *Psilocybe coprophila* (search
online) is smaller, does not stain blue,
and lacks psychoactivity.

Stropharia hardii G. F. Atk.

HARD'S STROPHARIA

Description: Cap 2.5-10 cm wide, convex then flattening, slightly sticky when moist, smooth when young, developing small matted fibers or scales near the margin at maturity, dirty yellow to yellowish-brown, darkest centrally. Gills attached, close, pale initially, later gray, finally purplish-brown. Stalk 4-12 cm long, up to 2 cm thick, equal, sticky in youth, later dry, smooth to slightly scaly, whitish, the base attached to a few white rhizomorphs. Partial veil membranous, white, leaving a ring on the stalk. Flesh whitish. Odor farinaceous or not distinctive. Taste not distinctive.

Spore Print: Blackish-brown.

Occurrence: Scattered or in groups under hardwoods or on hardwood debris. Summer-fall.

Edibility: Unknown.

Microscopic Features: Spores 6-9 × 3-5 μm, elliptic, smooth, apical pore present. Pale purplish-brown.

Comments: The conifer equivalent of this species, *Stropharia hornemannii* (search online) has a shaggy stalk below the partial veil. The edible *Cortinarius caperatus* has a rusty spore print and white powder on the cap.

Stropharia rugosoannulata Farl. ex Murrill

WINE CAP, KING STROPHARIA

Description: Cap 4-15 (or more) cm wide, hemispheric then broadly convex with a small umbo, sticky initially, later dry, smooth, reddish-brown or wine red, fading markedly in age. Margin often hung with veil fragments. Gills attached, crowded, white, becoming purplish-black. Stalk 7-20 cm long, to 3 cm thick, equal or with a small bulb, solid, smooth or finely hairy, white, the base displaying white mycelium and rhizomorphs. The partial veil is a thick white skirt with a grooved upper surface and cogwheeling splits underneath. Flesh white. Odor and taste not distinctive.

Spore Print: Purplish-brown to black.

Occurrence: Scattered, in groups or clusters on wood chips, mulch, or straw, in gardens or on lawns. Summer-fall.

Edibility: Choice, especially when young.

Microscopic Features: Spores 10-14 × 7-9 μm, elliptic, smooth. Pale purplish-brown.

Comments: This cultivated edible is a helpful companion for garden vegetables and, according to Tradd Cotter, a mycoremediator for coliform bacteria in chicken houses.

These more or less vase-shaped mush-rooms are typically, but not always, found on the ground in wooded areas. Most are brightly colored. A few are **hygrophanous**, fading markedly as the cap dries. The undersurfaces of caps can be nearly smooth or feature gill-like ridges that run down the stalk (**decurrent**), perhaps forking, fusing, or interconnecting via wrinkles known as **crossveins**. These false gills are usually thicker, shorter, and more triangular in cross section than true gills. True gills have parallel sides (faces).

Recent work on the genus *Cantharellus* by multiple research groups has altered classical species concepts. For years we've known that *Cantharellus cibarius* is a European species, genetically distinct from American golden chanterelles. Until late in 2016 we did not know that the Peach Chanterelle shown in field guides and online resources was a misidentification caused by the mistaken submission of a genetic sequence to GenBank, the repository for genomic information. The descriptions used here for *Cantharellus* species rely heavily on the work of Bart Buyck and coauthors. While several details remain to be ironed out, the general outline of *Cantharellus* in the Southeast now appears to be on firm ground. Unfortunately, the same can't always be said for how these species present in the field. A few are highly variable and might merit subdivision into new species. Others can be almost indistinguishable without access to a molecular research lab.

Three taxonomic changes are of particular note. First, the American species corresponding most closely to the European *Cantharellus cibarius* is *C. tenuithrix*, which may or may not include genetically similar forms currently labeled *C. phasmatis*, *C. deceptivus*, and *C. flavus*. Second, we now have multiple species of smooth chanterelle; *Cantharellus lateritius* is joined by *C. flavolateritius* and *C. velutinus*. The latter is variable in appearance, with a pink form previously misidentified as *C. persicinus*. (Another smooth chanterelle, a conjoined type called *Cantharellus confluens*, didn't sur-vive the reshuffle as a separate species.) Third, the true *Cantharellus persicinus* is a little guy, here given the common name of Little Peach Chanterelle.

We are happy to report that name changes have not altered the tastiness of the mushrooms in question. Those that were previously edible remain so.

Cantharellus appalachiensis R. H. Petersen
APPALACHIAN CHANTERELLE
Description: Cap 1-5 cm wide, convex with
a depressed center and an elevated,
wavy, or even crimped margin at
maturity. The upper surface is covered
with tiny matted fibers when young,
becoming smooth when mature, pale
to dark yellowish-brown, darkest over
the center, dingy yellow to yellowish-
orange in age. Lower surface pale
yellow to pale orange-yellow, with
decurrent, forked, rounded gill-like
ridges, often crossveined. Stalk 1.5-6 cm
long, up to 1.3 cm wide, nearly equal or
tapered downward, becoming hollow
in age, nearly smooth, pale yellowish-
brown, often with yellowish-orange
tones. Flesh thin, brittle or soft, pale
yellowish-brown to buff. Odor and taste
not distinctive.
Spore Print: Yellowish-salmon.
Occurrence: Scattered, in groups or
clusters in mixed woods or hardwoods.
Summer-fall.
Edibility: Unknown.
Microscopic Features:
Spores 6-10 × 4-6 μm, elliptic to oblong,
smooth. Hyaline.
Comments: The false gills of the brown-
capped *Craterellus tubaeformis* (search
online) are typically browner, grayer, or
lilac-tinged.

Cantharellus cinnabarinus
(Schwein.) Schwein.
**CINNABAR CHANTERELLE,
CINNABAR-RED CHANTERELLE**
Description: Cap 1-4.5 cm wide, convex
at first, then typically funnel-shaped,
the margin incurved at first, becoming
uplifted and wavy. Upper surface nearly
smooth, cinnabar red to reddish-orange,
fading to pale pinkish-orange in age.
Lower surface similarly colored with
decurrent, rounded gill-like ridges
and crossveins. Stalk 2-5 cm long,
3-10 mm thick, nearly equal or tapered
downward, often curved, cinnabar
red to reddish-orange or pale pinkish-
orange. Flesh thin, whitish or tinged
reddish-orange. Odor not distinctive.
Taste slightly peppery or not distinctive.
Spore Print: Pinkish-cream.
Occurrence: Scattered or in groups on soil
or among mosses. Late spring-fall.
Edibility: Edible.
Microscopic Features:
Spores 6-11 × 4-6 μm, elliptic to oblong,
smooth. Hyaline.
Comments: Compare with the yellower
Cantharellus persicinus. Two recently
described small orange- or cinnabar-
colored species, *Cantharellus texensis*
(search online) and *C. corallinus* (search
online), differ from *C. cinnabarinus* only
microscopically and genetically. Either
might occur in the Carolinas.

CHANTERELLES AND SIMILAR FUNGI

Cantharellus lateritius (Berk.) Singer
SMOOTH CHANTERELLE
Description: Cap 1.5-12 cm wide, convex
at first, then uplifted or funnel-shaped,
sometimes showing a low umbo.
The thin and initially inrolled margin
becomes wavy or lobed. Upper surface
dry, smooth to minutely fuzzy, yellow-
orange to yellow. Lower surface colored
the same or paler, nearly smooth or
with decurrent, shallow wrinkles or
gill-like ridges and crossveins. Stalk 1.5-
8 cm long, up to 2.5 cm thick, tapered
downward, smooth, solid, pale yellow
to orange-yellow. Flesh white. Odor
fragrant or not distinctive. Taste not
distinctive.
Spore Print: Pale pinkish-yellow.
Occurrence: Scattered, in groups, or in
conjoined clusters under hardwoods,
especially oaks. Late spring-fall.
Edibility: Choice.
Microscopic Features:
Spores 7.5-12 × 4.5-6.5 µm, elliptic,
smooth. Hyaline.
Comments: The undersurface of
Cantharellus tenuithrix has pronounced
gill-like ridges. *Cantharellus flavolateritius* (search online) and yellow
forms of *C. velutinus* differ genetically
but may be hard to distinguish in the
field. Both species are edible.

Cantharellus persicinus R. H. Peterson
LITTLE PEACH CHANTERELLE
Description: Cap up to 30 mm or, rarely,
45 mm wide, convex or irregularly
folded, perhaps slightly depressed at
maturity. Upper surface dry, smooth,
some shade of pale yellow or orange,
often with white powder at the cap
margin, hygrophanous. Lower surface
pink becoming a lavender-tinged
orange, with decurrent forking and
occasionally fusing gill-like ridges that
lack prominent crossveins. Stalk 33-45
mm long and up to 4 mm wide, nearly
equal or tapering downward, solid,
colored like the upper cap surface, often
whitened at the base. Flesh white when
fresh, yellowing when dry. Odor not
distinctive.
Spore Print: Pale yellow.
Occurrence: Single or scattered under oak
or other hardwoods. Summer.
Edibility: Unknown.
Microscopic Features:
Spores 9.5-11 × 6-7 µm, elliptic, smooth.
Comments: A misidentified gene sequence
caused this species to be confused with
Cantharellus velutinus (pink form).
Another small chanterelle, *Cantharellus
minor* (search online), has yellow gill-
like ridges.

CHANTERELLES AND SIMILAR FUNGI

Cantharellus tenuithrix complex
Buyck & V. Hofstetter
**CHANTERELLE,
GOLDEN CHANTERELLE**

Description: Cap typically 4-7 cm wide, inrolled at first, often lobed or wavy and uplifted in age. Upper surface dry, egg yellow to bright orange. Lower surface similarly colored with decurrent, gill-like ridges lacking prominent cross-veins. Stalk 18-26 mm long, 7-10 mm thick, nearly equal, whitish to pale yellow. Flesh white, slowly staining rusty orange. Odor like apricots. Taste not distinctive.

Spore Print: Pale cream.

Occurrence: Solitary, scattered, or in groups in or near woods. Late spring-fall.

Edibility: Choice.

Microscopic Features:
Spores 7-8.5 × 3.5-4.5 μm, elliptic or peanut-shaped, smooth.

Comments: Formerly *Cantharellus cibarius*. Specimens with whitish gill-like ridges in youth may represent *Cantharellus phasmatis* (see photo on p. 20) or *C. deceptivus* (search online). The slender and smaller *Cantharellus septentrionalis*, aka *C. altipes* (search online), has a stalk length approximating cap diameter (up to 55 mm). *Cantharellus lateritius* has lower gill folds. The poisonous *Omphalotus illudens* has true gills with parallel sides.

Cantharellus velutinus
Buyck & V. Hofstetter
PEACH CHANTERELLE

Description: Cap to 8 cm wide, inrolled at first, becoming uplifted or funnel-shaped, the margin thin and often wavy or lobed. Upper surface moist or dry, minutely fuzzy to scaly, peach- to pinkish-orange, the fuzz whitening when dry. Lower surface pale pinkish-orange with decurrent, rounded gill-like ridges and crossveins. Stalk to 8 cm long and 1.5 cm thick, may taper downward, solid, colored like the cap, base white, bruising dirty brown. Flesh generally whitish, sometimes orange-yellow in the cap. Odor faintly fruity or not distinctive. Taste not distinctive.

Spore Print: Whitish, turning pale yellow when dry.

Occurrence: Scattered under mixed or deciduous woods with oak. Summer-fall.

Edibility: Edible.

Microscopic Features:
Spores 7-8.5 × 4-5 μm, ellipsoid, smooth. Hyaline.

Comments: Previously misidentified as *Cantharellus persicinus*. Highly variable in color, we have described the pink form of *Cantharellus velutinus*. Yellow forms resemble *Cantharellus lateritius* or *C. tenuithrix*. *Cantharellus cinnabarinus* is smaller and brighter reddish-orange.

Craterellus fallax A. H. Sm.
BLACK TRUMPET
Description: Cap 1-8 cm wide, deeply
funnel-shaped. Margin inrolled at first,
becoming uplifted and wavy or lobed.
Upper surface minutely scaly or fibrous,
grayish- to dark brown or blackish.
Lower surface similarly colored or paler,
often with orange tints and bruising
blackish, smooth or showing shallow,
decurrent veinlike ridges. The stalk is
a tubular extension of the cap, hollow
almost to the base, dark brown to
blackish. Flesh thin, fibrous or brittle,
colored like the cap. Odor fragrant or
not distinctive. Taste not distinctive.
Spore Print: Pale pinkish-orange.
Occurrence: Scattered, in groups or
clusters, often in moss banks under
hardwoods or mixed woods. Late
spring-fall.
Edibility: Choice.
Microscopic Features:
Spores 11-14 × 7-9 µm, broadly elliptic,
smooth. Hyaline.
Comments: Look-alikes with prominent
veinlike ridges include the sickly sweet
Craterellus foetidus (search online) and
Craterellus cinereus (see photo on p. 20),
which is odorless and densely clumped.

Craterellus ignicolor (R. H. Petersen)
Dahlman, Danell & Spatafora
FLAME-COLORED CHANTERELLE
Description: Cap 1-8 cm wide, convex
with a central depression that usually
perforates into the hollow stalk. Margin
incurved, sometimes wavy or lobed.
Upper surface with tiny, erect, fibrous
scales especially at the margin (use a
hand lens), yellow-orange to brownish-
orange. Lower surface pale yellow to
orange-yellow at first, usually pinkish to
lavender in age, with slightly decurrent
gill-like ridges that are forked or crossveined. Stalk 2-6 cm long, 3-12 mm
thick, nearly equal, hollow, yellow-
orange or yellow. Flesh thin, orange
to yellow-orange. Odor and taste not
distinctive.
Spore Print: Pale pinkish-yellow.
Occurrence: Scattered, in groups or
clusters, often among damp woodland
mosses. Summer-fall.
Edibility: Edible.
Microscopic Features:
Spores 7.5-12 × 4.5-6.5 µm, elliptic,
smooth. Hyaline.
Comments: The cap of *Cantharellus minor*
(search online) measures 0.5-3 cm wide
and doesn't usually perforate. It has a
long solid stalk and is uniformly orange
to yellow-orange.

CHANTERELLES AND SIMILAR FUNGI

Craterellus odoratus (Schwein.) Fr.
FRAGRANT CHANTERELLE
Description: Fruitbody up to 16 cm high and wide, consisting of small, densely clustered caps. Caps 1.3-5 cm wide, trumpet- to funnel-shaped. Upper surfaces smooth, moist or dry, bright orange at the center with a paler, wavy and lobed margin. Lower surfaces pale orange- to creamy yellow, smooth or slightly wrinkled. Individual stalks to 5 cm long, hollow after rising from a common base that can be 1-2 cm thick, smooth, often dusted with white toward the base. Flesh thin, orange. Odor fragrant, unpleasant, or not distinctive. Taste not distinctive.
Spore Print: Pale apricot.
Occurrence: Solitary, scattered, or in groups on the ground in woodlands. Spring-fall.
Edibility: Edible.
Microscopic Features:
 Spores 8-12 × 4-6.5 μm, elliptic to narrowly oval, smooth. Hyaline.
Comments: *Cantharellus odoratus* is a synonym. The clustered fruitbody resembles an orange coral made of trumpets. Conjoined clumps of *Cantharellus lateritius* are larger and have solid stalks.

Gloeocantharellus purpurascens (Hesler) Singer
Description: Cap up to 12 cm wide, an inverted cone initially showing a scalloped and inrolled margin, later flat to centrally depressed, dry, coated with tiny flattened fibers, yellow-orange to orange-pink, bruising violet. Lower surface whitish, bruising violet, with strongly decurrent, nearly distant, gill-like ridges that irregularly fork. Stalk 4-10 cm long, 8-20 mm thick, tapering downward, dry, solid, covered with small fibers, creamy yellow when young, colored in age like the upper surface of the cap, bruising pale violet. Flesh firm, whitish. Odor anise-like. Taste mildly bitter or not distinctive.
Spore Print: Brown.
Occurrence: Solitary to scattered on the ground in mixed forests, usually with hemlock. Summer-fall.
Edibility: Unknown.
Microscopic Features:
 Spores 7-13.5 × 3.5-5.5 μm, ellipsoid to obovoid, finely warted. Pale brown.
Comments: *Gomphus purpurascens* is a synonym. This oddball relative of stinkhorns and coral fungi is uncommonly encountered and is the only representative of its genus to occur in North America.

Turbinellus floccosus
(Schwein.) Earle ex Giachini & Castellano
SCALY VASE CHANTERELLE

Description: Fruitbody up to 18 cm high. Cap 4-16 cm wide, funnel-shaped and deeply depressed, with a thin, wavy margin that is often lobed. Upper surface covered with coarse orange to reddish-orange scales over a paler orange ground color, becoming orange-brown in age. Lower surface creamy white to pale yellow, with strongly decurrent, close, forked, veinlike ridges. Stalk up to 10 cm long, 1-5 cm wide, tapering downward, nearly smooth, whitish to pale yellow. Flesh whitish. Odor and taste not distinctive.

Spore Print: Brownish-yellow.

Occurrence: Solitary, scattered, or in groups under conifers or in mixed woods. Summer-fall.

Edibility: Not recommended; a common cause of gastrointestinal upset.

Microscopic Features: Spores 11-15 × 7-8 μm, elliptic, warted. Hyaline.

Comments: *Gomphus floccosus* is a synonym. *Turbinellus kauffmanii* (search online) is similar but has coarse, dark brown scales and a whitish to pale brown lower surface and stalk.

Boletes are fleshy, stalked mushrooms that produce their spores inside tubes and disperse them through pores visible on the underside of the cap. The tubes and pores resemble a layer of miniature, tightly packed soda straws standing on end. Boletes generally grow on the ground and form mycorrhizal relationships with trees. Unlike polypores, another pored group, the tube layer of a bolete is typically easy to peel away from the flesh of the cap. Polypores are also tougher in texture and mainly grow on wood.

Identifying boletes to species requires attention to several things. Caps can characteristically be dry or sticky/slimy. There may be a velvety fuzz, scales, flattened fibers called **fibrils**, or characteristic cracking. The cap margin might overhang the pores like a drip edge on a roof (**sterile margin**) or be **shaggy** with partial veil remnants. The connection between the pore surface and stalk may be sunken (**depressed**) or running down the stalk (**decurrent**). Species-specific bruising or staining reactions of the cap, cut flesh, and pore surface are frequent and diagnostic when they occur. These may be slow to develop or change over time. Surface characteristics of the stalk are key features as well. Stalks may be shaggy, ribbed, finely roughened, or smooth. Some are decorated with flat or rounded speckles known as **resinous dots**. Stalks might bristle with **scabers**, raised tufts of tissue reminiscent of singed hair. In other species the stalk is sheathed in whole or part by a netlike **reticulation**. A few boletes even sport a partial veil. Spore color is another important feature; it will differ from the color of the pores.

Poisonous boletes do occur. Inedibility may also result from bitterness or an unappetizingly slimy consistency. The Carolinas are home to tasty species as well. But sadly, if *Boletus edulis* (King Bolete, Cep or Porcini) occurs in our region, it is vanishingly rare.

Use the following key to identify unknown boletes.

KEY TO BOLETES

1a Pores greatly distorted or gill-like, moderately to strongly running down the stalk; stalk lacking a ring, scabers, resinous dots and smears, or reticulation .... Group A (p. 198)

1b Mushroom not as above 2

2a Stalk with fine to coarse scabers... Group B (p. 205)

2b Mushroom without scabers 3

3a Pores somewhat elongated and radially arranged, and/or stalk decorated with resinous dots or smears, and/or evidence of a partial veil such as a ring, annular zone, or veil remnants hanging from the margin of the cap........................... Group C (p. 211); see also *Boletellus ananas* (p. 230) and *Pulveroboletus ravenelii* (p. 242)

3b Mushroom not entirely as above. Pores generally angular or round, not notably elongated or radially arranged 4

4a Cap surface gray. Pore surface whitish, pale gray, or dingy brown. Stalk coarsely reticulated. Exterior of stalk base usually becoming yellow at maturity....................... .... *Retiboletus griseus* (p. 243)

4b Mushroom not entirely as above 5

5a Pore surface often white at first (not dark brown), maturing to tan or pinkish-tan (not a shade of yellow or green) .... Group D (p. 218)

5b Pore surface not as above 6

6a Stalk flesh brittle, developing cavities or hollow at maturity .... Group A (p. 198)

6b Stalk flesh not as above 7

7a Pores some shade of red, pink, or yellow-orange (not yellow) .... Group A (p. 198)

7b Mushroom not entirely as above .... Group E (p. 228); see also *Tylopilus tabacinus* (p. 226)

Boletinellus merulioides (Schwein.) Murrill

ASH TREE BOLETE

Description: Cap 4-12.5 cm wide, often kidney-shaped, depressed to nearly funnel-shaped in age, lightly velvety, smooth, yellow- to olive- or reddish-brown. Pores decurrent, elongated and radially arranged with gill-like ridges and cross-walls, yellow, golden-yellow, or olive, slowly staining greenish-blue. Stalk 2-4 cm long, 6-25 mm thick, dry, solid, central or eccentric, brownish to blackish at the base, sometimes mottled with reddish-brown, staining reddish-brown when bruised. Flesh yellow, sometimes bruising bluish, usually reddish-brown around larval tunnels. Odor unpleasant or not distinctive. Taste pungent or not distinctive.

Spore Print: Olive-brown.

Occurrence: Solitary or in groups near or under ash trees. Summer-fall.

Edibility: Edible.

Microscopic Features: Spores 7-11 × 6-7.5 μm, broadly elliptical to nearly globose, smooth. Pale yellow.

Comments: *Gyrodon merulioides* is a synonym. This bolete is not mycorrhizal with ash trees. Instead it has a mutually beneficial relationship with an aphid that parasitizes ash trees.

Boletus subluridellus A. H. Sm. & Thiers

Description: Cap 5-12 cm wide, convex, margin sterile, dry, velvety, bright red to pinkish- or orange-red to bay, quickly bruising blackish-blue. Pores pinkish to dark red, becoming orange-red in age, quickly bruising blue. Stalk 4-10 cm long, 1.5-2.5 cm thick, equal, dry, solid, yellow, darkening upward from the base in age, finely roughened overall. Flesh yellow, quickly staining dark blue. Odor pungent. Taste not distinctive.

Spore Print: Olive-brown.

Occurrence: Solitary, scattered, or in groups with oak or in mixed woods. Summer-fall.

Edibility: Unknown.

Microscopic Features: Spores 11-15 × 4-6 μm, subfusoid with a minute apical pore, smooth. Yellowish.

Comments: *Boletus rufocinnamomeus* (search online) has a brick red cap with honey yellow overtones that becomes cinnamon-brown in age and does not bruise blackish-blue. *Suillellus subvelutipes* has a more orange to brownish cap and usually has red hairs at the stalk base. Compare with *Suillellus subluridus*, which has a more yellow-orange to purplish-red cap.

Butyriboletus floridanus (Singer)
G. Wu, Kuan Zhao & Zhu L. Yang

Description: Cap 4-15 cm wide, dry, somewhat velvety, color ranging from pinkish to red, purplish-red, or brownish-red, the margin yellowish or whitish. Pores various shades of reddish-orange, pinkish, purple-red, and yellow with reddish tints, often beaded with yellow droplets when young. Stalk 4-10 cm long, 1-2.5 cm thick, bulbous at first, becoming club-shaped or nearly equal with red reticulation over the upper one-half or more, dry, solid, yellow at the apex and red below or sometimes red overall. Flesh yellow, quickly bruising dark blue. Odor and taste not distinctive.

Spore Print: Olive-brown.

Occurrence: Scattered or in groups with oaks. Summer-early winter.

Edibility: Edible.

Microscopic Features:
Spores 13-18 × 4-5 μm, ellipsoid to fusoid, smooth. Pale yellow-brown.

Comments: *Floridanus* means "Florida," the state where this bolete was originally collected. *Boletus frostii* ssp. *floridanus*, *Exsudoporus floridanus*, and *Suillellus floridanus* are synonyms. *Butyriboletus frostii* is darker red and has a more coarsely reticulated stalk.

Butyriboletus frostii (J. L. Russell)
G. Wu, Kuan Zhao & Zhu L. Yang

FROST'S BOLETE

Description: Cap 5-15 cm wide, smooth, sticky when moist, blood red to candy-apple red, often with a yellow marginal band, faded yellowish areas may appear in age. Pores dark red, paler in age, usually with golden droplets when young, bruising blackish-blue. Stalk 4-12 cm long, 1-2.5 cm thick, equal or enlarged downward with coarse red reticulation on the upper portion or overall, dry, solid, dark red to pinkish-red, bruising blackish-blue, base white to yellowish. Flesh whitish to yellow, bruising blackish-blue. Odor not distinctive. Taste sour.

Spore Print: Olive-brown.

Occurrence: Scattered or in groups under hardwoods, or in mixed woods. Summer-fall.

Edibility: Edible.

Microscopic Features:
Spores 11-17 × 4-5 μm, elliptical, smooth. Brownish.

Comments: The epithet *frostii* honors American mycologist Charles C. Frost (1805-80). *Boletus frostii* and *Exsudoporus frostii* are synonyms. *Butyriboletus floridanus* has a lighter red cap and less prominent stalk reticulation, and it does not taste sour.

BOLETES

199

Chalciporus rubinellus (Peck) Singer
PURPLE-RED BOLETE
Description: Cap 2-4.5 cm wide, dry,
velvety when young, cracked in age,
red or reddish, yellowing in age.
Pores angular, bright rose-red at first,
becoming dull rose-red to pinkish when
mature. Stalk 2-3.5 cm long, 6-12 mm
thick, equal, dry, solid, red or reddish,
sometimes mixed with yellow, lacking
yellow basal mycelium. Flesh bright
yellow, unchanging. Odor and taste not
distinctive.
Spore Print: Brown.
Occurrence: Scattered or in groups in
conifer or mixed woods. Summer-fall.
Edibility: Unknown.
Microscopic Features:
Spores 12-15 × 3-5 μm, subfusoid,
smooth. Pale yellow-brown.
Comments: One of the smallest eastern
boletes, and the only one in the genus
lacking yellow basal mycelium. The
cap stains blood red, then dingy orange
with the application of NH_4OH. *Boletus
rubinellus* and *Suillus rubinellus* are
synonyms. *Chalciporus piperatus*
(search online) has a peppery taste.
Chalciporus rubritubifer (search online),
which might occur in South Carolina,
has an orange-yellow to orange-brown
cap.

Gyroporus castaneus (Bull.) Quél.
CHESTNUT BOLETE
Description: Cap 3-10 cm wide, margin
often split and flaring in age, dry,
velvety to bald, yellow-brown to
orange- or reddish-brown. Pores
whitish or yellowish. Stalk 3-9 cm
long, 6-16 mm thick, nearly equal or
constricted at the apex and base, dry
and uneven in texture, stuffed with
soft pith at first, developing cavities
or hollowing at maturity, colored like
the cap or paler toward the apex. Flesh
brittle, white. Odor faintly pungent or
not distinctive. Taste not distinctive.
Spore Print: Pale yellow.
Occurrence: Scattered or in groups with
hardwoods or in mixed woods. Year-
round.
Edibility: Edible.
Microscopic Features:
Spores 8-13 × 5-6 μm, elliptical to ovoid,
smooth. Hyaline.
Comments: *Gyroporus purpurinus* has a
vinaceous to burgundy cap and stalk.
Look-alikes with solid stalks and
nonbrittle flesh include *Aureoboletus
roxanae* (see photo on p. 21), with a dull
orange stalk apex, and *Austroboletus
gracilis* var. *gracilis*, which has pores
aging to pinkish-brown.

Gyroporus cyanescens (Bull.) Quél.
STAINING BLUE BOLETE
Description: Cap 4-12 cm wide, dry, covered with matted hairs or scales, straw yellow to pale olive, sometimes with darker streaks, bruising greenish-blue to dark blue. Pores white, yellowish-green, or tan, bruising greenish- to dark blue. Stalk 3-9 cm long, 6-16 mm thick, equal or swollen in the middle or below, textured like the cap, smoother in maturity, dry, stuffed becoming hollow or chambered, colored like the cap or paler and bruising greenish- to dark blue. Flesh whitish to pale yellow, brittle, bruising greenish- to dark blue. Odor and taste not distinctive.

Spore Print: Pale yellow.

Occurrence: Scattered or in groups in hardwood and mixed woods. Summer-fall.

Edibility: Edible.

Microscopic Features:
Spores 8-10 × 5-6 μm, elliptical, smooth. Hyaline.

Comments: *Boletus cyanescens*, *Gyroporus cyanescens* var. *cyanescens*, and *G. cyanescens* var. *violaceotinctus* are synonyms. A variety with flesh that does not bruise blue has been collected in North Carolina.

Gyroporus purpurinus Singer ex Davoodian & Halling
RED GYROPORUS
Description: Cap 2-8 cm wide, margin often splitting in age, dry, velvety, sometimes finely cracked when mature, purplish-red to burgundy with a paler or yellowish margin, fading from the margin toward the center in age. Pores whitish to buff, yellowing in age. Stalk 3-6 cm long, 3-10 mm thick, equal or enlarged downward, scurfy to velvety, dry, hollow, purplish-red to burgundy, sometimes whitish on the upper portion. Flesh brittle, white, unchanging. Odor and taste not distinctive.

Spore Print: Yellow.

Occurrence: Scattered or in groups in mixed woods. Summer-fall.

Edibility: Edible.

Microscopic Features:
Spores 8-11 × 5-7 μm, ovoid to ellipsoid, smooth. Yellowish.

Comments: Too rare to pick for the table, this bolete should be left to propagate. *Boletus castaneus* f. *purpurinus* is a synonym. *Gyroporus castaneus* has yellow- to orange- or reddish-brown cap and stalk. *Austroboletus gracilis* var. *gracilis* has a solid stalk and pinkish-brown pores when mature.

BOLETES

201

Gyroporus subalbellus Murrill

Description: Cap 2.5-12 cm wide, dry, nearly bald, color varying from apricot- to pinkish-buff, pinkish- to orange-cinnamon, or pale yellow to whitish, browning in age or when handled. Pores whitish when young, becoming pale to dull yellow when mature, sometimes slowly turning pinkish-cinnamon when bruised or in age. Stalk 4-10 cm long, 1-3 cm thick, enlarged downward, smooth, dry, hollow or chambered when mature, whitish, soon flushed pinkish to pinkish-orange especially toward the base, frequently with cinnamon, brownish, or olive stains. Flesh brittle, white, unchanging. Odor and taste not distinctive.

Spore Print: Yellowish-buff.

Occurrence: Scattered or in groups in mixed woods. Summer-fall.

Edibility: Edible.

Microscopic Features: Spores 8-14 × 4-6 µm, ellipsoid to ovoid, smooth. Hyaline.

Comments: *Subalbellus* means "somewhat whitish." *Suillus subalbellus* is a synonym. Compare with *Tylopilus peralbidus*, which is similar but has bitter-tasting flesh and a pinkish-brown spore print.

Phylloporus boletinoides A. H. Sm. & Thiers

Description: Cap 2-10 cm wide with a strongly incurved sterile margin, dry, velvety to minutely scaly, almost smooth when mature, dark pinkish-brown, fading to dull yellow-brown. Pores elongated, gill-like with numerous crossveins, radially arranged and strongly decurrent, pale olive-buff, darkening in age, sometimes tinged blue-green near the margin; may slowly bruise blue-green to dark blue. Stalk 2.5-6 cm long, 7-16 mm thick, equal or tapered downward, dry, solid, smooth, pale yellow at the apex, pale cinnamon below, basal mycelium white. Flesh whitish, sometimes cinnamon-brown in the base, slowly bruising bluish-gray to gray. Odor not distinctive. Taste mildly acidic or not distinctive.

Spore Print: Olive-brown.

Occurrence: Scattered in mixed pine/oak woods. Summer-winter.

Edibility: Unknown.

Microscopic Features: Spores 11-16 × 5-6.5 µm, subcylindrical to narrowly oval, smooth. Brownish.

Comments: *Phylloporus leucomycelinus* and *P. rhodoxanthus* (search online) have redder caps and yellow to golden-yellow pores.

Phylloporus leucomycelinus Singer

Description: Cap 4-8 cm wide with a sterile incurved margin, dry, velvety, often finely cracked when mature, dark red to reddish-brown, fading especially over the disc. Pores gill-like, decurrent and crossveined, yellow to golden-yellow. Stalk 4-8 cm long, 5-13 mm thick, equal or pinched at the base, usually with noticeable ribs at the apex, roughened with reddish points or dots over a yellow ground color, basal mycelium whitish. Flesh white to pale yellow. Odor and taste not distinctive.

Spore Print: Yellowish-brown.

Occurrence: Under hardwoods, especially oak and beech. Summer-fall.

Edibility: Edible.

Microscopic Features: Spores 8-14 × 3-5 μm, ellipsoid to fusoid, smooth. Pale yellowish.

Comments: *Phylloporus rhodoxanthus* (search online) is similar but has yellow basal mycelium. *Phylloporus boletinoides* has a paler cap and olive-buff pores that may slowly stain bluish-green to dark blue. The gills and flesh of *Paxillus involutus* stain reddish-brown.

Rubroboletus dupainii
(Boud.) Kuan Zhao & Zhu L. Yang

Description: Cap 2.5-11 cm wide with a sterile margin, smooth, slimy to sticky, shiny when dry, purplish- to pinkish-red, sometimes with yellow spots. Pores red, becoming orange-red, fading to yellow toward the margin, bruising blue. Stalk equal or club-shaped with a pinched base, dry, solid, yellow, coated with fine reddish points and dots that are denser toward the base, basal mycelium white. Flesh whitish to yellow, reddish toward the stalk base, quickly bruising blue then blackish-blue. Odor musky or not distinctive. Taste not distinctive.

Spore Print: Olive-brown.

Occurrence: Scattered or in groups with hardwoods and in mixed woods. Summer-fall.

Edibility: Unknown.

Microscopic Features: Spores 10-17 × 3.5-6 μm, fusiform-ellipsoid to elliptical, with prominent oil drops, smooth. Light yellow.

Comments: *Boletus dupainii* and *Suillellus dupainii* are synonyms. Previously known only from Europe, the first collection from the United States was from North Carolina in 2002 made by American mycologist Owen McConnell.

Suillellus subluridus Murrill

Description: Cap 4-11.5 cm wide with a sterile margin that becomes even, dry, bald or velvety, often cracked in age, orange-pink to orange-yellow with reddish tints, maturing to brownish-red, bruising dark blue. Pores usually yellow when young, especially near the margin, becoming purplish- to dark red before fading toward orange-yellow, bruising blue. Stalk 5-12 cm long, 1.2-3.5 cm thick, equal with a pinched base or tapered in either direction, sometimes longitudinally lined but not reticulate, dry, solid, smooth and yellow at the apex, covered with tiny reddish points and dots below, bruising blue. Flesh yellow, sometimes bruising blue. Odor weakly fetid or not distinctive. Taste not distinctive.

Spore Print: Olive-brown.

Occurrence: Scattered or in groups in hardwoods or mixed woods. Summer-fall.

Edibility: Unknown.

Microscopic Features:
Spores 9-14 × 4-6 µm, fusoid to subfusoid, smooth. Yellow.

Comments: *Boletus subluridus* is a synonym. *Boletus flammans* (search online) and *B. carminiporus* (search online) have reticulation on the stalks.

Suillellus subvelutipes (Peck) Murrill
RED-MOUTH BOLETE

Description: Cap 6-13 cm wide, dry, velvety to bald, sometimes cracked in age, yellow-orange to reddish-brown, quickly bruising blue-black. Pores some shade of red or orange, duller in age, quickly bruising blue to blackish. Stalk 3-10 cm long, 1-2 cm thick, equal, dry, solid, scurfy, usually yellow at the apex and mostly red with yellow tinges below, quickly bruising blue or black; mature specimens often sprout stiff red hairs at the base. Flesh bright yellow, quickly bruising dark blue, then fading to whitish. Odor not distinctive. Taste acidic or not distinctive.

Spore Print: Dark olive-brown.

Occurrence: Scattered or in groups with hardwoods, sometimes with conifers. Summer-fall.

Edibility: Listed as poisonous, but some people eat it without harm.

Microscopic Features:
Spores 13-18 × 5-6.5 µm, fusoid to subventricose, smooth. Brownish.

Comments: *Boletus subvelutipes* is a synonym. *Neoboletus luridiformis* (search online) and *Boletus subluridellus* lack the basal hairs.

Harrya chromapes (Frost) Halling, Nuhn, Osmundson & Manfr. Binder
CHROME-FOOTED BOLETE
Description: Cap 3-15 cm wide, dry or slightly sticky when moist, pink, rose-colored, or grayish when young, fading to pinkish-tan to brownish. Pores white, becoming pinkish to pinkish-tan in age. Stalk equal or tapered in either direction, often bent at the base, dry, solid, white to pinkish, initially covered with pink, reddish, or whitish scabers, bright yellow at the base. Flesh white, unchanging, bright yellow at the base. Odor not distinctive. Taste slightly lemony or not distinctive.
Spore Print: Pinkish- to reddish-brown
Occurrence: Solitary or in groups with hardwoods and conifers. Summer-fall.
Edibility: Edible.
Microscopic Features:
Spores 11-17 × 4-5.5 µm, nearly oblong to narrowly oval, smooth. Hyaline to brownish.
Comments: The genus *Harrya* was erected to honor American mycologist Harry D. Thiers (1919-2000). *Harrya chromapes* is the only species of this genus reported from eastern North America. *Boletus chromapes*, *Leccinum chromapes*, and *Tylopilus chromapes* are synonyms.

Leccinellum albellum
(Peck) Bresinsky & Manfr. Binder
Description: Cap 2-8 cm wide, margin even or with a band of sterile tissue, moist or dry, bald or faintly velvety, often with small cracks, shallow depressions, or dimples in age, color white to buff, pinkish-gray, or brown, sometimes with yellow or even bluish tints; a gelatinous layer often lies beneath the cap cuticle. Pores white, becoming buff to pale gray. Stalk 5-9 cm long, 6-10 mm thick, equal to enlarged downward, dry, solid or stuffed toward the base, whitish, sometimes bruising orange-yellow, covered with white scabers that may darken to brownish or gray. Flesh white, watery. Odor and taste not distinctive.
Spore Print: Olive-brown.
Occurrence: Scattered or in groups with hardwoods, especially oak. Summer-fall.
Edibility: Edible.
Microscopic Features:
Spores 14-22 × 4-6 µm, elliptical to subfusiform, smooth. Brownish-yellow.
Comments: Specimens exhibiting a range of colors commonly grow near one another. Compare with the firmer fleshed *Leccinum scabrum*.

BOLETES

Leccinellum crocipodium (Letell.) Watling

Description: Cap 4-15 cm wide, margin incurved well into maturity, wrinkled, pitted, and sometimes coarsely cracked in age, dark brown to blackish-brown, fading toward pale yellow-brown. Pores yellowish, usually bruising brownish. Stalk enlarging downward or tapered in either direction, dry, solid, light yellow, often reddish at the base, with brown scabers that darken to blackish-brown in age. Flesh light yellow, staining pinkish-, reddish-, or brownish-gray. Odor and taste not distinctive.

Spore Print: Honey yellow.

Occurrence: Scattered or in groups with hardwoods, especially oak. Summer-winter.

Edibility: Edible.

Microscopic Features:
Spores 14-20 × 6-9 μm, fusiform, smooth. Yellowish.

Comments: *Crocipodium* means "saffron foot," a reference to the ground color of the stalk. *Leccinum nigrescens* is a synonym. *Leccinum rugosiceps* has an orange-yellow cap and paler scabers. The stalks of *Boletus separans*, *Xerocomus hortonii*, and *Boletus variipes* lack scabers.

Leccinum chalybaeum Singer

Description: Cap 4-13 cm wide, sticky when fresh, shiny when dry, smooth or covered with fine matted hairs, may develop small cracks in age, buff to pinkish-buff at first, becoming yellow-brown, often tinged bluish- or greenish-gray especially near the margin. Pores whitish to beige, typically bruising olive to brown. Stalk 4-8 cm long, 1-2 cm thick, equal or enlarged downward, dry, solid, whitish with dingy white scabers that darken to brown. Flesh almost woody, white, bruising pink, then slowly pinkish-brown to purplish-gray or blackish. Odor and taste not distinctive.

Spore Print: Olive-brown.

Occurrence: Scattered or in groups with oak, or in mixed oak/pine woods. Summer-fall.

Edibility: Edible.

Microscopic Features:
Spores 16-18 × 5-6 μm, fusoid, smooth. Brownish.

Comments: *Leccinum scabrum*, often associated with birch, has a uniformly yellow- to gray-brown or dark brown cap, blackish scabers, and different staining reactions in the stalk flesh.

Leccinum insigne
A. H. Sm., Thiers, & Watling
ASPEN SCABER STALK
Description: Cap 7.5-15 cm wide with a band of sterile tissue that remains as flaps on the margin well into maturity, dry, texture granular to fibrous, orange to rusty cinnamon or brick red at first, becoming brownish-orange. Pores whitish when young, becoming yellowish to olive-brown, usually bruising brownish. Stalk 7-12 cm long, 1-2 cm thick, equal or enlarged downward, frequently pinched at the base, dry, solid, whitish, covered with brownish to blackish scabers. Flesh white, bruising purplish-gray to purplish-black without any reddish tints. Odor and taste not distinctive.
Spore Print: Yellow-brown to olive-brown.
Occurrence: Scattered or in groups with aspen or birch. Summer-fall.
Edibility: Edible.
Microscopic Features:
Spores 11-16 × 4-5 μm, elliptical, smooth. Yellowish.
Comments: The nearly identical *Leccinum vulpinum* grows with conifers.

Leccinum rubropunctum (Peck) Singer
ASHTRAY BOLETE
Description: Cap 2-9 cm wide, furrowed or wrinkled, sometimes smooth, slightly sticky or dry, bald, chestnut red or reddish-brown. Pores bright golden-yellow when young, becoming yellow to brownish-yellow when mature, unchanging. Stalk 4-10 cm long, 1-2 cm thick, tapered downward, dry, solid, yellow covered with reddish dots and points, basal mycelium pale yellow. Flesh yellowish, unchanging. Odor unpleasant, similar to old cigarette butts. Taste unpleasant.
Spore Print: Olive-brown.
Occurrence: Scattered or in groups with conifers and hardwoods. Summer-winter.
Edibility: Edible.
Microscopic Features:
Spores 16-22 × 5.5-7.5 μm, subfusiform to somewhat oblong, smooth. Brownish.
Comments: *Boletus rubropunctus* is a synonym. *Hemileccinum subglabripes* (search online) is similar, but the stalk has a sparser covering of points and dots, spores measuring 11-17 × 3-5 μm, and flesh that lacks a distinctive odor. Old specimens of *Hortiboletus rubellus* may have brownish caps, but the pores bruise blue.

Leccinum rugosiceps (Peck) Singer
WRINKLED LECCINUM

Description: Cap 5-15 cm wide with a sterile margin, dry, wrinkled or pitted and often with fine yellow cracks, orange-yellow overall, browning with age, darkest centrally. Pores yellowish, darkening toward olive-brown, unchanging when bruised or slowly bruising darker to blue-green. Stalk equal or tapered at either end, dry, solid, yellow to brownish, covered with pale brown scabers that darken in age and may form lines resembling reticulation. Flesh white or pale yellow, slowly bruising reddish or burgundy, sometimes faintly, most noticeable where the cap and stalk meet. Odor not distinctive. Taste not distinctive or astringent.

Spore Print: Olive-brown.

Occurrence: Solitary or in groups with oak, especially pin oak. Summer-fall.

Edibility: Edible.

Microscopic Features:
Spores 15-21 × 5-6 µm, fusiform, smooth. Brownish.

Comments: *Boletus rugosiceps* is a synonym. *Leccinellum crocipodium* has a darker cap, darker scabers, and differently staining flesh. *Boletus longicurvipes* has a sticky cap.

Leccinum scabrum (Bull.) Gray
COMMON SCABER STALK

Description: Cap 4-12 cm wide, bald or with matted fibrils that break up into tiny flattened scales in age, grayish- to yellow-brown or dark brown. Pores grayish-white when young, often with brown spots, becoming gray to brownish in age, bruising brownish. Stalk equal or enlarged downward, dry, solid, whitish to pale tan, may have blue-green stains near the base, covered with dark brown to blackish scabers that are fine at the apex and coarser below. Flesh whitish, variably staining: sometimes blue or yellow near the base, or slowly reddish then brownish or pale gray after several hours. Odor and taste not distinctive.

Spore Print: Brown.

Occurrence: Solitary, scattered, or in groups under birch. Summer-fall.

Edibility: Edible.

Microscopic Features:
Spores 14-22 × 4-6.5 µm, fusiform, smooth. Brownish.

Comments: *Leccinum oxydabile*, *L. roseo-fractum*, and *L. rotundifoliae* are all synonyms. Compare with *Leccinum chalybaeum*, which is associated with oak.

Leccinum snellii A. H. Sm., Thiers & Watling
SNELL'S BOLETE
Description: Cap 3-9 cm wide, dry, smooth, brown to blackish, typically with paler mottling, initially covered with brownish-black fibrils, fading to yellowish-brown as the fibrils erode. Pores whitish, becoming grayish to grayish-brown, sometimes bruising yellowish or brown. Stalk 4-11 cm long, 1-2 cm thick, equal or slightly enlarged downward, dry, solid, whitish but frequently blue-green near the base or where damaged, densely covered with gray to black scabers. Flesh whitish, bruising reddish, sometimes slowly, especially where the cap and stalk meet, darkening to purple-gray or black after one hour or more. Odor and taste not distinctive.
Spore Print: Brown.
Occurrence: Scattered or in groups under hardwoods, especially yellow birch. Spring-fall.
Edibility: Edible.
Microscopic Features: Spores 16-22 × 5-7.5 µm, fusoid, smooth. Brownish.
Comments: This bolete is named in honor of American boletologist Walter H. Snell (1889-1980).

Leccinum vulpinum Watling
FOXY BOLETE
Description: Cap 5-20 cm wide with a sterile, often splitting margin that leaves flaps on immature caps, dry or slightly sticky, sometimes finely cracked in age, dull orange to brick or rusty red or reddish-brown. Pores whitish at first, becoming dingy and olive-buff to pale grayish-brown, slowly bruising darker brown to olive. Stalk equal or enlarging downward, dry, solid, whitish, sometimes stained blue near the base, covered with brown scabers that blacken in age. Flesh white, sometimes initially staining pinkish but always slowly staining grayish or brownish-black. Odor and taste not distinctive.
Spore Print: Brown.
Occurrence: Under conifers, especially pines and Norway spruce. Summer-fall.
Edibility: Edible.
Microscopic Features: Spores 10-18 × 3.5-5 µm, fusiform to subfusiform, smooth. Brownish.
Comments: An older name, *Leccinum aurantiacum*, refers to a European species that doesn't actually occur here. *Leccinum piceinum* is a synonym. *Leccinum insigne* grows under hardwoods.

Sutorius eximius
(Peck) Halling, Nuhn & Osmundson
LILAC-BROWN BOLETE

Description: Cap 5-12 cm wide, dry, bald to velvety, purplish- to grayish-brown, usually with a white bloom when young. Pores dark purple- to chocolate-brown, then reddish-brown in age. Stalk 4.5-9 cm long, 1-4 cm thick, equal or enlarged downward, dry, solid, pale purplish-gray, covered with a layer of darker purple-brown tiny scales. Flesh whitish to gray, or reddish- to brownish-lilac. Odor pungent or not distinctive. Taste slightly bitter or not distinctive.

Spore Print: Pinkish-brown.

Occurrence: Scattered or in groups with conifers, or in mixed woods with oak. Summer-fall.

Edibility: Poisonous.

Microscopic Features:
Spores 11-17 × 3.5-5 μm, narrowly subfusoid, smooth. Hyaline to brownish.

Comments: *Leccinum eximium* and *Tylopilus eximius* are synonyms. This bolete could be mistaken for a species of *Leccinum* because of the purple-brown scales on its stalk. *Tylopilus griseocarneus* has a reticulated stalk. *Tylopilus plumbeoviolaceus* has paler pores and more intensely bitter flesh.

BOLETES

210

Bothia castanella
(Peck) Halling, Baroni & Manfr. Binder
BOTH'S BOLETE
Description: Cap 2.5-10 cm wide, dry, covered with matted hairs, becoming bald in age, brown to yellow-brown, reddish-brown, or burgundy. Pores slightly decurrent to decurrent, coarse, angular to elongated, radially arranged, pinkish-brown or buff, staining yellow-brown to dark rusty brown. Stalk 2-7 cm long, 6-20 mm thick, equal or tapered downward, sometimes enlarged toward the base, dry, solid, colored like the cap but paler, reticulate on the upper portion or more, basal mycelium white. Flesh whitish, sometimes slowly bruising pale rust. Odor not distinctive. Taste mildly acidic or not distinctive.
Spore Print: Yellow-brown.
Occurrence: Scattered or in groups with oak. Summer-fall.
Edibility: Unknown.
Microscopic Features:
Spores 8-11 × 4.5-5.5 µm, ovate to narrowly elliptical, smooth. Yellowish.
Comments: This bolete has been placed in seven different genera because of its combination of macroscopic and microscopic features. *Suillus castanellus*, *Boletinus castanellus*, *Boletinus squarrosoides*, and *Xerocomus castanellus* are all synonyms.

Strobilomyces dryophilus
Cibula & N. S. Weber
Description: Cap 3-12 cm wide, dry, whitish, covered with coarse, cottony, grayish-pink to pinkish-brown scales, the margin fringed with cottony pieces of similarly colored partial veil. Pores white, becoming gray then black, bruising reddish-orange, then black. Stalk 4-8 cm long, 1-2 cm thick, equal or enlarged at the base, dry, solid, pinkish-tan to brownish, reticulate above the shaggy ring zone, shaggy below. Partial veil cottony, whitish to pinkish-tan, leaving a ring zone on the stalk. Flesh whitish, quickly bruising orange-red, then blackish. Odor and taste not distinctive.
Spore Print: Brownish-black.
Occurrence: Scattered or in groups with oak. Summer-winter.
Edibility: Edible.
Microscopic Features:
Spores 9-12 × 7-9 µm, subglobose to short-elliptical, covered by a distinct and complete reticulum. Grayish.
Comments: The nearly identical *Strobilomyces strobilaceus* and *S. confusus* (search online) have darker purplish-gray to blackish caps and sometimes grow under different hardwood species or pines.

BOLETES

211

Strobilomyces strobilaceus (Scop.) Berk.
OLD MAN OF THE WOODS
Description: Cap 3-15.5 cm wide, dry,
whitish to gray under coarse, cottony,
flattened or erect and sometimes
overlapping scales in shades of
purplish- to dark gray or black, the
margin fringed with pieces of gray
partial veil. Pores white, darkening
to black in age, bruising reddish to
reddish-brown then black. Stalk 4-12 cm
long, 1-2.5 cm thick, equal or enlarged
at the base, dry, solid, reticulate above
the ring zone, shaggy below, colored
like the cap. Partial veil gray, cottony.
Flesh whitish, quickly bruising orange-
red, then black. Odor and taste not
distinctive.
Spore Print: Brownish-black.
Occurrence: Scattered under hardwoods,
mixed woods, or pines. Summer-fall.
Edibility: Edible.
Microscopic Features:
Spores 9.5-15 × 8.5-12 μm, short-
elliptical to globose, covered by a
distinct reticulum. Grayish.
Comments: *Strobilomyces floccopus* is a
synonym. *Strobilomyces dryophilus*
is paler in color. The spores of
Strobilomyces confusus (search online)
are irregularly ridged but not reticulate.

Suillus acidus (Peck) Singer
SOUR-CAP SUILLUS
Description: Cap 5-16 cm wide, sticky
when moist, shiny when dry, smooth,
yellowish at first, becoming tan or
yellowish- to pinkish-brown, usually
streaked or spotted, the margin
incurved and initially fringed with
tags of partial veil. Pores pale yellow
with yellowish droplets when young,
later dingy yellow, sometimes slowly
bruising reddish-brown. Stalk 4-10 cm
long, 6-12 mm thick, equal or enlarged
downward, solid, whitish to pale yellow,
covered with pinkish-brown dots and
smears that darken with age. Partial veil
cottony, slimy, yellow, leaving a sticky
ring around the stalk. Flesh whitish,
yellow, or orange-yellow, sometimes
slowly bruising reddish-brown. Odor
not distinctive. Taste of the slime
typically acidic.
Spore Print: Brown.
Occurrence: Scattered or in groups with
pines. Summer-fall.
Edibility: Edible.
Microscopic Features:
Spores 8-11 × 3-5 μm, elliptical to
subfusoid, smooth. Brownish.
Comments: *Suillus acidus* var. *intermedius*,
S. intermedius, and *S. subalutaceus*
are synonyms. The sour slime is a
distinguishing characteristic.

Suillus americanus (Peck) Snell
CHICKEN-FAT SUILLUS
Description: Cap 3-13 cm wide, sticky when moist, bald or with inconspicuous flattened fibrils and scales, bright yellow to brownish-yellow, streaked reddish, the margin tagged with bits of pale partial veil. Pores angular, sometimes elongated and radially arranged, usually slightly decurrent, yellow at first, then browner, slowly bruising reddish-brown. Stalk 3-9 cm long, 3-10 mm thick, equal, dry, solid but cavitating, yellow with reddish- to dark brown dots and smears, wine-colored bruising typical. Partial veil rarely leaves evidence on the stalk. Flesh yellow, bruising pinkish-gray to purplish-brown. Odor and taste not distinctive.
Spore Print: Brown.
Occurrence: Usually in groups or clusters with white pine. Summer-fall.
Edibility: Edible.
Microscopic Features:
Spores 8-11 × 3-4 µm, nearly fusiform, smooth. Brownish.
Comments: Cap scales of *Suillus hirtellus* are tufted and darker than the cap. *Suillus subaureus* is orange at the stalk apex, has pores that do not bruise reddish, and may grow under hardwoods.

Suillus cothurnatus Singer/(Frost)
SLIPPERY JILL
Description: Cap 1.6-6 cm wide, sometimes with an umbo, smooth, sticky, orange-yellow to yellow-, olive-, reddish-, or grayish-brown, the margin incurved and fringed with veil remnants. Pores often radially arranged, yellow to orange-yellow, becoming brownish-yellow. Stalk 2.5-6 cm long, 5-10 mm thick, equal or tapered downward, dry, solid, whitish to yellowish, with reddish-brown dots and smears that darken in age, basal mycelium pinkish-orange. Partial veil thick, baggy, whitish and sticky, leaving a ring on the stalk. Flesh yellow to orange-tan, marbled, bruising purple-gray. Odor and taste not distinctive.
Spore Print: Brown.
Occurrence: Scattered or in groups under pines. Year-round.
Edibility: Edible.
Microscopic Features:
Spores 8-10 × 2.5-3.5 µm, ellipsoid to subcylindric, smooth. Brownish.
Comments: *Suillus salmonicolor* (search online) is larger and has a more orange cap, a thicker veil, and salmon-orange flesh in the stalk base; it is also edible. *Suillus acidus* has sour-tasting slime. The larger *Suillus luteus* has a purple-tinted partial veil.

BOLETES

Suillus decipiens (Peck) Kuntze

Description: Cap 4-9 cm wide, dry, partly covered with hairs or small scales, dull yellow, orange, tan, or pale reddish-brown, bruising grayish to blackish, the margin incurved and fringed with remnants of veil tissue. Pores elongated and radially arranged, yellow to orange-yellow, browning when bruised or in age. Stalk 4-7 cm long, 7-16 mm thick, usually enlarged downward and curved at the base, dry, solid, cottony to velvety or hairy, often bright yellow-orange above the ring zone, yellower below. Partial veil whitish to gray, leaving a fragile ring on the stalk. Flesh yellow, orange toward the stalk base, sometimes darkening and developing red tints. Odor and taste not distinctive.

Spore Print: Pale brown.

Occurrence: Scattered or in groups in oak/pine woods. Summer-fall.

Edibility: Edible.

Microscopic Features:
Spores 9-12 × 3.5-4 μm, cylindrical to subelliptic, smooth. Hyaline to brownish-yellow.

Comments: *Suillus spraguei* has red scales in youth. *Suillus hirtellus* lacks a veil.

Suillus granulatus (L.) Roussel
BUTTERBALL

Description: Cap 5-12 cm wide, smooth, sticky or slimy, some shade of pale yellow to orange-cinnamon or pinkish-brown, which usually appears streaked and "checkered." Pores initially whitish to pinkish-buff, becoming yellow, often beaded with pinkish-cinnamon droplets when young, sometimes bruising dull cinnamon. Stalk 4-8 cm long, 1-2.5 cm thick, equal, solid, dry, covered with pinkish-tan to brownish dots and smears over a whitish ground color that yellows especially near the apex. Flesh white to yellow, unchanging. Odor and taste not distinctive.

Spore Print: Brown.

Occurrence: Scattered or in groups with pines. Summer-fall.

Edibility: Edible.

Microscopic Features:
Spores 7-10 × 2.5-3.5 μm, oblong or tapered slightly to the apex, smooth. Brownish.

Comments: *Suillus lactifluus* is a synonym. The white stalk of *Suillus neoalbidipes* (search online) lacks noticeable resinous dots. *Suillus bovinus* (search online) also lacks the dots and has a cap with a whitish margin.

Suillus hirtellus (Peck) Snell

Description: Cap 5-12 cm wide, dry or slightly sticky, yellow, typically staining wine brown, covered with tufts of reddish, brownish, or grayish fibrils and scales, the margin initially fringed with tufts of sterile tissue. Pores radially arranged and slightly elongated, sometimes beaded with whitish droplets, pale yellow becoming olive-yellow or orange-buff, may bruise wine brown or rarely blue-green. Stalk 3-8 cm long, 1-2 cm thick, equal or enlarged downward, dry, solid, smooth, pale yellow, covered with yellowish dots and smears that darken to brownish-black, red tints sometimes present near the base, basal mycelium white. Partial veil absent. Flesh yellow, may erratically and weakly bruise blue. Odor and taste not distinctive.

Spore Print: Brown.

Occurrence: Scattered or in groups with conifers. Summer-winter.

Edibility: Edible.

Microscopic Features:
Spores 7-13 × 3-3.5 μm, nearly oblong, smooth. Brownish.

Comments: The stalk of *Suillus decipiens* lacks resinous dots. Compare with *Suillus americanus*.

Suillus luteus (L.) Roussel
SLIPPERY JACK

Description: Cap 5-12 cm wide with a sterile margin that is usually hung with bits of partial veil, smooth, sticky or slimy, shiny when dry, some shade of yellowish- to reddish-brown. Pores white to pale yellow, then darker yellow to olive-yellow at maturity. Stalk 3-8 cm long, 1-2.5 cm thick, equal, solid, white becoming pale yellow at the apex with resinous dots and smears above the ring, often with purplish or brown tints below. Partial veil white on top and tinted purplish on the underside, usually leaving a large, flaring skirt on the stalk. Flesh white to yellow. Odor and taste not distinctive.

Spore Print: Brown.

Occurrence: Scattered or in groups with pines. Summer-winter.

Edibility: Edible.

Microscopic Features:
Spores 7-9 × 2.5-3 μm, nearly oblong, smooth. Brownish.

Comments: *Suillus cothurnatus*, known as Slippery Jill, is smaller, and its veil lacks purplish tints. *Suillus brevipes* (search online) has a shorter stalk and lacks a ring.

Suillus spraguei
(Berk. & M. A. Curtis) Kuntze
PAINTED SUILLUS
Description: Cap 4-12 cm wide, dry, cottony or velvety, covered with red to purplish-red fibrils and soft scales that fade in age and expose yellow flesh between them, the margin hung with tatters of veil tissue. Pores elongated, radially arranged, sometimes slightly decurrent, yellow, darkening to brownish-yellow and bruising reddish to brownish. Stalk 4-12 cm long, 1-2.5 cm thick, equal, sometimes with a swollen base, dry, solid, yellowish, covered below the ring with cottony red scales that may form concentric bands. Partial veil, white, fibrous, leaving a ring on the stalk. Flesh yellow, sometimes bruising reddish. Odor and taste not distinctive.
Spore Print: Olive-brown.
Occurrence: Scattered or in groups, exclusively under white pine. Spring-fall.
Edibility: Edible.
Microscopic Features:
Spores 8-12 × 3.5-5 µm, elliptical, smooth. Brownish.
Comments: *Suillus pictus* is a synonym. *Suillus decipiens* strongly resembles old and faded *S. spraguei* but is not limited to partnerships with white pine.

Suillus subaureus (Peck) Snell
Description: Cap 3-14 cm wide with an inrolled margin, sticky, shiny when dry, covered with matted scarlet to reddish-brown fibers over a yellower ground color. Pores radially arranged, subdecurrent, sometimes beaded with clear droplets when young, yellow-orange, becoming brownish-yellow. Stalk 4-8 cm long, 1-2 cm thick, equal, sticky and sometimes beaded with droplets, dry in age, solid, orange at the apex, yellow below, the lower portion with raised, bright yellow dots that darken in age. Flesh yellow, bruising reddish in the cap and slowly brownish in the stalk. Odor not distinctive. Taste acidic or not distinctive.
Spore Print: Brown.
Occurrence: Scattered or in groups with hardwoods or in mixed woods. Summer-fall.
Edibility: Edible.
Microscopic Features:
Spores 7-10 × 2.7-3.5 µm, narrowly elliptical to subfusiform, smooth. Brownish.
Comments: The brownish pores of *Suillus tomentosus* bruise blue. *Suillus punctipes* (search online) has brownish pores and spicy-smelling flesh. *Bothia castanella* has a reticulated stalk.

Suillus tomentosus (Kauffman) Singer
BLUE-STAINING SLIPPERY JACK
Description: Cap 5-12 cm wide, dry, covered at first with grayish, yellowish, or reddish-brown fibers and scales over a yellow to orange-yellow ground color, in age often bald with an uplifted, wavy margin. Pores attached to slightly decurrent, sometimes beaded with yellowish droplets when young, brown to reddish-brown, yellowing at maturity, bruising blue. Stalk 5-12 cm long, 1-2.5 cm thick, equal or enlarged downward, dry, solid, yellow to orange-yellow with orange or brown resinous dots and smears. Flesh yellow, inconsistently bruising blue, often slowly. Odor and taste not distinctive.
Spore Print: Brown.
Occurrence: Scattered or in groups with conifers. Summer-fall.
Edibility: Edible.
Microscopic Features:
Spores 7-12 × 3-5 µm, fusoid to elongate-ovoid, smooth. Yellowish.
Comments: This is the only *Suillus* with pores that bruise blue. *Tylopilus sordidus* is darker brown, lacks resinous dots, and has whitish rather than yellow flesh.

Austroboletus gracilis var. *gracilis* (Peck) Wolfe

GRACEFUL BOLETE

Description: Cap 3-10 cm wide, convex, dry, sometimes cracked in age, maroon to reddish-brown, or tawny to yellow-brown. Pores white, becoming pinkish or burgundy-tinged in age, staining brownish when bruised. Stalk 7.5-18 cm long, 6-10 mm thick, long and slender in relation to the cap diameter, enlarged downward, often curved, solid, colored like the cap or paler, with elevated riblike lines that sometimes form an obscure, narrow reticulation over at least the upper half, basal mycelium white. Flesh white or tinged pink. Taste slightly tart or not distinctive.

Spore Print: Pinkish- to reddish-brown.

Occurrence: Scattered or in groups in conifer and hardwood forests. Spring-fall.

Edibility: Edible.

Microscopic Features:
Spores 10-17 × 5-8 μm, narrowly ovoid to subelliptic, pitted. Pale brown.

Comments: *Tylopilus gracilis* and *Porphyrellus gracilis* are synonyms. *Gyroporus castaneus* and *G. purpurinus* are similar but have white pores, hollow stalks, yellow spore prints, and smooth spores.

Austroboletus subflavidus (Murrill) Wolfe

WHITE COARSELY RIBBED BOLETE

Description: Cap 3-10 cm wide, convex, becoming flat and slightly depressed, dry, somewhat velvety, cracked in age, white at first, becoming buff, yellowish, or grayish, often tinged pale pinkish-orange. Pores white to grayish, becoming pinkish, sometimes with clear droplets when young. Stalk 4.5-14.5 cm long, 7-30 mm thick, equal or tapered downward, dry, solid, colored like the cap, with raised and coarsely ribbed reticulation that looks pitted. Flesh white in the cap, shading to yellow in the stalk base. Odor fruity. Taste bitter.

Spore Print: Reddish-brown.

Occurrence: Scattered or in groups under oak and pine. Spring-fall.

Edibility: Inedible.

Microscopic Features:
Spores 15-20 × 6-9 μm, fusoid, minutely pitted. Brownish.

Comments: *Subflavidus* means "nearly yellow." *Tylopilus subflavidus* and *Porphyrellus subflavidus* are synonyms. *Tylopilus rhoadsiae* is similar but has distinct brown reticulation when mature that is not so coarsely ribbed and pitted, and a club-shaped stalk with a pinched base.

Tylopilus alboater (Schwein.) Murrill
BLACK VELVET BOLETE
Description: Cap 3-15 cm wide, often with a sterile margin, dry, velvety, finely cracked when mature, dark grayish-brown to black, usually covered with a whitish bloom when young. Pores white, sometimes with a gray tinge at first, becoming dull pinkish-brown, typically bruising reddish, then slowly black. Stalk 4-10 cm long, 2-4 cm thick, equal or enlarged downward, dry, solid, colored like the cap, often paler near the apex, usually covered with a whitish bloom, sometimes slightly reticulate at the apex. Flesh dense and firm when fresh, white or gray-tinged, bruising pinkish to reddish-gray, finally blackening. Odor and taste not distinctive.
Spore Print: Pinkish-brown.
Occurrence: Solitary to scattered with hardwoods, especially oak. Spring-fall.
Edibility: Edible.
Microscopic Features:
Spores 7-11 × 3.5-5 μm, narrowly oval, smooth. Hyaline.
Comments: *Tylopilus atronicotianus* has an olive-brown cap and a disagreeable odor. The pores of *Tylopilus griseocarneus* are black in youth.

Tylopilus atronicotianus Both
FALSE BLACK VELVET BOLETE
Description: Cap 7.5-20 cm wide with a sterile margin, dry, bald, somewhat shiny, olive- to bronzy brown, some-times tinged yellow. Pores initially white, darkening to reddish-brown, bruising pinkish-cinnamon then blackish. Stalk 6-12 cm long, 1.5-4.5 cm thick, equal, tapered in either direction or bulbous, dry, solid, powdery, coated with black hairs, sometimes finely reticulate at the whitish apex, vinaceous-gray or dark brown below, black near the base, which may be pointed, rootlike, and white. Cap flesh white, slowly bruising pink or reddish, then blackish, stalk flesh gray to blackish. Odor musty, disagreeable. Taste unpleasant or not distinctive.
Spore Print: Reddish-brown.
Occurrence: Scattered or in groups in mixed woods with oak or hemlock. Summer-fall.
Edibility: Unknown.
Microscopic Features:
Spores 7.5-10.5 × 4-5 μm, narrowly oval, smooth. Hyaline.
Comments: *Tylopilus alboater* differs by having a somewhat velvety, blackish cap without brown tones, and flesh lacking a distinctive odor.

BOLETES

Tylopilus badiceps (Peck) A. H. Sm. & Thiers
BEVELED-CAP BOLETE
Description: Cap 4-8 cm wide, velvety at first but smoother at maturity, maroon aging to purplish- or reddish-brown, the margin characteristically having an abrupt bevel or crease. Pores white, eventually tan, may bruise brown. Stalk 4-5 cm long, 1.5-3 cm thick, equal or enlarged downward, dry, solid, apex sometimes reticulate, colored like the cap or bluish-purple nearly overall, usually white at the apex and base. Flesh white, sometimes slowly bruising pinkish to brown. Odor sweet, like molasses, or not distinctive. Taste not distinctive.
Spore Print: Pinkish-brown.
Occurrence: Scattered or in groups with oaks. Summer-fall.
Edibility: Edible.
Microscopic Features:
Spores 8-11 × 3.5-4.5 µm, narrowly elliptic, smooth. Hyaline to yellowish.
Comments: *Tylopilus plumbeoviolaceus* and *T. felleus* taste bitter. The reddish-brown colors of *Tylopilus ferrugineus* lack purple or violet tones, and the margin of the cap is plain, not abruptly beveled.

Tylopilus balloui (Peck) Singer
BURNT ORANGE BOLETE
Description: Cap 5-12 cm wide, dry, initially bright orange to bright orange-red, fading to dull orange, cinnamon, or tan. Pores white to whitish, becoming tan or pinkish in age, bruising brown. Stalk 2.5-12 cm long, 6-25 mm thick, equal or swollen on the lower portion, smooth or roughened, dry, solid, sometimes with fine reticulation at the apex, whitish or tinged yellow to orange, bruising brown. Flesh white, bruising pinkish-tan to violet-brown. Odor not distinctive. Taste bitter or not distinctive.
Spore Print: Pale brown to reddish-brown.
Occurrence: Scattered or in groups in grassy areas or woods, especially near oak, beech, or pine. Summer-fall.
Edibility: Edible.
Microscopic Features:
Spores 5-11 × 3-5 µm, elliptic, smooth. Hyaline to brownish.
Comments: *Rubinoboletus balloui* is a synonym. The epithet *balloui* is sometimes incorrectly spelled *ballouii*. Somewhat similar *Leccinum rugosiceps* has a wrinkled cap.

Tylopilus felleus (Bull.) P. Karst.
BITTER BOLETE
Description: Cap 5-30 cm wide, smooth, usually dry but sometimes sticky when moist, initially pinkish- to reddish-purple, browning with or without purplish tints and fading toward tan in age. Pores white, becoming vinaceous or pinkish-tan, often bruising brown. Stalk 4-20 cm long, 1-3 cm thick, enlarging downward and typically bulbous, prominently reticulated over the upper third or more, dry, solid, usually white at the apex and base, brown in between, frequently bruising olive or olive-brown. Flesh white, may bruise reddish. Odor not distinctive. Taste extremely bitter.
Spore Print: Pinkish-brown.
Occurrence: Solitary or in groups on the ground or, rarely, on decaying wood with conifers or in mixed woods. Summer-fall.
Edibility: Inedible because of the bitter taste.
Microscopic Features: Spores 11-17 × 3-5 µm, subfusoid, smooth. Brownish.
Comments: The extremely bitter flesh rules out *Boletus edulis* (search online). The stalks of *Tylopilius plumbeoviolaceus* and *T. rubrobrunneus* are not prominently reticulated.

Tylopilus ferrugineus (Frost) Singer
Description: Cap 4-12 cm wide with an incurved and sometimes sterile margin that is usually wavy or lobed in age, dry, velvety, reddish- to dark brown. Pores whitish, becoming pinkish-buff, bruising brown. Stalk 3-10 cm long, 1.5-2.5 cm thick, equal, dry, solid, sometimes reticulate at the apex or over the upper half but often smooth, usually whitish at the apex and reddish- to dull brown below, basal mycelium white. Flesh white, slowly bruising pink then brownish. Odor and taste not distinctive.
Spore Print: Pinkish-brown.
Occurrence: Scattered or in groups with oaks. Summer-fall.
Edibility: Edible.
Microscopic Features: Spores 8-13 × 3-5 µm, subfusoid to ellipsoid, smooth. Yellowish.
Comments: *Tylopilus badiceps* has maroon or violet tints and a beveled margin. *Austroboletus gracilis* var. *gracilis* has a longer, thinner build. Take care not to confuse with similarly colored bitter species of *Tylopilus*.

Tylopilus griseocarneus Wolfe & Halling

Description: Cap 4-11 cm wide, dry, velvety, sometimes cracked in age, some dark shade of dull reddish-, olive- or grayish-brown to nearly black. Pores black, becoming gray in age, bruising grayish-orange or darker gray. Stalk 4.5-8.5 cm long, 1.2-3 cm thick, equal or tapered in either direction, dry, solid, blackish-brown to gray, often paler at the apex, often finely and darkly powdery, with prominent reticulation on the upper one-third or overall. Flesh grayish, bruising orange to orange-red, then finally black. Odor and taste not distinctive.

Spore Print: Pinkish to pinkish-gray.

Occurrence: Scattered or in groups with oak or pine. Summer-winter.

Edibility: Unknown.

Microscopic Features:
Spores 8-14 × 3-5 μm, fusiform-elliptic, smooth. Hyaline.

Comments: *Sutorius eximius* is similar, but its stalk lacks reticulation. *Tylopilus alboater* has whitish pores at first. *Strobilomyces* spp. have shaggy caps with partial veil remnants on the margin.

Tylopilus indecisus (Peck) Murrill

Description: Cap 5-17 cm wide, dry, velvety, pale brown to yellowish- or occasionally reddish-brown. Pores white at first, becoming pinkish-brown, bruising brown. Stalk 4-10 cm long, 1-3 cm thick, equal or enlarged downward, dry, solid, reticulated at the apex, whitish at first, then pale brown from the base up, bruising brown. Flesh white, sometimes slowly bruising brownish or pinkish. Odor and taste not distinctive.

Spore Print: Pinkish- to reddish-brown.

Occurrence: Scattered or in groups with hardwoods, or in pine/oak woods. Summer-fall.

Edibility: Edible.

Microscopic Features:
Spores 10-15 × 3-5 μm, narrowly subfusiform, smooth. Brownish.

Comments: *Tylopilus badiceps* has a dark brown to maroon cap with a beveled margin. The cap and stalk of *Tylopilus ferrugineus* are darker shades of reddish-brown. *Tylopilus tabacinus* has yellowish-brown pores at maturity, its cap is usually larger, and it frequently grows in grassy areas.

Tylopilus intermedius A. H. Sm. & Thiers
PARCHMENT BITTER BOLETE
Description: Cap 6-15 cm wide, often crinkled or finely textured like parchment, sometimes powdery, whitish but may be tinged with pink, brownish-yellow, or tan and bruises brown in age. Pores white, becoming pale tan to pinkish, slowly bruising brown. Stalk 8-14 cm long, 1-4 cm thick, club-shaped or bulbous at the base, weakly to distinctly reticulate, dry, solid, colored like the cap, bruising brownish. Flesh white, very slowly bruising dark brown. Odor pungent or not distinctive. Taste bitter.
Spore Print: Pinkish to pinkish-brown.
Occurrence: Scattered or in groups with hardwoods, especially oak, or with pine. Summer-fall.
Edibility: Inedible.
Microscopic Features:
Spores 10-15 × 3-5 µm, nearly oblong, smooth. Hyaline to brownish.
Comments: Compare with *Tylopilus peralbidus*, which lacks stalk reticulation, and *T. rhoadsiae*, which has prominent stalk reticulation but nonstaining flesh. *Boletus pallidus* has whitish or pale yellow pores that turn greenish-yellow in age.

Tylopilus peralbidus
(Snell & Beardslee) Murrill
Description: Cap 4.5-13 cm wide, dry, smooth or velvety, finely cracked in age, white at first, then brownish-yellow to tan and finally brown, bruising cinnamon to brown. Pores whitish, becoming buff or pink-tinged, bruising brown. Stalk 4.5-11 cm long, 1.3-4 cm thick, equal or tapered in either direction, usually with a pointed base, dry, solid, smooth, white to brownish or colored like the cap, bruising brown. Flesh white, may slowly bruise pale pinkish-brown or buff. Odor unpleasantly resembling bleach. Taste bitter.
Spore Print: Pinkish-brown.
Occurrence: Scattered or in groups in grassy areas, along roads, or in forests with oak or pine. Spring-fall.
Edibility: Unknown.
Microscopic Features:
Spores 7-12 × 2.3-3.5 µm, cylindric or cylindric-subclavate, smooth. Pale honey yellow.
Comments: *Boletus peralbidus* is a synonym. Other whitish boletes in the Carolinas, *Tylopilus intermedius* and *T. rhoadsiae*, have reticulated stalks. The pore surface of *Boletus pallidus* becomes yellowish, not pinkish.

Tylopilus plumbeoviolaceus
(Snell & Dick) Singer

VIOLET-GRAY BOLETE

Description: Cap 4-15 cm wide with a sterile margin, smooth, shiny, sometimes cracked, brownish to grayish-brown or dull cinnamon, at times with purplish tints especially toward the margin, not staining when bruised. Pores initially white, then pale to pinkish-tan, may bruise pinkish-brown. Stalk 8-12 cm long, 1-2 cm thick, equal or enlarged downward, dry, solid, smooth below a narrow zone of apical reticulation, purple, fading to purple-tinged shades of gray or brown, basal mycelium white. Flesh white, sometimes browning around insect damage. Odor pungent or not distinctive. Taste very bitter.

Spore Print: Purplish-brown.

Occurrence: Solitary or in small groups in forests with oak. Summer-fall.

Edibility: Inedible.

Microscopic Features:
Spores 10-13 × 3-4 μm, elliptical, smooth. Brownish.

Comments: *Tylopilus violatinctus* is very similar, but the cap bruises rusty violet to purplish, and the stalk apex is typically whitish.

Tylopilus rhoadsiae (Murrill) Murrill

Description: Cap 6-15 cm wide, dry, velvety or smooth, shiny at times, white to whitish, usually tinged with buff, grayish-buff, pinkish, or pinkish-tan, maturing to tan, pinkish-brown, or golden-brown. Pores white at first, becoming dull pinkish, not staining when bruised. Stalk 3-11.5 cm long, 1-4.5 cm thick, equal or enlarged downward to a pinched base, prominently reticulated over the entire length or at least on the upper half, dry, solid, white or colored like the cap, basal mycelium white. Flesh white, unchanging. Odor not distinctive. Taste bitter.

Spore Print: Pinkish to wine-brown.

Occurrence: Scattered or in groups with pines or oaks. Summer-winter.

Edibility: Inedible.

Microscopic Features:
Spores 11-13.5 × 3.5-4.5 μm, oblong-elliptic, smooth. Hyaline to pale yellow.

Comments: The stalk of *Tylopilus intermedius* has finer, less prominent stalk reticulation and pores that slowly bruise brownish. *Tylopilus peralbidus* lacks stalk reticulation.

BOLETES

Tylopilus rubrobrunneus
Mazzer & A. H. Sm.

REDDISH-BROWN BITTER BOLETE

Description: Cap 8-30 cm wide, dry, mostly smooth, sometimes cracked in age, dark to bright purple at first, becoming purple-brown, dark reddish-brown, or dull brown. Pores whitish to very pale brownish at first, then dingy pinkish-brown, bruising brown. Stalk 6-20 cm long, 1-5 cm thick, equal or enlarged downward, sometimes finely reticulate at the apex but otherwise smooth, dry, solid, white to brown, developing olive or olive-brown stains from the base upward with age or handling. Flesh white, sometimes slowly bruising brown. Odor not distinctive. Taste very bitter.

Spore Print: Pinkish-brown.

Occurrence: Scattered, in groups or clusters in hardwoods or mixed oak/pine woods. Summer-fall.

Edibility: Inedible.

Microscopic Features:
Spores 10-14 × 3-4.5 μm, suboblong to nearly fusoid, smooth. Brownish.

Comments: *Tylopilus plumbeoviolaceus* and *T. violatinctus* look similar but don't have olive-brown stains on the stalk. *Tylopilus felleus* also lacks olive stains and has a prominently reticulated stalk.

Tylopilus sordidus
(Frost) A. H. Sm. & Thiers

Description: Cap 4.5-13 cm wide initially with a sterile margin, dry, smooth or velvety, cracking in age, gray- to olive- or dark brown, frequently with green-blue tints along the margin. Pores large, eventually 1-2 mm wide, initially whitish to grayish-buff, then pinkish-brown, finally reddish- or yellow-brown, bruising blue-green or blue, changing to brick red. Stalk 4-10 cm long, 1-2 cm thick, equal, finely roughened, dry, solid, brown, with dark longitudinal streaks, tinged with green or blue-green near the apex, paler below, whitish at the base. Flesh whitish, sometimes with red tints, bruising blue-green. Odor slightly pungent or not distinctive. Taste unpleasant or not distinctive.

Spore Print: Reddish-brown.

Occurrence: Scattered or in groups with conifers or hardwoods. Summer-fall.

Edibility: Unknown.

Microscopic Features:
Spores 10-14 × 4-6 μm, subelliptical, smooth. Brownish.

Comments: *Sordidus* means "dirty or smoky." *Suillus tomentosus* has yellowish pores and flesh. *Tylopilus porphyrosporus* (search online) has dark reddish- or blackish-brown pores.

Tylopilus tabacinus (Peck) Singer

Description: Cap 4.5-18 cm wide, commonly with a wavy margin, dry, smooth or velvety, developing fine cracks, yellow-brown to orange-brown or tobacco brown. Pores white to pale tan, more yellow-brown in age, with darker patches and stains. Stalk 4-16.5 cm long, 2.5-6 cm thick, enlarged downward or bulbous when young, nearly equal in age, with prominent reticulation over the upper portion and often smooth below, dry, solid, colored like the cap. Flesh white, browning in age, usually slowly bruising pinkish-buff. Odor typically not distinctive. Taste slightly bitter or not distinctive.

Spore Print: Pinkish-brown.

Occurrence: Scattered or in groups with oak and pine. Summer-fall.

Edibility: Unknown.

Microscopic Features: Spores 10-17 × 3.5-4.5 µm, fusoid to elliptical, smooth. Hyaline to pale honey yellow.

Comments: The yellow-tinged pore surface separates this from pink-tinged species such as the very bitter *Tylopilus felleus* and edible *T. indecisus. Boletus durhamensis* has an olive-brown spore print and mild-tasting flesh.

Tylopilus variobrunneus
Roody, A. R. Bessette & Bessette
VARIABLE BROWN-NET BOLETE

Description: Cap 4-12 cm wide, initially with a sterile margin, dry, velvety becoming nearly bald, dark greenish- or blackish-brown when young, maturing to medium or chestnut brown. Pores whitish, becoming yellow-brown to brownish-pink, bruising pinkish-brown. Stalk 4-10 cm long, 1.2-3 cm thick, equal or enlarged downward above a typically pinched base, prominent white reticulation near the apex, brown reticulation below, dry, solid, whitish on the upper portion, brown lower down, basal mycelium white. Flesh whitish, slowly bruising pinkish to brownish-pink, usually dark brown around insect damage. Odor not distinctive. Taste bitter, astringent, or not distinctive.

Spore Print: Pinkish-brown.

Occurrence: Scattered or in groups with oaks or in mixed oak/pine woods. Summer-fall.

Edibility: Edible.

Microscopic Features: Spores 9-13 × 3-4.5 µm, subfusiform to subelliptic, smooth. Brownish.

Comments: The distinctly two-tone stalk helps distinguish this species from *Tylopilus felleus* and the edible look-alikes *T. ferrugineus* and *T. badiceps.*

Tylopilus violatinctus T. J. Baroni & Both
PALE VIOLET BITTER BOLETE
Description: Cap 7.5-14 cm wide with a
  strongly incurved sterile margin at first,
  dry, velvety becoming almost bald,
  sometimes cracking in age, grayish-
  to bluish-violet, maturing to pale
  purplish or brownish, bruising rusty to
  dark violet. Pores white to dull pink at
  first, then pale brownish, may bruise
  brown. Stalk 8-15 cm long, 1-3.8 cm
  thick, equal or enlarged downward,
  nearly smooth or finely reticulate at
  the apex, dry, solid, white at the apex
  and base, otherwise colored like the
  cap or paler, at times bruising yellow to
  yellow-brown. Flesh white, sometimes
  bruising pale gray. Odor pungent or not
  distinctive. Taste intensely bitter.
Spore Print: Reddish-brown.
Occurrence: Scattered or in groups with
  conifers or hardwoods. Spring-fall.
Edibility: Unknown.
Microscopic Features:
  Spores 7-10 × 3-4 µm, subfusiform,
  smooth. Pale yellow.
Comments: *Tylopilus plumbeoviolaceus*
  has a nonbruising cap and a dark
  purple stalk. The stalk of *Tylopilus
  rubrobrunneus* bruises olive-brown.

Veloporphyrellus conicus
(Ravenel) B. Ortiz, Yan C. Li & Zhu L. Yang
**CONICAL SHAGGY-CAPPED
BOLETE**
Description: Cap 2.5-9.5 cm wide, conical
  becoming convex, dry, shaggy or
  scaly, usually with ridges and small
  depressions when mature, pinkish-
  tan to yellow-brown, sometimes with
  a tinge of orange, showing white flesh
  between the scales, the margin fringed
  with remnants of sterile tissue when
  young. Pores white, then grayish-pink
  to pinkish-brown. Stalk slender, 4-7 cm
  long, 6-18 mm thick, equal, smooth or
  finally wrinkled, dry, solid, white or
  yellow, sometimes with pinkish tints
  especially in the midportion. Flesh
  white, unchanging. Odor fruity or not
  distinctive. Taste not distinctive.
Spore Print: Pinkish-brown.
Occurrence: Scattered with pines or in
  mixed woods. Summer-fall.
Edibility: Edible.
Microscopic Features:
  Spores 14-21 × 4-6 µm, elongate-fusoid,
  smooth. Hyaline to honey yellow.
Comments: *Tylopilus conicus* is a synonym.
  Boletellus ananas and *Suillus spraguei*
  have yellow pores.

Aureoboletus auriporus (Peck) Pouzar
ACIDIC GOLDEN-PORED BOLETE
Description: Cap 2-8 cm wide with a
sterile margin, moist and sticky when
fresh, coated with tiny fibrils, pinkish-
to vinaceous-brown. Pores golden-
yellow, becoming brownish-yellow in
age, typically slowly staining brick red.
Stalk 4-11.5 cm long, 6-17 mm thick,
narrowed abruptly at the base, sticky,
pale yellow at the apex, streaked pale
pinkish-brown below, basal mycelium
white. Flesh white to yellowish,
vinaceous under the cuticle, sometimes
faintly staining blue or pinkish when
exposed. Odor often pungent. Taste of
cap surface and flesh usually acidic.
Spore Print: Olive-brown.
Occurrence: Scattered, or in groups under
oak. Summer-fall.
Edibility: Edible.
Microscopic Features:
   Spores 11-16 × 4-6 μm, fusiform-elliptic,
   smooth. Brownish.
Comments: *Auriporus* means "golden
pores." *Boletus auriporus* is a synonym.
Aureoboletus innixus is similar but often
grows in clusters joined at the stalk
bases. It has a darker brown, dry cap
that does not taste acidic, and flesh with
a pungent odor.

Aureoboletus innixus
(Frost) Halling, A. R. Bessette & Bessette
CLUSTERED BROWN BOLETE
Description: Cap 3-7.5 cm wide, margin
sterile, dry, slightly velvety, often
cracked in age, yellow-brown, or
reddish-brown to cinnamon, may
develop purplish or reddish tones near
the margin. Pores bright yellow at first,
becoming dull yellow in age. Stalk
3-6 cm long, 1-1.6 cm thick, usually
enlarged downward, swollen above a
tapered base, club-shaped, solid; surface
sticky near the base, yellowish, streaked
with dark brown tones, basal mycelium
yellow. Flesh white to pale yellow,
sometimes with vinaceous tinges
beneath the cap cuticle. Odor pungent.
Taste mildly acidic or not distinctive.
Spore Print: Olive-brown.
Occurrence: Scattered or in clusters with
hardwoods, especially with oak. Spring-
fall.
Edibility: Edible.
Microscopic Features:
   Spores 8-11 × 3-5 μm, elliptical, smooth.
   Brownish.
Comments: *Boletus innixus*, *B. caespitosus*,
and *Pulveroboletus innixus* are all synonyms. *Aureoboletus auriporus* is similar,
but it has a sticky cap that tastes acidic.

Aureoboletus russellii
(Frost) G. Wu & Zhu L. Yang
RUSSELL'S BOLETE
Description: Cap 3-13 cm wide with a strongly incurved margin, dry, velvety, becoming cracked with scalelike patches in age, yellowish- to reddish-brown or olive-gray. Pores yellow to greenish-yellow, sometimes bruising brighter yellow. Stalk 10-20 cm long, 1-2 cm thick, deeply grooved and ridged like shaggy bark or honeycomb, equal, dry, solid, often curved at the base, reddish-brown to pinkish-tan. Flesh yellow, may slowly bruise brown. Odor and taste not distinctive.
Spore Print: Olive to olive-brown.
Occurrence: Scattered, with oak, hemlock, or pine. Summer-fall.
Edibility: Edible.
Microscopic Features:
Spores 15-20 × 7-11 µm, elliptical, longitudinally lined with deep grooves. Brownish.
Comments: *Boletellus russellii* and *Frostiella russellii* are synonyms. *Heimioporus betula* has a bald, shiny, red to orange cap and pitted spores. Mycologist Charles Frost named this bolete to honor his friend the American botanist John Lewis Russell (1808-73).

Baorangia bicolor complex
(Kuntze) G. Wu, Halling & Zhu L. Yang
RED AND YELLOW BOLETE
Description: Cap 5-12.5 cm wide, velvety when young, often cracked when dry or mature, dark red to rose-red, fading toward tan. Pores bright yellow when young, becoming olive-yellow, bruising blue, tubes less than 1 cm long. Stalk 5-10 cm long, 2-5 cm thick, equal or enlarged downward, solid, smooth, yellow at the apex, reddish below, unchanging or slowly bruising blue, not reticulate or rarely so at the apex. Flesh yellow, deeper yellow in the stalk, unchanging or slowly or weakly staining blue. Odor and taste not distinctive.
Spore Print: Olive-brown.
Occurrence: Scattered or in groups with oak. Summer-fall.
Edibility: Edible.
Microscopic Features:
Spores 8-12 × 3.5-5 µm, oblong to slightly ventricose, smooth. Brownish.
Comments: *Boletus bicolor* is a synonym. *Boletus sensibilis* has longer tubes, quickly bruises blue on all parts, and smells like curry. *Boletus pallidoroseus* has a pale rose-pink cap, a yellowish margin, and flesh smelling of bouillon.

BOLETES

229

Boletellus ananas (M. A. Curtis) Murrill
PINEAPPLE BOLETE
Description: Cap 3-10 cm wide, with overlapping purplish-red scales that become pinkish to tan in age, the margin hung with white remnants of partial veil. Pores yellow, sometimes tinged reddish-brown, bruising blue. Stalk 6-15.5 cm long, 7-16 mm thick, enlarged downward, bald to slightly fibrillose, white to tan, may have a reddish zone near the apex. Flesh whitish, staining yellowish, then blue, and finally grayish. Odor and taste note distinctive.
Spore Print: Rusty brown to dark brown.
Occurrence: Scattered or in groups on decaying wood or on the ground, with oak and pine. Spring-fall.
Edibility: Inedible.
Microscopic Features:
Spores 15-24 × 7-11 µm, fusoid, with conspicuous, spiraling longitudinal ridges, often with an indistinct apical pore. Brownish.
Comments: *Ananas* is the pineapple genus, referring to the cap scales. *Boletus ananas* is a synonym. Compare with somewhat similar *Veloporphyrellus conicus*. Also see *Suillus spraguei*, which has a shaggy red stalk.

Boletus auripes Peck
Description: Cap 4-13 cm wide, rounded at first, becoming nearly flat, dry, finely velvety to nearly bald, yellowish, grayish, or chestnut brown, becoming paler in age. Pores yellow at first, becoming olive-yellow, unchanging or bruising yellow-orange, often depressed at the stalk when mature. Stalk 7-10 cm long, 2-3 cm thick, typically bulbous when young, becoming club-shaped to almost equal when mature, dry, solid, golden-yellow with yellow reticulation on at least the upper portion. Flesh bright yellow, intensifying when rubbed. Odor and taste not distinctive.
Spore Print: Yellow-brown to olive-brown.
Occurrence: Solitary or in groups with hardwoods, especially oak and beech. Summer-fall.
Edibility: Edible.
Microscopic Features:
Spores 10-14 × 3-5 µm, ellipsoid-cylindric to subfusoid, smooth. Yellowish.
Comments: *Auripes* means "golden-yellow foot." *Boletus aureissimus* (search online) is very similar but has more delicate stalk reticulation and a honey yellow to bright yellow or yellow-orange cap. *Ceriomyces aureissimus* var. *castaneus* (search online) also similar, has a velvety purplish-brown cap.

Boletus durhamensis
B. Ortiz, Bessette & McConnell

Description: Cap 2-17 cm wide, broadly
convex with a sterile margin, dry, feltlike to velvety, rusty brown, becoming
yellowish-brown in age, usually
yellowish along the margin. Pores
dark cinnamon-brown, unchanging or
darkening slightly when bruised. Stalk
2.8-7.5 cm long, 1-2 cm thick, equal
or enlarged downward, solid, yellow
powdered with cinnamon-brown and
typically with fine cinnamon-brown
reticulation at the apex. Flesh white,
tinged with yellowish-tan. Odor and
taste not distinctive.

Spore Print: Olive-brown.

Occurrence: Solitary, scattered, or in
groups with hardwoods or in grassy
areas near willow oak, white oak, and
sometimes red maple, sweetgum, and
dogwood. Summer-fall.

Edibility: Unknown.

Microscopic Features:
Spores 7-12 × 3.7-5 μm, ellipsoid,
smooth. Hyaline.

Comments: *Durhamensis* refers to
Durham, North Carolina, where this
bolete was first collected by American
mycologist Owen McConnell. See *Boletus
vermiculosoides*, which has blue-staining
flesh, and *Tylopilus tabacinus*, which has
bitter-tasting flesh.

Boletus ferrugineus Schaeff.
RUSTY IRON BOLETE

Description: Cap 5-11 cm wide, margin
even or sterile, dry, slightly velvety,
sometimes cracked in age, dark olive
to olive-yellow to reddish-brown.
Pores yellowish, often bruising bluish.
Stalk 3-10 cm long, 1.5-2.5 cm thick,
equal or tapered downward, usually
with a pinched base, dry, solid, with
raised longitudinal lines that may
resemble reticulation at the apex or
below, pale yellow or whitish, usually
streaked with brown, whitish near the
base, basal mycelium yellowish. Flesh
yellow with a reddish line beneath the
cuticle, pinkish around larval tunnels,
sometimes slightly bruising blue. Odor
slightly pungent or not distinctive.
Taste not distinctive.

Spore Print: Olive-brown.

Occurrence: Scattered or in groups in
mixed woods, usually with conifers.
Summer-fall.

Edibility: Edible.

Microscopic Features:
Spores 10-14 × 4.5-5 μm, oblong to
ventricose, smooth. Brownish.

Comments: Compare with *Boletus subtomentosus* var. *subtomentosus* (search
online) and *Xerocomellus chrysenteron*
(search online). *Boletus spadiceus* and
Xerocomus ferrugineus are synonyms.

Boletus longicurvipes Snell & A. H. Sm.
LONG CURVED-FOOTED BOLETE
Description: Cap 2.5-11 cm wide, smooth or slightly wrinkled-pitted, sticky or slimy, shiny, yellow to brown-orange, often with green tones. Pores yellow, becoming greenish, may bruise yellow or brownish. Stalk 5-9 cm long, 1-2 cm thick, equal or enlarged downward, usually curved at the bottom, dry, solid, whitish to yellowish, often with pinkish-red to pinkish-tan tints, covered with raised white to yellowish dots darkening to red-brown. Flesh white to yellow, sometimes staining pink, then reddish, and finally dingy slate, the stalk flesh sometimes bruising blue in the base or erratically overall. Odor not distinctive. Taste acidic or not distinctive.
Spore Print: Olive- to gray-brown.
Occurrence: Solitary or scattered in mixed woods and hardwoods with oak, pine, and hemlock. Summer-fall.
Edibility: Edible.
Microscopic Features:
Spores 13-19 × 4-6.5 μm, narrowly subfusiform to oblong, smooth. Brownish.
Comments: Molecular analysis indicates that *Boletus longicurvipes* and *B. viscidocorrugis* are synonyms.

Boletus luridellus (Murrill) Murrill
Description: Cap 4-12 cm wide, margin sterile, dry, velvety or nearly bald, yellow- to amber- or red-brown, sometimes streaked brown over a yellow ground color, becoming paler in age. Pore surface yellow at first, becoming greenish- to olive-yellow, bruising blue. Stalk 4.5-9.5 cm long, 1-3 cm thick, equal or tapered in either direction, sometimes swollen near the middle, dry, solid, yellow at the apex and yellow to brownish-red overall, apex with brown reticulation; lower down the stalk is often dotted and streaked with dark red or brownish-red and bruises blue. Flesh yellow, red in the stalk base, quickly bruising blue. Odor and taste not distinctive.
Spore Print: Olive-brown.
Occurrence: Scattered or in groups with oak and pine. Summer-fall.
Edibility: Edible.
Microscopic Features:
Spores 12-17 × 4-6 μm, fusoid, smooth. Pale yellow-brown.
Comments: A difficult bolete to identify because of its variable colors. *Luridellus* means "dirty brownish," referring to the cap color. *Boletus subsensibilis* is a synonym.

Boletus miniato-olivaceus Frost
RED AND OLIVE VELVET-CAP
Description: Cap 5-15 cm wide, with an incurved sterile margin, dry, velvety, rose-red, becoming rose-pink with olive tones, then olive-yellow when mature, bruises blue. Pores yellow, aging to olive-yellow with reddish tints, quickly bruising blue then slowly brownish. Stalk 6-12.5 cm long, 1-2 cm thick, equal or tapered in either direction, with a pinched base, dry, solid, roughened with reddish dots, occasionally longitudinally lined, yellow with reddish tints, sometimes reticulate on the upper portion, typically bruising dark blue, basal mycelium yellow. Cap flesh white to pale yellow, slowing bruising blue; stalk flesh yellow, sometimes bruising blue. Odor and taste not distinctive.
Spore Print: Olive-brown.
Occurrence: Scattered or in groups with conifers or hardwoods. Summer-fall.
Edibility: Reportedly poisonous.
Microscopic Features:
Spores 10-18 × 4-7 µm, fusoid-subelliptical, smooth. Yellowish-brown.
Comments: *Boletus sensibilis* is similar, but the cap lacks olive tones, and the flesh smells like curry.

Boletus nobilissimus Both & R. Riedel
Description: Cap 9.5-15 cm wide, with an incurved sterile margin that becomes uplifted at maturity, dry, tufted with fine hairs, pitted to corrugated, yellow to vinaceous-brown, sometimes mottled with these colors. Pores stuffed, white, becoming yellow then greenish-yellow to olive when mature. Stalk 8.5-11.5 cm long, 2.9-6 cm thick, club-shaped to bulbous, with elongated and sometimes raised reticulation that is white at the apex and base and pale brown in the midsection. Flesh white, staining brown in the stalk base. Odor fragrant. Taste not distinctive.
Spore Print: Brownish-olive.
Occurrence: Scattered or in groups in mixed oak/pine woods. Summer-fall.
Edibility: Edible.
Microscopic Features:
Spores 11-15.5 × 4.4-5.5 µm, subfusiform, smooth. Hyaline.
Comments: *Boletus nobilis* (search online) is similar but has a much smoother cap and a whitish stalk with delicate, nonraised reticulation. Compare with *Boletus edulis* (search online), which grows with conifers and has a cap that is neither strongly pitted nor corrugated.

Boletus oliveisporus (Murrill) Murrill

Description: Cap 5-18 cm wide with a sterile margin, dry, velvety, often cracked when mature, initially reddish-orange becoming somewhat shiny and dull gray- to cinnamon-brown, quickly bruising blue-black. Pores yellow at first, becoming olive-yellow, bruising blue. Stalk 4-12 cm long, 1-2.5 cm thick, equal or tapered in either direction, dry, solid, bald or covered with raised brown dots, yellow with reddish tinges when young, becoming olive-brown from the base upward in age, longitudinally lined, sometimes reticulate on the upper portion or nearly overall. Flesh yellow, bruising blue when exposed. Odor and taste not distinctive.

Spore Print: Olive-brown.

Occurrence: Solitary or in groups with pines or in mixed pine/oak woods. Summer-fall.

Edibility: Unknown.

Microscopic Features:

Spores 11-17 × 4-6 μm, fusoid, smooth. Brownish.

Comments: *Cyanoboletus pulverulentus* (search online) is similar but has raised ridges on the stalk and a smaller, darker brown cap. *Suillellus subvelutipes* has red to orange pores.

Boletus pallidoroseus Both

PALE ROSE BOLETE

Description: Cap 6-17 cm wide, dry, bald to velvety, rose- or purplish-pink, yellowish along the margin, becoming pale orange-brownish, not bruising blue. Pores yellow becoming olive-brown, bruising blue, tubes only to 5-6 mm long. Stalk 6-8 cm long, 1.5-3 cm thick, equal or enlarged downward, apex sometimes reticulate, dry, solid, covered at first with fine matted hairs or powder, later nearly bald, yellow above and shades of pink below, bruising blue. Flesh yellow, golden-yellow in the stalk, bruising blue slowly and faintly in the cap, sometimes also in the stalk. Odor like beef bouillon or rotted meat. Taste not distinctive.

Spore Print: Brownish-olive.

Occurrence: Scattered or in groups with oak and beech. Summer-fall.

Edibility: Unknown.

Microscopic Features:

Spores 9-12 × 3.5-5.5 μm, subfusiform, smooth. Yellowish.

Comments: *Boletus sensibilis* has longer tubes and quickly bruises blue on all parts. The *Baorangia bicolor* complex also has shallow tubes, as well as odorless flesh.

Boletus pallidus Frost
PALLID BOLETE
Description: Cap 4.5-15 cm wide, the center sometimes depressed, dry, smooth, often cracked in age, whitish to pale brownish, developing rose tints. Pores whitish to pale yellow, becoming greenish-yellow, bruising greenish-blue then grayish-brown (very young specimens may not bruise, or stain grayish-brown only). Stalk 5-12 cm long, 1-2.5 cm thick, equal or enlarged downward, dry, solid, smooth or slightly reticulate at the apex, the apex sometimes yellow; overall the stalk is whitish developing brown streaks and/or reddish tints toward the base, may bruise slightly blue. Flesh white to pale yellow, may bruise blue or pinkish. Odor not distinctive. Taste mild or slightly bitter.

Spore Print: Olive or olive-brown.

Occurrence: Solitary or in groups in hardwoods, or in mixed oak/pine woods. Summer-fall.

Edibility: Edible.

Microscopic Features:
Spores 9-15 × 3-5 μm, narrowly oval to subfusoid, smooth. Pale brown.

Comments: *Tylopilus intermedius* has grayish-buff to dull pinkish pores and intensely bitter flesh.

Boletus patrioticus
T. J. Baroni, Bessette & Roody
PATRIOTIC BOLETE
Description: Cap 3-13 cm wide, margin sterile, dry, velvety, olive becoming pinkish to brick or dark red, usually retaining olive tints when mature. Pores pale yellow, becoming olive-yellow, bruising blue. Stalk 2.5-10 cm long, 1-2 cm thick, usually enlarged downward, often with a pinched base, dry, solid, scurfy, color varying from rose-red on the upper portion to olive toward the base, sometimes a mixture of these colors over a yellow ground color, basal mycelium whitish. Flesh whitish, pinkish-red under the cap cuticle, dingy yellow to brownish toward the base, slowly staining blue beneath the reddish areas, bruising blue-green or sometimes rose-red elsewhere. Odor not distinctive. Taste acidic.

Spore Print: Olive-brown.

Occurrence: Solitary or in groups with oak or in mixed woods. Spring-fall.

Edibility: Unknown.

Microscopic Features:
Spores 10-13 × 4-5.5 μm, subfusiform, smooth. Golden-brown.

Comments: *Patrioticus* means "patriotic," referring to the red, white, and blue staining of the flesh.

BOLETES

235

Boletus rubricitrinus (Murrill) Murrill

Description: Cap 3-15 cm wide, sometimes slightly depressed, margin sterile, dry, bald or velvety, rose- to brick red or tawny cinnamon, fading toward olive- or yellowish-browns, usually bruising blue-black. Pores yellow, then olive-yellow, bruising blue; tubes 8-20 mm deep. Stalk 5-12 cm long, 1.5-3.5 cm thick, equal or tapered in either direction, sometimes swollen near the base, dry, solid, usually longitudinally lined, sometimes weakly reticulate at the apex, yellow with dull red to red-brown streaks and dots especially toward the base, bruising blue-green to blue-black. Flesh yellow, bruising blue. Odor not distinctive. Taste slightly acidic.

Spore Print: Olive-brown.

Occurrence: Under oak or in mixed oak/pine woods. Spring-fall.

Edibility: Edible.

Microscopic Features:
 Spores 13-19 × 5-8 μm, fusoid to subfusoid-ellipsoid, smooth. Yellowish.

Comments: *Rubricitrinus* means "red and lemon-yellow." *Ceriomyces rubricitrinus* is a synonym. The cap of *Xerocomus sclerotiorum* usually has a yellow margin. *Lanmaoa carminipes* (search online) has tubes less than 8 mm deep.

Boletus sensibilis Peck
SENSITIVE BOLETE

Description: Cap 5-16 cm wide, margin even, dry, velvety, bald in age, orange- to brick red, aging to rose or cinnamon, bruising blue. Pores yellow, browning in age, instantly bruising blue; tubes 8-12 mm long. Stalk 8-12 cm long, 1-3.5 cm thick, equal or enlarged downward, dry, solid, sometimes reticulate at the apex, yellow with pink or red on the lower portion, quickly bruising blue. Flesh yellow, brighter in the stalk, rapidly bruising blue. Odor like fenugreek or curry. Taste not distinctive.

Spore Print: Olive-brown.

Occurrence: Scattered or in groups with hardwoods, especially oak. Summer-fall.

Edibility: Edible, although previously reported as toxic.

Microscopic Features:
 Spores 10-13 × 3.5-4.5 μm, suboblong to slightly ventricose, smooth. Brownish.

Comments: *Boletus pallidoroseus* has a similar smell but shorter tubes and does not bruise blue in all parts. *Boletus miniato-olivaceus* and the *Baorangia bicolor* complex lack the curry odor and have different bruising patterns.

Boletus separans Peck
LILAC BOLETE
Description: Cap 5-15 cm wide, convex, dry, velvety or bald, pitted and wrinkled, creamy white tinged with lilac- to reddish-brown, or sometimes purple, becoming yellowish-brown or bronze when mature. Pores white, then yellowish to brownish in age. Stalk 6-15 cm long, 1-3 cm thick, equal or enlarged downward, dry, solid, colored like the cap, often with lilac tones in the midportion, sometimes purplish overall or yellow near the apex, finely reticulate at least on the upper half, reticulation sometimes hard to see. Flesh white, unchanging. Odor not distinctive. Taste sweet and nutty or not distinctive.

Spore Print: Pale reddish-brown.

Occurrence: Solitary or in groups with hardwoods or with pines. Year-round.

Edibility: Edible.

Microscopic Features:
Spores 12-16 × 3.5-5 µm, narrowly subfusiform, smooth. Brownish.

Comments: *Xanthoconium separans* is a synonym. Lilac areas stain blue with NH_4OH. *Boletus nobilissimus* and *B. nobilis* (search online) lack any purplish tones.

Boletus speciosus Frost
SHOWY BOLETE
Description: Cap 7-16 cm wide, convex, dry, finely velvety to nearly bald, bright rose-red to rose-pink, becoming orange-red to olive-brown, bruises blackish-blue. Pores yellow, becoming olive-yellow, quickly bruising blue then reddish-brown. Stalk 5-12 cm long, 1.6-4 cm thick, equal or enlarged downward, base often abruptly narrowed, dry, solid, reticulate on the upper half or overall, yellow on the upper portion, pinkish-red to pinkish-brown below, bruising blue. Flesh yellow, staining gray-blue. Odor like iodine or not distinctive. Taste not distinctive.

Spore Print: Olive-brown.

Occurrence: Solitary or in groups with hardwoods and pines. Summer-fall.

Edibility: Edible.

Microscopic Features:
Spores 11-15 × 3-5.5 µm, narrowly oblong to subfusoid, smooth. Yellowish-brown.

Comments: *Ceriomyces speciosus* is a synonym. *Butyriboletus brunneus* (search online) has a reddish- to yellow- or olive-brown cap. Also compare with *Butyriboletus roseopurpureus* (search online), which has a pinkish-purple cap that becomes purple-red or mottled with these colors in age.

Boletus variipes Peck
VARIABLE-STALK BOLETE
Description: Cap 6-20 cm wide, dry,
velvety to bald, often cracked at
maturity, creamy to yellowish-tan,
grayish- to yellow-brown, or dark
brown. Pores white, becoming yellowish to yellowish-olive in age. Stalk
8-15 cm long, 1-3.5 cm thick, equal
or enlarged downward, dry, solid,
whitish to yellow- or grayish-brown,
usually covered with white or brown
reticulation. Flesh white, unchanging or
slowly staining pale pinkish-gray when
exposed. Odor and taste not distinctive.
Spore Print: Olive-brown.
Occurrence: Scattered or in groups with
hardwoods, sometimes conifers.
Spring-fall.
Edibility: Edible.
Microscopic Features:
Spores 12-18 × 4-6 µm, subfusoid,
smooth. Yellow.
Comments: *Boletus variipes* var. *variipes*
and *B. variipes* var. *fagicola* are synonyms. *Tylopilus felleus* is similar but has
bitter-tasting flesh and a pore surface
that pinkens in age. *Boletus atkinsonii*
(search online), also similar, has a
cap surface roughened with tufts of
hyphae, a whitish stalk covered with
fine brownish reticulation, and smaller
spores.

Boletus vermiculosoides A. H. Sm. & Thiers
WORMY BOLETE
Description: Cap 4-12 cm wide, dry,
covered with tiny matted fibers, yellow
at first, becoming brown in age. Pores
initially dark brown, turning paler in
age, bruising blackish-blue then very
slowly fading to dull brownish-orange.
Stalk 4-10 cm, 1-2 cm thick, equal, dry,
solid, coated with brownish powder
over a whitish or pale yellow ground
color with olive tints, bruising blue
then dark brown. Flesh yellow, quickly
bruising blue. Odor pungent. Taste
astringent or not distinctive.
Spore Print: Olive-brown.
Occurrence: Solitary or in groups with oak.
Summer-fall.
Edibility: Unknown.
Microscopic Features:
Spores 9-12 × 3-4 µm, elliptical,
smooth. Brownish.
Comments: *Boletus vermiculosus* (search
online) is very similar but has a dark
brown to grayish- or reddish-brown
cap that stains vinaceous with the
application of KOH, and larger spores.
Vermiculosoides means "resembling
Boletus vermiculosus." *Vermiculosus*
means "infested with insect larvae,"
which both of these species usually are.

Buchwaldoboletus lignicola (Kallenb.) Pilát

Description: Cap 2.5-12 cm wide with a
substantial inrolled and sterile margin,
dry, suedelike, reddish- to yellow-
brown, often darker along the margin,
sometimes bruising darker brown. Pores
attached to slightly decurrent, yellow
to golden, becoming greenish-yellow,
bruising greenish- to blackish-blue then
fading to reddish-brown. Stalk 3-8 cm
long, 6-25 mm thick, equal or tapered
in either direction, often eccentric, dry,
solid, velvety, golden-yellow at the
apex, reddish- to yellow-brown below,
bruising brown, often with fine reddish
apical reticulation, basal mycelium
yellow. Flesh yellow, bruising blue.
Odor not distinctive. Taste acidic or not
distinctive.

Spore Print: Olive-brown.

Occurrence: Solitary or scattered on pine
trees, stumps or roots. Summer-fall.

Edibility: Unknown.

Microscopic Features:
Spores 6-10 × 3-4 µm, ellipsoid,
smooth. Yellowish.

Comments: *Boletus lignicola* and *Pulveroboletus lignicola* are synonyms. *Buchwaldoboletus hemichrysus* (search
online) has a brighter yellow, powdery
cap, flesh without a distinctive odor,
and yellow pores that become reddish-
brown.

Heimioporus betula (Schwein.) E. Horak

SHAGGY-STALKED BOLETE

Description: Cap 3-9 cm wide with a sterile
margin, smooth, sticky and shiny when
moist, bright red, orange, yellow, or a
combination of these, the margin often
yellow. Pores yellow or greenish-yellow,
sometimes bruising blue. Stalk 10-20
cm long, 6-20 mm thick, often curved
near the base, covered with coarse
and shaggy reticulation, dry, solid,
various shades of reds and yellows,
basal mycelium white and cottony.
Flesh yellow, sometimes tinged orange
beneath the cap, pinkish elsewhere.
Odor not distinctive. Taste acidic.

Spore Print: Olive-brown.

Occurrence: Scattered under pine,
hemlock, hardwoods, or rhododendron.
Summer-fall.

Edibility: Edible.

Microscopic Features:
Spores 15-19 × 6-10 µm, narrowly
elliptical, ornamented with a loose
reticulum and scattered minute pits,
typically with a distinct apical pore.
Brownish.

Comments: The stalks are particularly
good for cooking. *Austroboletus betula*
and *Heimiella betula* are synonyms.
Aureoboletus russellii is dry-capped and
less colorful. *Austroboletus subflavidus*
is found along the coastal plain.

BOLETES

239

Hortiboletus rubellus
(Krombh.) Simonini, Vizzini & Gelardi
RUBY BOLETE
Description: Cap 2-8 cm wide, dry, velvety, usually finely cracked in age, dark red, fading toward olive-brown at maturity. Pores yellow, bruising blue-green. Stalk 3-8 cm long, 5-13 mm thick, equal, enlarged or tapered downward, often with a narrowed base, dry, solid, yellow at the apex, with reddish-orange dots and points, bruising brown. Flesh yellow above and reddish-orange toward the base, slowly bruising blue-green. Odor and taste not distinctive.
Spore Print: Olive-brown.
Occurrence: Scattered or in groups in grassy areas or under hardwoods, especially oak and beech. Summer-fall.
Edibility: Unknown.
Microscopic Features:
Spores 10-13 × 4-5 µm, elliptical, smooth. Brownish.
Comments: *Boletus rubellus* and *Xerocomus rubellus* are synonyms. *Hortiboletus campestris* (search online) has stalk flesh without reddish-orange in the base. *Boletus subfraternus* (search online) has large, irregular pores, and its cap does not become cracked. *Boletus harrisonii* (search online) differs microscopically and lacks reddish-orange dots and points on its stalk.

Imleria badia (Fr.) Vizzini
BAY BOLETE
Description: Cap 4-9 cm wide, maturing to nearly flat or centrally depressed with a margin that is often upturned, dry to sticky, smooth or slightly velvety, chestnut to yellow-brown, sometimes with olive tones. Pores yellow to greenish-yellow, quickly bruising greenish- to grayish-blue. Stalk 4-9 cm long, 1-2 cm thick, equal or enlarged downward, dry, solid, smooth to slightly roughened, basal mycelium white. Flesh white, usually staining yellow except near the tube layer, where it bruises bluish. Odor and taste not distinctive.
Spore Print: Olive-brown.
Occurrence: Solitary or scattered under conifers, or on decayed conifer stumps. Summer-fall.
Edibility: Edible.
Microscopic Features:
Spores 10-14 × 4-5 µm, elliptical to fusiform, smooth. Yellow.
Comments: *Boletus badius* and *Xerocomus badius* are synonyms. *Xanthoconium affine* has white pores that stain yellow to brownish when bruised. *Tylopilus* species have white or pinkish-brown pores and pinkish-brown spore prints.

Neoboletus pseudosulphureus
(Kallenb.) W. Klofac

Description: Cap 4-20 cm wide, dry, covered with tiny matted fibrils, becoming bald in age, bright yellow, aging duller to tawny usually with central tints of brownish-red, quickly bruising bluish-black. Pores bright yellow, becoming greenish- then brownish-yellow, quickly bruising blue then slowly brownish. Stalk 4-12 cm long, 2-5 cm thick, enlarged downward, sometimes reticulate on the upper portion, dry, solid, bright yellow, may have reddish tints especially near the base, bruising like the pores. Flesh bright yellow to greenish-yellow in the cap, yellow in the upper portion of the stalk, dark red at the base, quickly bruising blue. Odor not distinctive. Taste acidic, astringent, or not distinctive.

Spore Print: Olive-brown.

Occurrence: Scattered or in groups under hardwoods or in mixed oak/pine woods. Summer-fall.

Edibility: Unknown.

Microscopic Features:
Spores 10-16 × 4-6 μm, fusoid to ellipsoid-fusoid, smooth. Brownish-yellow.

Comments: *Boletus pseudosulphureus* is a synonym. *Retiboletus ornatipes* does not bruise blue.

Pulveroboletus auriflammeus
(Berk. and M. A. Curtis) Singer

FLAMING GOLD BOLETE

Description: Cap 4-9 cm wide, dry, velvety or powdery, sometimes with fine cracks, bright orange-yellow or brownish-orange. Pores radially elongated, yellow to yellow-orange, sometimes with red tinges. Stalk equal or tapered in either direction, sometimes club-shaped with a pinched base, coarsely reticulate on the upper portion or overall, young specimens sometimes with raised longitudinal ribs, dry, solid, slightly powdery, colored like the cap, basal mycelium white. Flesh white to pale yellow. Odor not distinctive. Taste acidic or not distinctive.

Spore Print: Olive-brown.

Occurrence: Scattered or clustered under hardwoods, especially oak, or in mixed woods. Summer-fall.

Edibility: Unknown.

Microscopic Features:
Spores 8-12 × 3-5 μm, subellipsoid to subfusiform, smooth. Hyaline.

Comments: *Boletus auriflammeus* is a synonym. *Boletus aurantiosplendens* (search online) is similar but has an orange to brownish-yellow cap, a yellow to apricot orange stalk with reddish-brown streaks, and brighter yellow pores without crimson tints.

Pulveroboletus curtisii (Berk.) Singer

Description: Cap 3-9.5 cm wide with a sterile and initially incurved margin, slimy or sticky when fresh, dusted with orange powder when young, later smooth, bright yellow to orange-yellow, sometimes developing brownish tints or whitish areas in age. Pores at first whitish to bright yellow-orange, in age dull and brownish. Stalk 6-12 cm long, 6-13 mm thick, equal, solid, sticky or slimy when fresh, roughened near the apex, smoother below, pale yellow to yellow, the base covered with cottony white mycelium. Flesh whitish, unchanging when exposed. Odor not distinctive. Cap slime tastes acidic.

Spore Print: Olive-brown.

Occurrence: Scattered or in groups in conifer or mixed woods. Summer-fall.

Edibility: Unknown.

Microscopic Features:
Spores 9.5-17 × 4-6 μm, elliptical to subventricose, smooth. Yellowish.

Comments: *Boletus curtisii* is a synonym. This mushroom was named after the nineteenth-century North Carolina mycologist Moses Ashley Curtis. The slime stains fingers yellow.

Pulveroboletus ravenelii (Berk. & M. A. Curtis) Murrill

RAVENEL'S BOLETE

Description: Cap 2.5-10 cm wide, margin incurved and usually fringed with remnants of partial veil, sticky when moist, otherwise dry, powdery at first, then smooth, bright yellow, becoming reddish-orange to reddish-brown centrally. Pores bright yellow, turning olive at maturity, bruising greenish-blue. Stalk 4-14.5 cm long, 6-16 mm thick, equal, dry, solid, bright yellow, smooth above the ring or ring zone, slightly roughened below. Partial veil cottony and bright yellow, leaving a fragile ring near the apex. Flesh white to yellow, bruising pale blue then brownish. Odor not distinctive or somewhat spicy. Taste acidic.

Spore Print: Olive-brown to olive-gray.

Occurrence: Scattered or in groups with conifers or rhododendron. Summer-fall.

Edibility: Edible.

Microscopic Features:
Spores 8-10.5 × 4-5 μm, elliptical to oval, smooth. Brownish.

Comments: *Boletus melleoluteus* (search online) is a similar but uncommon bolete that grows with hardwoods. *Suillus tomentosus* bruises blue but lacks a partial veil.

Retiboletus griseus
(Frost) Manfr. Binder & Bres.
GRAY BOLETE
Description: Cap 5-14 cm wide, dry, covered with matted, grayish fibrils or scales when mature, gray to brownish-gray, sometimes developing yellow tints. Pores white to grayish or gray-brown, pinkish-brown in age, sometimes bruising dirty gray. Stalk 4-14.5 cm long, 1-3.5 cm thick, equal or tapered downward and often curved, dry, solid, covered with coarse yellowish reticulation that darkens to brownish-black, ground color white to gray, occasionally with reddish stains, yellowing from the base upward. Flesh whitish, yellow in the base of the stalk, yellow-brown around insect damage, sometimes slowly bruising brownish. Odor and taste not distinctive.
Spore Print: Olive-brown.
Occurrence: Scattered in mixed hardwoods. Summer-fall.
Edibility: Edible.
Microscopic Features:
Spores 9-13 × 3-5 μm, fusoid to oblong, smooth. Brownish.
Comments: *Boletus griseus* is a synonym. *Boletus griseus* var. *fuscus* (search online) is a former variety, now in synonymy, with *Retiboletus griseus*. It has a purplish- to dark brown cap in youth.

Retiboletus ornatipes
(Peck) Manfr. Binder & Bres.
ORNATE-STALKED BOLETE
Description: Cap 4-20 cm wide, dry, powdery or velvety or smooth and shiny, some shade of yellow to brownish- or dull gray. Pores yellow, becoming brownish-yellow in age, bruising yellow-orange to brownish. Stalk 8-15 cm long, 1-2.5 cm thick, variably shaped, dry, solid, yellowish, usually covered with coarse brown reticulation overall, bruising darker yellow or brown. Flesh yellow, rarely bruising blue in the base of the stalk. Juice stains fingers yellow. Odor not distinctive. Taste typically very bitter.
Spore Print: Olive- to yellow-brown.
Occurrence: Scattered or clustered under hardwoods or in mixed woods. Spring-fall.
Edibility: Edible.
Microscopic Features:
Spores 9-13 × 3-4 μm, oblong to slightly ventricose with an obtuse apex, smooth. Brownish.
Comments: *Boletus ornatipes* is a synonym. *Retiboletus griseus* lacks the bitter taste. *Pulveroboletus auriflammeus* is smaller and less robust.

Xanthoconium affine (Peck) Singer

Description: Cap 4-11.5 cm wide, dry, velvety, dark brown to golden-brown, sometimes with white or pale yellow spots. Pores white at first, becoming yellowish to yellow-brown, bruising yellow to brownish. Stalk 3-10 cm long, 1-2 cm thick, equal or tapered in either direction, smooth or having brown reticulation, dry, solid, whitish, sometimes with brownish streaks. Flesh white, unchanging. Odor and taste not distinctive.

Spore Print: Bright yellow-brown.

Occurrence: Scattered, in groups or clusters with pines and hardwoods, especially oak or beech. Spring-fall.

Edibility: Edible.

Microscopic Features:
Spores 9-16 × 3-5 µm, narrowly ventricose to nearly cylindrical, smooth. Yellowish.

Comments: Spotted or reticulated specimens were previously published as named varieties. *Xanthoconium purpureum* (search online) is similar but has a purplish-red to maroon cap. *Xanthoconium chattoogaense* (search online), known only from the Chattooga River region in the Nantahala National Forest, N.C., grows under oaks, red maple, and rhododendron; it has an odor of rotting meat.

Xanthoconium stramineum (Murrill) Singer

Description: Cap 4-9 cm wide with a sterile margin, dry, smooth but often cracking or uneven at maturity, white at first, becoming whitish to straw-colored, sometimes tinged brown. Pores whitish when young, becoming buff or pale yellow-brown at maturity, not bruising. Stalk equal or enlarging downward to a swollen base, smooth, dry, solid, white to whitish. Flesh white, sometimes slowly bruising pinkish-brown. Odor fruity, unpleasant, or not distinctive. Taste somewhat bitter or not distinctive.

Spore Print: Brownish-yellow.

Occurrence: Scattered or in groups with oak and pine. Summer-fall.

Edibility: Edible.

Microscopic Features:
Spores 10-15 × 2.5-4 µm, cylindrical, smooth. Hyaline to yellowish.

Comments: *Stramineum* means "straw-colored." *Boletus albisulphureus* (search online) is very similar but is differentiated by its reticulate stalk. The pores of *Boletus pallidus* typically bruise blue, and *Gyroporus subalbellus* has a brittle stalk that hollows in age.

Xerocomus hortonii
(A. H. Sm. & Thiers) Manfr. Binder & Besl
CORRUGATED BOLETE
Description: Cap 4-10 cm wide, dry or
 sometimes sticky, deeply pitted and
 corrugated, orange- to reddish-brown
 or reddish-tan. Pores yellow, becoming
 olive-yellow, rarely bruising blue. Stalk
 6-10 cm long, 1-2 cm thick, equal or
 enlarged downward, dry, solid, smooth
 to lightly powdery, sometimes with
 delicate reticulation on the upper half,
 pale yellow to tan, sometimes reddish
 at the base. Flesh whitish to pale yellow.
 Odor and taste not distinctive.
Spore Print: Olive-brown.
Occurrence: Scattered or in groups in
 mixed woods, especially with oak,
 hickory, beech, and hemlock. Spring-
 fall.
Edibility: Edible.
Microscopic Features:
 Spores 12-15 × 3.5-4.5 μm, somewhat
 boat-shaped, smooth. Yellow.
Comments: *Boletus hortonii* is a synonym.
 The cap surface flashes blue-green,
 then stains olive-brown with NH_4OH.
 Leccinum rugosiceps has brown scabers
 and red-bruising flesh. The pore surface
 of *Boletus nobilissimus* is initially white.
 Hemileccinum subglabripes (search
 online) has a smoother cap.

Xerocomus sclerotiorum nom. prov.
A. E. Bessette, M. E. Smith, A. R. Bessette &
H. Hitchcock
WHITEY'S BOLETE
Description: Cap 4-10 cm wide, with
 a bright yellow sterile margin, dry,
 smooth, pinkish- to rose-red with olive
 tints when young, rose- to brownish-
 pink when mature, slowly bruising
 blackish-blue. Pores bright yellow,
 becoming dull- to brownish-yellow
 in age, bruising blue. Stalk 4.5-9 cm
 long, 1-2 cm thick, equal or enlarged
 downward, dry, solid, yellow at the
 apex, covered below the apex with
 red or red-brown dots, longitudinally
 lined, sometimes reticulate at the apex,
 bruising blue, basal mycelium white.
 Flesh yellow, sometimes pinkish under
 the cap cuticle, bruising blue to blue-
 green, sometimes erratically and slowly.
 Odor not distinctive. Taste acidic.
Spore Print: Olive-brown.
Occurrence: Scattered or in groups with
 hardwoods. Summer-fall.
Edibility: Edible.
Microscopic Features:
 Spores 12-18 × 4-6 μm, subfusoid-
 fusiform, smooth. Hyaline to pale
 brownish-yellow.
Comments: The common name honors
 Dr. Harold "Whitey" Hitchcock. *Boletus
 rubricitrinus* lacks the yellow cap margin.

POLYPORES

The average polypore is easy to recognize as such. It's a tough or woody clamshell with pores instead of gills underneath, and it grows on wood. But polypores can be as inventive as they are stiff. Some species stretch elements of the group concept to the point that they can be confused with gilled mushrooms, tooth fungi, parchments, or even terrestrial boletes. In youth, some species are squeezably soft and watery.

Polypores make their livings as parasites or recyclers of woody plants. **Brown rotters** digest cellulose. They leave dead wood a darker brown than they found it. **White rotters** have learned to feed on lignin as well, bleaching wood white. The lignin-eating innovation seems to have evolved approximately 300 million years ago at the end of the Carboniferous Period, the time when deposition of major coal deposits ceased. But for white rotters, today's forests might still grow atop slowly compressing mounds of deadfall. Termites would love it; hikers, not so much.

Differential characteristics among the polypores include pore size, shape (round, angular, mazelike, gill-like, or toothlike), and whether or not the pores are **decurrent** (running down the stalk, if present). In a few species the fresh pore surface is said to **glance** (shine like highlights in polished wood when held at a certain angle). **Perennial** polypores have more than one layer of tubes and pores, one below the other. Some species have **zoned** (striped) caps or flesh; others don't (**azonate**). When collecting a polypore for identification, note the host species whenever possible.

Members of the polypore group are used as food, medicine, fiber, and tinder; for papermaking; and for fiber and fabric dyeing. Among the personal effects found with Ötzi, the posthumously famous 5,300-year-old iceman discovered in the Alps, were two polypores. The Tinder Conk, *Fomes fomentarius*, was part of his fire-starting kit. He most likely carried the Birch Polypore, *Fomitopsis betulina*, for medicinal purposes. Both species occur in the Carolinas. **Recent research has revealed that, contrary to popular wisdom, at least one polypore occasionally found in our region, *Hapalopilus nidulans* (see comment under *Hapalopilus croceus*), can be deadly poisonous if ingested.**

Use the following key to identify unknown polypores.

KEY TO POLYPORES

1a Fruitbody an irregular growth resembling charred wood, deeply cracked and brittle with a golden-brown interior. No pore surface evident. Occurs on living birch trunks, occasionally on ironwood, elm, or beech. Not found on cherry or other fruit trees ....*Inonotus obliquus* (p. 280)
1b Fruitbody not as above 2
2a Pores notably elongated, sometimes into gill-like structures, or broken into toothlike projections, not simply round or angular ....Group A (p. 248); see also *Coltricia montagnei* (p. 256) and *Trametes villosa* (p. 274)
2b Pores predominantly round or angular, ranging in size from tiny to large 3
3a Fruitbody growing, or appearing to grow, on the ground but may be attached to buried roots .... Group B (p. 253); see also *Ganoderma curtisii* (p. 265), *Laetiporus cincinnatus* (p. 268), and *Heterobasidion annosum* (p. 267)

3b Fruitbody growing from wood 4

4a Flesh of fruitbody white, creamy, or pale brown, not notably zoned with a darker
    color but may contain a thin dark line .... Group C (p. 262);
    see also *Fistulina hepatica* (p. 276), *Rhodofomes cajanderi* (p. 282),
    and *Pseudofistulina radicata* (p. 261)

4b Flesh of fruitbody darker or, if partially white, zoned with a darker color ....
    .... Group D (p. 276);
    see also *Ganoderma* (pp. 265-66), *Laetiporus* (pp. 268-69), *Oxyporus populinus* (p. 271),
    Phaeolus schweinitzii (p. 260), and *Porodaedalea pini* (p. 251)

Cerrena unicolor (Bull.) Murrill
MOSSY MAZE POLYPORE
Description: Fruitbody 4-10 cm wide, consisting of somewhat flattened, stalkless caps, sometimes laterally fused and forming extensive rows. Caps fan-shaped to semicircular or irregular. Upper surface lobed, usually grooved, covered with a dense layer of short, stiff hairs arranged in zones, whitish, grayish, pale brown, or green when covered by algae. Margin fairly sharp, lobed and wavy. Pores 1-4 per mm, mazelike, often splitting and becoming toothlike in age, whitish to pale buff, becoming smoky to grayish-brown at maturity. Flesh up to 3 mm thick, corky to tough, whitish to pale brown, with a thin dark zone near the cap surface.

Spore Print: White.

Occurrence: Typically in overlapping clusters, sometimes solitary or scattered, on hardwoods or rarely conifers. Year-round.

Edibility: Inedible.

Microscopic Features: Spores 5-7 × 2.5-4 μm, cylindric-ellipsoid, smooth. Hyaline.

Comments: *Unicolor* means "one color." *Daedalea unicolor* is a synonym. The flesh of *Daedaleopsis confragosa* lacks the dark zone.

Daedalea quercina (L.) Pers.
THICK-MAZE OAK POLYPORE
Description: Cap 5-20 cm wide, semicircular to kidney-shaped, stalkless, convex to nearly flat, leathery to corky or woody. Upper surface velvety, becoming smooth, then cracked or furrowed in age, often concentrically zoned in shades of brownish-yellow, tan, brown, or black. Margin blunt and whitish. Pores mazelike with tough, thick walls, sometimes with elongated pores near the margin, whitish to grayish-brown. Flesh up to 1 cm thick, tough, dull white to pale brown. Odor and taste not distinctive.

Spore Print: White.

Occurrence: On decaying hardwoods, especially oak. Year-round.

Edibility: Inedible.

Microscopic Features: Spores 5-6 × 2-3.5 μm, cylindric, smooth. Hyaline.

Comments: The pore surfaces of *Lenzites betulina* and *Gloeophyllum spp.* mimic a gilled mushroom. *Cerrena unicolor* has a smaller cap covered with short stiff hairs and often a green coat of algae. The mazelike pores have thin walls, as do those of *Daedaleopsis confragosa*.

Daedaleopsis confragosa (Bolton) J. Schröt.
THIN-MAZE FLAT POLYPORE
Description: Cap 3-16 cm wide, slightly
convex to nearly flat, semicircular to
kidney-shaped, stalkless. Upper surface
coarsely wrinkled, rough and scaly
at first, becoming velvety to nearly
smooth in age, with concentric zones of
creamy white, grayish, and/or shades
of brown. Margin thin and sharp. Pores
mazelike or sometimes elongated,
whitish to pale brown; they bruise
pinkish-brown. Flesh up to 1.2 cm thick,
tough, whitish to pale brown.
Spore Print: White.
Occurrence: Solitary, scattered, or in
groups on decaying wood, especially
hardwood. Year-round.
Edibility: Inedible.
Microscopic Features:
Spores 7-11 × 2-3 µm, cylindric to
allantoid, smooth. Hyaline.
Comments: *Daedaleopsis septentrionalis*
is nearly identical, but it has grayish
gill-like pores. *Daedalea quercina* has
a larger and thicker fruitbody with a
conspicuously mazelike pore surface.
The pore surface of *Trametes aesculi* is
similar, but the cap of that species is
usually whitish to pale tan and lumpy.

Daedaleopsis septentrionalis
(P. Karst.) Niemela
Description: Cap 3-7 cm wide, slightly
convex to nearly flat, semicircular
to kidney-shaped, stalkless. Upper
surface somewhat bumpy and uneven,
concentrically zoned with bands of
brownish-yellow, brownish-orange, and
various shades of brown. Margin thin
and sharp, wavy, whitish to brownish.
Pores distinctly gill-like, elongated and
sinuous, whitish to grayish, becoming
brownish in age; they bruise pinkish-
brown. Flesh up to 1.2 cm thick, tough,
whitish to pale brown.
Spore Print: White.
Occurrence: Solitary, scattered, or in
overlapping groups on decaying birch
wood. Year-round.
Edibility: Inedible.
Microscopic Features:
Spores 7-12 × 2-3.5 µm, cylindric to
allantoid, smooth. Hyaline.
Comments: *Septentrionalis* means "northern." *Gloeophyllum septentrionalis* is a
synonym. *Daedaleopsis confragosa* is
nearly identical, but it has mazelike or
sometimes elongated, but not gill-like,
pores and occurs on several species of
deciduous or occasionally conifer wood.
The gill-like pores of *Lenzites betulina*
are white and don't change color when
bruised.

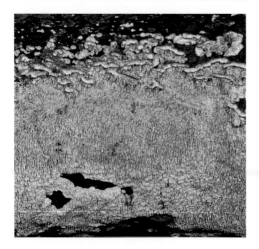

Irpex lacteus (Fr.) Fr.
MILK-WHITE TOOTHED POLYPORE

Description: Fruitbody a stalkless, crust-like mass that usually produces some fused caps. Caps 1-3 cm wide, shell-shaped to semicircular, convex to nearly flat, typically laterally fused. Upper surface dry, azonate to faintly zoned, velvety, white to creamy white. Margin sharp. Pores angular, 2-3 per mm, white to creamy. Tubes up to 6 mm long, becoming jagged or toothlike in age. Flesh to 1.5 mm thick, tough, stiff or somewhat flexible, white to pale tan.

Spore Print: White.

Occurrence: In spreading, overlapping clusters on decaying hardwoods. Year-round.

Edibility: Inedible.

Microscopic Features: Spores 5-7 × 2-3 µm, oblong to cylindric, straight or curved, smooth. Hyaline.

Comments: *Trichaptum* species also have toothlike pores, but they are violet to purple-brown in youth and fade to buff in age. *Schizopora paradoxa* (search online) forms a spreading crustlike mass with mazelike pores that often split and form toothlike edges. Also compare with *Sarcodontia pachyodon*.

Lenzites betulina (L.) Fr.
GILLED POLYPORE, MULTICOLOR GILL POLYPORE

Description: Cap 3-10 cm wide, shelflike, stalkless, nearly flat, kidney-shaped to semicircular, tough, usually flexible. Upper surface velvety to hairy, with multicolored concentric zones in shades of white, pink, gray, yellow, orange, brown, and sometimes green if covered with algae. Margin sharp. Pores conspicuously gill-like, sometimes forked, occasionally with elongated pores near the margin, white to creamy white. Flesh up to 2 mm thick, tough, white.

Spore Print: White.

Occurrence: On decaying hardwoods, especially birch, oak, and willow, rarely on conifers. Summer-early winter.

Edibility: Inedible.

Microscopic Features: Spores 4-6 × 2-3 µm, cylindric to allantoid, smooth. Hyaline.

Comments: *Betulina* means "birch," a common host tree. *Gloeophyllum* species have brown gill-like pores and prefer conifers. *Daedalea quercina* and *Daedaleopsis confragosa* have mazelike pores.

Osmoporus mexicanus
(Mont.) Y. C. Dai & S. H. He

Description: Cap 3-10 cm wide, shelflike and flattened, broadly attached, stalkless. Upper surface finely velvety when young, especially along the margin, soon becoming bald and roughened, often shallowly furrowed, grayish at first, developing concentric zones of dull brown to rusty brown, gray, or blackish. Margin sharp, often wavy. Pores distinctly gill-like, elongated and sinuous, brownish-yellow to reddish-brown, occasionally rounded near the margin. Flesh tough and leathery, rusty brown. Odor and taste not distinctive.

Spore Print: White.

Occurrence: Solitary or in groups or fused clusters on decaying conifer wood. Year-round.

Edibility: Inedible.

Microscopic Features:
Spores 9-12.5 × 3.5-4 μm, cylindrical, slightly curved, smooth. Hyaline.

Comments: *Gloeophyllum mexicanum* (Mont.) Ryvarden is a synonym. The very similar *Gloeophyllum sepiarium* (see photo on p. 22) has a bright yellowish-red to reddish-brown cap darkening to grayish or blackish in age, an orange- to brownish-yellow or whitish margin, and mazelike pores that are thick and elongated.

Porodaedalea pini (Brot.) Murrill
OCHRE-ORANGE HOOF POLYPORE

Description: Fruitbody perennial, stalkless, up to 20 cm or more wide, hoof-shaped to shelflike or spreading on the host. Upper surface coated with fine matted hairs toward the margin or nearly overall, concentrically zoned and furrowed, rough and cracked in age, reddish-brown to dark brown or blackish. Margin thick, rounded, covered with matted hairs, brownish-yellow when young, becoming yellow-brown to dark reddish-brown and crusty. Pores circular to angular or mazelike, 1-4 per mm, yellowish to yellow-brown. Flesh up to 3 cm thick, corky to woody, reddish- to yellowish-brown, lustrous, usually containing one or more thin black layers.

Spore Print: Brown.

Occurrence: Solitary to clustered on living conifers. Year-round.

Edibility: Inedible.

Microscopic Features:
Spores 4.5-7 × 3.5-5 μm, ovoid, smooth. Hyaline. Setae abundant.

Comments: *Phellinus pini* is a synonym. This virulent parasite on the heartwood of mature conifers causes red ring rot. Red-Cockaded Woodpeckers nest in the rot cavities.

POLYPORES

Sarcodontia pachyodon (Pers.) Spirin

Description: Fruitbody a spreading crust and stalkless, overlapping caps on wood. Caps 2-5 cm wide, fan-shaped, convex. Upper surface nearly smooth, azonate, white to creamy white, becoming brownish-yellow in age. Margin sharp and incurved. Pores gill-like to mazelike or more circular near the margin, breaking up to form flattened teeth up to 1.5 cm long at maturity, white to creamy white, darkening in age. Flesh 3-8 mm thick, leathery to tough, white to pale cream. Odor and taste not distinctive.

Spore Print: White.

Occurrence: On living hardwood trees, especially oak. Year-round.

Edibility: Inedible.

Microscopic Features:
Spores 5-7 × 5-6.5 µm, subglobose, thick-walled, smooth. Hyaline.

Comments: *Spongipellis pachyodon* is a synonym. *Spongipellis unicolor* (search online) has whitish to pale buff caps that become brownish or tawny in age, and large circular to angular pores that become somewhat mazelike but don't form teeth.

Trichaptum biforme (Fr.) Ryvarden
VIOLET TOOTHED POLYPORE

Description: Cap 2-6 cm wide, semicircular to fan-shaped, convex, stalkless. Upper surface distinctly zoned and variously colored, white to grayish, reddish-brown, violet, etc. Margin thin, typically violet when fresh. Pores angular, 3-5 per mm, splitting and becoming toothlike, violet to purple-brown, fading to buff in age. Flesh up to 1.5 mm thick, tough, white to yellowish. Odor and taste not distinctive.

Spore Print: White.

Occurrence: In overlapping clusters on decaying hardwoods. Year-round.

Edibility: Inedible.

Microscopic Features:
Spores 5-8 × 2-2.5 µm, cylindric, smooth. Hyaline.

Comments: *Trichaptum sector* (search online), another hardwood species, has gray or dark purplish-brown or blackish pores. *Trichaptum abietinum* (search online) is a conifer-dweller with a hairy, pale gray upper surface and violet pores that break up into jagged but not toothlike structures. *Trichaptum fuscoviolaceum* (search online) is very similar to *T. abietinum* but has pores that split to form distinct teeth.

Abortiporus biennis (Bull.) Singer
ABORTED POLYPORE
Description: Fruitbody occurs in two
distinct forms, one a distorted mass of
whitish and brownish tissue covered
with pores. The nondistorted form is
a typical shelving polypore, 8-16 cm
wide, almost circular to rosette-like,
becoming irregularly undulating and
lobed in age. Upper surface smooth to
slightly pitted, finely velvety, whitish,
becoming yellow-brown at maturity.
Margin thin, whitish, staining reddish-
brown. Pores angular to elongated and
sinuous, whitish, staining reddish-
brown, 1-3 per mm. Stalk 4-7 cm long,
2-3 cm thick, colored like the upper
surface, often covered with adhering
debris. Flesh duplex, white to tan, soft
on the outer portion, firm and corky
on the inner portion, staining reddish.
Odor unpleasant. Taste not distinctive.
Spore Print: White.
Occurrence: Solitary or grouped on
decaying hardwood or on the ground
attached to buried roots. Summer-fall.
Edibility: Unknown.
Microscopic Features:
Spores 4.5-7 × 3.5-5 μm, ellipsoid.
Hyaline.
Comments: The distorted form is
commonly found.

Albatrellus cristatus
(Schaeff.) Kotl. & Pouzar
CRESTED POLYPORE
Description: Cap 5-20 cm wide, convex,
circular to irregularly lobed. Upper
surface smooth to slightly velvety,
often forming coarse scales or cracks,
especially at the center, yellowish-
green to olive or brown. Margin thin,
incurved. Pores decurrent, white with
yellowish stains, 2-4 per mm. Stalk 2.5-
7.5 cm long, 1-2.5 cm thick, irregular,
sometimes branched, smooth, whitish
to greenish or colored like the cap. Flesh
tough, whitish, staining yellowish-
green. Odor not distinctive. Taste bitter
or mild.
Spore Print: White.
Occurrence: Solitary or more often in
fused clusters in hardwoods or mixed
woods, especially with oak, rarely with
conifers. Summer-early winter.
Edibility: Inedible.
Microscopic Features:
Spores 5-7 × 4-5 μm, broadly elliptic to
subglobose, smooth. Hyaline.
Comments: The Goat's Foot, *Albatrellus
pes-caprae* (search online), has a wooly
to scaly, reddish-brown to dark brown
cap that is yellowish between the
scales, a thick, eccentric stalk, and
large, angular, white pores.

POLYPORES

Albatrellus ellisii (Berk.) Pouzar

Description: Cap 5-20 cm wide, circular, semicircular, fan-shaped or irregularly lobed. Upper surface dry, covered with coarse scales composed of matted fibers, greenish-yellow to dull yellow-orange. Margin incurved at first. Pores perhaps slightly decurrent, circular to angular, 1-2 per mm, sometimes torn on older specimens, cream-colored or yellowish in age, slowly staining greenish when bruised. Stalk 5-12 cm long, 2-6 cm thick, nearly equal or tapered downward to a narrow base, solid, coated with matted fibers, greenish-yellow to dull yellow-orange. Flesh firm, azonate, cream-colored to pale tan. Odor and taste not distinctive.

Spore Print: White.

Occurrence: On the ground in conifer or mixed woods, especially with pines. Fall.

Edibility: Unknown.

Microscopic Features: Spores 8-14 × 5-8 μm, ellipsoid to lacrimoid, smooth. Hyaline.

Comments: A distinctively colored species that is not commonly collected. *Albatrellus pes-caprae* (search online) has a wooly to scaly, reddish-brown to dark brown cap showing yellow flesh between the scales.

Albatrellus ovinus (Schaeff.) Kotl. & Pouzar

SHEEP POLYPORE

Description: Cap 5-16 cm wide, convex, circular to kidney-shaped, sometimes fused. Upper surface smooth, whitish to creamy yellow or pale grayish, becoming cracked with pale yellow flesh showing in the cracks at maturity. Margin incurved at first. Pores angular near the stalk, round near the margin, 2-5 per mm, white to pale yellow, sometimes with reddish tints, not staining when bruised. Stalk 2.5-7.5 cm long, 1-3.5 cm thick, central or eccentric, enlarged downward or nearly equal, often with an asymmetrically swollen base, white to pale brownish-yellow. Flesh thick, firm, white, drying yellowish. Odor and taste not distinctive.

Spore Print: White.

Occurrence: Scattered or in groups under conifers or hardwoods. Fall-early winter.

Edibility: Edible.

Microscopic Features: Spores 3.5-5 × 2.5-3.5 μm, ovoid to subglobose, smooth. Hyaline.

Comments: *Albatrellus confluens* (search online) has a pinkish-buff to pale orange cap that is often fused with others, has 3-5 pores per mm, and grows under conifers.

Bondarzewia berkeleyi
(Fr.) Bondartsev & Singer
BERKELEY'S POLYPORE
Description: Fruitbody 20-125 cm wide,
a large overlapping cluster of caps
attached to a central stalk. Caps 6-25
cm wide, fan-shaped, convex, laterally
fused and forming rosettes. Upper
surface wrinkled, pitted, obscurely
to conspicuously zoned, whitish to
grayish, yellowish or tan. Margin
wavy and blunt, not blackening when
bruised. Pores angular to irregular, 0.5-2
per mm, white to cream. Stalk 4-12 cm
long, 3-5 cm thick, solid, roughened,
dingy yellow to brownish. Flesh up to
3 cm thick, corky to tough, white. Odor
not distinctive. Taste mild when young,
bitter in age.
Spore Print: White.
Occurrence: Usually solitary on the ground
at the base of hardwood trees and
stumps. Summer-fall.
Edibility: Edible when young and tender.
Microscopic Features:
 Spores 7-9 × 6-8 μm, globose,
 ornamented with prominent ridges and
 spines. Hyaline, amyloid.
Comments: *Berkeleyi* honors British
mycologist Miles Joseph Berkeley
(1803-89). The cap margins of *Meripilus
sumstinei* blacken when bruised.

Cladomeris umbellata (Pers.) Quél.
UMBRELLA POLYPORE
Description: Fruitbody up to 50 cm wide,
a compound cluster of numerous
circular caps attached to a central
branching stalk. Cap 2-4 cm wide,
nearly flat with a depressed center.
Upper surface showing radial fibers or
small scales, grayish-brown to yellow-
brown, sometimes dull white. Margin
thin, even, entire. Pores decurrent,
angular, 1-3 per mm, white. Stalk
white, branching. Flesh up to 1 mm
thick, dense, white. Odor and taste not
distinctive.
Spore Print: White.
Occurrence: Solitary or in groups at the
base of hardwood stumps or trees. Late
spring-fall.
Edibility: Edible.
Microscopic Features:
 Spores 7-10 × 3-4 μm, cylindric,
 smooth. Hyaline.
Comments: *Polyporus umbellatus* is a
synonym. The central stalk arises from
an underground, blackish sclerotium
that is easily broken off when the
fruitbody is picked. Compare with
Grifola frondosa, which has fan-shaped
caps that fuse laterally and are laterally
attached to their branches of the
common stalk.

POLYPORES

255

Coltricia cinnamomea (Jacq.) Murrill
SHINY CINNAMON POLYPORE
Description: Cap 1.2-5 cm wide, circular to irregular, nearly flat or slightly depressed, tough. Upper surface concentrically zoned, silky, shiny, bright reddish-cinnamon to amber-brown, with dark rusty brown bands. Margin thin and sharp, faintly lined, often lacerated. Pores angular, nondecurrent, 2-4 per mm, dark reddish-brown to yellow-brown. Stalk 1-4 cm long, 1.5-6 mm thick, central, nearly equal or tapered downward, velvety, dark reddish-brown. Flesh up to 1 mm thick, tough, rusty brown.
Spore Print: Yellowish-brown.
Occurrence: Solitary, in groups, or laterally fused, in various habitats, especially woodland paths and along roadsides. Summer-early winter.
Edibility: Inedible.
Microscopic Features:
Spores 6-10 × 4.5-7 μm, elliptic, smooth. Hyaline.
Comments: The cap of *Coltricia perennis* (search online) is up to 11 cm wide and dull brownish-orange to pale cinnamon; it has a decurrent pore surface.

Coltricia montagnei (Fr.) Murrill
MONTAGNE'S POLYPORE
Description: Cap 4-13 cm wide, convex to flat, often depressed over the center, sometimes fused. Upper surface uneven, finely velvety to matted hairy, azonate or inconspicuously zoned, cinnamon to dark reddish-, or blackish-brown. Margin paler with blunt edges. Pores relatively large and variable, circular to angular or concentric gill-like plates, whitish to cinnamon or grayish-brown, darkening in age. Stalk 2-5 cm long, 5-15 mm thick, usually tapered downward, somewhat velvety, cinnamon to dark rusty brown. Flesh soft and corky on the upper portion, dense and tough on the lower portion. Odor not distinctive. Taste bitter.
Spore Print: Pale brown.
Occurrence: Solitary or in groups, often fused, under hardwoods or in mixed woods. Summer-fall.
Edibility: Inedible.
Microscopic Features:
Spores 9-14 × 5.5-7.5 μm, ellipsoid, smooth, pale golden-yellow. Slightly destrinoid.
Comments: *Montagnei* honors French mycologist Jean Pierre Montagne (1784-1866). *Onnia tomentosa* has smaller pores and occurs under conifers.

Grifola frondosa (Dicks.) Gray
HEN OF THE WOODS, MAITAKE
Description: Fruitbody a dense cluster of overlapping and partially fused caps up to 60 cm wide, attached to branches arising from a short and thick common stalk. Caps 2-8 cm wide, fan- to petal-shaped, laterally attached. Upper surface bald or finely wooly-matted, zoned, gray to brownish-gray, dark brown in age. Margin thin, wavy. Pores angular, 1-3 per mm, white. Stalk 2-4.5 cm long, up to 10 cm thick, repeatedly branched, white. Flesh up to 6 mm thick, fleshy, white. Odor and taste not distinctive.
Spore Print: White.
Occurrence: Solitary or in groups at the base of hardwood trees, especially oak. Late summer-fall.
Edibility: Edible.
Microscopic Features:
Spores 5-7 × 3.5-5 µm, oval to elliptic, smooth. Hyaline.
Comments: *Meripilus sumstinei* has thicker, shelflike caps and a white pore surface that stains black. The circular caps found in *Cladomeris umbellata* are attached centrally to branches of the common stalk.

Laetiporus persicinus
(Berk. & M. A. Curtis) Gilb.
Description: Fruitbody solitary or a rosette of caps 10-26 cm wide, circular to fan-shaped, soft initially, becoming tough. Upper surface azonate to faintly zoned, smooth or bumpy, initially pinkish-brown with a whitish margin, becoming darker brown with a blackish-brown margin. Margin blunt, wavy. Pores decurrent, circular, 3-4 per mm, whitish to pinkish-cream, becoming pale brown, bruising dark brown, sometimes exuding amber droplets. Stalk up to 10 cm long, 3-7 cm thick, solid, central or branched, dry, pinkish-brown, often binding leaves and soil at the base. Flesh up to 2 cm thick, soft, whitish. Odor resembling ham, bacon, or not distinctive. Taste unpleasant.
Spore Print: White.
Occurrence: Solitary or in groups attached to roots near the base of living oaks or pines. Year-round.
Edibility: Unknown.
Microscopic Features:
Spores 6.5-8 × 4-5 µm, ovoid to ellipsoid, smooth. Hyaline.
Comments: *Persicinus* means "peach-colored." *Laetiporus cincinnatus* has brighter colors and no distinct odor.

POLYPORES

Meripilus sumstinei
(Murrill) M. J. Larsen & Lombard
BLACK-STAINING POLYPORE
Description: Fruitbody a cluster of overlapping caps up to 50 cm wide, attached to a common stalk. Individual caps 6-20 cm wide, fan- to spoon-shaped. Upper surface velvety, dull orange with black stains when young, becoming yellowish-brown, or grayish to blackish at maturity. Margin wavy, blackening when bruised or in age. Pores angular, 3-6 per mm, white, bruising dark brown or black. Stalk 1-3 cm long, up to 12 cm thick, brownish-orange to brownish. Flesh up to 1.6 cm thick, fleshy to fibrous, white. Odor and taste not distinctive.
Spore Print: White.
Occurrence: Solitary or in groups at the base of hardwood trees and stumps. Summer-fall.
Edibility: Edible when young.
Microscopic Features:
Spores 6-7 × 4.5-6 µm, oval to nearly round, smooth. Hyaline.
Comments: *Grifola frondosa* has gray to brownish-gray caps with thinner flesh and a white pore surface that does not stain black. Also compare with *Laetiporus persicinus*.

Microporellus dealbatus (Jungh.) Ryvarden
Description: Cap 2-10 cm wide, circular to fan- or kidney-shaped. Upper surface somewhat velvety to nearly bald, distinctly zoned with buff to brown, pale grayish-brown or pale smoky gray colors. Margin thin, sharp, whitish. Pores angular to irregularly rounded, minute, 8-10 per mm, white, becoming cream and finally brownish-yellow at maturity. Stalk 3-10 cm long, 3-12 mm thick, central to lateral, nearly equal or tapered in either direction, often twisted, dry, rigid, colored like the cap or paler. Flesh up to 4 mm thick, tough to hard and woody, white. Odor and taste not distinctive.
Spore Print: White.
Occurrence: Solitary, scattered, or in groups on the ground attached to buried wood in hardwoods or mixed woods. Year-round.
Edibility: Inedible.
Microscopic Features:
Spores 4.5-6 × 3.5-4.5 µm, ellipsoid to lacrimoid, smooth. Hyaline, weakly dextrinoid.
Comments: *Dealbatus* means "off-white." *Microporellus obovatus* has a lateral stalk, a paler spoon-shaped cap, and slightly smaller subglobose to ellipsoid spores.

Neoalbatrellus caeruleoporus (Peck) Audet
BLUE-PORED POLYPORE
Description: Cap 2.5-12 cm wide, convex
to broadly convex, circular to kidney-
shaped. Upper surface smooth to
slightly felty, grayish-blue to gray,
becoming brownish in age. Margin
incurved and wavy. Pores decurrent,
angular, blue to grayish-blue, 2-3 per
mm. Stalk 2.5-7 cm long, 6-25 mm
thick, central to eccentric, blue to
grayish-blue, pitted on the upper half,
smooth below. Flesh firm, whitish. Odor
and taste not distinctive.
Spore Print: White.
Occurrence: Solitary or in groups, usually
under hemlock. Summer-fall.
Edibility: Edible.
Microscopic Features:
Spores 4-6 × 3-5 μm, nearly round,
smooth. Hyaline.
Comments: *Caeruleoporus* means "blue
pores." *Albatrellus caeruleoporus* is a
synonym. *Albatrellus cristatus* has a
yellowish-brown to olive-brown or
yellowish-green cracked cap, and white
to greenish-yellow pore surface.

Onnia tomentosa (Fr.) P. Karst.
WOOLY VELVET POLYPORE
Description: Cap 4-17 cm wide, circular to
fan-shaped or irregular. Upper surface
velvety or matted hairy, wrinkled and
uneven or smooth, tan to brownish-
yellow or rusty brown. Margin blunt,
usually paler than the center. Pores
angular, 2-4 per mm, buff at first
becoming grayish-brown to dark
brown. Stalk 2-5 cm long, 6-20 cm
thick, sometimes rudimentary, velvety,
colored like the cap. Flesh up to 6 mm
thick, tough, yellowish-brown to rusty
brown. Odor and taste not distinctive.
Spore Print: Yellowish to pale brown.
Occurrence: Solitary or in groups or fused
clusters on the ground or wood under
conifers. Summer-early winter.
Edibility: Inedible.
Microscopic Features:
Spores 5-6 × 3-4 μm, elliptic, smooth.
Yellowish. Setae present.
Comments: *Inonotus tomentosus* is a
synonym. If you have old eyes, a hand
lens may be necessary to distinguish
this from a tooth mushroom. *Phaeolus
schweinitzii* has a larger cap and yellowish to greenish-yellow pores that stain
darker brown.

POLYPORES

Phaeolus schweinitzii (Fr.) Pat.
DYE POLYPORE
Description: Cap 4-26 cm wide, circular
to fan-shaped, flattened. Upper surface
matted hairy, faintly to distinctly zoned,
dull orange, becoming rusty brown
to dark brown in age. Margin sharp,
wavy or lobed, yellowish- to brownish-
orange. Pores decurrent, angular, 0.5-
5 per mm, yellow to greenish-yellow or
orange, bruising brown when young,
becoming yellowish-brown to dark
rusty brown in age. Stalk 2-7 cm long,
up to 5 cm thick, enlarged upward, pale
to dark brown. Flesh up to 3 cm thick,
tough, yellowish to reddish-brown.
Odor and taste not distinctive.
Spore Print: Whitish.
Occurrence: Solitary or in rosettes on
conifer wood or attached to buried
roots. Year-round.
Edibility: Inedible.
Microscopic Features:
Spores 5-9 × 3-5 µm, elliptic, smooth.
Hyaline.
Comments: *Schweinitzii* honors German
American botanist and mycologist
Lewis David de Schweinitz (1780-1834).
It is a virulent pathogen of conifers.
Onnia tomentosa has a smaller, tan to
brownish-yellow or rusty brown cap
and a buff to grayish-brown or dark
brown pore surface.

Polyporus radicatus Schwein.
ROOTING POLYPORE
Description: Cap 3-20 cm wide, circular,
convex to nearly flat, fibrous and
tough. Upper surface velvety to finely
scaly, sometimes roughened and finely
cracked, dry, yellowish- to reddish-
brown. Margin incurved, becoming
uplifted and wavy at maturity. Pores
angular, 2-3 per mm, white to creamy
yellow. Stalk 5-15 cm long, 6-25 mm
thick, central, scurfy, colored like the
cap or darker, attached to a tapered,
black, rootlike base up to 30 cm or more
long. Flesh up to 1 cm thick, tough,
white. Odor and taste not distinctive.
Spore Print: White.
Occurrence: Solitary, scattered, or in
groups attached to buried roots, usually
in hardwoods. Summer-fall.
Edibility: Inedible.
Microscopic Features:
Spores 12-15 × 6-8 µm, oblong to
elliptic, smooth. Hyaline.
Comments: *Picipes badius* is similar but
lacks the black, rootlike base. *Polyporus
melanopus* (search online) has a smaller,
pale yellow- to gray-brown cap with
radial fibrils, and a velvety stalk also
lacking the black, rootlike base.

Pseudofistulina radicata (Schwein.) Burds.

Description: Cap 3-7.5 cm wide, kidney-shaped to rounded or irregularly lobed. Upper surface coated with matted hairs, azonate, yellowish-brown, darkening in age. Margin sharp, smoothly arcing or deeply notched. Pores circular, 5-7 per mm, white to creamy white, becoming pinkish-buff to brownish-yellow at maturity. Stalk 4-10 cm long, up to 1 cm thick, usually tapered downward, lateral, typically rooting, sometimes branched, colored like the cap or darker near the apex, whitish to grayish below. Flesh up to 7 mm thick, fibrous, tough, white to pale buff. Odor and taste not distinctive.

Spore Print: White.

Occurrence: Solitary or scattered on the ground attached to buried wood, or on decaying hardwood logs and stumps. Late spring-fall.

Edibility: Inedible.

Microscopic Features:
Spores 3-4 × 2-3 μm, ovoid, smooth. Hyaline.

Comments: *Fistulina radicata* is a synonym. *Fistulina hepatica* has a larger reddish cap, a short lateral stalk, and reddish flesh. *Ganoderma curtisii* has a shiny cap.

Bjerkandera adusta (Willd.) P. Karst.
SMOKY POLYPORE

Description: Fruitbody spreading, often forming overlapping caps, stalkless. Cap 2-7.5 cm wide, shelflike or sometimes forming rosettes, tough. Upper surface finely velvety, azonate to faintly zoned, whitish to pale smoky gray. Margin sharp, whitish, darkening when bruised. Pores angular to irregularly rounded, 4-7 per mm, pale gray at first, becoming dark smoky gray. Flesh up to 6 mm thick, tough, pale buff, lacking a dark layer near the tubes. Odor and taste not distinctive.

Spore Print: White.

Occurrence: On hardwoods or sometimes conifers. Summer-early winter.

Edibility: Inedible.

Microscopic Features:
Spores 5-6 × 2.5-3.5 µm, short-cylindric, smooth. Hyaline.

Comments: *Adusta* means "scorched," a reference to the smoky gray colors. *Bjerkandera fumosa* (search online) has a paler pore surface and forms larger fruitbodies with flesh up to 1.5 cm thick that contains a thin dark line near the tube layer. That species often has an odor of anise.

Cerioporus leptocephalus (Jacq.) Zmitr.
ELEGANT POLYPORE

Description: Cap 3-6 cm wide, up to 1 cm thick, circular to kidney- or fan-shaped. Upper surface bald, azonate, tan to yellowish- or chestnut brown. Margin thin, sharp. Pores attached to somewhat decurrent, circular to angular, 5-7 per mm, pale buff. Stalk up to 7 cm long, 2-5 mm thick, central to lateral, bald, colored like the cap on the upper portion, black below. Flesh up to 7 mm thick, corky, azonate, pale buff. Odor and taste not distinctive.

Spore Print: White.

Occurrence: Solitary or in groups on decaying hardwood sticks or debris, occasionally on the wood of conifers. Late spring-early winter.

Edibility: Inedible.

Microscopic Features:
Spores 7.5-10 × 2.5-3 µm, cylindric to slightly allantoid, smooth. Hyaline.

Comments: *Leptocephalus* means "thin head," a reference to the cap. *Polyporus elegans* and *P. leptocephalus* are synonyms. *Cerioporus varius* = *Polyporus varius* (search online) is similar, but it has a much shorter, paler stalk and a pale buff, radially lined cap.

Cerioporus squamosus (Huds.) Quél.
DRYAD'S SADDLE

Description: Cap 5-40 cm wide, kidney- to fan-shaped, circular or funnel-shaped, fleshy when young, fibrous and tough in age. Upper surface ground color whitish to yellowish or pale yellow-brown, covered with concentrically arranged, flattened, reddish-brown scales. Margin thin, arcing smoothly or lobed. Pores decurrent, angular, large, 0.25-1 per mm, white to yellowish. Stalk 1-12 cm long, 1-5 cm thick, lateral or eccentric, sometimes rudimentary, whitish on the upper portion, brown to blackish at the base. Flesh up to 4 cm thick, soft and corky when young, becoming tough at maturity, white. Odor and taste like cucumber or watermelon rind.

Spore Print: White.

Occurrence: Solitary or in groups or overlapping clusters on decaying hardwoods. Spring and fall.

Edibility: Edible, especially the cap margins, when young and tender.

Microscopic Features:
Spores 16-20 × 6-9 μm, cylindric, smooth. Hyaline.

Comments: Sometimes called the Pheasant's Back Polypore. *Polyporus squamosus* is a synonym.

Cryptoporus volvatus (Peck) Shear
VEILED POLYPORE,
CRYPTIC GLOBE FUNGUS

Description: Cap 1.5-5 cm wide, nearly round to hoof-shaped, stalkless. Upper surface azonate, smooth or wrinkled, whitish to tan or pale yellow-brown, sometimes coated with a clear, lacquerlike layer. Pores white to pinkish or pale brown, circular, 3-5 per mm, covered by a thick, whitish to yellowish membranous veil that tears open at maturity. Flesh up to 2 cm thick, soft and corky, white. Odor not distinctive. Taste slightly bitter.

Spore Print: Pinkish-buff.

Occurrence: Solitary, scattered, or in groups on trunks and stumps of recently killed conifers. Spring through fall.

Edibility: Inedible.

Microscopic Features:
Spores 12-16.5 × 3.5-5 μm, cylindric, smooth. Hyaline.

Comments: Insects and other tiny arthropods often bore holes in the membrane. *Cryptoporus volvatus* means "hidden pores surrounded by a veil." The fruitbody of *Fomitopsis ochracea* is tough, even in youth.

POLYPORES

263

Fomitopsis betulina
(Bull.) B. K. Cui, M. L. Han & Y. C. Dai
BIRCH POLYPORE

Description: Cap 3-25 cm wide, shell- to kidney-shaped, corky when fresh. Upper surface smooth when young, breaking up into scales and patches in age, pale brown with darker brown streaks. Margin rounded and inrolled like a curb around the sunken pore surface. Pores circular to angular, 3-5 per mm, becoming toothlike or jagged in age, white at first, then pale brown to yellowish-brown. Stalk up to 6 cm long and thick, sometimes rudimentary or lacking, lateral, white to brown. Flesh 1-5 cm thick, fibrous, tough, white. Odor and taste not distinctive.

Spore Print: White.

Occurrence: Solitary, scattered, or in groups on birch trees. Year-round.

Edibility: Edible, but most people find it tough and somewhat bitter.

Microscopic Features:
Spores 4-6 × 1.5-2 μm, cylindric to allantoid, smooth. Hyaline.

Comments: The pores of young specimens may not be visible, even with a hand lens. *Piptoporus betulinus* is a synonym.

Fomitopsis ochracea complex
Ryvarden & Stokland
RED-BELTED POLYPORE

Description: Fruitbody perennial, 7-38 cm wide, stalkless, shelflike to hoof-shaped, usually with a thick, rounded margin. Upper surface often covered at first with sticky reddish-brown resin, concentrically furrowed, thickened at the point of attachment, hard, finely cracked or nearly smooth, greenish-gray to grayish or blackish-brown with the resin, if present, persisting longest near the margin. Margin whitish, creamy yellow, or reddish. Pores circular, 3-5 per mm, creamy white, staining yellow. Flesh up to 4 cm thick, corky to woody, creamy white to pale brown.

Spore Print: Whitish.

Occurrence: Solitary or in groups typically on conifers but also on hardwoods. Year-round.

Edibility: Inedible.

Microscopic Features:
Spores 6-9 × 3.5-4.5 μm, cylindric to elliptic, smooth. Hyaline.

Comments: Commonly listed in field guides as *Fomitopsis pinicola*, a Eurasian species that differs genetically from American specimens. The combination of dark cap, pale flesh, and perennial growth pattern distinguishes it from other hard polypores covered here.

Ganoderma applanatum (Pers.) Pat.
ARTIST'S CONK

Description: Fruitbody perennial, 5-65 cm wide, shelflike to somewhat hoof-shaped, stalkless, woody. Upper surface thick, crusty, concentrically furrowed, thickened at the attachment point, finely cracked and roughened, dull brown to blackish-brown. Margin thin, often whitish to yellowish. Pores circular, 4-6 per mm, white, staining brown when bruised, becoming yellowish to brownish in age. Flesh up to 6 cm thick, corky to woody, brown. Odor and taste not distinctive.

Spore Print: Brown.

Occurrence: Solitary or in overlapping groups on a wide variety of hardwoods. Year-round.

Edibility: Inedible.

Microscopic Features: Spores 7-11 × 5-7.5 µm, broadly elliptic, truncate, with a thick double wall. Pale brown.

Comments: Durable and detailed pictures are created by scratching the pore surface with a sharp object. *Ischnoderma resinosum* has larger pores. *Ganoderma lobatum* (search online) has a dark brown cap with a thin, fragile crust that cracks in age, a yellowish margin, and a cream to yellowish-buff pore surface bruising purplish-brown.

Ganoderma curtisii (Berk.) Murrill
GOLDEN REISHI

Description: Cap 3-20 cm wide, fan- to kidney-shaped. Upper surface uneven with concentric shallow furrows, varnished and shiny, brownish-yellow when young, partly becoming dull red when mature. Margin sharp or blunt, yellow to brownish-yellow. Pores circular, 4-6 per mm, whitish to yellowish, becoming brownish in age and staining brown. Stalk 3-12 cm long, 1-3 cm thick, lateral to nearly central, varnished, darker than the cap in shades of brownish-yellow or reddish-brown. Flesh up to 1.5 cm thick, corky when fresh, becoming tough and rigid, white on the upper portion, brown below.

Spore Print: Brown.

Occurrence: Solitary or in groups on stumps, roots, and trunks of hardwoods. Year-round.

Edibility: Used medicinally.

Microscopic Features: Spores 9-13 × 5-7 µm, ovoid, truncate, coarsely echinulate. Pale brown.

Comments: *Ganoderma meredithiae* (search online) is nearly identical but grows exclusively on pine stumps or the base of pine trees. *Ganoderma sessile* is stalkless or nearly so.

POLYPORES

Ganoderma sessile Murrill
LING CHIH

Description: Cap 3–25 cm wide, semi-circular, fan- to kidney-shaped or irregular, stalkless or with a rudimentary stalk. Upper surface roughened and uneven with a few shallow furrows, varnished and shiny, dark red to reddish-brown, becoming brownish-yellow toward the margin. Margin blunt, whitish. Pores circular, 4–6 per mm, white, becoming yellowish to dull brown and staining brown. Flesh up to 3 cm thick, corky when fresh, becoming tough and rigid, brown or yellowish.

Spore Print: Brown.

Occurrence: Solitary or in groups or overlapping clusters on stumps, roots, or the base of standing hardwood trees. Year-round.

Edibility: A medicinal tea is brewed from the fruitbody.

Microscopic Features:
Spores 9–12 × 5.5–8 μm, ellipsoid, echinulate. Brown.

Comments: Although illustrated and labeled as *Ganoderma lucidum* in many American field guides, molecular analysis has shown that it does not occur in North America. *Ganoderma curtisii* has a conspicuous stalk.

Ganoderma tsugae Murrill
HEMLOCK VARNISH SHELF

Description: Cap 6–31 cm wide, fan- to kidney-shaped. Upper surface smooth or wrinkled, varnished and shiny, concentrically zoned and shallowly furrowed, brownish-red to mahogany or reddish-orange, rarely blue to bluish-green. Margin bright whitish. Pores circular to angular, 4–6 per mm, white to creamy white, becoming brown in age or when bruised. Stalk 3–15 cm long, 1–4 cm thick, typically lateral, varnished and colored like the cap. Flesh up to 3 cm thick, corky or tough, whitish. Odor and taste not distinctive.

Spore Print: Brown.

Occurrence: Solitary or in groups on decaying conifer wood, typically hemlock. Year-round.

Edibility: The young margin is edible when soft. Also used medicinally.

Microscopic Features:
Spores 9–11 × 6–8 μm, elliptic, truncate, with a thick double wall. Pale brown.

Comments: *Ganoderma sessile* and *G. curtisii* grow on hardwoods. *Ganoderma meredithiae* (search online) is a southern species growing exclusively on pines.

Gelatoporia dichroa (Fr.) Ginns

Description: Cap up to 10 cm wide, variable from shelflike to spreading in rows, stalkless. Upper surface velvety to nearly bald, somewhat zoned, whitish to brownish- or grayish-yellow. Margin sharp and undulating. Pores round to angular, 4-6 per mm, grayish-pink to purplish or reddish-brown, with a whitish margin when immature. Tubes gelatinous when fresh, separable as a layer from the flesh. Flesh white, up to 4 mm thick, soft and fibrous or cottony when fresh, drying hard and resinous.

Spore Print: White.

Occurrence: In overlapping, fused groups on decaying hardwoods, sometimes on conifers or old, woody polypores. Summer-early winter.

Edibility: Inedible.

Microscopic Features:
Spores 3.5-5.5 × 0.5-1.5 μm, allantoid to cylindrical, smooth. Hyaline, inamyloid.

Comments: *Gloeoporus dichrous* is a synonym. The color pattern can resemble an upside-down species of *Stereum*, a group that lacks pores (use a hand lens).

Heterobasidion annosum (Fr.) Bref.

CONIFER-BASE POLYPORE

Description: Cap 2.5-25 cm wide, variable from shelflike to spreading in rows, semicircular to irregular, stalkless. Upper surface uneven and roughened with shallow furrows, indistinctly zoned, velvety or bald becoming incrusted, brown, then blackish in age. Margin rounded, wavy. Pores circular to angular, 4-5 per mm, ivory to pinkish-cream, glancing, smooth. Flesh up to 1 cm thick, corky, azonate, ivory. Odor and taste not distinctive.

Spore Print: White.

Occurrence: Solitary or in groups at the base of conifers and rarely on deciduous trees. Year-round.

Edibility: Inedible.

Microscopic Features:
Spores 4.5-6.5 × 3.5-4.5 μm, subglobose to ovoid, minutely echinulate. Hyaline.

Comments: A major root rot pathogen of North American conifers, particularly in commercial plantations and second-growth stands that have been thinned. *Cerrena unicolor* can occur on conifers but has mazelike pores that often break up into teeth.

Ischnoderma resinosum (Schrad.) P. Karst.
**RESINOUS POLYPORE,
STEAK OF THE WOODS**
Description: Cap 7-26 cm wide, shelflike,
stalkless, fan-shaped to semicircular,
convex to flattened, fleshy and soft
when young and fresh, becoming tough
or brittle in age, occasionally exuding
amber drops of fluid. Upper surface
concentrically and radially furrowed,
faintly to distinctly zoned, velvety
at first, covered with a thin, glossy,
resinous crust on mature specimens,
dull brownish-orange to dark brown.
Margin thick, rounded, whitish to
brownish-yellow. Pores angular to
circular, 4-6 per mm, white, staining
brown when bruised and browning in
age. Flesh up to 2.5 cm thick, soft or
tough, whitish to pale yellow. Odor and
taste not distinctive.
Spore Print: Whitish.
Occurrence: Solitary to clustered on
decaying hardwoods. Year-round.
Edibility: Edible, when young and tender.
Microscopic Features:
Spores 4.5-7 × 1.5-2.5 µm, cylindric to
allantoid, smooth. Hyaline.
Comments: *Resinosum* is a reference to
the amber-colored droplets sometimes
exuded by the fruitbody. *Ganoderma
applanatum* is a perennial species with
smaller pores.

Laetiporus cincinnatus (Morgan) Burds.,
Banik & T. J. Volk
WHITE-PORED SULPHUR SHELF
Description: Fruitbody a large rosette of
convex to nearly flattened, laterally
fused caps attached to a central
branching stalk. Cap 3-25 cm wide,
petal- to fan-shaped. Upper surface
velvety, radially wrinkled, bright orange
to pinkish-orange. Margin blunt, wavy,
sometimes lobed, white to pinkish-
cream. Pores circular, 3-4 per mm,
white. Stalk 4-9 cm long, 2-5 cm thick,
whitish. Flesh up to 2 cm thick, fleshy
to fibrous, white. Odor and taste not
distinctive.
Spore Print: White.
Occurrence: On the ground attached to
roots at the base of oak trees or stumps,
rarely on other hardwood species.
Summer-early spring.
Edibility: Edible.
Microscopic Features:
Spores 4.5-5.5 × 3.5-4 µm, oval to
elliptic, smooth. Hyaline.
Comments: *Bondarzewia berkeleyi*
has duller colors and larger pores.
Laetiporus sulphureus has orange caps
with yellow margins and yellow pores,
and typically grows on logs and tree
trunks.

Laetiporus sulphureus (Bull.) Murrill
CHICKEN OF THE WOODS, SULPHUR SHELF
Description: Cap 5-30 cm wide, shelflike, fan- to petal-shaped. Upper surface somewhat velvety, dry, often wrinkled and roughened, bright to dull orange, fading to orange-yellow then whitish in age. Margin blunt, wavy, often lobed, pale orange. Pores angular, 3-4 per mm, bright sulfur yellow. Stalk lateral and rudimentary or absent, colored like the upper cap surface. Flesh up to 2 cm thick, fleshy to fibrous when fresh, becoming tough and brittle in age, whitish or yellow. Odor and taste not distinctive.
Spore Print: White.
Occurrence: In overlapping clusters or rosettes, sometimes solitary, on hardwoods, especially oak, rarely on conifers. Fall-early winter.
Edibility: Edible and good.
Microscopic Features:
Spores 5-8 × 3.5-5 μm, oval to elliptic, smooth. Hyaline.
Comments: The bright yellow pore surface of this prized culinary species distinguishes it from other representatives of *Laetiporus* in the Carolinas.

Leiotrametes lactinea
(Berk.) Welti & Courtec
Description: Cap 5-25 cm wide, shelflike, semicircular to fan- or kidney-shaped. Upper surface typically uneven and conspicuously warted, concentrically zoned or shallowly furrowed, color a variable mixture of whitish to grayish and pale to dark brown. Margin thick and blunt. Pores initially round, becoming angular in age, 2-3 per mm, white to cream, dull yellow to brownish in age. Stalk absent or stubby. Flesh up to 2 cm or more thick, corky, white to yellowish. Odor and taste not distinctive.
Spore Print: White.
Occurrence: Solitary or in groups or overlapping clusters, on decaying hardwoods, especially oak. Year-round.
Edibility: Inedible.
Microscopic Features:
Spores 5-7 × 2.5-3.2 μm, oblong-elliptic to cylindric, smooth. Hyaline.
Comments: *Trametes lactinea* is a synonym. *Trametes aesculi* has a thin, sharp margin and highly variable pores with circular, mazelike, and sometimes gill-like components.

Neofavolus alveolaris
(DC.) Sotome & T. Hatt.

HEXAGONAL POLYPORE

Description: Cap 2-6.5 cm wide, convex to somewhat funnel-like, circular to kidney-shaped. Upper surface with tiny flattened scales or fibers, orange-yellow to reddish-orange, fading to pale yellow or tan in age. Margin thin, inrolled at first, somewhat fringed. Pores hexagonal or multisided, up to 1 × 2 mm in size, decurrent, radially arranged, cream to pale yellow. Stalk up to 1 cm long, 3-6 mm thick, lateral to nearly central. Flesh tough, creamy. Odor and taste not distinctive.

Spore Print: White.

Occurrence: Solitary or in groups on fallen branches of hardwoods. Spring–fall.

Edibility: Edible but tough.

Microscopic Features:
Spores 9-11 × 3-3.5 µm, cylindrical, smooth. Hyaline.

Comments: *Favolus alveolaris*, *Hexagonia alveolaris*, and *Polyporus mori* are synonyms. *Lentinus arcularius* = *Polyporus arcularius* (search online) has a circular, orange-brown cap with a fringed margin, and white to cream honeycomb pores. *Lentinus brumalis* = *Polyporus brumalis* (search online) has a darker cap and smaller, randomly arranged pores.

Niveoporofomes spraguei (Berk. & M. A. Curtis) B. K. Cui, M. L. Han & Y. C. Dai

Description: Cap 5-9 cm wide, up to 4 cm thick, semicircular and shelflike to irregular and spreading, stalkless. Upper surface azonate, with flattened hairs or nearly bald, smooth or roughened, white to ivory or pale brownish-yellow, usually with greenish-blue to grayish-blue stains. Margin rounded or acute, colored like the cap, reddish, or greenish-blue to grayish-blue. Pores circular to angular, 3-6 per mm, white to buff or pale brown. Flesh up to 4 cm thick, corky or tough, azonate, white to brownish-yellow. Odor not distinctive. Taste variously described as slightly acidic, bitter, or not distinctive.

Spore Print: White.

Occurrence: Solitary or in groups or clusters on hardwoods. Summer–early winter.

Edibility: Inedible.

Microscopic Features:
Spores 5.5-7 × 4-5 µm, ovoid to broadly ellipsoid, smooth. Hyaline.

Comments: *Spraguei* honors C. J. Sprague, who collected it as an undescribed species. *Fomitopsis spraguei* is a synonym. The fruitbody of *Postia caesia* is comparatively soft and bruises blue.

Oxyporus populinus (Schumach.) Donk
MOSSY MAPLE POLYPORE
Description: Fruitbody perennial, cap
3-20 cm wide, fan- to kidney-shaped,
convex, stalkless. Upper surface
covered with dense matted hairs, white
to creamy white, green when covered
with moss. Margin sharp, uneven.
Pores circular to angular, 4-7 per mm,
white to creamy white. Flesh up to
2 cm thick, corky to fibrous and tough,
white to yellowish-brown. Older pore
layers separated from each other by
thin sheets of flesh. Odor and taste not
distinctive.
Spore Print: White.
Occurrence: Usually solitary on hardwood
trees, especially maple. Year-round.
Edibility: Inedible.
Microscopic Features:
Spores 3.5-5.5 μm, subglobose, smooth.
Hyaline.
Comments: *Populinus* refers to poplar
trees, a misnomer since it occurs on
maples. *Trametes aesculi* is similar but
has much larger pores. *Perenniporia*
fraxinophila (search online) also greens
when covered with moss or algae;
it grows on ash and has a brown to
blackish cap with a white margin.

Picipes badius (Pers.) Zmitr. & Kovalenko
BLACK-FOOTED POLYPORE
Description: Cap 4-20 cm wide, circular
to irregular, convex to funnel-shaped.
Upper surface smooth, shiny or dull,
pale reddish-brown with a darker center
when young, darkening to reddish-
brown with a blackish-brown center.
Margin incurved at first, thin, acute,
wavy or lobed at maturity. Pores circular
to angular, 5-7 per mm, white to pale
buff. Stalk 1-3 cm long, 3-16 mm thick,
nearly equal or tapered downward,
central or eccentric, smooth, reddish-
brown near the apex, black below. Flesh
thin, tough, white. Odor and taste not
distinctive.
Spore Print: White.
Occurrence: Solitary, scattered, or in
groups on decaying hardwoods. Late
spring-early winter.
Edibility: Inedible.
Microscopic Features:
Spores 6-10 × 3-5 μm, cylindric,
smooth. Hyaline.
Comments: *Badius* means "reddish
brown." *Polyporus badius* is a synonym.
The smaller *Picipes melanopus* (search
online) has a pale yellow-brown to
gray-brown cap with radial fibrils; the
velvety—not smooth—stalk is black on
the lower half or overall.

271

Poronidulus conchifer (Schwein.) Murrill
LITTLE NEST POLYPORE
Description: Fruitbody at first a small
  splash cup. An area of the rim then
  extends as a stalkless cap with pores
  on the underside. Cup up to 1.6 cm
  wide, concentrically zoned, smooth,
  brown at first, becoming brown and
  white, sometimes not obvious after the
  cap develops. Cap 1-5 cm wide, fan- to
  kidney-shaped, flattish and sometimes
  forming secondary cups, zoned with
  whites, yellows, and browns. Margin
  thin, wavy. Pores angular, 2-4 per mm,
  white to yellowish. Flesh less than 1 mm
  thick, tough, white. Odor and taste not
  distinctive.
Spore Print: White.
Occurrence: Solitary or in groups on
  decaying hardwood. Summer–early
  winter.
Edibility: Inedible.
Microscopic Features:
  Spores 5-7 × 1.5-2.5 μm, cylindric,
  smooth. Hyaline.
Comments: *Trametes conchifer* is a
  synonym. The cups produce asexual
  spores that are dispersed by raindrops
  as in bird's-nest fungi. Identification of
  this oddball is difficult when the splash
  cups are not obvious.

Postia caesia (Schrad.) P. Karst.
BLUE CHEESE POLYPORE
Description: Cap 2-8 cm wide, shelflike,
  semicircular, broadly convex to
  flattened, stalkless. Upper surface
  velvety or covered with matted hairs,
  sometimes bald, smooth, whitish,
  often with bluish tints and/or bruising
  intensely blue. Margin sharp, smoothly
  arcing. Pores angular, sometimes split
  or torn, 3-6 per mm, whitish to grayish,
  usually staining blue. Flesh up to 1 cm
  thick, soft, spongy, watery when fresh,
  white, becoming yellowish or grayish
  in age. Odor usually fragrant. Taste not
  distinctive.
Spore Print: Bluish.
Occurrence: Usually solitary, sometimes
  in groups on conifers or hardwoods.
  Summer-fall.
Edibility: Inedible.
Microscopic Features:
  Spores 5.5-7.5 × 1-2 μm, cylindric to
  allantoid, smooth. Hyaline.
Comments: *Oligoporus caesius* and
  Tyromyces caesius are synonyms.
  Niveoporofomes spraguei has a whitish
  to ivory cap usually with greenish-blue
  stains, and corky to tough flesh. *Postia
  fragilis* (search online) has a whitish cap
  that stains reddish-brown when bruised
  or on drying.

Trametes aesculi (Fr.) Justo

Description: Cap 5-30 cm wide, up to 3 cm thick, shelflike, semicircular to fan- or kidney-shaped, corky when fresh, rigid when dry. Upper surface bald, concentrically zoned, uneven to warted, sometimes smooth at the margin, color white to cream, buff, gray, or pale brownish-yellow, occasionally blackish from the base in age. Margin thin, sharp, arcing smoothly or lobed. Pores 1-2 per mm, highly variable with circular, mazelike, and sometimes gill-like components. Stalk absent or stubby, up to 3 cm long, colored like the cap. Flesh up to 1.5 cm thick, tough to woody, white to pale cream. Odor and taste not distinctive.

Spore Print: White.

Occurrence: Solitary or in groups on decaying hardwoods. Year-round.

Edibility: Inedible.

Microscopic Features:
Spores 5-7 × 2-3 μm, cylindric to ellipsoid, smooth. Hyaline.

Comments: *Trametes elegans* is a synonym. *Trametes gibbosa* (search online) is nearly identical, but the cap has a velvety texture or fuzzy surface when viewed with a hand lens.

Trametes pubescens (Schumach.) Pilát

Description: Cap 3-6 cm wide, semicircular to kidney-shaped or irregularly shelflike, sometimes fusing laterally, stalkless. Upper surface finely hairy to nearly smooth, azonate or very faintly zoned, creamy white to yellowish-buff. Margin often lined or shallowly furrowed. Pores angular, 3-5 per mm, creamy white, turning yellowish in age. Flesh up to 5 mm thick, corky or tough, whitish. Odor and taste not distinctive.

Spore Print: White.

Occurrence: In groups or overlapping clusters on decaying hardwoods, rarely on conifers. Summer-fall.

Edibility: Inedible.

Microscopic Features:
Spores 5-7 × 1.5-2 μm, cylindric, smooth. Hyaline.

Comments: *Pubescens* means "downy or hairy." *Trametes ochracea* (search online) has a zoned cap in shades of white and brown; the white pores become tan in age. *Trametes versicolor* has a strongly zoned cap and a white to grayish pore surface.

Trametes versicolor (L.) Lloyd
TURKEY-TAIL

Description: Cap 2-10 cm wide, fan-shaped to kidney-shaped, stalkless, thin, tough. Upper surface silky to velvety, with conspicuous concentric zones of colors that may include orange, green, blue, brown, or gray. Margin thin, sharp. Pores circular to angular, 3-5 per mm, white to grayish. Flesh up to 3 mm thick, tough, white to creamy white, with a thin black layer below the cap surface.

Spore Print: White.

Occurrence: Solitary or in groups or overlapping clusters, in rows or rosettes on wood. Year-round.

Edibility: Inedible, used medicinally.

Microscopic Features:
Spores 5-6 × 1.5-2 μm, cylindric to allantoid, smooth. Hyaline.

Comments: *Versicolor* means "of various colors." Turkey-tail extracts have a long been used in Chinese medicine; some have empirically documented immunostimulant properties. *Trametes ochracea* (search online) has a paler and less strongly zoned cap, and its upper flesh lacks the black layer. *Stereum ostrea* lacks pores.

Trametes villosa (Sw.) Kreisel

Description: Cap up to 7 cm wide and 1-2 mm thick, shelflike, stalkless, semicircular to fan-shaped, often fused laterally, occasionally spreading crustlike below the cap. Upper surface covered with coarse, elongated, and somewhat flattened hairs, distinctly zoned, white to grayish or sometimes dirty brown. Margin thin, wavy or lobed. Pores angular, thin-walled, 1-3 per mm, often breaking up to become toothlike, white to cream or brownish in age. Flesh up to 1.5 mm thick, tough, white, lacking a black layer. Odor and taste not distinctive.

Spore Print: White.

Occurrence: In groups or clusters on decaying conifers or hardwoods. Year-round.

Edibility: Inedible.

Microscopic Features:
Spores 5.5-8.5 × 2.5-3.5 μm, cylindric to allantoid, smooth. Hyaline.

Comments: *Villosa* means "hairy or shaggy." The gray colors and large, ragged pores distinguish this from most other species. *Trametes hirsuta* (see photo on p. 22) has caps up to 18 mm thick with smaller, nontoothed pores, 3-4 per mm.

Tyromyces chioneus (Fr.) P. Karst.
WHITE CHEESE POLYPORE
Description: Cap 2-10 cm wide,
semicircular to petal- or tongue-shaped,
convex to nearly flat, stalkless. Upper
surface smooth to slightly velvety,
azonate, dry, soft, white at first, becoming pale yellow to pale grayish in age.
Margin thin, sharp, sometimes uneven.
Pores angular to circular, 3-5 per mm,
white to pale cream. Flesh up to 2 cm
thick, soft, spongy, white. Odor fragrant
when fresh, often disappearing soon
after collection. Taste not distinctive.
Spore Print: White.
Occurrence: Solitary, scattered, or in
groups on decaying hardwoods.
Summer-early winter.
Edibility: Inedible.
Microscopic Features:
Spores 4-5 × 1.5-2 µm, cylindric,
typically curved, smooth. Hyaline.
Comments: The upper surface of *Postia
caesia* has blue tints and often bruises
intensely blue, especially on the
margin. *Postia fragilis* (search online)
has a whitish cap that stains reddish-
brown when bruised or on drying.
Oxyporus populinus may appear similar
but is perennial and tougher in texture.

Fistulina hepatica (Schaeff.) With.
BEEFSTEAK POLYPORE
Description: Cap 7-25 cm wide, fan-
shaped. Upper surface smooth to
velvety, gelatinous, sometimes sticky,
reddish-orange to pinkish-red or dark
red, often exuding red juice when
squeezed. Margin rounded or sharp,
often wavy. Pores circular, 1-3 per mm,
whitish to pinkish-yellow, darkening
in age or when bruised. Tubes crowded
but not fused together (use a hand
lens). Stalk up to 8 cm long, colored like
the cap. Flesh 2-5 cm thick, tender and
juicy when fresh, becoming fibrous,
whitish, pinkish, or reddish with a
meaty grain. Odor not distinctive. Taste
sour.
Spore Print: Pinkish-salmon.
Occurrence: Solitary or in groups on trunks
and stumps of oaks. Summer-fall.
Edibility: Edible, with a citruslike flavor.
Microscopic Features:
Spores 4-6 × 2.5-4 µm, oval to
lacrimoid, smooth. Hyaline.
Comments: *Pseudofistulina radicata* has a
smaller, pale yellowish-brown cap up to
7.5 cm wide, a whitish pore surface, and
a rooting stalk up to 10 cm long.

Fomes fasciatus (Sw.) Cooke
SOUTHERN CLAM SHELL
Description: Fruitbody perennial, 7-18 cm
wide, convex, hoof- to fan-shaped or
semicircular, stalkless. Upper surface
velvety and slightly roughened when
young, becoming hard and nearly
smooth at maturity, concentrically
furrowed, grayish with concentric zones
of reddish- and grayish-brown, often
dark brown to blackish-brown in age.
Margin curved and somewhat blunt.
Pores circular, 4-5 per mm, pale brown
to dark grayish-brown. Flesh up to 4 cm
thick at the base, hard and crusty near
the upper surface, fibrous to granular
and corky below, faintly to distinctly
zoned, lustrous golden-brown. Odor
and taste not distinctive.
Spore Print: White.
Occurrence: Solitary, in groups, or
sometimes in overlapping clusters on
hardwood trees, logs, and stumps. Year-
round.
Edibility: Inedible.
Microscopic Features:
Spores 10-14 × 4-5 µm, cylindric,
smooth. Hyaline.
Comments: *Fasciatus* means "banded,"
a reference to the concentric zones of
this polypore. Compare with *Fomes
fomentarius*.

Fomes fomentarius (L.) Fr.
TINDER CONK, TINDER POLYPORE
Description: Fruitbody perennial, 6-20 cm wide, hoof-shaped, stalkless, woody. Upper surface concentrically furrowed and zoned, hard, thick, crusty, thickest at the zone of attachment, smooth or finely cracked and roughened, pale to dark gray or sometimes pale to dark brown. Margin blunt, extending beyond the slightly concave pore surface. Pores circular, 3-5 per mm, pale brown. Flesh up to 3 cm thick, tough to woody, yellowish-brown. Odor and taste not distinctive.
Spore Print: White.
Occurrence: Solitary or in groups on decaying hardwood, especially birch and beech. Year-round.
Edibility: Inedible.
Microscopic Features: Spores 12-20 × 4-7 μm, cylindric, smooth. Hyaline.
Comments: Historically used to carry fire and as a source of felt. Compare with *Fomes fasciatus* and *Fomitiporia robusta*. *Phellinus everhartii* (search online) has a yellowish-brown to black cap and typically grows on oak. *Phellinus igniarius* (search online) has orange-brown flesh mixed with white mycelial threads; it grows on various hardwoods.

Fomitiporia robusta
(P. Karst.) Fiasson & Niemelä
Description: Fruitbody perennial, up to 20 cm wide, hoof-shaped to shelflike, stalkless. Upper surface bald, furrowed, incrusted and cracked, brown to blackish. Margin rounded, yellowish-brown, becoming brown to blackish in age. Pores circular, 7-9 per mm, yellowish- to grayish-brown. Flesh up to 3 cm thick. Upper portion shiny, yellowish-brown, zoned, woody. Lower portion paler brown with white streaks near the tubes and point of attachment.
Spore print: White.
Occurrence: Solitary or in groups on decaying hardwoods, especially oak. Year-round.
Edibility: Inedible.
Microscopic Features: Spores 6-8.5 × 5.5-7 μm, subglobose, smooth. Hyaline. Setae usually absent.
Comments: *Phellinus robustus* is a synonym. *Phellinus everhartii* (search online) has a yellowish- to reddish-brown pore surface that glances with a golden luster, brown spores, and frequent setae. *Phellinus igniarius* (search online) is hoof-shaped to shelflike and has a brown pore surface, tubes stuffed with white material, brown spores, and setae that are abundant to rare.

POLYPORES

Fuscoporia gilva
(Schwein.) T. Wagner & M. Fisch.
MUSTARD YELLOW POLYPORE
Description: Cap 3-12 cm wide, fan-shaped to shell-shaped or sometimes spreading across the host, stalkless. Upper surface velvety to nearly bald, often wrinkled, sometimes zoned, brownish-yellow to bright rusty yellow when young, soon becoming dark yellowish- to reddish-brown with a conspicuous yellow margin when fresh. Margin sharp. Pores variable, round to angular or irregular, 2-5 per mm, bright reddish-brown, darkening in age or when bruised. Flesh up to 5 mm thick, yellowish to tawny. Odor and taste not distinctive.

Spore Print: White.

Occurrence: Solitary or in groups on hardwood trees, logs, and stumps, especially oak; sometimes on pine. Year-round.

Edibility: Inedible.

Microscopic Features:
Spores 4-5 × 3-3.5 μm, ellipsoid to ovoid, smooth. Hyaline.

Comments: *Gilva* means "dull pale yellow." *Phellinus gilvus* is a synonym. *Ischnoderma resinosum* has whitish flesh. *Phaeolus schweinitzii* is much larger and usually grows in overlapping clusters or rosettes on buried conifer roots.

Globifomes graveolens (Schwein.) Murrill
SWEET KNOT
Description: Fruitbody 5-21 cm wide and long, a nearly round to cylindric or hoof-shaped, stalkless mass of small, overlapping caps arising from a solid central core. Caps laterally fused with long overhanging margins. Upper surface radially wrinkled, dull yellow-brown with a tan margin when young, becoming dark brown to grayish-black in age. Margins rounded, petal-shaped and projecting. Pores circular, 3-5 per mm, purplish-gray, becoming dark grayish-brown. Flesh up to 6 mm thick, tough, yellowish-brown. Odor sweet, resembling apples or green fodder, or not distinctive. Taste not distinctive.

Spore Print: Brown.

Occurrence: Solitary or in groups on trunks and logs of hardwoods, especially oak. Summer-fall.

Edibility: Inedible.

Microscopic Features:
Spores 9-14 × 3-4.5 μm, cylindric, smooth. Hyaline to pale brown.

Comments: *Polyporus graveolens* is a synonym.

Hapalopilus croceus (Pers.) Donk.

Description: Cap 5-20 cm wide, shelflike, fan-shaped to semicircular, convex, stalkless. Upper surface velvety and bright orange at first, becoming brownish-orange and smooth to roughened with gummy tufts of hyphae. Margin thick, blunt. Pores angular, 2-3 per mm, bright reddish-orange when fresh, brownish when dry. Flesh up to 3 cm thick, soft and watery when fresh, becoming corky to brittle, bright orange when fresh, becoming darker orange to brownish. Odor not distinctive. Taste slightly bitter.

Spore Print: White.

Occurrence: Solitary or in groups on oak or chestnut. Late spring-fall.

Edibility: Unknown; possibly deadly poisonous.

Microscopic Features:
Spores 4-7 × 3-4.5 μm, broadly ellipsoid, smooth. Hyaline.

Comments: *Croceus* means "saffron-colored." The cap stains red to carmine with KOH. *Hapalopilus nidulans* (search online) has a less robust, cinnamon to brownish-orange cap and pores, stains light violet to purplish with KOH, and grows on a wide variety of hardwoods.

Inonotus hispidus (Bull.) P. Karst.

SHAGGY POLYPORE

Description: Cap 10-30 cm wide, convex, semicircular to fan-shaped, stalkless. Upper surface broadly attached, azonate, covered with stiff, bright reddish-orange hairs that become reddish-brown to blackish in age. Margin rounded and blunt, bright sulfur yellow when young. Pores angular to irregularly rounded, 1-3 per mm, uneven, yellow at first, becoming brownish-yellow then yellowish-brown to blackish in age. Flesh up to 7.5 cm thick, somewhat zoned, soft or tough, yellow to brownish-orange with darker zones, immediately staining brownish when exposed. Odor somewhat acidic and pleasant. Taste not distinctive.

Spore Print: Brown.

Occurrence: Solitary or in groups on living hardwood trees, especially oak and walnut. Summer-early winter.

Edibility: Inedible.

Microscopic Features:
Spores 8-11 × 6-8 μm, subglobose to ovoid, thick-walled, smooth, brown, setae sometimes present, up to 30 μm long. Dark brown.

Comments: *Hispidus* means "having stiff hairs." Dyers often seek out this species for the gold and brown colors it produces.

POLYPORES

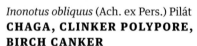

Inonotus obliquus (Ach. ex Pers.) Pilát
CHAGA, CLINKER POLYPORE, BIRCH CANKER
Description: Fruitbody perennial, 10–40 cm wide, stalkless, a rough and irregular blackened canker reminiscent of charred wood rising from a wound in tree bark. The outer surface is dark brown or black, deeply cracked, hard and brittle. Inner portion corky, bright yellow- to rusty brown.
Occurrence: Solitary or in groups on standing birch trees, occasionally also found on alder, beech, elm, or ironwood, but not on cherry. Year-round.
Edibility: Inedible but sometimes ground and steeped to make Chaga tea.
Comments: The visible fungus is a sterile mass of woody tissue. The actual fruitbody is rarely observed and quickly deteriorated by insects. A significant reduction in the population of this fungus has occurred because of widespread commercial harvesting.

Nigroporus vinosus (Berk.) Murrill
Description: Cap 2–12 cm wide, shelflike, stalkless, leathery or tough, becoming brittle as it dries. Upper surface velvety to nearly bald, sometimes zoned, violet to vinaceous-brown at first, becoming purplish-brown to dark violet at maturity. Margin thin, sharp. Pores irregularly rounded, 7–8 per mm, purplish-brown to dark violet or smoky black. Flesh up to 6 mm thick, vinaceous-brown or paler. Odor and taste not distinctive.
Spore Print: White.
Occurrence: Solitary or in groups or overlapping clusters on hardwoods or conifers. Year-round.
Edibility: Inedible.
Microscopic Features:
Spores 3.5–4.5 × 1–1.5 μm, allantoid to cylindrical, smooth. Hyaline.
Comments: *Vinosus* means "wine-red," a reference to colors of the fruitbody. Compare with *Rhodofomes cajanderi*, which has a pinkish- to reddish-brown or grayish-brown cap and rosy pink to pinkish-brown pores. *Bjerkandera adusta* lacks the purplish colors.

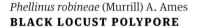

Phellinus robineae (Murrill) A. Ames
BLACK LOCUST POLYPORE
Description: Fruitbody perennial, up to
35 cm wide, shelflike to hoof-shaped,
stalkless. Upper surface covered with
matted hairs, azonate, yellowish-brown
at first, becoming bald, blackish, scaly
and deeply cracked in age. Margin
rounded, yellowish-brown when young,
blackish in age. Pores circular, 7-8 per
mm, yellowish- to reddish-brown. Flesh
up to 2.5 cm thick, arranged in stratified
layers, woody, yellowish-brown to light
reddish-brown. Odor fragrant or not
distinctive. Taste not distinctive.
Spore Print: Brown.
Occurrence: Solitary or in groups on
stumps and trunks of black locust trees.
Year-round.
Edibility: Inedible.
Microscopic Features:
Spores 5-6 × 4.5-5 μm, ovoid to
subglobose, smooth. Reddish-brown.
Comments: *Fomitiporia robusta* may have
a similar appearance but rarely, if ever,
occurs on black locust. The same is
probably true of another oak-lover,
Phellinus everhartii (search online).

Pseudoinonotus dryadeus
(Pers.) T. Wagner & M. Fisch.
WEEPING POLYPORE
Description: Cap 13-36 cm wide, convex,
fan-shaped or top-shaped, sometimes
rounded, stalkless. Upper surface
smooth, azonate, becoming finely
cracked in age, whitish when very
young, soon buff to brown, typically
exuding amber droplets when fresh.
Margin blunt, ivory or colored like
the cap. Pores circular to angular, 4-6
per mm, buff, becoming dark brown.
Flesh up to 15 cm thick, soft or tough,
zoned, bright yellowish-brown at first,
becoming reddish-brown in age, mottled
when cut. Odor and taste not distinctive.
Spore Print: White.
Occurrence: Solitary or in groups at the
base, on stumps, or along roots of oak
trees. Year-round.
Edibility: Inedible.
Microscopic Features:
Spores 6-8 × 5-7 μm, subglobose,
smooth, setae rare or frequent,
ventricose, often hooked. Hyaline,
dextrinoid.
Comments: *Dryadeus* refers to oak trees.
Inonotus dryadeus is a synonym. The
presence of amber droplets is a good
field identification feature. *Inocutis
dryophila* (search online) has 1-3
angular pores per mm.

POLYPORES

281

Pycnoporus cinnabarinus (Jacq.) P. Karst.
CINNABAR-RED POLYPORE
Description: Cap 3-14 cm wide, up to
2 cm thick, convex to nearly flat,
semicircular to kidney-shaped, tough,
stalkless. Upper surface dry, azonate,
typically roughened or wrinkled,
occasionally smooth, bright or dull
reddish-orange, sometimes mixed with
yellow or brownish tints. Margin sharp
or rounded. Pores circular to angular or
sometimes elongated, 2-4 per mm, pale
or dark orange-red. Flesh up to 1.5 cm
thick, corky or tough, reddish-orange.
Odor and taste not distinctive.
Spore Print: White.
Occurrence: Solitary or in groups on
decaying hardwoods, rarely on conifers.
Year-round.
Edibility: Inedible.
Microscopic Features:
Spores 4.5-8 × 2.5-4 µm, cylindric to
slightly allantoid, smooth. Hyaline.
Comments: *Cinnabarinus* means "reddish-
orange to bright brick red." The flesh
stains black with KOH. The smaller
Pycnoporus sanguineus (search online)
has a thinner cap and dark red pore
surface. *Pycnoporellus fulgens* (search
online) has a pale to dark orange or
rusty cap. *Hapalopilus croceus* is larger,
yellower, and stains red with KOH.

Rhodofomes cajanderi
(P. Karst.) B. K. Cui, M. L. Han & Y. C. Dai
ROSY POLYPORE
Description: Fruitbody perennial, 3-14
or rarely up to 20 cm wide, convex to
nearly flat, semicircular and shelflike
to fan-shaped or irregular, tough,
becoming corky to brittle when dry,
stalkless. Upper surface with flattened
fibrils, smooth or somewhat roughened,
typically faintly zoned, pinkish- to
reddish-brown or grayish-brown. Margin
fairly sharp, typically whitish when
young. The lower surface may spread
as a flat surface below the cap. Pores
circular to angular, 3-5 per mm, rosy
pink to pinkish-brown. Flesh tough, rosy
pink, becoming pinkish-brown in age.
Odor and taste not distinctive.
Spore Print: White.
Occurrence: Solitary to clustered on
decaying conifer wood, rarely on
hardwood. Year-round.
Edibility: Inedible.
Microscopic Features:
Spores 4-7 × 1.5-2 µm, allantoid,
smooth. Hyaline.
Comments: *Fomitopsis cajanderi* is a synonym. *Rhodofomes roseus* = *Fomitopsis
rosea* (search online) grows at high elevations, usually on spruce. The rose-pink
cap becomes cracked and darkens to
brownish-black; spores are cylindrical.

CRUST AND PARCHMENT FUNGI AND FIBER FANS

These fungi are thin and tough. Crusts and parchments are wood decomposers that may spread as a flat coating across a wooden surface, form caps reminiscent of colorfully banded (**zoned**) potato chips, or do a little of both. Fiber fans and one species of parchment grow on the ground as rosettes or flaring trumpet shapes. This group lacks the tubes and pores of polypores. Fertile surfaces can be bumpy or wrinkled but are not sandpapery rough, as in flat species of carbon and cushion fungi. Try those sections if you don't find what you're looking for here.

Crusts, parchments, and fiber fans are inedible. Fiber fans are used in papermaking and as dye sources for wool or silk. Other species are rarely of great interest to mushroom hunters except as a source of diagnostic confusion or, when found digesting the floor joists, horror.

Byssomerulius incarnatus (Schwein.) Gilb.

Description: Fruitbody consisting of stalkless caps, 3-8 cm long, 2-4 cm wide, semicircular to fan-shaped, somewhat leathery to cartilaginous. Upper surface moist or dry, bald to velvety, coral-pink when young and fresh, becoming pinkish-buff in age. Lower surface is a radial network of branched folds, whitish to pinkish or brownish. Flesh 2-4 mm thick, spongy to leathery, whitish to buff.

Spore Print: White.

Occurrence: In overlapping clusters on logs and stumps of hardwood trees, typically growing among fruitbodies of *Stereum ostrea* or other *Stereum* species. Summer-winter.

Edibility: Unknown.

Microscopic Features: Spores 4-5 × 2-3 µm, elliptic, smooth. Hyaline.

Comments: *Phlebia incarnata* and *Merulius incarnatus* are synonyms. It may be parasitic on *Stereum* species. *Phlebia tremellosa* (see photo on p. 23) is similar but has a hairier, white to pale yellow upper surface (when present) and a yellowish to brownish- or pinkish-orange lower surface that may spread across a log rather than shelf out to produce a cap.

Hydnochaete olivacea (Schwein.) Banker

BROWN-TOOTHED CRUST

Description: Fruitbody a spreading crust up to 20 cm long and 10 cm wide. Surface dry, leathery, dull yellowish- or reddish-brown, with jagged teeth up to 2 mm long. Margin sometimes brownish-yellow when young. Flesh up to 3 mm thick, leathery, brown. Odor and taste not distinctive.

Spore Print: White.

Occurrence: On the underside of fallen hardwood branches, especially oak. Year-round.

Edibility: Inedible.

Microscopic Features: Spores 5.5-7 × 1-1.5 µm, cylindrical to allantoid, smooth. Hyaline. Setae present on the teeth 30-150 × 9-14 µm, sharp and tapered at both ends, thick-walled, reddish-brown.

Comments: *Hymenochaete tabacina* (search online) forms a thin spreading crust with small, shelflike, concentrically zoned, stalkless caps that grow in overlapping clusters. *Hymenochaete corrugata* (search online) has a finely cracked, reddish-brown to reddish-gray surface, sometimes with a pinkish tint, and has flattened teeth.

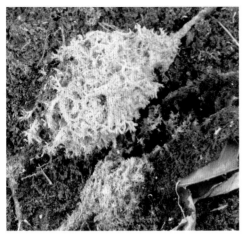 

Scorias spongiosa (Schwein.) Fr.

HONEYDEW EATER

Description: Fruitbody up to 6 cm high and 15 cm or more wide. At first a loosely stranded or tangled cobwebby mat, cream to buff, adhering to leaves and twigs; this thickens into a brownish-yellow mass resembling a gelatinous sponge and producing asexual spores. Months later, the mass darkens to brown or black and generates sexual ascospores.

Occurrence: Beneath colonies of the beech blight aphid, *Grylloprociphilus imbricator*, on leaves, twigs, and branches of American beech trees. The asexual stage of the fungus appears in late summer and persists through the winter. The sexual stage develops during spring.

Edibility: Inedible.

Microscopic Features: Ascospores 12-5 × 2.5-3 µm, cylindrical to elliptical, 3-septate, smooth. Yellowish-hyaline.

Comments: This so-called sooty mold feeds on the honeydew of beech blight aphids. Unlike the aphids, it does not attack the tree.

Sebacina incrustans (Pers.) Tul. & C. Tul.

Description: Fruitbody up to 16 cm wide or occasionally larger, a thin and irregularly shaped, tough and waxy to leathery crust with small lateral projections from the margins, whitish to pale tan.

Occurrence: On the ground, spreading and enveloping leaves, cones, twigs, plant stems, and debris. Spring-fall.

Edibility: Inedible.

Microscopic Features: Spores 11.5-15 × 6-8 µm, elliptic to ovoid, flattened to slightly depressed on one side, smooth. Hyaline.

Comments: *Incrustans* means "covered with a crustlike layer." Compare with *Helvellosebacina concrescens*, which is also pale in color, grows on the ground, and clasps or envelops plant stems and leaves; that species has a soft, rubbery to gelatinous fruitbody. *Tremellodendron schweinitzii* is a tough, coral-like mass of flattened and fused whitish fingers that grow erect on the ground, not engulfing parts of plants.

CRUST AND PARCHMENT FUNGI AND FIBER FANS

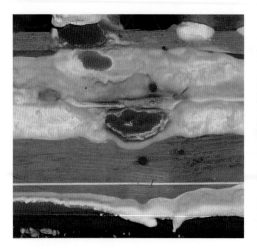

Serpula lacrymans (Wulfen) J. Schröt.
DRY ROT FUNGUS
Description: Fruitbody a spreading honey-comb of a crust producing pancake-like patches that may exceed 3 feet in diameter, sometimes on vertical surfaces also forming spongy, shelflike caps that project up to 10 cm. Pancake margin or upper cap surface thick, downy, whitish to cream-colored. Lower surface resembles an uneven honeycomb with angular, toothlike projections and small porelike depressions, brown to rusty cinnamon. Flesh pale brownish-yellow. Odor not distinctive when fresh, strongly unpleasant and musty when old. Taste not distinctive.

Spore Print: Brownish.

Occurrence: On conifer logs in the woods or in damp, poorly ventilated spaces on structural timber, spreading long distances across non-nutritious substrates such as stone, brick, or concrete via grayish mycelial cords. Year-round.

Edibility: Inedible.

Microscopic Features:
Spores 8–12 × 4.5–6 µm, elliptic, smooth, thick-walled. Pale yellow.

Comments: *Lacrymans* means "weeping," a reference to the large quantity of water this fungus exudes and the reaction of afflicted homeowners.

Stereum complicatum (Fr.) Fr.
CROWDED PARCHMENT
Description: Fruitbody a spreading crust of caps that are sometimes laterally fused. Cap up to 3 cm wide, fan-shaped. Upper surface dry, with fine silky hairs near the margin and stiff hairs at the base, concentrically zoned and variously colored from orange to grayish-orange, or reddish-brown, sometimes with shallow radial grooves. Margin often wavy or crimped. Lower surface smooth, pale orange to tan or grayish, exuding a red juice if cut when fresh and moist.

Spore Print: White.

Occurrence: In groups or dense overlapping clusters on twigs and branches of conifers and hardwoods, especially oak. Year-round.

Edibility: Inedible.

Microscopic Features:
Spores 5–6.5 × 2–2.5 µm, nearly cylindric, smooth. Hyaline.

Comments: *Stereum hirsutum* (search online) has a dense coating of stiff hairs on its upper surface, and its lower surface does not exude red juice when cut. The cap of *Stereum striatum* is pale gray to silvery or buff with radiating silky fibers.

Stereum ostrea (Blume & T. Nees) Fr.
FALSE TURKEY TAIL
Description: Cap up to 8 cm wide, sometimes laterally fused, with a narrow point of attachment, leathery, flexible. Upper surface covered with fine hairs, concentrically zoned with bands of reddish-brown, gray, yellow, and orange, frequently coated with green algae, may be reddish-brown when wet, margin often whitish. Lower surface smooth, reddish-brown to buff. Flesh thin, buff.
Spore Print: White.
Occurrence: In groups or dense clusters on hardwood branches, logs, and stumps. Year-round.
Edibility: Inedible.
Microscopic Features:
Spores 5-7.5 × 2-3 μm, cylindric, smooth. Hyaline.
Comments: It is often misidentified as the Turkey-tail, which has an undersurface covered by tiny white pores, a broader point of attachment, and a thin tube layer beneath the cap flesh. *Stereum hirsutum* (search online) is smaller, with a dense coating of stiff hairs on the upper surface. Also compare with *Xylobolus subpileatus*, which forms smaller fruitbodies and has smaller spores.

Stereum striatum (Fr.) Fr.
SILKY PARCHMENT
Description: Fruitbody a spreading crust of fan-shaped to shell-shaped caps that are often laterally fused. Cap up to 1.5 cm wide, rounded, somewhat flattened, attached to the substrate at a central point. Upper surface dry, shiny, pale gray to silvery or buff, with radiating silky fibers or tiny furrows. Lower surface smooth, buff to yellowish or brownish at first, whiter in age. Flesh very thin and tough. Odor and taste not distinctive.
Spore Print: White.
Occurrence: In groups or clusters on decaying twigs and branches of hardwoods, especially American hornbeam. Year-round.
Edibility: Inedible.
Microscopic Features:
Spores 6-8.5 × 2-3.5 μm, cylindrical, smooth. Hyaline.
Comments: *Striatum* means "finely furrowed or lined." Compare with *Stereum complicatum*, which has an orange to brownish-orange or reddish-brown upper surface and an orange to tan or grayish lower surface that sometimes exudes red juice when cut.

Terana coerulea (Lam.) Kuntze
VELVET BLUE CRUST
Description: Fruitbody composed of thin, rounded to irregular crusts up to 2 cm in diameter that fuse at the margins to form patches up to 16 or more cm in diameter. Surface dry, velvety, dark blue to blackish-blue with a paler margin.
Spore Print: White.
Occurrence: Usually seen only on the undersides of fallen and decaying hardwood logs and branches, especially oaks. Summer-winter.
Edibility: Inedible.
Microscopic Features:
Spores 6-10 × 4-5 μm, elliptic, smooth. Hyaline.
Comments: *Pulcherricium coeruleum* and *Corticium coeruleum* are synonyms. *Chondrostereum purpureum* (see photo on p. 23) appears as bright pink to brown or dark violet spreading patches that may be decorated with small frilly caps; it is a destructive parasite and decomposer of cherry, plum, and related fruit trees, also found on wild hardwoods or rarely on conifers.

Thelephora vialis Schwein.
VASE THELEPHORE
Description: Fruitbody 2.5-10 cm high, up to 15 cm wide, typically a semi-erect rosette of caps arising from a central stalk, but highly variable. Cap funnel-shaped or fused and somewhat vase-shaped. Upper surface minutely scaly, white to yellowish at the margin, elsewhere purple or brownish. Lower surface wrinkled and similarly colored. Stalk 1-5 cm long, 5-40 mm thick, enlarged downward, solid, whitish to grayish. Flesh thick, leathery, whitish to grayish. Odor faintly sharp and disagreeable, intensifies on drying, or not distinctive. Taste unpleasant or not distinctive.
Spore Print: Brown.
Occurrence: Solitary, scattered, or in groups under hardwoods, especially oaks. Summer-early winter.
Edibility: Inedible.
Microscopic Features:
Spores 4.5-8 × 4.5-6.5 μm, angular, warted, minutely spiny. Olive-buff.
Comments: *Thelephora terrestris* (see photo on p. 23) forms brown, circular to fan-shaped rosettes with coarsely torn margins, and brownish wrinkled and warted lower surfaces. *Thelephora palmata* (search online) forms coral-like, branched, brown tufts with spoon-shaped whitish tips and an intensely unpleasant odor.

Trichoderma peltatum
(Berk.) Samuels, Jaklitsch & Voglmayr

Description: Fruitbody up to 8 cm in diameter, shield-shaped to brainlike, attached to the substrate at a central point. Upper surface fleshy or leathery in texture, light tan. Lower surface smooth but showing shallow ridges that radiate from the point of attachment, lighter tan. Flesh leathery. Odor and taste not recorded; see below.

Occurrence: Solitary or in groups or fused clusters, usually on hardwood logs and branches, rarely on pines. Year-round.

Edibility: Unknown.

Microscopic Features:
Spores 2-6.5 × 2-5 µm, subglobose, finely spinulose. Hyaline.

Comments: *Peltatum* means "shield-shaped." *Hypocrea peltata* is a synonym. The large, stalked fruitbodies with radial ridges on the lower surface are distinctive, resembling parasitized gilled mushrooms growing on wood. Because this species thrives at body temperature and has been found in a human lung, smelling and tasting are not recommended.

Xylobolus subpileatus
(Berk. & M. A. Curtis) Boidin

Description: Fruitbody a spreading crust of shell-shaped, rigid caps that are often laterally fused. Cap up to 3.5 cm wide, rounded or somewhat flattened, attached at a central point. Upper surface shallowly grooved and concentrically zoned with bands of grayish-orange and various shades of brown, dry, covered with densely matted hairs; margin whitish or brownish. Lower surface smooth or covered with short hairs, white to pinkish-brown or brown. Flesh thin, leathery, orangish to brownish.

Spore Print: White.

Occurrence: Scattered, in groups or clusters on hardwoods, especially oaks. Year-round.

Edibility: Inedible.

Microscopic Features:
Spores 4-5 × 2-2.5 µm, cylindric, smooth. Hyaline.

Comments: *Stereum subpileatum* is a synonym. The Bleeding Broadleaf Crust, *Stereum rugosum* (search online), is similar, but its lower surface is brownish-yellow, stains red when scratched, and has much larger spores, 7-12 × 3.5-4.5 µm. See *Stereum ostrea*, which is larger, leathery, and flexible, and *Xylobolus frustulatus* (see photo on p. 23).

TOOTH FUNGI

The tooth fungi, as discussed here, are a genetically diverse group. The attribute they share in common is a fertile surface composed of "teeth" or soft spines that hang downward, like a field of cloned icicles. These usually occur on the underside of a cap, but in the genus *Hericium*, the entire fruitbody is covered with them. Teeth may be quite small. When in doubt, use a hand lens to distinguish them from jagged remnants of an eroded layer of polypore tubes. Tooth fungi may or may not have a stalk. Some are terrestrial. Others grow on wood. One species grows on fallen conifer cones. The consistency of the fruitbody ranges from gelatinous in one species to tough, crumbly, or woody in other species. A stalk with a flaky surface is said to be **scurfy**. The cap and/or flesh of some tooth fungi is **zoned**, striped with grainlike bands of color. Species without this feature are termed **azonate**. In some terrestrial species, the flesh consists of upper and lower layers that differ in color and consistency (**duplex**).

Good edibles can be found among the tooth fungi. Some species of *Hydnellum* and *Sarcodon* are used both as fabric and fiber dyes and in papermaking.

Auriscalpium vulgare Gray
PINECONE FUNGUS,
PINECONE TOOTH
Description: Cap 1-4 cm wide, semicircular to kidney-shaped, broadly convex; upper surface dry, densely hairy, pale brown to reddish-brown; margin entire or eroded, wavy, pale yellow-brown to pale reddish-brown, often with a hairy fringe, notched at the stalk; lower surface covered with 2-3-mm-long spines, whitish to pinkish, becoming brown at maturity. Flesh thin, leathery, white to pale brown. Stalk 2.5-7.5 cm long, 1.5-3 mm thick, enlarged downward, flexible, tough, densely hairy, dark reddish-brown, attached at the notch on the cap margin.
Spore Print: White.
Occurrence: Solitary or in groups on fallen cones of pine or Douglas fir. Summer-fall.
Edibility: Inedible.
Microscopic Features:
Spores 5-6 × 4-5.2 μm, subglobose, slightly roughened. Hyaline.
Comments: It is easy to identify because of its exclusive occurrence on fallen conifer cones. The cap and stalk stain black with KOH.

Climacodon pulcherrimus
(Berk. & M. A. Curtis) Nikol.
Description: Cap 3-10 cm wide, fan-shaped to semicircular, arising from a confluent spreading base; upper surface densely hairy, whitish to pale tan or pinkish-tan; lower surface covered with crowded short spines, 2.5-5 mm long, whitish at first, becoming pinkish-tan in age. Stalk absent, or a short lateral projection that may be furrowed. Flesh fibrous, flexible, white, exuding a creamy white, sticky sap when squeezed. Odor variously described as woody or resembling preserved figs. Taste not distinctive.
Spore Print: White.
Occurrence: In overlapping or fused clusters on decaying hardwoods. Summer-early winter.
Edibility: Inedible.
Microscopic Features:
Spores 4-5 × 2-2.5 μm, elliptic, smooth. Hyaline.
Comments: *Pulcherrimus* means "beautiful." *Steccherinum pulcherrimum* is a synonym. The cap and flesh stain pinkish to red with KOH. *Sarcodontia setosa* (search online) forms a yellow spreading crust with crowded waxy spines that slowly bruise reddish, and it has an unpleasant odor. It grows on hardwood logs and branches.

TOOTH FUNGI

291

Climacodon septentrionalis (Fr.) P. Karst.

NORTHERN TOOTH

Description: Cap 10-25 cm wide, 2.5-5 cm thick, stalkless, fan-shaped; upper surface hairy to roughened, whitish to creamy yellow when young, becoming yellow-brown in age; lower surface composed of crowded, flexible spines, 6-20 mm long, whitish with lacerated tips. Flesh whitish, zoned, tough, flexible. Odor and taste not distinctive when young, becoming like spoiled ham and bitter in age.

Spore Print: White.

Occurrence: In dense, overlapping clusters growing from a common base on wounds of standing hardwood trunks, especially maple. Summer-fall.

Edibility: Inedible.

Microscopic Features:
Spores 4-5.5 × 2.5-3 μm, elliptic, thick-walled, smooth. Hyaline.

Comments: *Climacodon* means "arranged like a ladder," a reference to the caps occurring in overlapping clusters that sometimes reach 38 or more cm high. *Septentrionalis* means "northern." *Irpex lacteus* vaguely resembles this species if it had melted and run down the side of a fallen log.

Hericium coralloides (Scop.) Pers.

COMB TOOTH

Description: Fruitbody 7-25 cm wide, 7-20 cm high, consisting of a cluster of spreading branches with spines arranged in rows along the branches like teeth on a comb, arising from a common base; white to salmon or pinkish. Spines up to 2.5 cm long, white, rather evenly distributed along the branches. Flesh thick, white, soft. Odor and taste not distinctive.

Spore Print: White.

Occurrence: Solitary or in groups hanging on decaying broadleaf logs and stumps. Late spring-fall.

Edibility: Edible.

Microscopic Features:
Spores 3-5 × 3-4 μm, oval to round, slightly roughened. Hyaline.

Comments: *Coralloides* means "resembling coral." The Bear's Head Tooth, *Hericium americanum* (search online), is similar but has spines arranged in clusters at the branch tips.

Hericium erinaceus (Bull.) Pers.

LION'S MANE, BEARDED TOOTH, SATYR'S BEARD

Description: Fruitbody up to 20 cm high and wide, a whitish to yellowish cushion-shaped mass giving rise to long spines and resembling a beard. Spines up to 9 cm long, white. Flesh thick, soft, white. Odor and taste not distinctive when young, becoming sour and unpleasant in age.

Spore Print: White.

Occurrence: Solitary or in groups on trunks, logs, and stumps of decaying hardwood trees. Summer-early winter.

Edibility: Edible.

Microscopic Features:
Spores 5-6.5 × 4-5.6 μm, oval to globose, smooth to slightly roughened. Hyaline.

Comments: *Erinaceus* means "resembling a hedgehog," a reference to the long spines.

Hydnellum aurantiacum (Batsch) P. Karst.

ORANGE ROUGH-CAP TOOTH

Description: Cap 5-18 cm wide, broadly convex; upper surface with irregular projections and cavities, finely velvety, whitish to orange-buff when young, becoming rusty brown with a rusty orange to whitish margin; lower surface covered with spines, 5-7 mm long, dark brown with grayish tips, running down the stalk. Stalk 2-7 cm long, 5-20 mm thick, enlarged downward to a bulbous base, covered with matted orange to brownish hairs, basal mycelium orange. Flesh tough, zoned, buff in the cap, rusty orange in the stalk. Odor pungent. Taste mildly bitter.

Spore Print: Brown.

Occurrence: Often fused and forming rosettes under conifers. Summer-early winter.

Edibility: Inedible.

Microscopic Features:
Spores 5-8 × 5-6 μm, subglobose, distinctly warted. Pale brown.

Comments: *Hydnellum ferrugipes* (search online) is similar but occurs under hardwoods, as does *H. piperatum* (search online), which tastes peppery hot. *Hydnellum peckii* also tastes acrid and exudes drops of red juice when young and fresh.

TOOTH FUNGI

Hydnellum caeruleum (Hornem.) P. Karst.
BLUISH TOOTH
Description: Cap 3-15 cm wide, top-shaped or nearly flat; upper surface azonate, velvety at first, becoming uneven, bumpy and pitted, whitish with bluish tints initially, sometimes pale brown along the margin, becoming dark brown at maturity, margin soft, velvety, white; lower surface covered with crowded, whitish or bluish decurrent spines, 3-10 mm long, that become brown with white tips in age. Stalk 2-6 cm long, 7-20 mm thick, enlarged or tapered downward, brown. Flesh in cap duplex, upper layer thin, spongy; lower layer tough, typically zoned blue, orange, and brown. Flesh in stalk mostly reddish-orange with blue areas. Odor and taste farinaceous.
Spore Print: Brown.
Occurrence: Scattered or in groups, often with fused caps, under conifers. Summer-early winter.
Edibility: Inedible.
Microscopic Features:
Spores 4.5-6 × 3.5-5.5 μm, subglobose to oblong, coarsely warted. Pale brown.
Comments: *Hydnellum suaveolens* (search online) has zoned white, blue, and violet flesh and a fragrant odor.

Hydnellum concrescens (Pers.) Banker
Description: Cap 2-12 cm wide, nearly flat or shallowly depressed; upper surface with irregular projections and cavities, finely velvety or bald, often strongly zoned, pinkish-brown and whitish, margin bruising dark brown when fresh; lower surface covered with crowded spines, 1-2 mm long, orange-white to brown, running down the stalk. Stalk 2-4 cm long, up to 2 cm thick, enlarged at the base, central to eccentric, colored like the cap. Flesh up to 5 mm thick, tough, flexible, duplex, zoned, colored like the cap. Odor and taste not distinctive.
Spore Print: Brown.
Occurrence: Solitary or in groups, often fused, under hardwoods, especially oaks. Summer-fall.
Edibility: Inedible.
Microscopic Features:
Spores 4-7 μm, subglobose, conspicuously warted. Brownish.
Comments: The flesh stains olive-green in KOH. *Hydnellum scrobiculatum* has an azonate or weakly zoned cap and grows under conifers or hardwoods. *Hydnellum spongiosipes* has an azonate cap and longer spines, up to 6 mm long.

Hydnellum cristatum (Bres.) Stalpers

Description: Cap up to 2 cm wide, convex to nearly flat, margin typically appearing lobed from fused caps; upper surface often with irregular projections, especially along the margin, finely velvety or with matted hairs, pitted, brownish-orange to reddish-brown over a cream ground color, bruising black, whitish to cream along the margin; lower surface covered with spines up to 5 mm long, crowded, pale orange to brownish-orange, running down the stalk. Stalk up to 7 cm long and 2 cm thick, often fused, nearly smooth, pale orange to dark brown. Flesh zoned, flexible or brittle, colored like the cap. Odor somewhat fragrant. Taste strongly acrid.

Spore Print: Brown.

Occurrence: Solitary or in groups, often fused, under hardwoods. Summer-fall.

Edibility: Inedible.

Microscopic Features:
Spores 5-6 × 4-5 μm, subglobose to globose, strongly warted. Brown.

Comments: *Cristatum* means "having crests or tufts," a reference to the cap margin. It is uncommon but widespread in the Carolinas.

Hydnellum peckii Banker

RED-JUICE TOOTH

Description: Cap 3-14 cm wide, broadly convex to nearly flat; upper surface dry, somewhat velvety at first, becoming uneven with numerous rounded to jagged projections especially over the center, white and often exuding drops of bright red juice when fresh, soon tinged pinkish, finally becoming dull brown to purplish-black; lower surface covered with spines, up to 6 mm long, pinkish or blackish-brown with paler tips, running down the stalk. Stalk 2-8 cm long, 1-3 cm thick, often with a swollen base, somewhat velvety, colored like the cap. Flesh tough, faintly zoned, reddish-brown. Odor variously described as fragrant, unpleasant, or not distinctive. Taste strongly acrid.

Spore Print: Brown.

Occurrence: Solitary, scattered, or in groups under conifers. Summer-early winter.

Edibility: Inedible.

Microscopic Features:
Spores 4.5-5.5 × 3.5-4.5 μm, subglobose, distinctly warted. Yellowish to pale brown.

Comments: *Peckii* honors mycologist and New York botanist Charles Horton Peck (1833-1917). *Hydnellum diabolus* is a synonym.

Hydnellum scrobiculatum (Fr.) P. Karst.
ROUGH HYDNELLUM
Description: Cap 3.5-14 cm wide, convex to nearly flat or depressed; upper surface roughened with pits, projections, and ridges, azonate or weakly zoned, variously colored with dull pink, vinaceous-brown, dark rusty cinnamon, and grayish-black, margin white with pinkish tints, staining purple-brown to brown-black; lower surface covered with spines up to 3 mm long, dark vinaceous-cinnamon with paler tips, running down the stalk. Stalk up to 3.5 cm long, 1-4 cm thick, variable, often fused, colored like the cap. Flesh tough, orange-brown to dark reddish-brown. Odor and taste farinaceous or not distinctive.
Spore Print: Brown.
Occurrence: Scattered or in groups, often fused, under conifers or hardwoods. Summer-early winter.
Edibility: Inedible.
Microscopic Features:
Spores 4.5-5.5 × 4-4.5 µm, somewhat angular, coarsely warted. Pale brown.
Comments: *Scrobiculatum* means "having pits." It might be confused with older specimens of *Hydnellum peckii*, but that species has peppery-tasting flesh. *Hydnellum concrescens* has a zonate cap.

Hydnellum spongiosipes (Peck) Pouzar
SPONGY-FOOTED TOOTH
Description: Cap 2-10 cm wide, broadly convex to irregularly flat; upper surface uneven, azonate, somewhat velvety, cinnamon-brown to reddish-brown, sometimes with a grayish bloom, darkening when bruised, margin with concentric ridges of secondary growth, often fused; lower surface covered with spines up to 6 mm long, brown with slightly paler tips, running down the stalk. Stalk up to 10 cm long, 5-20 mm thick, with a broad and spongy base, often fused and arising from a thick mycelial pad, dark reddish-brown to dark brown or grayish-brown. Flesh duplex with a thick, spongy, dark brown upper layer; the lower layer is thin, tough, cinnamon-brown. Odor and taste not distinctive.
Spore Print: Brown.
Occurrence: Scattered or in groups, under hardwoods. Summer-fall.
Edibility: Inedible.
Microscopic Features:
Spores 5.5-7 × 5-6 µm, subglobose, coarsely warted. Pale brown.
Comments: *Hydnellum ferrugineum* = *Hydnellum pineticola* (see photo on p. 24) lacks the very broad bulbous stalk base and grows under conifers.

Hydnum repandum L.
HEDGEHOG, SWEET TOOTH
Description: Cap 3-15 cm wide, broadly
convex, margin wavy, often deeply
lobed when mature; upper surface dry,
felty, pale brownish- to reddish-orange,
occasionally pale buff or yellow-orange,
staining dark orange when bruised;
lower surface covered with spines 3-10
mm long, creamy white to orange-
yellow and darkening when bruised,
running slightly down the stalk. Stalk
2.5-10 cm long, 1-3.5 cm thick, nearly
equal, solid, colored like the cap or
white with orange tints, bruising
orange-yellow. Flesh thick, firm, brittle,
white, staining orange-yellow when
bruised. Odor described as nutty, sweet,
or not distinctive. Taste peppery or not
distinctive.

Spore Print: White.

Occurrence: Solitary, scattered, or in
groups under conifers or hardwoods.
Late spring-fall.

Edibility: Edible.

Microscopic Features:
Spores 7-8.5 × 6-7 µm, subglobose,
smooth. Hyaline.

Comments: *Repandum* means "bent back,"
a reference to the margin of mature
specimens. *Hydnum umbilicatum*
(search online) has a smaller cap with a
deep central depression.

Mycorrhaphium adustum
(Schwein.) Mass Geest.
KIDNEY-SHAPED TOOTH
Description: Cap 2.5-7.5 cm wide, kidney-
shaped to fan-shaped or nearly circular,
broadly convex to nearly flat; upper
surface finely roughened to somewhat
velvety, whitish to tan, staining
smoky gray when bruised, margin
thin, wavy, faintly zoned, sometimes
blackish in age; lower surface covered
with tiny spines up to 3 mm long,
somewhat flattened, often fused and
appearing forked at their tips, white
at first, becoming pinkish-brown to
cinnamon-brown at maturity. Stalk
up to 3 cm long, 1-2 cm thick, lateral
to rudimentary or sometimes absent,
somewhat velvety, whitish to dull
cream. Flesh thin, tough, white. Odor
and taste not distinctive.

Spore Print: White.

Occurrence: Solitary, scattered, or in
groups, often fused and overlapping, on
decaying hardwood branches and logs,
especially oak. Summer-early winter.

Edibility: Inedible.

Microscopic Features:
Spores 2.5-4 × 1-1.5 µm, cylindrical,
smooth. Hyaline.

Comments: *Hydnum adustum* is a synonym. A hand lens may be necessary to
clearly visualize the spines.

Phellodon alboniger (Peck) Banker

Description: Cap 3-9 cm wide, broadly convex to nearly flat; upper surface finely velvety, grayish-white with a gray center when young, becoming brownish to blackish, margin blue-gray, becoming paler at maturity, staining blackish when bruised; lower surface covered with spines up to 4 mm long, pale grayish, running down the stalk. Stalk 4-10 cm long, 1-2 cm thick, with a bulbous base, felty, pale to dark brown. Flesh up to 1 cm thick, duplex with a spongy black upper layer and a lower layer that is firm and black. Odor fragrant. Taste slightly acrid or not distinctive.

Spore Print: White.

Occurrence: Scattered or in groups under conifers or hardwoods. Summer-late fall.

Edibility: Inedible.

Microscopic Features:
Spores 4.5-5.5 μm, globose to subglobose, coarsely echinulate, prominently apiculate. Hyaline.

Comments: *Alboniger* means "white and black." *Phellodon niger* (search online) has a dark smoky brown to blackish cap and thinner flesh (to 3 mm thick) that is less obviously duplex.

Phellodon confluens (Pers.) Pouzar

Description: Cap 4-9 cm wide, convex to broadly convex, often fused; upper surface azonate or sometimes faintly zoned when mature, conspicuously velvety and whitish to creamy buff when young, becoming brown and uneven with projecting ridges where the velvety layer wears away, margin with a narrow band of sterile tissue, white, becoming dark brown where bruised; lower surface covered with spines up to 3 mm long, grayish to dark vinaceous-brown, decurrent. Stalk 2-4 cm long, 1-3.5 cm thick, often fused, scurfy, spongy at the base, colored like the cap. Flesh duplex: upper layer soft, cottony, colored like the cap; lower layer zoned, firm, brown, bruising dark brown. Odor of fenugreek, maple syrup, or curry. Taste not distinctive.

Spore Print: White.

Occurrence: Scattered or in groups under conifers or hardwoods. Summer-fall.

Edibility: Inedible.

Microscopic Features:
Spores 4-5.5 × 4-5 μm, subglobose, spiny, strongly apiculate. Hyaline.

Comments: *Confluens* means "fused together." The flesh stains olive-green with $FeSO_4$.

Sarcodon scabrosus (Fr.) P. Karst.

Description: Cap 4-14 cm wide, convex; upper surface breaking into rough scales and furrows, pale pinkish-brown, becoming dark reddish-brown, margin typically wavy; lower surface covered with decurrent pale brownish spines up to 1 cm long, with whitish tips. Stalk 2.5-12 cm long, 1-3.5 cm thick, with a narrowed base; surface scurfy, brown, blue-green to olive-black toward the base. Flesh whitish, staining pinkish then brownish, grayish to blackish or grayish-green at the base. Odor farinaceous. Taste bitter.

Spore Print: Brown.

Occurrence: Solitary, scattered, or in groups under conifers. Summer-early winter.

Edibility: Inedible.

Microscopic Features: Spores 7-9 × 5.5-7.5 μm, subglobose, coarsely warted. Pale brown.

Comments: The Scaly Tooth, *Sarcodon imbricatus* (search online), is similar, but its stalk base is pale brown and its flesh is slightly bitter or not distinctive. *Sarcodon underwoodii* (search online) has an abruptly pointed, whitish stalk base, is extremely bitter, and grows under hardwoods. Compare with *Sarcodon joeides* (see photo on p. 24).

CLUSTERED CORALS AND CAULIFLOWERS

Like undersea corals, these fungi grow as clusters or clumps of solid, erect, noodle or branched structures. Many are brightly colored, at least at first, but some fade quickly to a nondescript tan. Branch tips may be colored differently than branches or have a species-specific shape. Where the tips are pointed or crowned with multiple points, these are oriented upward, not down as in the Tooth Fungi group. Cauliflowers can be distinguished from Jelly Fungi by their much larger size, tougher consistency, and growth on the ground at the base of trees rather than directly on wood. Coral species range from flexible to brittle but are *not* gelatinous or hard. Although a few grow on wood or decaying organic matter, most are terrestrial. Members of the large genus *Ramaria* are frequently difficult to distinguish. Some representative species are described here.

Cauliflowers are good edibles. Other species range from moderately poisonous to edible but mediocre.

Artomyces pyxidatus (Pers.) Jülich
CROWN-TIPPED CORAL
Description: Fruitbody up to 13 cm high and 10 cm wide, erect, coral-like, repeatedly branched, arising from a short, velvety, whitish to brownish, stalklike base. Branches 2-5 mm thick, erect, crowded, smooth, whitish to yellowish, or tan. Branch tips have crownlike points (use a hand lens) and are colored like the branches. Flesh tough or brittle. Odor not distinctive. Taste somewhat peppery or not distinctive.
Spore Print: White.
Occurrence: Solitary, scattered, or in groups on decaying hardwoods. Late spring-fall.
Edibility: Edible.
Microscopic Features:
Spores 4-5 × 2-3 μm, elliptic, smooth. Hyaline, amyloid.
Comments: *Clavicorona pyxidata* is a synonym. The crownlike branch tips and growth on decaying wood are the important field identification features. *Clavulina coralloides*, previously known as *C. cristata* (search online), grows on soil, as does *Tremellodendron schweinitzii*. *Lentaria micheneri* grows on leaf litter.

Clavaria fragilis Holmsk.
WHITE WORM CORAL
Description: Fruitbody 3-12 cm high, 2-5 mm thick, erect, wormlike to spindle-shaped, typically unbranched, tapered downward. Surface nearly smooth, white overall or sometimes yellowish near the tips. Flesh thin, brittle, white. Odor and taste not distinctive.
Spore Print: White.
Occurrence: In clusters on the ground in woodlands or sometimes grassy areas. Summer-early winter.
Edibility: Edible.
Microscopic Features:
Spores 4-7 × 3-5 μm, elliptic, smooth. Hyaline.
Comments: *Clavaria vermicularis* is a synonym. *Fragilis* refers to the brittle flesh. The Smoky Worm Coral, *Clavaria rubicundula* (search online), is very similar and also grows in clusters, but it has pinkish-buff to pale grayish-pink fruitbodies. *Clavulina rugosa* (search online) has an erect, compressed, and conspicuously wrinkled, white to grayish-white fruitbody that is unbranched or notched at the apex. *Xylaria hypoxylon* is powdery white at first and grows on decaying wood.

Clavaria zollingeri Lév.
MAGENTA CORAL
Description: Fruitbody up to 10 cm high, coral-like, repeatedly branched, arising from a smooth, whitish to pinkish-purple stalklike base. Branches erect, crowded, typically rounded, smooth, color variable, pinkish-purple, violet, or pale to dark purple. Branch tips rounded to bluntly pointed, colored like the branches but typically darker. Flesh brittle, reddish-purple. Odor not distinctive. Taste somewhat radish-like.
Spore Print: White.
Occurrence: Solitary, scattered, or in groups on the ground in mixed woods. Summer-fall.
Edibility: Edible.
Microscopic Features:
Spores 5-7.5 × 3-4.5 µm, elliptic to oval, smooth. Hyaline.
Comments: *Clavaria amethystina* = *Clavulina amethystina* is sometimes listed as a similar species in American field guides, but it is a European species that does not occur in North America. The Smoky Worm Coral, *Clavaria rubicundula* (search online), also grows in clusters, but it has pinkish-buff to pale grayish-pink fruitbodies. The fruitbody of *Clavulina amethystinoides* (search online) is sparingly branched and pinkish-tan to grayish-lilac or dull purple.

Clavulina cinerea (Bull.) J. Schröt.
GRAY CORAL
Description: Fruitbody up to 11 cm high, coral-like, repeatedly branched, arising from an inconspicuous stalklike base. Branches erect, crowded, rounded to somewhat flattened, often curved, smooth or wrinkled, sometimes longitudinally grooved, whitish at first, becoming ashy gray, sometimes blackened from the base upward. Branch tips pointed or blunt, but not crested, colored like the branches. Flesh tough or brittle, white. Odor and taste not distinctive.
Spore Print: White.
Occurrence: Solitary, scattered, or in groups in conifer or mixed woods. Late spring-fall.
Edibility: Edible.
Microscopic Features:
Spores 6.5-11 × 5-10 µm, oval to subglobose, smooth. Hyaline.
Comments: The Crested Coral, *Clavulina coralloides* = *Clavulina cristata* (search online), has a white to yellowish or pale pinkish-brown fruitbody usually with crested branch tips. The fruitbodies of both the Gray Coral and the Crested Coral may blacken from the base upward when attacked by *Helminthosphaeria clavariarum*, a parasitic fungus (search online).

CLUSTERED CORALS AND CAULIFLOWERS

Clavulinopsis aurantiocinnabarina
(Schwein.) Corner
ORANGE SPINDLE CORAL
Description: Fruitbody up to 14 cm high
and 1.5-8 mm thick, spindle-shaped to
wormlike, often somewhat flattened
with a conspicuous longitudinal
channel, hollow, apex usually pointed.
Surface smooth, reddish-orange, yellow
to whitish near the base. Flesh thin,
brittle, reddish-orange. Odor unpleasant
or not distinctive. Taste not distinctive.
Spore Print: Whitish to pale yellow.
Occurrence: Sometimes solitary but more
often in groups or clusters in grassy
areas or woodlands. Summer-fall.
Edibility: Edible.
Microscopic Features:
Spores 5-6.5 × 4.5-6 µm, subglobose,
smooth. Hyaline.
Comments: *Aurantiocinnabarina* means
"orange and cinnabar red." *Clavaria
aurantiocinnabarina* is a synonym.
Clavulinopsis laeticolor (search online)
has a deep golden-yellow fruitbody,
does not grow in clusters, and has
spores measuring 6-7 × 4.5-5 µm.

Clavulinopsis fusiformis (Sowerby) Corner
SPINDLE-SHAPED
YELLOW CORAL
Description: Fruitbody up to 14 cm high,
1.5-7 mm thick, spindle-shaped to
wormlike, sometimes slightly flattened
and showing a shallow longitudinal
groove, unbranched or occasionally
branched, with a pointed or rounded
apex. Surface smooth or wrinkled,
bright to dull yellow. Flesh thin, fibrous
or brittle, yellowish.
Spore Print: White to pale yellow.
Occurrence: In dense clusters on soil in
woodlands or fields. Late spring-fall.
Edibility: Edible.
Microscopic Features:
Spores 5-9 × 4-9 µm, broadly oval to
globose, smooth. Hyaline.
Comments: *Fusiformis* means "spindle-
shaped." The similar *Clavulinopsis
aurantiocinnabarina* is reddish-orange.
Clavulinopsis helveola (search online)
is smaller, light buffy-yellow, grows in
clusters, and has elliptic spores, 7-8 ×
2-3 µm. *Clavulinopsis laeticolor* (search
online) is smaller, golden-orange, but
it does not grow in clusters. The Fairy
Thread Coral, *Macrotyphula juncea*
(search online), is long, thin, threadlike,
pale brown; it grows singly, in groups,
or in small clusters on decaying leaves
and twigs.

CLUSTERED CORALS AND CAULIFLOWERS

303

Lentaria micheneri
(Berk. & M. A. Curtis) Corner

Description: Fruitbody up to 4 cm high, 1-2.5 cm wide, a cluster of branches arising from a common stalk. Branches erect, crowded, repeatedly forked, smooth or with velvety patches, pale orange to pale pinkish-orange or pale orange-buff. Branch tips pointed, often forked, colored like the branches. Stalk smooth or velvety, colored like the branches, with a conspicuous mat of white basal mycelium. Flesh tough, whitish. Odor not distinctive. Taste bitter.

Spore Print: White.

Occurrence: Solitary, scattered, or in groups on leaf litter and duff, under oak, beech, or pine. Summer-fall.

Edibility: Unknown.

Microscopic Features:
Spores 7-9 × 2.3-4.5 μm, narrowly elliptical, smooth. Hyaline.

Comments: Addition of $FeSO_4$ to the branches produces a green stain. *Lentaria byssiseda* (search online) is similar but has a pinkish-tan fruitbody with creamy white branch tips and much larger spores, 12-18 × 3-6 μm. *Tremellodendropsis semivestita* (search online) lacks the basal mat of mycelium and has larger spores.

Ramaria aurea complex (Schaeff.) Quél.

Description: Fruitbody up to 12 cm high, 10-15 cm wide, a cluster of branches arising from a common stalk. Branches erect, crowded, repeatedly forked, smooth, golden-yellow to golden-orange. Branch tips typically forked and pointed, colored like the branches. Stalk up to 5 cm thick, white. Flesh tough, white. Odor somewhat musty or not distinctive. Taste slightly bitter or not distinctive.

Spore Print: Yellow.

Occurrence: Solitary or in groups on the ground under hardwoods. Summer-fall.

Edibility: Unknown.

Microscopic Features:
Spores 9-11 × 3.5-5 μm, elliptic, with minute warts. Hyaline, inamyloid.

Comments: *Aurea* means "golden." Addition of $FeSO_4$ to the branches produces a green stain. We treat this as a species complex because several types of yellow coral have been identified as *Ramaria aurea*. Microscopic examination is needed for diagnostic certainty. *Ramaria spinulosa* (see photo on p. 25) has a stout stalk and main branches, blunt tips, and distinctly bitter flesh; it grows on the ground in hardwoods and mixed woods.

Ramaria botrytis (Pers.) Ricken
PINK-TIPPED CORAL MUSHROOM
Description: Fruitbody up to 20 cm high and 5-30 cm wide, a cauliflower-like cluster of branches arising from a common stalk. Branches erect, crowded, repeatedly forked, short, smooth, white to creamy white, becoming brownish in age. Branch tips forked, pointed or blunt, pinkish- to purplish-red. Stalk 1.5-5 cm thick, white, becoming brownish in age. Flesh firm, white. Odor not distinctive. Taste somewhat bitter or not distinctive.
Spore Print: Brownish-yellow to pale orange.
Occurrence: Solitary, scattered, or in groups on the ground under hardwoods or conifers. Summer-fall.
Edibility: Edible, but may cause a laxative effect.
Microscopic Features:
Spores 14-17 × 4.5-6 μm, narrowly elliptic, weakly longitudinally striate, smooth. Pale yellow.
Comments: *Botrytis* means "resembling a cluster of grapes." Addition of $FeSO_4$ to the branches produces a green stain. The Rose Coral, *Ramaria subbotrytis* (search online), has a rose-coral to salmon-pink fruitbody and smaller spores, 8-11 × 3-4 μm.

Ramaria fennica (P. Karst.) Ricken
Description: Fruitbody 6-12 cm high and 4-8 cm wide, a cluster of branches arising from a common stalk. Branches erect, crowded, rounded or flattened, repeatedly forked, smooth, brownish-yellow to olive- or grayish-brown, sometimes with lilac tinges on the lower branches. Branch tips typically forked and pointed, colored like the branches. Stalk lilac to purplish on the upper portion, whitish with yellow tints at the base. Flesh firm, whitish. Odor not distinctive. Taste slightly bitter.
Spore Print: Honey yellow.
Occurrence: Solitary, scattered, or in groups on the ground under hardwoods. Summer-fall.
Edibility: Unknown.
Microscopic Features:
Spores 9-12 × 4-5.5 μm, elliptical, finely roughened, sometimes with oil drops. Hyaline.
Comments: Addition of KOH to the lilac or violet areas produces a bright red stain. A green stain is produced when $FeSO_4$ is applied to the yellowish or brownish areas of the branches.

Ramaria formosa (Pers.) Quél.
YELLOW-TIPPED CORAL
Description: Fruitbody up to 20 cm high and 5-15 cm wide, a cluster of branches arising from a common stalk. Branches erect, crowded, rounded, repeatedly forked, smooth or wrinkled, coral-pink to pale salmon, becoming brownish in age. Branch tips typically forked and blunt, pale yellow, becoming brownish. Stalk thick, pinkish or whitish. Flesh fibrous or brittle, colored like the stalk. Odor not distinctive. Taste bitter.
Spore Print: Pale brownish-yellow.
Occurrence: Solitary, scattered, or in groups on the ground under conifers or hardwoods. Summer-fall.
Edibility: Poisonous, causing gastrointestinal distress.
Microscopic Features:
Spores 8-15 × 4-6 μm, elliptical, finely warted. Hyaline.
Comments: Addition of $FeSO_4$ to the branches produces a green stain. *Ramaria stricta* also has yellowish branch tips but grows on wood. *Ramaria conjunctipes* (search online) has yellow tips and saffron (yellow-salmon) branches arising from slender bases that touch but are not fused; odor and taste are not distinctive.

Ramaria grandis (Peck) Corner
Description: Fruitbody up to 20 cm high and 5-15 cm wide, a cluster of branches arising from a common stalk. Branches erect, crowded, rounded, repeatedly forked, smooth, brown to dark brown. Branch tips bluntly rounded, whitish. Stalk 1-6 cm long, 1-2 cm thick, deeply rooted. Flesh firm, white, rapidly staining purplish-brown when exposed. Odor not distinctive. Taste bitter.
Spore Print: Brown.
Occurrence: Solitary, scattered, or in groups on the ground under hardwoods. Summer-fall.
Edibility: Unknown.
Microscopic Features:
Spores 10-13 × 5-7 μm, obovate, spiny. Brownish.
Comments: Addition of $FeSO_4$ to the branches produces a green stain. *Ramaria murrillii* (search online) is very similar, but the branch tips are brown; it has narrowly elliptic, spiny spores, 8-9.5 × 3-4 μm.

Ramaria stricta (Pers.) Quél.
STRAIGHT-BRANCHED CORAL
Description: Fruitbody up to 14 cm high and 5-12 cm wide, a cluster of branches arising from a short base. Branches erect and nearly parallel, slender, crowded, rounded or somewhat flattened, repeatedly forked, smooth, pale yellow to orange- or pinkish-buff, bruising brown. Branch tips typically forked and pointed, pale yellow, browning with age. Base whitish on the lower portion, colored like the branches above. Flesh tough, whitish. Odor fragrant or not distinctive. Taste bitter.
Spore Print: Yellowish.
Occurrence: Solitary, scattered, or in groups on fallen branches, logs, and stumps of conifers or hardwoods. Summer-fall.
Edibility: Unknown.
Microscopic Features:
Spores 7-10 × 3.5-5.5 μm, ellipsoid, minutely roughened. Hyaline to pale yellow.
Comments: *Stricta* means "straight." Addition of $FeSO_4$ to the branches produces a green stain. *Clavaria stricta* is a synonym. *Ramaria concolor* (search online) is nearly identical, but both the branches and branch tips are yellowish-tan to pale cinnamon.

Ramariopsis kunzei (Fr.) Corner
WHITE CORAL
Description: Fruitbody up to 12 cm high and 4-10 cm wide, a cluster of branches arising from a short base. Branches 1-5 mm thick, erect, coral-like, repeatedly forked, smooth, white, often developing pinkish to pale apricot tinges in age. Branch tips forked, bluntly pointed, white. Bases clustered or fused into stalks. Flesh white, somewhat flexible. Odor and taste not distinctive.
Spore Print: White.
Occurrence: Solitary, scattered, or in groups on the ground in woods. Summer-fall.
Edibility: Edible with caution; see comments below.
Microscopic Features:
Spores 3-5.5 × 2.5-4.5 μm, broadly elliptic to subglobose, with minute spines. Hyaline.
Comments: Branches *do not* stain green when $FeSO_4$ is applied. The poisonous *Ramariopsis lentofragilis* (search online) has creamy white branches that do not develop pinkish to pale apricot tinges but do stain green with $FeSO_4$. The spores are slightly larger: 4-7 × 3.5-5 μm. Cases of severe abdominal pain and general body weakness have been reported.

Sparassis americana R. H. Petersen
AMERICAN CAULIFLOWER MUSHROOM

Description: Fruitbody 15-30 cm high and wide, a rounded, lettucelike cluster of flattened branches attached to a common, partially buried stalklike base. Base 5-14 cm long, 2-5 cm thick, tough, dark brown to blackish. Branches densely arranged, with leaf- to fanlike curly, flexible, smooth, azonate lobes, whitish, cream to pale yellow or tan. Flesh thin, white. Odor fragrant or not distinctive. Taste not distinctive.

Spore Print: White.

Occurrence: Solitary or in groups on the ground in conifer or mixed woods, sometimes on well-decayed conifer logs and stumps. Summer-fall.

Edibility: Edible.

Microscopic Features: Spores 5-7 × 3-4 µm, oval, smooth. Hyaline.

Comments: Previously identified as *Sparassis crispa*, DNA studies have proven that *S. crispa* is a European species that does not occur in North America. The edible Cauliflower Mushroom, *Sparassis spathulata* = *Sparassis herbstii* (search online), differs by growing with hardwoods and having zoned, spoon-shaped, less flexible branches that are widest at the tips.

Tremellodendron schweinitzii (Peck) G. F. Atk.
JELLIED FALSE CORAL

Description: Fruitbody 2.5-12 cm high and 5-15 cm wide, a cluster of branches arising from a common base. Branches erect, densely arranged, flattened, smooth, flexible, white at first, then yellowish to brownish in age. Branch tips squared off or forked and pointed, white. Bases fused, not forming distinct stalks. Flesh tough, somewhat cartilaginous or thickly gelatinous, white. Odor not distinctive. Taste bitter and unpleasant.

Spore Print: White.

Occurrence: Scattered or in groups on the ground in hardwoods or mixed woods. Summer-fall.

Edibility: Inedible.

Microscopic Features: Spores 7-12 × 4-6 µm, allantoid, smooth. Hyaline.

Comments: *Tremellodendron pallidum* is a synonym. *Tremellodendropsis semivestita* (search online) also has flexible, tough, flattened, whitish branches, but they are attached to a conspicuous, brownish, central stalk. Its branch tips are typically blunt, and the spores are much larger: 12-18 × 6-7 µm. Similar corals, including *Clavulina coralloides* = *Clavulina cristata* (search online) and *Ramariopsis kunzei*, are more brittle and easily break.

JELLY FUNGI

This is a traditional grouping of species based primarily on a gelatinous or rubbery consistency rather than any genetic relationship. Most grow on wood and are sensitive to moisture, swelling or shriveling and hardening rapidly in response to atmospheric conditions. For this reason, they are best observed shortly after rains. Some have a leafy, clustered shape. Others could be confused with a coral, an earth club, a cup fungus, or in one bizarre instance, a tooth mushroom.

If your specimen doesn't appear here, check those sections. Gelatinous flesh doesn't necessarily translate to a smooth, wet surface. Some jellies are hairy, others **scurfy** (flaky). The upper or inner surface often has a different look than the lower/outer surface.

Although jellies are considered edible, only the American Wood Ear, *Auricularia angiospermarum*, has much of a culinary following. Others are said to taste like sautéed water.

Auricularia angiospermarum
Y. C. Dai, F. Wu, & D. W. Li
AMERICAN WOOD EAR
Description: Fruitbody up to 8 cm
    wide, ear-shaped to irregularly cup-
    shaped, sometimes with a lobed
    margin. Exterior (upper surface)
    wrinkled, minutely velvety, reddish-
    brown. Interior (under surface)
    smooth, yellowish- to reddish-brown
    or purplish-brown. Stalkless. Flesh
    rubbery-gelatinous, tough. Odor and
    taste not distinctive.
Occurrence: Typically in groups or fused
    clusters, sometimes solitary, on
    hardwood branches, logs, and stumps.
    Year-round.
Edibility: Edible.
Microscopic Features:
    Spores 12–15 × 4–6 μm, allantoid,
    smooth. Hyaline.
Comments: *Auricularia nigricans* =
    Auricularia polytricha (search online)
    is similar, but its exterior is covered
    by a dense layer of fine grayish hairs.
    The Conifer Wood Ear, *Auricularia
    americana* (search online), is also similar
    but grows on conifer wood. The Tree
    Ear, *Auricularia auricula* (search online),
    is described and illustrated in most
    American mushroom field guides, but
    it is a European species. Thinly sliced
    American Wood Ear is an ingredient in
    our version of hot-and-sour soup.

Bulgaria inquinans (Pers.) Fr.
**BLACK JELLY DROPS,
POOR MAN'S LICORICE**
Description: Fruitbody 2–4 cm wide, 1.5–
    3.5 cm high, nearly round to top-shaped
    when young, becoming saucer-shaped
    in age. Upper surface smooth, shiny,
    black. Lower surface scurfy, brown to
    blackish-brown. Flesh relatively thick,
    rubbery-gelatinous to tough, blackish.
    Odor and taste not distinctive.
Occurrence: In groups or clusters on
    decaying hardwoods, especially oak.
    Summer-fall.
Edibility: Unknown.
Microscopic Features:
    Spores 9–16 × 6–7 μm, kidney-shaped
    to elliptic, smooth. Each ascus contains
    spores of two color forms: upper four
    dark brown, lower four hyaline.
Comments: *Exidia glandulosa* has a dark
    reddish-brown to black, gland- to
    brainlike fruitbody that is typically
    fused and forms extensive rows or
    masses.

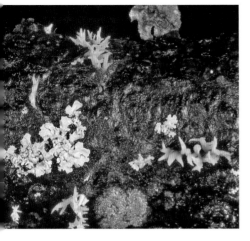

Calocera cornea (Batsch) Fr.

HORN-LIKE TUNING FORK

Description: Fruitbody up to 2 cm high and 3 mm wide, consisting of erect, antlerlike spikes, simple or sometimes branched, flexible, rubbery-gelatinous, smooth, yellow to orange-yellow. Flesh colored like the exterior, rubbery-gelatinous. Odor and taste not distinctive.

Occurrence: Scattered or in groups or clusters on branches and logs of decaying wood, especially hardwood. Summer-fall.

Edibility: Unknown, but too small to be of culinary interest.

Microscopic Features:
Spores 7-11 × 3-4.5 μm, cylindric to allantoid, 1-septate at maturity, smooth. Hyaline to pale yellow.

Comments: *Cornea* means "small horn." *Calocera viscosa* (search online) has a larger, golden-yellow to orange-yellow, erect fruitbody that is antlerlike and repeatedly forked.

Dacrymyces chrysospermus Berk. & M. A. Curtis

ORANGE JELLY

Description: Fruitbody up to 3 cm high, 1-6 cm wide, a spreading, brainlike mass, yellow-orange to orange or reddish-orange, whitish near the point of attachment, fading to pale yellow in age. Flesh rubbery-gelatinous to soft, colored like the exterior, reduced to liquid during prolonged wet weather, hard and shriveled when dry.

Occurrence: In clusters on decaying conifer branches, logs, and stumps. Year-round.

Edibility: Edible but flavorless.

Microscopic Features:
Spores 17-25 × 6-8 μm, cylindric to allantoid, 7-9 septate at maturity, smooth. Yellowish.

Comments: *Chrysospermus* means "having golden spores." *Dacrymyces palmatus* is a synonym. *Tremella mesenterica* is similarly colored but grows on decaying hardwood; it takes a leafier form, like a head of leaf lettuce.

Dacryopinax spathularia
(Schwein.) G. W. Martin

Description: Fruitbody up to 2.5 cm
high, 5-10 mm wide, shoehorn- to
spatula-shaped with a wavy margin,
or fan-shaped with deeply cut lobes,
longitudinally ribbed, bright yellow-
orange to orange. Stalk round at the
base, becoming flattened upward,
darkening in age. Flesh rubbery-
gelatinous, colored like the exterior.
Odor and taste not distinctive.

Occurrence: In groups or clusters on
decaying wood. Summer-fall.

Edibility: Unknown.

Microscopic Features:
Spores 8-12 × 3.5-5 μm, allantoid,
1-septate at maturity, smooth.
Yellowish.

Comments: *Spathularia* means "spoon-
shaped." *Guepinia spathularia* is a
synonym. *Dacryopinax elegans* (search
online) is similar, but the fruitbody
is dark amber-brown to blackish-
brown, lacks deeply cut lobes, and
has larger spores, 11-16 × 4.5-6.5 μm.
Less colorful look-alikes also include
Spathularia flavida, which grows on the
ground or in moss, and the much larger
Spathulariopsis velutipes.

Exidia glandulosa (Bull.) Fr.
**BLACK WITCHES' BUTTER,
BLACK JELLY ROLL**

Description: Fruitbody up to 1.3 cm
high, 1-2 cm wide, gland-, blister-,
or brainlike, fused together and
forming extensive irregular and soft-
gelatinous masses up to 20 cm or more
wide. Exterior smooth or somewhat
roughened, shiny, dark reddish-brown
to blackish-brown or black, becoming
a black crust when dry. Flesh soft,
gelatinous, colored like the exterior
or paler, reduced to liquid during
prolonged wet weather. Odor and taste
not distinctive.

Occurrence: In large clusters on decaying
hardwood branches and logs. Year-
round.

Edibility: Edible but flavorless.

Microscopic Features:
Spores 10-16 × 4-5 μm, allantoid,
smooth. Hyaline.

Comments: *Glandulosa* means "resembling
glands." *Tremella glandulosa* is a synonym. *Exidia recisa* forms irregularly
lobed to cushion-shaped fruitbodies
that are yellowish-brown to purplish-
brown or cinnamon-brown.

Exidia recisa (Ditmar) Fr.
AMBER JELLY ROLL
Description: Fruitbody up to 2 cm high,
1.5-3.5 cm wide, irregularly lobed with
concave depressions or cushion-shaped,
somewhat erect, with a stalklike base,
forming extensive irregular clusters
up to 12 or more cm wide. Exterior
shiny, smooth to somewhat roughened,
yellowish- to purplish-brown or
cinnamon-brown. Flesh soft to rubbery-
gelatinous, colored like the exterior
or paler, reduced to liquid during
prolonged wet weather. Odor and taste
not distinctive.
Occurrence: In groups or clusters on
decaying hardwood logs or branches.
Year-round.
Edibility: Unknown.
Microscopic Features:
Spores 11-15 × 3-5.5 μm, allantoid,
smooth. Hyaline.
Comments: *Recisa* means "cut back or
cut off," a reference to its cushion
shape. *Exidia nucleata* (search online)
is very similar, but its interior contains
numerous hard, whitish, seedlike
granules. *Exidia glandulosa* forms
glandlike to blisterlike fruitbodies that
are dark reddish- to blackish-brown
or black. *Camarops petersii* has harder
flesh and a wet, dog's-nose surface.

Helvellosebacina concrescens
(Schwein.) Oberw., Garnica & K. Riess
Description: Fruitbody a soft, rubbery-
gelatinous, irregular, membranelike,
spreading mass, up to 15 or more
cm wide. Exterior bald, smooth or
wrinkled, whitish to grayish. Flesh
thin, rubbery-gelatinous, colored like
the surface or paler. Odor and taste not
distinctive.
Occurrence: On the ground clasping and
enveloping plant stems and leaves.
Summer-fall.
Edibility: Unknown.
Microscopic Features:
Spores 9-14 × 5-8 μm, elliptic to oval or
subglobose, smooth. Hyaline.
Comments: *Concrescens* means "curdled
or congealed." *Tremella concrescens*
is a synonym. This species might be
mistaken for the egg mass of an insect.
Sebacina incrustans also clasps and
envelops plant stems, leaves, branches,
and cones, but the fruitbody is fibrous-
tough, whitish to pale tan, and forms
small, lateral projections. Compare
with the branched, fingerlike lobes of
Sebacina sparassoidea, which do not
clasp and envelop plant stems or leaves.

JELLY FUNGI

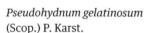

Pseudohydnum gelatinosum
(Scop.) P. Karst.
JELLY TOOTH
Description: Fruitbody 2-5 cm high, 2-7 cm wide, consisting of a gelatinous cap and stalk. The cap is shoehorn- to tongue-shaped or hemispheric with an incurved margin, often crimped near the stalk. Upper surface minutely velvety, translucent, whitish or grayish, sometimes brown or yellowish. Lower surface covered with decurrent, tiny, soft, whitish spines. Stalk up to 6 cm long or sometimes lacking, lateral, somewhat flattened at the apex, tapered downward, bald, smooth, colored like the cap. Flesh rubbery-gelatinous, translucent. Odor and taste not distinctive.
Occurrence: Solitary, scattered, or in groups on decaying conifer wood. Late summer-fall.
Edibility: Edible but flavorless.
Microscopic Features:
   Spores 5-7 µm, globose, smooth. Hyaline.
Comments: The rubbery-gelatinous consistency and soft spines make this species easy to recognize. Typical tooth mushrooms have fibrous, not gelatinous, flesh.

Sebacina sparassoidea (Lloyd) P. Roberts
WHITE CORAL JELLY
Description: Fruitbody up to 16 cm wide, a compound mass of fused, erect, gelatinous, hollow, branched lobes that are typically fingerlike with blunt tips. Exterior somewhat translucent, white at first, becoming creamy white then yellowish-brown in age. Flesh gelatinous to rubbery, colored like the exterior or paler. Odor and taste not distinctive.
Occurrence: Solitary or in groups on the ground or well-decayed wood in hardwoods or mixed woods. Summer-fall.
Edibility: Unknown.
Microscopic Features:
   Spores 9-11 × 5-6 µm, broadly ovoid, smooth. Hyaline.
Comments: *Sparassoidea* means "resembling *Sparassis*," the genus of cauliflower mushrooms. It is also called Dead Man's Rubber Glove. *Tremella reticulata* is a synonym. Compare with *Helvellosebacina concrescens*, which forms an irregular, membranelike, spreading mass that clasps and envelops plant stems and leaves. *Ductifera pululahuana* (see photo on p. 26) forms a whitish, convoluted, brainlike mass on barkless, decaying hardwood. It has allantoid to oval spores, 9-12 × 4.5-7 µm.

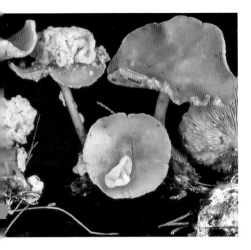

Syzygospora mycetophila (Peck) Ginns
COLLYBIA JELLY
Description: Fruitbody 3-25 mm wide, consisting of irregular cup-shaped or brain- to tumorlike growths that are typically fused. Exterior bald, smooth or wrinkled, pale yellow to brownish-yellow. Flesh rubbery-gelatinous, colored like the exterior. Odor and taste not distinctive.
Occurrence: In dense clusters on the cap, gills, or stalk of *Gymnopus dryophilus*. Summer-fall.
Edibility: Unknown.
Microscopic Features:
Spores 6-9 × 1.5-2.5 μm, elliptic to cylindric, smooth. Hyaline.
Comments: *Mycetophila* means "fungus loving." *Christiansenia mycetophila* is a synonym. This species is easy to identify because of the distinctive shape and exclusive occurrence on *Gymnopus dryophilus* mushrooms.

Tremella foliacea Pers.
JELLY LEAF
Description: Fruitbody up to 10 cm high and 25 cm wide, a lettucelike cluster consisting of rubbery-gelatinous, leaflike folds. Exterior smooth, pale to dark reddish-brown or rarely pale brownish-yellow. Flesh rubbery-gelatinous, colored like the exterior or paler. Odor and taste not distinctive.
Occurrence: Solitary or scattered on decaying wood. Summer-fall.
Edibility: Edible but flavorless.
Microscopic Features:
Spores 8-12 × 7-9 μm, oval to subglobose, smooth. Hyaline.
Comments: *Foliacea* means "having leaves." *Auricularia angiospermarum* is similarly colored, but the fruitbodies are ear-shaped to irregularly cup-shaped. *Ionomidotis irregularis* (search online) grows singly or in clusters on decaying wood, where it forms tough, asymmetrical cups or ruffled leaf fruitbodies up to 3 cm wide and high. The inner surface is black and relatively smooth; the outer (upper) surface has a brownish, scurfy coating over a pimpled black underlayment.

JELLY FUNGI

Tremella fuciformis Berk.
SILVER EAR, WHITE JELLY MUSHROOM

Description: Fruitbody up to 3 cm high and 7 cm wide, a jellylike mass of delicate, leaflike, complex lobes. Exterior shiny, translucent, silvery white. Flesh soft, gelatinous, colored like the exterior or paler, reduces to liquid during prolonged wet weather. Odor and taste not distinctive.

Occurrence: Solitary or scattered on decaying branches and logs of hardwoods, especially oaks. Summer-early winter.

Edibility: Edible but flavorless.

Microscopic Features:
Spores 8-14 × 5-8 μm, elliptic, smooth. Subglobose conidia, up to 4.5 × 3 μm, are sometimes present as well. Hyaline.

Comments: *Fuciformis* means "shaped like seaweed." This is a tropical species with a northern range extending into the Southeast. *Ductifera pululahuana* (see photo on p. 26) is similar, but the white is closer to opaque.

Tremella mesenterica Retz.
WITCHES' BUTTER

Description: Fruitbody up to 10 cm wide, a spreading, irregularly lobed and folded mass often resembling bunched leaves. Exterior bald, smooth, shiny, pale yellow to golden-yellow or orange-yellow. Flesh soft to rubbery-gelatinous, colored like the exterior or paler, reduces to liquid during prolonged wet weather, hard and shriveled when dry.

Occurrence: Solitary, in groups, or in clusters on hardwood branches, logs, and stumps, especially beech and oak. Year-round.

Edibility: Edible but flavorless.

Microscopic Features:
Spores 10-18 × 8-12 μm, broadly elliptical, smooth. Subglobose, smooth conidia measuring 3-4.5 × 2.5-3.5 μm may also be present. Hyaline.

Comments: *Mesenterica* means "resembling the middle intestine." *Tremella lutescens* is a synonym. If found near a small species of *Stereum*, often *S. hirsutum* (search online), consider *Tremella aurantia* (search online). *Dacrymyces chrysospermus* is white at the point of attachment, more brainlike in appearance, and grows on conifer wood.

JELLY FUNGI

STINKHORNS

These are the preadolescent boys of kingdom Fungi. The outrageously constructed fruitbodies "hatch" from eggs. The ruptured "eggshell" remaining at the base is termed a **volva**. The volva is anchored to the underlying stinkhorn mycelium by thick cords called **rhizomorphs**. Mature stinkhorns stink, a lot, thanks to a slathering of green to brown, spore-containing, fly-attracting glop. This type of **spore mass** is known in mycological circles as the gleba, a word creation that would do any kid proud. Flies wade around in it, enjoy a meal, and then propagate the stinkhorn by tracking gleba wherever they go next. In other words, stinkhorns are a devious and disgustingly charming group.

Edibility: stinkhorns are not known to be dangerously toxic. One species, not found in the Carolinas, has a place in Chinese cuisine and herbal medicine. A few daredevil mycophagists—and really, what other term fits this case?—feel compelled to sample the eggs of our native stinkhorns and report, usually negatively, on the experience. **Before attempting to join that group, cut what you think is a stinkhorn egg in two, top to bottom.** Amanitas, some of which are deadly, also begin as eggs. Inside them you'll find what appears to be a baby capped mushroom. Small species of puffball, poisonous earthballs, and a few truffles could also be confused with stinkhorn eggs.

Aseroe rubra Labill.

**FUNGUS FLOWER,
STARFISH STINKHORN**

Description: Immature fruitbody an egg up
to 4 cm wide, rounded, whitish to pale
grayish-brown, with basal rhizomorphs
and a gelatinous interior. The egg
ruptures at the top and gives rise to a
cylindrical stalk and central disc with
radiating, tapered arms and gleba at
the stalk apex, leaving a saclike volva at
the base. Stalk 4-6.5 cm long, 1.5-3 cm
thick, spongelike, hollow, pinkish to
reddish, forming a flattened disc with
5-11 radiating, chambered arms that
are often forked near the midportion
and curled at the tip. Arms up to 4.5 cm
long, bright red. Gleba covering the disc
and interior base of the arms, slimy,
fetid, dark olive-brown.

Occurrence: Solitary or in groups on wood
mulch, leaf litter, or soil. Spring-fall.

Edibility: Inedible.

Microscopic Features:
Spores 4.5-7 × 1.7-2.5 μm, elliptic to
cylindric, truncate, smooth. Hyaline
to brownish.

Comments: Originally described from
Tasmania but has escaped around
Charleston.

Clathrus columnatus Bosc

COLUMNED STINKHORN

Description: Immature fruitbody an egg
up to 7 cm wide, nearly round, whitish,
with a gelatinous interior. It gives rise to
a stalkless mature stage up to 16 cm tall,
consisting of 2-5 spongy, erect, curved,
delicate, orange to reddish-orange
or rosy red columns fused at their
tips. The volva at the base is saclike,
wrinkled and tough, whitish, attached
to the ground by one or more whitish
rhizomorphs. Gleba is olive-brown,
slimy, fetid, deposited on the underside
of the columns.

Occurrence: Solitary, scattered, or in
groups on the ground in grassy areas,
wood chips, woodlands, or marginal
areas. Year-round.

Edibility: Inedible.

Microscopic Features:
Spores 3.5-5 × 1.5-2.5 μm, smooth,
elliptic. Yellowish-brown.

Comments: *Linderia columnata* is a
synonym. *Phallogaster saccatus* has a
club-shaped to pear-shaped fruitbody,
2.5-5 cm high, 1-3.5 cm wide. It is white
to pinkish-lilac, has a dark green gleba,
and grows on decaying wood.

Lysurus periphragmoides (Klotzsch) Dring
STALKED LATTICE STINKHORN
Description: Immature fruitbody an egg
up to 4.5 cm wide, round to elongated,
white to buff, with a gelatinous interior,
attached to the ground by several
whitish rhizomorphs. The mature form
consists of a head, stalk, and volva.
Head a swollen and rounded terminal
network of conjoined latticelike arms.
Arms sharply angled and distinctly
corrugated, pinkish to pinkish-orange,
sometimes yellowish or whitish. Stalk
up to 16 cm high, 1-2 cm wide, hollow,
colored like the arms. Volva oval,
membranous, white to buff. Gleba
slimy, fetid, dark olive-green, filling
the interior of the head and extending
outward from the latticelike arms.
Occurrence: Solitary or in groups on the
ground or on mulch. Year-round.
Edibility: Inedible.
Microscopic Features:
Spores 4-4.5 × 1.5-2 µm, elliptical,
smooth. Pale brown.
Comments: *Periphragmoides* means
"around something that resembles a
palisade," a reference to the latticelike
arms and head.

Mutinus elegans (Mont.) E. Fisch.
ELEGANT STINKHORN
Description: Immature fruitbody an egg
up to 2.5 cm wide, round to oval, white,
with a gelatinous interior, attached to
the ground by a white rhizomorph. The
mature form consists of a stalk with an
indistinct head portion, and a volva.
Stalk up to 18 cm high, 1.2-2.5 cm wide,
roughened, orange to pinkish-orange or
rarely pink, tapered from the middle in
both directions, the apex with a narrow
opening. The volva is saclike, wrinkled,
tough, whitish. Gleba covering the
upper third or more of the stalk, olive-
green, slimy, fetid.
Occurrence: Scattered, in groups, or in
clusters on wood chips, leaf litter, or
soil. Year-round.
Edibility: Inedible.
Microscopic Features:
Spores 4-7 × 2-3 µm, elliptic, smooth.
Pale yellowish-green.
Comments: *Mutinus ravenelii* (search
online) has a clearly defined head and
a pitted, pinkish-red stalk. *Phallus
rubicundus* (search online) has a flaring,
thimblelike cap and a pitted stalk
coated with an olive-brown gleba.

Phallogaster saccatus Morgan
CLUB-SHAPED STINKHORN
Description: Fruitbody egglike, up to
5 cm high, 1-3.5 cm wide, pear-shaped
and narrowed toward the base, or
sometimes nearly round, white to
pinkish or pinkish-lilac on the upper
portion, white toward the base,
smooth at first, then forming irregular
depressions that perforate to expose the
gleba. Interior gelatinous. Base attached
to the substrate by whitish to pinkish
rhizomorphs. Gleba slimy, dark green,
fetid.
Occurrence: Solitary or in groups on
decaying wood or wood chip mulch.
Year-round.
Edibility: Inedible.
Microscopic Features:
Spores 4-5.5 × 1.5-2 μm, subcylindric,
smooth. Greenish.
Comments: *Saccatus* means "having a
saclike container." The distinctive
club-shaped fruitbody and occurrence
on wood make this stinkhorn easy to
identify.

Phallus ravenelii Berk. & M. A. Curtis
RAVENEL'S STINKHORN
Description: Immature fruitbody an
egg up to 4.5 cm wide, oval to pear-
shaped, whitish to pinkish-lilac,
interior gelatinous, with pinkish-lilac
rhizomorphs. Mature fruitbody a head,
stalk, and volva. Head up to 4.5 cm high,
1.5-4 cm wide, conical to ovoid, with a
white-rimmed apical opening, granular
to wrinkled, lacking pits, covered by
gleba. Stalk up to 16 cm high, 1.5-3 cm
wide, roughened, spongy, hollow,
whitish. The volva is tough, wrinkled,
whitish to pinkish-lilac. Gleba slimy,
greenish- to olive-brown, fetid.
Occurrence: Scattered or in groups on or
near woody debris. Year-round.
Edibility: Inedible.
Microscopic Features:
Spores 3-4 × 1-1.5 μm, cylindric,
smooth. Hyaline.
Comments: *Ravenelii* honors Henry William Ravenel (1814-87), South Carolina
mycologist and botanist. *Phallus
hadriani* (search online) is similar, but
its head is conspicuously pitted. The
Netted Stinkhorn, *Dictyophora duplicata*
(search online), is larger and has a pitted
head, and its stalk is surrounded at the
apex by a white, netlike, flaring veil.

Pseudocolus fusiformis (E. Fisch.) Lloyd
STINKY SQUID
Description: Immature fruitbody an egg
2-3.5 cm wide, oval to pear-shaped,
grayish-brown to pale gray, often finely
cracked, with a gelatinous interior,
attached by white rhizomorphs. The
mature form consists of a multiarmed
stalk and volva. Stalk 2-4.5 cm long,
1.5-3 cm thick, roughened, spongy,
hollow, with 3-5 arms, whitish at the
base, yellow to orange above. Arms 2-7
cm long, pitted, arched, tapered upward
and often united at their apices, yellow
to orange. Volva tough, wrinkled,
grayish-brown to pale gray. Gleba olive-
green to dark green, drying nearly
black, slimy, fetid, borne on the inner
side of the arms.
Occurrence: Scattered or in groups on
soil in conifer or mixed woods, or in
landscaping wood chips. Summer-fall.
Edibility: Inedible.
Microscopic Features:
Spores 4.5-5.5 × 2-2.5 μm, elliptic-
ovoid, smooth. Hyaline.
Comments: *Fusiformis* means "fused," a
reference to the tips of the arms.

PUFFBALLS, EARTHBALLS, EARTHSTARS, AND SIMILAR FUNGI

The common trait in this group is the production of spores inside a single balloonlike spore case, or **peridium**. Spores are often discharged through a small hole developing at the apex. The peridium may be thin, as in puffballs, or consist of multiple layers that include a thick rind. Some stoutly jacketed earthballs form underground and erupt upward to daylight. The outer layer of peridium in the earthstars splits open as starlike rays to expose a thin inner capsule filled with spores. **Hygroscopic** rays open or close in response to water or humidity. The peridium of stalked puffballs is raised off the ground. In the genus *Calostoma*, the stalk is comprised of a coarsely woven lattice resembling a loose column of seaweed. The interior of a peridium may be uniformly colored, speckled with small differently colored structures called **peridioles,** or traversed by a cordlike **columella** of nonspore tissue. The spore mass inside the peridium of puffballs, earthballs, earthstars, and similar fungi is called a **gleba**.

Some species in this group are edible, at least when young. Others are poisonous. *Pisolithus arhizus* is a source of fiber and fabric dyes.

Astraeus morganii
Phosri, Watling & M. P. Martin
BAROMETER EARTHSTAR
Description: Fruitbody up to 9 cm wide,
1-2.5 cm high when fully expanded,
consisting of a rounded peridium and
starlike rays. Peridium nearly round or
somewhat flattened, finely roughened,
with one irregular porelike mouth,
whitish to grayish or grayish-brown.
Gleba white at first, becoming brown
and powdery at maturity. Rays 6-12,
hygroscopic, up to 5 cm long, yellow-
brown to reddish-brown or grayish to
nearly black; inner surface often finely
cracked.
Occurrence: Solitary, scattered, or in
groups on sandy soil, with oaks or
pines. Year-round.
Edibility: Inedible.
Microscopic Features:
Spores 7.5-10 µm, globose, distinctly
warted. Brown.
Comments: American collections of this
earthstar have traditionally been called
Astraeus hygrometricus, a European
species. *Geastrum arenarium* (see photo
on p. 28) is similar but smaller; its rays
are not hygroscopic and not finely
cracked, and it has much smaller spores
that measure 3-4 µm.

Bovista pusilla (Batsch.) Pers.
Description: Fruitbody 6-20 mm wide,
consisting of a peridium with a small,
pinched, cordlike rooting base.
Peridium rounded or somewhat
flattened, forming a small apical pore
at maturity, covered with a fine fibrous
coating that collapses and separates
into very small patches or becomes
powdery, white at first, becoming dull
yellow to dark brown in age. Gleba
filling the entire peridium, white,
becoming greenish-yellow then brown
and powdery at maturity.
Occurrence: Scattered or in groups in
cemeteries, lawns, fields, yards, and
other open grassy areas. Summer-fall.
Edibility: Unknown.
Microscopic Features:
Spores 3.2-4.3 µm, globose, smooth or
finely warted, with a very short pedicel,
often with one large oil drop. Brownish.
Comments: *Pusilla* means "very little,"
an appropriate name for this easily
overlooked puffball. *Lycoperdon
pusillum* is a synonym. *Lycoperdon
acuminatum* (search online) is smaller
yet, 3-9 mm wide; it has a pointed egg
shape and grows on the bark of living
trees.

Calostoma cinnabarinum Desv.
HOT LIPS, RED SLIMY-STALKED PUFFBALL

Description: Fruitbody a peridium with an outer and inner layer supported by a thick, short stalk. Peridium 1-2 cm wide and high, oval to nearly round. Outer layer thick, gelatinous, with small, orange-red seedlike pieces. Inner layer smooth, thin-walled, bright reddish-orange, fading to orange-yellow, with a slitlike mouth surrounded by liplike bright red ridges. Gleba white, becoming buff and powdery. Stalk 1.5-4 cm long, 1-2 cm thick, spongy, coarsely networked and pitted, reddish-orange to pale reddish-brown, covered by a thick gelatinous layer coated with debris.

Occurrence: Scattered or in groups under hardwoods, especially oak, or in mixed woods, often buried up to the peridium. Summer-fall.

Edibility: Inedible.

Microscopic Features:
Spores 14-22 × 6-9 μm, oblong-elliptic, pitted. Hyaline.

Comments: *Calostoma lutescens* has a yellow peridium. *Calostoma ravenelii* (search online) has a scurfy grayish peridium that lacks a gelatinous layer.

Calostoma lutescens (Schwein.) Burnap
COLLARED CALOSTOMA

Description: Fruitbody consisting of a peridium supported by an elongated stalk. Peridium 1.5-2 cm wide and high, oval to nearly round. Outer layer thin, gelatinous, forming a torn ring around the bottom of the inner layer. Inner layer smooth, thin-walled, yellow, with a slitlike mouth surrounded by liplike bright red ridges. Gleba white, becoming buff and powdery. Stalk 5-9 cm long, 1.5-2 cm thick, spongy, coarsely reticulate and pitted, pale yellow to brown, covered with a gelatinous layer coated with debris.

Occurrence: Scattered or in groups on the ground or on well-decayed stumps in woodlands. Summer-early winter.

Edibility: Inedible.

Microscopic Features:
Spores 5.5-8 × 5.5-8 μm, globose, pitted. Hyaline.

Comments: *Calostoma cinnabarinum* has a bright reddish-orange peridium. *Calostoma ravenelii* (search online) has a scurfy grayish peridium, lacking a gelatinous layer and the torn ring around the base of the peridium.

Calvatia craniiformis (Schwein.) Fr.
SKULL-SHAPED PUFFBALL
Description: Fruitbody up to 20 cm high and wide, consisting of a peridium with a conspicuous sterile base attached to the ground by white rhizomorphs. Peridium skull-shaped to pear-shaped, typically furrowed, initially smooth, cracking into irregular patches as it matures, white, becoming grayish to pale tan. Gleba white and firm, becoming greenish-yellow and finally olive-brown and powdery at maturity. Sterile base large, occupying most of the lower one-third of the fruitbody, chambered, white, becoming yellow-brown, and finally dark brown in age.

Occurrence: Solitary, scattered, or in groups in grassy areas or in woodlands. Summer-fall.

Edibility: Edible when the gleba is white.

Microscopic Features:
Spores 2.5-3.5, globose, nearly smooth or with minute spines, with a very short pedicel, yellowish.

Comments: *Calvatia cyathiformis* (search online) is very similar, but its mature gleba is dull purple. *Calvatia rubroflava* (search online) is whitish and becomes yellow to orange when handled or in age.

Calvatia gigantea (Batsch) Lloyd
GIANT PUFFBALL
Description: Fruitbody consisting of a peridium and a gleba. The peridium is very large, 20-50 cm wide, nearly round or somewhat flattened, attached to the ground by a thick, cordlike basal rhizomorph. Peridium white to creamy white, soft, resembling deerskin, cracking irregularly in age. Gleba soft, white, becoming yellow-green and finally greenish-brown.

Occurrence: Solitary, scattered, or in groups in pastures, parks, golf courses, and woodlands. Summer-fall.

Edibility: Edible when the gleba is white.

Microscopic Features:
Spores 3.5-5 μm, globose, weakly echinulate or nearly smooth. Pale brown.

Comments: At maturity, this soccer ball of a puffball is commonly attacked by a gray bread mold called *Syzygites megalocarpus* (search online). The Giant Puffball has minimal taste, but there's a lot of it. Think of it as fungal tofu.

Geastrum fornicatum (Huds.) Hook.
ARCHED EARTHSTAR
Description: Fruitbody up to 6 cm wide when fully expanded, consisting of a peridium and starlike rays. Peridium 2-2.5 cm high and wide, rounded or somewhat flattened, attached to a short stalk that may be surrounded at the base by a tiny collar, splitting open and forming a large porelike mouth at the top when mature, whitish at first, becoming brown. Gleba firm and whitish at first, becoming blackish-brown and powdery. Rays usually 4-5, up to 5 cm long, bent strongly backward and downward, clasping a thick mass of hyphae and debris, brown.

Occurrence: Scattered or in groups among leaves or organic debris in landscaped areas, or woodlands. Summer-early winter.

Edibility: Inedible.

Microscopic Features:
Spores 3.5-4.5 μm, globose, warted. Dark brown.

Comments: *Geastrum coronatum* (search online) is very similar, but its pore mouth is sharply defined by a silky area outlined by a shallow groove.

Geastrum saccatum Fr.
ROUNDED EARTHSTAR
Description: Fruitbody up to 5 cm wide, consisting of a broadly conic to rounded peridium and starlike rays. Peridium 1.2-2 cm wide and high, broadly conic to rounded, brownish to grayish-brown, stalkless, splitting open and forming a large porelike mouth surrounded by a conspicuous paler disclike zone. Gleba white and firm at first, becoming brown to purplish-brown and powdery at maturity. Rays 5-7, bent strongly backward and downward at maturity, forming a distinct saclike container surrounding the peridium, brown.

Occurrence: Solitary, scattered, or in groups among leaf litter in woodlands. Summer-early winter.

Edibility: Inedible.

Microscopic Features:
Spores 3.5-4.5 μm, globose, finely warted. Brown.

Comments: *Geastrum fimbriatum* (search online) is similar, but its porelike mouth lacks a conspicuous paler disclike zone. The Saltshaker Earthstar, *Myriostoma coliforme* (search online), has a finely roughened, silvery-brown to grayish-brown peridium with several pore mouths that open at maturity.

Lycoperdon americanum Demoulin
SPINY PUFFBALL
Description: Fruitbody consisting of a peridium and gleba. The peridium is 2.5-5 cm wide and high, nearly round or somewhat flattened, white, becoming brownish in age, coated with clusters of long white spines with fused tips that turn brown in age and fall off, leaving a netlike pattern on the surface; a pore mouth opens at maturity. Gleba firm, white at first, becoming purple-brown and powdery.
Occurrence: Scattered or in groups, often among leaves and debris in woodlands. Late spring-fall.
Edibility: Edible when the gleba is white.
Microscopic Features:
Spores 4-6 μm, globose, warted. Purple-brown.
Comments: Some authors consider *Lycoperdon echinatum* to be a synonym. A mature stage of this puffball is illustrated in the Color Key to the Major Groups of Fungi (p. 28). *Lycoperdon pulcherrimum* (search online) has spines that are fused at their tips, but they do not darken in age or leave marks on the peridium when they fall away.

Lycoperdon marginatum Vittad.
PEELING PUFFBALL
Description: Fruitbody consisting of a peridium and gleba. The peridium is 1-5 cm wide, supported by a somewhat tapered, sterile, stalklike base. Peridium nearly round at first, becoming slightly flattened to pear-shaped at maturity, white, covered with short spines or warts that break off in irregular sheets to expose the nearly smooth, pale to dark olive-brown or reddish-brown inner surface with a single, apical pore mouth. Gleba firm and white at first, becoming olive-brown to grayish-brown and powdery at maturity.
Occurrence: Scattered or in groups on the ground, usually in mixed woods. Summer-early winter.
Edibility: Unknown.
Microscopic Features:
Spores 3.5-4.5 μm, globose, punctate to nearly smooth, sometimes with a short pedicel. Pale brown.
Comments: Other puffballs have spines or warts that do not break off in sheets. The Tumbling Puffball, *Bovista pila* (search online), has a smooth, white peridium when young that becomes brown to bronze and papery thin at maturity.

Lycoperdon perlatum Pers.

**DEVIL'S SNUFFBOX,
GEM-STUDDED PUFFBALL**

Description: Fruitbody 2.5-8 cm high,
2-6.5 cm wide, consisting of a peridium
with a large, stalklike sterile base.
Peridium pear-shaped to turban-
shaped, covered with short spines and
granules that easily break off, white at
first, becoming yellow-brown in age; a
rounded, apical pore mouth appears at
maturity. Gleba firm and white when
young, becoming yellow to olive and
finally olive-brown and powdery at
maturity.

Occurrence: Solitary, scattered, or in
clusters on the ground under conifers or
hardwoods. Summer–early winter.

Edibility: Edible when the gleba is white.

Microscopic Features:
Spores 3.5-4.5 µm, globose, weakly
spiny. Pale brown.

Comments: *Perlatum* means "widespread,"
a reference to the distribution of this
common puffball. Compare with
Lycoperdon pyriforme, which grows in
dense clusters on wood. The Stalked
Puffball, *Tulostoma brumale* (search
online), has a small, brownish peridium
supported by a slender stalk, and an
elevated porelike mouth.

Lycoperdon pyriforme Schaeff.

PEAR-SHAPED PUFFBALL

Description: Fruitbody consisting of a
peridium and gleba. The peridium is
1.5-5 cm wide and high, pear-shaped
to nearly round, whitish at first, soon
becoming yellowish- to reddish-brown,
coated with tiny granules or spines,
the lower portion tapered downward
perhaps forming a short, sterile stalklike
base that is often compressed; an apical
pore opens at maturity, gleba white
and firm at first, becoming greenish-
yellow and finally dark olive-brown and
powdery when mature.

Occurrence: Scattered or in dense,
squeezed clusters on decaying wood,
sawdust, or organic debris. Summer–
early winter.

Edibility: Edible when the gleba is white.

Microscopic Features:
Spores 3-4.5 µm, globose, smooth. Pale
brown.

Comments: *Pyriforme* means "pear-
shaped." Compare with *Lycoperdon
perlatum*, which has a longer stalklike
sterile base and usually grows on the
ground. *Lycoperdon subincarnatum*
(see photo on p. 28) is 1-3 cm wide, has
reddish- to purplish-brown spines, and
grows on mossy hardwood logs and
stumps.

Lycoperdon radicatum Durieu & Mont.

Description: Fruitbody 2.5-9 cm wide, nearly round to top-shaped, attached to the ground by a firm, cordlike, tapered and rooting base. Peridium white, scurfy, coated with soft, white pyramid-shaped warts that are often fused at their tips to form tiny bundles (use a hand lens), which become dull orange-yellow and wear away in age; the peridium eventually splits open at the top to form a slit or pore. Gleba white and spongy when young, becoming yellow-brown and powdery. Sterile base cup-shaped, whitish to orange-yellow.

Occurrence: Scattered or in groups on soil in open areas, fields, pastures, and woodlands, especially with oak and pine. Late spring–fall.

Edibility: Unknown.

Microscopic Features:
Spores 4-5 × 3.5-4.5 μm, oval, smooth, with one large oil drop and a conspicuous pedicel. Hyaline.

Comments: *Bovistella radicata* is a synonym.

Pisolithus arhizus (Scop.) Rauschert

DYE-MAKER'S FALSE PUFFBALL

Description: Fruitbody 5-15 or more cm high, 3.5-12 cm wide, consisting of a peridium and stalklike rooting base. Peridium tapered downward, pear-shaped to oval or club-shaped, thin, smooth, shiny, dingy yellow to yellow-brown, splitting irregularly at maturity and exposing numerous tiny yellowish to brownish peridioles embedded in a black gelatinous matrix. Gleba produced by the disintegrating peridioles is reddish-brown to dark brown and powdery at maturity.

Occurrence: Solitary, scattered, or in groups in sandy soil, usually under oaks and pines, often with Prickly Pear cactus, typically partially buried. Summer–early winter.

Edibility: Inedible.

Microscopic Features:
Spores 7-12 μm, globose, spiny. Brownish.

Comments: This species is used to dye wool various shades of brown or black. *Pisolithus tinctorius* is a synonym.

Rhizopogon nigrescens Coker & Couch

Description: Fruitbody consisting of a peridium and gleba. The stalkless peridium is 1-4 cm wide, thin, yellowish when young, becoming dark brown to blackish, staining reddish-brown then brown when bruised. Gleba firm and whitish when young, olive-brown at maturity.

Occurrence: Scattered or in groups, often partially buried, in sandy soil under pines. Summer–early winter.

Edibility: Unknown.

Microscopic Features:
Spores 6-9 × 2-3.5 μm, subfusoid to oblong, smooth. Hyaline to pale yellow.

Comments: *Rhizopogon atlanticus* (search online) has a pinkish-cinnamon to brown peridium that does not stain when bruised, and a whitish to pale brown gleba; the spores measure 7-8.5 × 3-4 μm. *Rhizopogon roseolus* (see photo on p. 28) has a whitish peridium when very young; it becomes reddish-brown in age and stains reddish when bruised; the whitish to olive-buff gleba stains reddish-brown when exposed, and the spores measure 6.4-8.5 × 3-3.7 μm.

Rhopalogaster transversarius (Bosc) J. R. Johnst.

Description: Fruitbody 3-9.5 cm high, 1.5-4.5 cm wide, club-shaped, consisting of a peridium and a narrowed stalk with several basal rhizomorphs; the gleba is traversed by a central columella. Peridium scurfy, reddish- to yellowish-brown, becoming pale brownish-yellow in age, rupturing irregularly to expose the mature gleba. Columella central, whitish, extending upward from the base of the stalk and extensively branching crosswise through most of the peridium. The gleba distinctly chambered like a honeycomb, gelatinous at first, conspicuously marbled or veined, dull red to reddish-brown, slowly staining blackish when exposed, becoming olive-brown and powdery in age.

Occurrence: Solitary, scattered, or in groups on decaying organic matter including leaf litter, mulch, or wood chips in oak and pine woods. Summer–winter.

Edibility: Unknown.

Microscopic Features:
Spores 5.5-7.5 × 3-4.5 μm, elliptic, smooth, pale brown.

Comments: *Transversarius* means "lying crosswise," a reference to the branches of the columella.

Scleroderma bovista Fr.

Description: Fruitbody 1.5-4.5 cm wide and high, consisting of a peridium attached to the soil by a thick stalklike base. The peridium is nearly round to somewhat flattened, smooth when young, soon developing fine cracks and divided into small scalelike patches, straw yellow to reddish-brown, splitting irregularly on the top and sides in age. Gleba dark blackish-brown, powdery at maturity. The stalklike base is 5-35 mm long, 12-30 mm wide, composed of a dense mass of rhizomorphs and trapped sand.

Occurrence: Solitary, scattered, or in groups on sandy soil in grassy areas, waste areas, and oak/pine woods. Summer-fall.

Edibility: Poisonous, causing gastrointestinal distress.

Microscopic Features:
Spores 10-16 μm, globose, with a partial to complete reticulum. Brown.

Comments: *Bovista* means "puffball." *Scleroderma meridionale* (search online) is similar but has a prominent stalklike base, 2.5-9 cm long, 2-4.5 cm wide, and a thicker-walled peridium that splits into irregular lobes at maturity.

Scleroderma citrinum Pers.
COMMON EARTHBALL, PIGSKIN POISON PUFFBALL

Description: Fruitbody consisting of a peridium and gleba. The peridium is 2.5-10 cm wide and high, nearly round or somewhat flattened, thick and rindlike, pale brown to golden-brown, finely cracked and covered with coarse warts, attached to the substrate by a thick, stalklike mycelial base. The peridium wall is white in cross section, slowly staining pinkish when rubbed. An irregular pore mouth forms on the upper surface. Gleba is white, solid and firm only when very young; it soon turns dark gray to purplish-black and powdery at maturity.

Occurrence: Scattered or in groups on the ground or decaying wood. Summer-fall.

Edibility: Poisonous, causing gastrointestinal distress.

Microscopic Features:
Spores 8-12 μm, globose, strongly reticulate. Dull brown.

Comments: This is one of the most commonly encountered and easily identified earthballs. It is sometimes parasitized by a small bolete, *Pseudo-boletus parasiticus* (search online), with a tawny olive cap, pale lemon yellow flesh, a similarly colored stalk, and a yellowish to olive-brown pore surface.

Scleroderma michiganense
(Guzmán) Guzmán

Description: Fruitbody consisting of a
peridium and gleba. The peridium is
2.5-6 cm wide and high, attached to the
soil by white rhizomorphs. Peridium
rounded to somewhat flattened or
shaped like an inverted pear, yellowish
then reddish-brown in age, staining
reddish-brown when bruised, smooth
to finely cracked, splitting irregularly
in age. The wall of the peridium is
1-2.5 mm thick, whitish to yellowish.
Gleba white when young, becoming
blackish and powdery when mature.

Occurrence: Scattered or in groups
on sandy soil or organic debris in
hardwoods. Summer-fall.

Edibility: Unknown, but likely poisonous.

Microscopic Features:
Spores 14-20 μm, globose, with long
spines and a complete reticulum. Dull
brown.

Comments: *Scleroderma cepa* (search
online) is very similar, but its peridium
is round to slightly flattened, pale
pinkish-brown to pale yellowish-
brown, and becomes dark brown where
handled or in age. It has smaller spores
that measure 8-10 μm; they have sharp
spines but lack reticulation.

Scleroderma polyrhizum (J. F. Gmel.) Pers.
EARTHSTAR SCLERODERMA

Description: Fruitbody 4-12 cm wide
when closed, expanding to 16 cm and
resembling a giant earthstar when
fully open, attached to the ground by a
rootlike mass of tough fibers. Peridium
round to oval or irregular, 3-10 mm
thick, hard, rindlike, rough, finely
cracked to somewhat scaly, whitish to
straw-colored or pale yellow-brown,
splitting open into rays and exposing
the gleba. Rays 4-8, thick, brown to
blackish-brown. Gleba firm and white
at first, becoming brown to purplish-
brown and finally blackish-brown and
powdery at maturity.

Occurrence: Scattered or in groups,
often partially buried in sandy soil,
driveways, or graveled lots. Summer-
early winter.

Edibility: Poisonous, causing
gastrointestinal upset.

Microscopic Features:
Spores 5-10 μm, globose, spiny,
sometimes forming a partial reticulum.
Purple-brown.

Comments: Sometimes incorrectly spelled
"*polyrhizon.*" *Polyrhizum* means "many
roots," a reference to the mass of fibers
anchoring the fruitbody. *Scleroderma
geaster* is a synonym.

Zelleromyces cinnabarinus
Singer & A. H. Sm.
MILKY FALSE TRUFFLE

Description: Fruitbody consisting of a peridium and gleba. The peridium is 1-3 cm wide, connected to the substrate by white basal mycelium. The peridium is nearly round or irregularly compressed and lobed, smooth, brick red to dull orange-brown. The interior is chambered or marbled with sterile tissue and contains a distinctly branching columella. Gleba firm and orangish-white at first, exuding a white latex when fresh specimens are cut, in age becoming granular and brownish. Odor pungent like rubber or not distinctive. Taste not distinctive.

Occurrence: Scattered, in groups, or clustered on the ground or buried underground, with pines. Summer-fall.

Edibility: Unknown.

Microscopic Features: Spores 12-18 × 11-16 µm, globose to broadly elliptic, thick-walled, ornamented with warts and ridges that form a broken reticulum. Hyaline to pale yellow, amyloid.

Comments: *Cinnabarinus* means "the color of cinnabar," a reference to the peridium. *Rhizopogon* species are similar and are also mycorrhizal with pines, but they lack latex and a columella.

Bird's-nest fungi look like tiny paper cups with eggs in them. Cups of immature specimens are usually lidded by a papery membrane that subsequently disappears. They grow on wood, leaves, or other decaying matter. The "eggs," known as **peridioles**, contain spores. Think of peridioles as miniature puffballs, a group to which the bird's-nests are related. Spores are typically dispersed by the splash force of raindrops falling into cups. The Sphere Thrower or Cannon Fungus, *Sphaerobolus stellatus*, is very small, only up to 3 mm wide, and also grows on wood, dung, and other decaying matter. Its tiny puffball-like spore case splits open at maturity to form a miniature star-shaped structure that surrounds a tiny single peridiole. When light and moisture conditions are right, the peridiole is forcibly shot, or thrown up to ten feet away.

Bird's-nests and the Sphere Thrower are considered inedible.

Crucibulum laeve (Huds.) Kambly
COMMON BIRD'S-NEST
Description: Fruitbody consisting of a cup and egglike peridioles. Cup somewhat cylindric and tapered downward, 6-10 mm wide at the top, 6-10 mm high, protected when young by a white, membranelike lid and covered overall by yellowish-orange fibers that open at maturity. Interior smooth, whitish. Exterior hairy to wooly, yellowish-orange, becoming paler yellow in age. Peridioles 1.5-2 mm wide, lens-shaped, whitish, each attached on the underside by a tiny, coiled cord.

Occurrence: Scattered or in groups on fallen twigs and branches, wood chips, and garden mulch. Year-round.

Edibility: Inedible.

Microscopic Features:
Spores 8-10 × 4-5.5 μm, elliptic, smooth. Hyaline.

Comments: *Crucibulum vulgare* is a synonym. *Cyathus* species are similar, but they have grayish-brown to gray or blackish peridioles.

Cyathus striatus (Huds.) Willd.
SPLASH CUPS
Description: Fruitbody consisting of a cup and egglike peridioles. Cup 6-10 mm high, cone-shaped, covered by a white, membranous lid when young. Interior vertically lined, smooth, shiny, gray to grayish-white. Exterior hairy, reddish- to chocolate or grayish-brown. Peridioles 1.5-3 mm in diameter, flattened and often vaguely triangular, dark gray, attached to the cup interior by a tiny, coiled cord.

Occurrence: Scattered or in dense groups on twigs, bark, and wood chips. Year-round.

Edibility: Inedible.

Microscopic Features:
Spores 15-20 × 8-12 μm, elliptic, smooth. Hyaline.

Comments: *Hypocrea latizonata* (search online) is a parasitic fungus that often forms a distinctive white band around the outside of the cups. Look-alikes with cup interiors that are not vertically lined include *Cyathus stercoreus* (see photo on p. 29), which has dark gray to black peridioles, a hairy cup exterior, and a smooth interior that is not vertically lined, and *Cyathus olla* (search online), which has grayish-brown peridioles and a smooth to minutely hairy cup exterior.

Sphaerobolus stellatus Tode
**CANNON FUNGUS,
SPHERE THROWER**

Description: Fruitbody consisting of
a spore case and a single egglike
peridiole. Spore case 1.5-3 mm wide,
nearly round, white to yellow-orange,
splitting at maturity into 4-9 star-
shaped to toothlike rays that expose
the peridiole. Peridiole 1.5-2.5 mm
in diameter, whitish to dull yellow or
reddish-brown to dark brown.

Occurrence: Solitary or in groups on
decaying wood, sawdust, compost,
and dung. Spring-fall.

Edibility: Inedible.

Microscopic Features:
Spores 7-10 × 3.5-5 μm, oblong, smooth.
Hyaline.

Comments: *Sphaerobolus stellatus*
means "star-shaped sphere thrower."
Sphaerobolus dentatus is a synonym.
The peridiole is forcibly ejected
in response to moisture and light.
Pleurocolla compressa (search online)
has a small, 1.5-5 mm, gelatinous to
rubbery, stalkless, cushion-shaped
fruitbody that is whitish at first,
becomes yellowish to orange-yellow at
maturity, and grows in dense clusters
on decaying wood.

CUP FUNGI

This often colorful group is comprised of species with caps shaped like a cup, saucer, or animal ear. There are no gills, tubes, pores, or teeth. Spores are produced on the *top* (inner) surface of the cup. Blowing air across some of the larger species or stamping the ground beside a terrestrial clump might cause a mass ejection of spores that rise like a cloud of smoke. Cup fungi may grow on wood, on dung, or on the ground.

Differentiating between species of split cup fungi, species in the genus *Otidea*, can be a challenge. The surest way to resolve the uncertainty may be microscopic features such as spore details and the shape of **paraphyses**. Say what? Imagine the fertile (inner) surface of a cup as a microscopic lawn. Among the blades of grass stand tubular spore factories that function—minus gunpowder—like Roman candle fireworks. Without support, these spore cannons would fall over and blast the fungus in the cup, apparently not a winning evolutionary strategy. Enter paraphyses, the grass in the cup's lawn. These sterile stalks crowd around the spore cannons, keeping them pointed skyward. In some species the tips of paraphyses are characteristically bent or curled into a hook shape. In *Otidea rainierensis* the tips swell into clublike bulbs.

The edibility of cup fungi is largely unknown. Toxic hydrazine compounds have been found in some species. Cases of gastrointestinal distress have been reported as well. Enjoy cups for their looks.

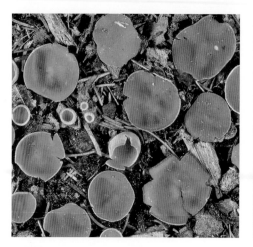

Aleuria aurantia (Pers.) Fuckel
ORANGE PEEL FUNGUS
Description: Fruitbody 1-10 cm wide, cup- to saucer-shaped, margin occasionally torn at maturity. Inner surface smooth and bright orange to yellow-orange. Outer surface pale orange, downy in youth becoming smooth in age. Stalkless. Flesh thin, pale orange, brittle. Odor and taste not distinctive.
Occurrence: Solitary or in flattened clumps. Under trees or in grassy, disturbed soil, in gardens, or along roadsides. Spring-fall.
Edibility: Edible but tasteless.
Microscopic Features:
Spores 17-24 × 9-11 µm, elliptic, coarsely warted and reticulate, usually with projecting spines at one or both ends. Spores typically contain 2 oil drops. Hyaline.
Comments: The Orange Peel looks like its namesake. It is much larger and more orange than *Bisporella citrina*, which grows on decaying wood. The bright orange color separates it from larger cups, such as *Otidea rainierensis*. Also compare with the Blue-staining Cup, *Caloscypha fulgens* (see photo on p. 30), which stains dark bluish-green, especially toward the margin.

Ascocoryne cylichnium (Tulasne) Korf
PURPLE JELLY DROPS
Description: Fruitbody 3-10 mm wide and 3-20 mm tall. Pinkish-purple inside and out. Shape varies from stubby columns to shallow cups and puffy cushions with dimpled centers. Texture somewhat wrinkled. Margin lobed or wavy. A rudimentary stalk may be present. Flesh violet-pink, rubbery-gelatinous. Odor and taste not distinctive.
Occurrence: In dense clusters (which may distort the cup shape) on damp logs and stumps, especially beech. Fall.
Edibility: Unknown.
Microscopic Features:
Spores 18-30 × 4-6 µm, elliptic, smooth. Mature spores divided by several internal septa. Paraphyses filiform and unbranched. Hyaline.
Comments: *Ascocoryne sarcoides*, also called Purple Jelly Drops (search online), is nearly identical but has branched paraphyses and smaller spores, 11-18 × 3.5-5 µm, that have a single septum. This cup fungus produces a mild antibiotic that helps protect trees against invasion by heart rot fungi.

Bisporella citrina (Batsch) Korf & S. E. Carp.

YELLOW FAIRY CUPS

Description: Fruitbody 1-3 mm wide, saucer-shaped. Inner surface smooth and bright yellow. Outer surface also smooth but often paler than the inner surface. A tiny, rudimentary stalk may be identifiable. Flesh thin and dry. Odor and taste not distinctive.

Occurrence: In groups and clumps on decaying wood. Summer-fall.

Edibility: Unknown.

Microscopic Features:

Spores 9-14 × 3-5 µm, elliptic, smooth, with an oil drop at each end. May be septate at maturity. Hyaline.

Comments: Despite the brilliant coloration, this wood recycler is more apparent to youthful eyes, especially to children who meet it at eye level on a fallen log or fence post. Microscopic analysis is needed to positively distinguish Yellow Fairy Cups from look-alike species. Yellow jellies, such as *Dacrymyces chrysospermus* and *Tremella mesenterica*, have a different shape and gelatinous flesh.

Chlorociboria aeruginascens (Nyl.) Kanouse ex C. S. Ramamurthi, Korf & L. R. Batra

BLUE-GREEN WOOD STAIN

Description: Fruitbody 3-8 mm wide, saucer-shaped to nearly flat, typically asymmetrical. Blue-green, sometimes with hints of yellow. Inner surface smooth or wrinkled. Outer surface finely roughened. Stalk usually off-center, 3-6 mm long, tapering downward. Flesh thin. Odor and taste not distinctive.

Occurrence: Scattered groups of cups on decaying, deciduous logs. Early summer-fall.

Edibility: Unknown.

Microscopic Features:

Spores 6-10 × 1-2.5 µm, elliptical to irregularly fusiform, smooth, with an oil drop at each end. Hyaline.

Comments: An equally colorful cousin, *Chlorociboria aeruginosa* (search online), has a more consistently round cup and central stalk but can be identified with certainty only by the larger spores, 8-15 × 2-4 µm. The mycelium of these species stains wood blue-green. This blue-green stained wood has been used in decorative woodwork.

Disciotis venosa (Pers.) Arnould
VEINED CUP
Description: Fruitbody 4-21 cm wide,
initially cup-shaped but flattening.
Outer edges irregular, often rolling up
or splitting. Inner surface reddish- to
yellowish-brown, radially wrinkled and
puckering at center, occasionally raising
secondary edges there. Outer surface
pale brown, slightly scurfy. Stalk
short, thick, often ribbed. Flesh thick,
brittle. May smell of chlorine. Taste not
distinctive.
Occurrence: Solitary or scattered under
conifers or hardwoods. Spring.
Edibility: Edible with caution. Poisonous if
uncooked.
Microscopic Features:
Spores 19-30 × 12-16 μm, broadly
elliptic, smooth, lacking oil drops. Pale
yellow.
Comments: This flapjack of a cup is related
to the morels and false morels. The
Veined Cup is larger and thicker and
may have a stronger odor than *Peziza
varia*. The lumpy and wrinkled inner
surface of *Gyromitra ancilis*—possibly
the same as *Discina perlata*—(both
are searchable online) is not radially
arranged; spores are 25-45 × 11-16 μm,
containing a large, central oil drop,
sometimes flanked by two smaller ones.

Galiella rufa (Schwein.) Nannf. & Korf
HAIRY RUBBER CUP
Description: Fruitbody 1-3 cm wide and
up to 3 cm tall. Cup interior smooth,
tan to reddish-brown. Exterior surface
brown to black, velvety or finely hairy
in youth, may become wrinkled at
maturity. Cap margin finely toothed.
Stalk, when present, up to 1 cm long
and 5 mm wide. Flesh thick, dark
and gelatinous. Odor and taste not
distinctive. Overall impression rubbery.
Occurrence: Solitary or in small groups
on hardwood logs or fallen sticks.
Summer-fall.
Edibility: Edible, requiring specific
preparation to make it palatable.
Microscopic Features:
Spores 18-20 × 8-10 μm, elliptic with
tapering ends. Texture appears finely
rough. Hyaline.
Comments: The Hairy Rubber Cup is aptly
named but could as easily have become
known as the Peanut Butter Cup.
Wolfina aurantiopsis is a bit larger, with
a pale yellow cup interior. The flesh of
that species is pale yellow and tough,
becoming corky when dry.

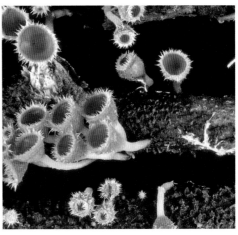

Humaria hemisphaerica
(F. H. Wigg.) Fuckel
BROWN-HAIRED WHITE CUP
Description: Fruitbody 1-3 cm wide and
1-2 cm tall. Deeply cup-shaped. Interior
surface white to pale gray, smooth.
Outer surface brownish-yellow, covered
with stiff brown hairs, some of which
project like eyelashes over the cup
margin. No stalk. Flesh thin, brittle.
Odor and taste not distinctive.
Occurrence: Scattered or in loose groups
on soil, in moss or humus, or on
decaying wood. Late spring-fall.
Edibility: Unknown.
Microscopic Features:
Spores 22-27 × 10-13 μm, broadly
elliptic. Surface warted in Melzer's
reagent but not in KOH. Oil drops at
each end of the spore may disappear at
maturity. Hyaline.
Comments: This pint-sized beauty could
have been named the Coconut Cup.
A larger, northern species, *Jafnea
semitosta* (see photo on p. 30), might
occur in the Carolinas. It is 2-5 cm
wide × 2-7 cm tall, with a pale interior
and hairy brownish-yellow exterior. The
spores are also longer, 25-35 × 10-12 μm.

Microstoma floccosum (Schwein.) Raitv.
SHAGGY SCARLET CUP
Description: Fruitbody 3-10 mm wide and
1-4.5 cm tall. Goblet-shaped with a long
stalk. Interior of cup bright red, smooth.
Outer surface pink to red, covered with
white hairs that project like eyelashes
over the cup margin. The narrow, whiter
stalk is 2-3.5 cm long. Flesh thin. Odor
and taste not distinctive.
Occurrence: Gregarious on decaying
hardwood branches. Summer-early fall.
Edibility: Unknown.
Microscopic Features:
Spores 20-35 × 15-17 μm, elliptic to
fusiform, smooth. Covered, when
fresh, by a thick hyaline coating. Spores
hyaline as well.
Comments: The Eyelash Cup, *Scutellinia
scutellata*, forms a larger, stalkless cup
with dark brown eyelashes. The Scarlet
Cups, *Sarcoscypha* spp., have wider
cups and lack eyelashes.

Otidea rainierensis Kanouse
BROWN CLUSTERED EAR CUP
Description: Fruitbody 2-4 cm wide and 2-3 cm tall. Cup-shaped, split down the short side. Interior smooth, creamy to pinkish-buff. Exterior smooth, chamois-colored. White mycelial threads at base of cup and on stalk. Stalk 5-10 mm long and 3-5 mm thick. Flesh thin, brittle. Odor and taste not distinctive.
Occurrence: Solitary or clustered on the ground under hardwoods and possibly elsewhere. Summer.
Edibility: Unknown.
Microscopic Features:
Spores 11.5-12.5 × 5.5-6.5 μm, broadly elliptic, smooth. Two oil drops. Color hyaline to pale yellow. Paraphyses have bulbed apices, not hooked.
Comments: This was formerly known as *Otidea kauffmanii*. *Otidea onotica* (search online) is twice the size, usually with elongated, ear-shaped cups and spores measuring 12-13 × 6-7 μm. *Sowerbyella unicisa* (search online) is smaller, with basal mycelial threads colored yellow to brownish-orange, and spores measuring 14-15.5 × 6.5-8.5 μm.

Peziza phyllogena Cooke
COMMON BROWN CUP
Description: Fruitbody 3-15 cm wide. Cup-shaped, flattening with age. Inner surface smooth, brown, with hints of pink, purple, or olive. Outer surface similarly colored but has a granular texture. Attachment to the substrate is small and central but doesn't form a stalk. Flesh thin, brittle. Odor and taste not distinctive.
Occurrence: Scattered or clustered on rich soil or decaying wood. Late spring.
Edibility: Reportedly edible.
Microscopic Features:
Spores 16-21 × 8-10 μm, elliptic, finely warted. Two oil drops. Hyaline.
Comments: This species was formerly known as *Peziza badioconfusa*. A similar species, *Peziza badia* (search online) fruits in the fall; its spores are decorated by a fine netting rather than warts. *Peziza domiciliana* (search online) is smaller and paler in color and grows on surfaces in and around homes. *Disciotis venosa* is larger and has thicker flesh. *Auricularia angiospermarum* has a lateral attachment to the logs on which it grows.

Peziza varia (Hedw.) Alb. & Schwein.
RECURVED CUP
Description: Fruitbody 5-11.5 cm wide. Cup- to saucer-shaped but often splits at the margin and rolls outward (recurves). Inner surface smooth, usually with a puckered center, pale yellow-brown to dark brown. Outer surface whitish and finely fuzzy (may require a hand lens). Small, central point of attachment with little or no stalk. Flesh thin, brittle. Odor and taste not distinctive.

Occurrence: Solitary or in groups on decaying hardwoods or ground nearby. Late spring-early fall.

Edibility: Unknown.

Microscopic Features: Spores 14-16 × 8-10 μm, elliptic, smooth. No oil drops. Hyaline.

Comments: This species or species complex is also called Palamino Cup. Mycologists disagree about how many species are contained within the general physical description given above. *Peziza repanda* doesn't differ significantly from *P. varia* and is considered a synonym here. Taxonomic uncertainty is one reason for the variance in expert opinions regarding edibility.

Sarcoscypha austriaca (Beck ex Sacc.) Boud.
SCARLET CUP
Description: Fruitbody 2-7 cm wide. Initially rounded and cup-shaped, shallow and irregular at maturity. Inner surface bright scarlet, often wrinkling with age. Outer surface rough or scurfy, white to pale orange or pinkish-red. Stalk, if present, short and thick. Flesh pink, thin. Odor and taste not distinctive.

Occurrence: Often found in groups on fallen sticks in hardwood or mixed forests. Early spring.

Edibility: Nonpoisonous.

Microscopic Features: Spores 20-38 × 9-16 μm, elongated elliptic with truncated ends, smooth, with multiple small oil drops, less than 3 μm in diameter. Hyaline.

Comments: This early splash of springtime red has a close relative, *Sarcoscypha dudleyi* (search online), that is indistinguishable but for the latter's rounded spore ends and 2 large oil drops in the spores. *Sarcoscypha occidentalis* is smaller, has a prominent stalk, and occurs later in the season. *Scutellinia scutellata* has dark eyelashes.

CUP FUNGI

Sarcoscypha occidentalis (Schwein.) Sacc.
STALKED SCARLET CUP

Description: Fruitbody 5-16 mm wide and 1.2-4.5 cm tall. Shallowly cup-shaped. Interior bright red, smooth and shiny. Outer surface pink, lacking white hairs. Stalk 1-3.5 cm long and up to 3 mm thick, smooth, white. Flesh thin. Odor and taste not distinctive.

Occurrence: Scattered or in small groups on fallen sticks and possibly leaves. Late spring-fall.

Edibility: Unknown.

Microscopic Features:
Spores 18-22 × 10-12 μm, elliptic, smooth, with two or more oil drops. Hyaline.

Comments: These resemble drops of blood on the forest floor. The lack of eyelashes separates them from *Microstoma floccosum* and *Scutellinia scutellata*. *Sarcoscypha austriaca* is much larger and fruits in early spring.

Scutellinia scutellata (L.) Lambotte
EYELASH CUP

Description: Fruitbody 3-20 mm wide. Shallow cup to flattened saucer. Interior smooth, shiny, bright orange to red. Outer surface brownish, covered with stiff dark brown to black hairs that fringe the cup margin as eyelashes. No stalk. Flesh thin, reddish, brittle. Odor and taste not distinctive.

Occurrence: Scattered to clustered on decaying wood or damp, rich woodland soil. Late spring-fall.

Edibility: Inedible.

Microscopic Features:
Spores 16-21 × 10-14 μm, elliptic. Smooth when young, minutely warted at maturity. Young spores contain multiple oil drops. Hyaline.

Comments: The Eyelash Cup is a cutie, no doubt about it. *Scutellinia erinaceus* (see photo on p. 30) is smaller, 0.5 cm or less in diameter, with a yellow to orange inner surface. The dark eyelashes of these two species distinguish them from *Microstoma floccosum*, which has white eyelashes. *Sarcoscypha occidentalis* lacks eyelashes of any color.

Urnula craterium (Schwein.) Fr.
DEVIL'S URN

Description: Fruitbody 2-7 cm wide and 4.5-11 cm tall. Goblet-shaped. The mouth is initially narrow, expanding with age as the rim splits and peels back. Cup interior black and smooth. Exterior dark brown to black, wooly when young. Stalk 2-4 cm long and 5-10 mm thick, black. Flesh leathery. Odor and taste not distinctive.

Occurrence: In groups on decaying or buried wood. Early spring.

Edibility: Unknown.

Microscopic Features:
Spores 25-35 × 10-15 μm, broadly elliptic, smooth, lacking oil drops. Hyaline.

Comments: The Devil's Urn, aka the Black Tulip, appears around the time morels do.

Wolfina aurantiopsis
(Ellis) Seaver ex Eckblad

Description: Fruitbody up to 7 cm wide. The shallow cups have a smooth interior and are dull yellow to brownish-yellow or orangish in color. Cup exterior brown to black, wooly in youth. The outer surface is further textured by indistinct, closely spaced vertical ridges or "projecting folds" (imagine wooly corduroy). Stalkless with a broad attachment. Flesh thick, pale and firm, corky when dry. Odor and taste not distinctive.

Occurrence: Solitary or in small groups on decaying sticks or buried wood. Summer-fall.

Edibility: Inedible.

Microscopic Features:
Spores 27-33 × 16-18 μm, broadly elliptic, smooth but with a granular interior. Hyaline to slightly yellow.

Comments: This species is less common than *Galiella rufa*, a cup that is usually smaller and has a darker inner surface. When these features aren't conclusive, the tough, pale flesh of *Wolfina aurantiopsis* sets it apart. Surprisingly, the two species are not closely related.

CUP FUNGI

Wynnea americana Thaxt.
RABBIT EARS

Description: Fruitbody 2.5-14 cm wide, 6-13 cm tall. Composed of multiple, rabbit-ear-shaped structures. Interior surfaces pink to brownish-orange, darkening with age. Exterior surfaces are dark brown to black and have a warted texture. The ears are joined by short stalks arising from a tough knot of brown tissue. Flesh in ears brown, tough. Flesh in stalks whitish. Odor and taste not distinctive.

Occurrence: Solitary to scattered under hardwoods or, occasionally, in mixed woods. Summer-fall.

Edibility: Unknown.

Microscopic Features: Spores 32-40 × 15-16 μm, elliptic, tipped with short spines. Dark and light bands run the length of the spore (like caraway seed). Spores contain multiple oil drops.

Comments: Rabbit Ears are a fun find. Not only do they look exotic, but they might perform for you. Stamping the ground around a clump or fanning the air above it may raise a smoky cloud of spores.

The fertile surface in this group is the outer surface of the mushroom head or, in some members of the genus *Helvella*, the top surface of a cap lacking gills, pores, or teeth. The head section of true morels features a pattern of ridges and spore-producing pits. In false morels and some Helvellas, the head is comprised of warped or heavily wrinkled plates. All species of true morel found in the Carolinas are hollow. In the other genera, interiors usually contain at least some cobwebby material, chambers, or crumpled wads of stalk tissue.

Apart from the highly prized species of *Morchella*, we do not recommend eating mushrooms in this group. Some others *are* edible by most people, when properly cooked, but it is too easy to make mistakes. Certain *Gyromitra* species contain enough of the toxin gyromitrin to cause seizures, kidney failure, and death. Even morels must be thoroughly cooked to eliminate the low concentration of toxic hydrazine compounds. Some unfortunate people suffer gastrointestinal distress after consuming both alcohol and morels. **Note: cooking does not remove lead, arsenic, or other heavy metals that may be found in the soil.** Morels and some other fungi concentrate these metals in their flesh. Consuming them has resulted in hospitalizations for heavy metal poisoning. Don't eat morels from old apple orchards unless you are certain that pesticides containing these metals were never used there. Also think twice before consuming morels found along heavily traveled roads. Remember leaded gasoline? The lead from that decades-old car exhaust is still in the soil.

Gyromitra brunnea Underw.
GABLED FALSE MOREL
Description: Cap 4-12 cm broad and 4-9 cm high, composed of 2-4 distorted plates that are often roughly saddle-shaped and fused where they touch. Upper surfaces yellow- to red-brown, moist when fresh. Undersurfaces pale and granular in texture. Stalk 2.5-10 cm long and 4-9 cm thick, pale, ribbed and filled with wads of stalk material. Flesh brittle. No distinctive smell or taste.

Occurrence: On the ground around hardwoods. Spring.

Edibility: Not recommended; has caused headaches and gastric distress.

Microscopic Features:
Spores 25-30 × 13-15 μm, ellipsoid, finely reticulate, multiple short projections on the ends of mature spores, 1-3 oil drops. Hyaline.

Comments: Also known as *Discina brunnea, D. fastigiata,* and *Gyromitra fastigiata.* The cap of *Gyromitra caroliniana* (search online) is intricately pitted and ridged, seldom showing the pale underside of a plate. The cap of *Gyromitra esculenta* is brainlike and has a smaller stalk and smaller spores.

Gyromitra esculenta (Pers.) Fr.
FALSE MOREL
Description: Cap 3-5 cm broad and 4-10 cm high, deeply wrinkled and convoluted. Upper surface reddish- to orange-brown, moist when fresh. Undersurface and stalk pale pink to yellow-tan. Stalk 2-7 cm long and 2-3 cm thick, usually with a few ribs near the base, internally chambered and, in youth, stuffed with cottony material. Flesh brittle. Lacks distinctive odor or taste.

Occurrence: Solitary or in groups under conifers or in mixed woods. Spring.

Edibility: Can be deadly poisonous.

Microscopic Features:
Spores 16-28 × 7-13 μm, ellipsoid, smooth, 2 oil drops. Hyaline.

Comments: Also called the Beefsteak Morel, Red Morel, and Lorchel. Although something with this name is edible in Europe and a few Americans are able to eat our version after elaborate preparation, just don't. Similar species include *Gyromitra brunnea, G. infula,* and *G. caroliniana* (search online).

Gyromitra infula (Schaeff.) Quél.
SADDLE-SHAPED FALSE MOREL
Description: Cap 2.5-10 cm wide and 2-20 cm high, usually warped into a saddle shape (rarely with 3 raised portions), edges rolled under. Upper surface typically wrinkled or convoluted, dark brown to reddish- or yellowish-brown. Moist when fresh. Lower surface and stalk whitish to pinkish-buff. Stalk 2-6 cm long and 2-2.5 cm thick, not ribbed, finely granular, hollow or internally chambered. Flesh brittle. Odor not distinctive.

Occurrence: On well-rotted wood or humus. Summer-fall.

Edibility: Poisonous.

Microscopic Features:
Spores 18-23 × 7-10 μm, elliptic, smooth, with 2 large oil drops. Hyaline.

Comments: This species fruits in the summer or fall, not spring, and often grows directly from rotting wood. Several fairy saddles, including *Helvella albella* (search online), *H. atra* (search online), and *H. latispora* (search online) are strongly saddle-shaped but smaller. *Helvella crispa* is pale overall, with a ribbed and chambered stalk.

Helvella crispa (Scop.) Fr.
FLUTED WHITE HELVELLA
Description: Cap 2-6 cm wide and 1-4 cm high, saddle-shaped to irregularly lobed, edges rolled under when young but flaring with maturity. Entire mushroom creamy white to pale buff. Upper surface smooth or slightly wrinkled, dry. Undersurface finely hairy. Stalk 2.5-9 cm long and 1-3 cm thick, heavily ribbed and pitted, internally chambered. Flesh brittle. Odor not distinctive.

Occurrence: On the ground in the woods. Summer-early winter.

Edibility: Not recommended.

Microscopic Features:
Spores 16-22 × 10-14 μm, broadly elliptic, smooth, containing 1 large oil drop and sometimes smaller ancillary ones. Hyaline.

Comments: Europeans eat their version of the Fluted White Helvella, but edibility of the North American variety is not established. The cap of a related species, *Helvella sulcata* (see photo on p. 31), is pale to dark gray.

Helvella macropus (Pers.) P. Karst.
LONG-STALKED GRAY CUP
Description: Cap 1.5-4 cm wide and 4-12 mm high, deeply cup-shaped in youth, saucer-shaped at maturity. The initially inrolled margins relax with age. Inner surface grayish-brown to dark brown, smooth or finely wrinkled. Lower surface gray to grayish-brown, densely fuzzy or hairy, especially near the margin. Stalk 4-6 cm long and 1.5-4 mm thick, enlarging downward, fuzzy, solid, gray to gray-brown, whitening at the base. Flesh thin. Odor not distinctive.
Occurrence: Solitary or grouped on the ground, in moss or on decaying wood in forested areas. Summer-fall.
Edibility: Not edible.
Microscopic Features:
Spores 18-25 × 10.3-12.2 μm, elliptic to almost spindle-shaped at maturity, smooth to slightly roughened. One central oil drop, flanked by 2 smaller ones. Hyaline.
Comments: This easily overlooked "species" is probably an umbrella name for multiple species yet to be reliably differentiated.

Morchella americana Clowez & Matherly
YELLOW MOREL
Description: Fruitbody 4-22 cm tall (occasionally much larger). Head 2-11 cm high and 1.5-4 cm wide, usually oval or cylindrical, a busy network of randomly arranged ridges and pits. Color of mature specimens yellowish-brown. Young mushrooms may be yellowish or pale gray with dark pits. Tops of ridges not blackened. Head and stalk connect at the base of the head; both are hollow. Stalk has a granular surface and widens with age, often ribbed. Flesh brittle. Odor not distinctive.
Occurrence: Scattered, in groups or clusters under ash or elm or in apple orchards, also with other hardwoods, near streams, or with conifers. Spring.
Edibility: Choice, but must be cooked.
Microscopic Features:
Spores 17-24 × 11-15 μm elliptic, smooth. Hyaline.
Comments: *Morchella esculentoides* is a synonym. Previously known as *Morchella esculenta* and, when old and huge, *M. crassipes*. The smaller *Morchella diminutiva* usually has a conical head with fewer, more vertically oriented, ridges and pits.

Morchella angusticeps Peck
**COMMON EASTERN
BLACK MOREL**
Description: Fruitbody to 18 cm tall. Head
2.5-9 cm high and 2-6 cm wide, grayish-
brown to blackish-brown, bluntly
conical in youth but sharpening with
age, covered by a network of vertically
oriented pits and ridges with darkened
tops. Head attached to stalk at the base
of the head; in youth this connection
is sunken. Head and stalk hollow. Stalk
tan, granular in texture, widening with
age. Flesh brittle. Odor not distinctive.
Occurrence: Scattered or in groups,
primarily found in the mountains with
hardwoods such as tulip poplar, cherry,
and ash, sometimes with pine. Spring.
Edibility: Choice, but must be cooked.
Microscopic Features:
Spores 22-28 × 11-15 µm, elliptic,
smooth. Hyaline.
Comments: In *Morchella punctipes* the
stalk attaches about midway up
inside the head. Black morels found
in landscape mulch may be *Morchella
elata* or *M. importuna* (search online),
both edible species.

Morchella diminutiva M. Kuo, Dewsbury,
Moncalvo & S. L. Stephenson
WHITE MOREL, POPLAR MOREL
Description: Fruitbody 3-10 cm tall. Head
1.5-5 cm high and 1-3 cm wide, often
conical, covered by a coarse net of
vertically oriented ridges and pits. Color
gray to yellowish in youth, yellow-
brown at maturity. Neither pits nor
ridges are darkened. Head and stalk
hollow, joined at the base of the head,
without a sunken rim. Stalk smooth or
granular, widening and lengthening
with age. Flesh brittle. Odor not
distinctive.
Occurrence: Solitary, scattered, or in
groups with tulip poplar, ash, hickory,
and apple; also found with other
hardwoods or in grass at the edge of the
woods. Absent from the coast. Spring.
Edibility: Choice, but must be cooked.
Microscopic Features:
Spores 18-26 × 10-18 µm, elliptic,
smooth. Hyaline.
Comments: Also known as the Tulip Morel.
Previously classified as *Morchella
deliciosa*. The head of *Morchella
angusticeps* is much darker than the
stalk and has blackened ridges.

Morchella punctipes Peck
EASTERN HALF-FREE MOREL
Description: Fruitbody to 18 cm tall. Head 1.5-4.5 cm wide, 1-4 cm high, conical, covered with a loose arrangement of vertically oriented ridges and pits. Head color brown, ridgetops darkening with age. Head and stalk hollow. Stalk begins short but grows absurdly long, attached well up inside the head, but not at the very top. Stalk pale tan, granular in texture, often vertically ribbed. Flesh fragile. Odor not distinctive.

Occurrence: Scattered or in groups under hardwoods, mainly in the mountains. Spring.

Edibility: Edible.

Microscopic Features: Spores 22-30 × 10-18 μm, elliptic, smooth. Hyaline.

Comments: Formerly known as *Morchella semilibera*, this morel is ho-hum in the kitchen. *Morchella angusticeps* has a darker color scheme and a connection between head and stalk at the base of the head. *Verpa bohemica* (search online) and *V. conica* (see photo on p. 31), found north and west of the Carolinas, are not entirely hollow; cap and stalk join at the apex of the cap underside.

EARTH TONGUES AND EARTH CLUBS

This is a mixed bag of ground-, wood-, or water-dwelling fungi shaped like vertical clubs, twigs, or stalks with odd-looking heads. Many species resemble spoons, spatulas, or oversized insect antennae. The heads may be textured or minutely hairy but are not sandpapery to the touch, a trait found in stalked members of the *Cordyceps* and carbon fungi groups. If you don't find your mushroom here, search those sections as well as the corals.

Most earth tongues and clubs are of unknown edibility. The fairy clubs, *Clavariadelphus* species, are edible, if not particularly tasty.

Clavariadelphus americanus
(Corner) Methven
FAIRY CLUB
Description: Fruitbody 3-15 cm high and
1-3 cm wide in the upper portion, cylindric when young, becoming broadly
club-shaped, usually unbranched,
tapered downward to a whitish stalklike
base that is sometimes curved. Surface
dry, smooth to longitudinally wrinkled,
orange-buff to orange- or reddish-
brown, slowly bruising brownish. Flesh
thick, firm or spongy, whitish, slowly
bruising brownish when cut. Odor not
distinctive. Taste bitter to unpleasant or
not distinctive.
Spore Print: White.
Occurrence: Scattered or in groups with
oaks and pines. Summer-fall.
Edibility: Edible.
Microscopic Features:
Spores 8-12 × 4-6 μm, broadly ovoid,
smooth. Hyaline.
Comments: *Americanus* means
"American." *Clavariadelphus pistillaris*
(search online) is nearly identical but
grows exclusively with beech trees.

Clavariadelphus truncatus Donk
FLAT-TOPPED CORAL
Description: Fruitbody 5-15 cm high and
2.5-7 cm thick, club- to top-shaped with
a flattened and sometimes depressed
apex, tapered downward, usually
unbranched but sometimes forked,
narrowing to a white, stalklike base
densely covered with white mycelium.
Surface dry, longitudinally wrinkled,
smooth near the base, golden- to
orange-yellow or pale brownish-orange.
Flesh thick, firm or spongy, white.
Odor not distinctive. Taste sweet or not
distinctive.
Spore Print: Pale brownish-yellow.
Occurrence: Scattered or in groups with
conifers. Summer-fall.
Edibility: Edible.
Microscopic Features:
Spores 9-12 × 5-8 μm, broadly elliptic,
smooth. Hyaline with yellow oil drops.
Comments: *Truncatus* means "appearing
cut off." *Clavariadelphus unicolor*
(search online) is similar, but its
fruitbody is pinkish to reddish-brown,
and it grows with oaks or pines.

Cudonia lutea (Peck) Sacc.
YELLOW CUDONIA
Description: Cap 1-1.5 cm wide, broadly convex to somewhat flattened, irregularly rounded, margin strongly inrolled, dry, smooth to distinctly furrowed or brainlike, pale yellow to pale brownish-orange. Stalk 1.5-4.5 cm long, 3-6 mm thick, smooth or finely granular, pale yellow. Flesh fleshy-fibrous, soft but not gelatinous, pale yellow. Odor and taste not distinctive.
Occurrence: In groups or clusters on leaf litter under hardwoods, especially beech. Summer-fall.
Edibility: Unknown.
Microscopic Features:
Spores 40-75 × 1.8-2.5 μm, needlelike, multiseptate, smooth. Hyaline.
Comments: *Lutea* means "yellow." *Cudonia circinans* (search online) is nearly identical but has a creamy yellow to pale brown cap and a pale brown stalk, and it grows on the ground or on decaying wood with conifers. The spores are smaller: 30-45 × 1.8-2.2 μm. *Leotia lubrica* is also similar, but it has a moist, gelatinous fruitbody.

Leotia lubrica (Scop.) Pers.
**OCHRE JELLY CLUB,
JELLY BABIES**
Description: Fruitbody consisting of a gelatinous head and stalk. Head 6-30 mm wide, irregularly rounded and flattened, smooth to distinctly furrowed or brainlike, margin strongly inrolled. Surface moist, smooth, slippery, pale dull yellow to orange-yellow, sometimes with a greenish tint. Stalk 2-5 cm long, 6-10 mm thick, enlarged downward, moist, smooth, slippery, pale dull yellow to orange-yellow. Flesh soft, gelatinous, yellowish. Odor and taste not distinctive.
Occurrence: In groups or clusters on the ground or well-decayed logs in the woods. Year-round.
Edibility: Unknown.
Microscopic Features:
Spores 18-25 × 4-6 μm, cylindric-oblong to fusiform, often curved, multiseptate at maturity, smooth. Hyaline.
Comments: *Lubrica* means "smooth or slippery." Specimens with a pea-green head *and* stalk are thought to be attacked by the parasitic fungus *Coryne atrovirens* (search online). *Leotia viscosa* is similar but has a dark green head and pale yellow to orange-yellow stalk.

Leotia viscosa Fr.

GREEN-HEADED JELLY CLUB

Description: Fruitbody consisting of a gelatinous head and stalk. Head 6-20 mm wide, irregularly rounded and flattened, smooth to distinctly furrowed or brainlike, margin distinctly inrolled. Surface moist, smooth, slippery, dark green to blackish-green. Stalk 2-4 cm long, 6-10 mm thick, equal or enlarged downward, smooth, slippery, pale yellow to orange-yellow. Flesh soft, gelatinous, greenish. Odor and taste not distinctive.

Occurrence: Scattered, grouped, or clustered in woodland soil, sand dunes, or other sandy areas. Year-round.

Edibility: Unknown.

Microscopic Features:
Spores 18-20 × 5-6 μm, narrowly elliptic to fusiform with rounded ends, straight or curved, multiseptate at maturity, smooth. Hyaline.

Comments: Also known as Green-capped Jelly Babies. Specimens with a pea-green head and stalk are thought to be attacked by a parasitic fungus called *Coryne atrovirens* (search online). *Leotia lubrica* is very similar but has a yellow to orange-yellow head.

Microglossum rufum (Schwein.) Underw.

ORANGE EARTH TONGUE

Description: Fruitbody consisting of a head and stalk. Head 3-16 mm wide and 1-3.5 cm high, tongue- to spoon-shaped or cylindric. Surface smooth, dull or shiny, often longitudinally furrowed or compressed, yellow-orange to orange. Stalk 1.5-4.5 cm long, 1.5-5 mm thick, equal or tapered downward, often longitudinally furrowed, granular or finely scaly, yellow to orange-yellow. Flesh firm, yellowish. Odor and taste not distinctive.

Occurrence: Scattered, in groups or clusters on the ground, among mosses, or on decaying wood. Summer-fall.

Edibility: Unknown.

Microscopic Features:
Spores 18-38 × 4-6 μm, allantoid to fusiform, aseptate when young, 5-10 septate in age, smooth. Hyaline.

Comments: The head of *Spathularia flavida* is some shade of yellow over a whitish stalk. *Spathulariopsis velutipes* has a reddish-brown stalk and dense, orange, basal mycelium. *Clavulinopsis fusiformis* and *C. aurantiocinnabarina* have a consistently clustered growth habit and lack a distinct head.

Mitrula elegans Berk.

SWAMP BEACON

Description: Fruitbody 2-5 cm high, consisting of a head and stalk. Head 6-20 mm high, 3-12 mm wide, spindle- to pear-shaped, elliptic or irregularly rounded. Surface shiny, smooth to slightly wrinkled, translucent yellow to orange, becoming dull orange in age. Stalk 2-4 cm long, 1.5-3 mm thick, slightly enlarged downward, shiny, smooth, whitish to pale translucent gray, sometimes with a pinkish tint. Flesh somewhat gelatinous, yellowish. Odor and taste not distinctive.

Occurrence: Scattered or in groups in wet areas on decaying leaves and twigs in woodlands and bogs. Spring-summer.

Edibility: Unknown.

Microscopic Features: Spores 11-18 × 1.5-3 µm, narrowly elliptic or slightly clavate, smooth. Hyaline.

Comments: *Mitrula lunulatospora* (search online) is very similar and occurs in the same habitats but has a pale pink head. *Vibrissea truncorum* (search online) has a yellow head 1.5-6 mm wide and a tiny grayish stalk; it grows on partially or completely submerged branches in streams during spring-early summer.

Spathularia flavida Pers.

Description: Fruitbody up to 6 cm high, consisting of a fan-shaped head and a distinct stalk. Head 1-3.5 cm high and 1-4 cm wide, flattened, fan-shaped, wavy to lobed or irregularly folded. Surface dry, smooth, pale yellow to brownish-yellow or yellow-orange. Stalk 1-2.5 cm long, 2-10 mm thick, tapered downward, dry, smooth, whitish. Flesh thin, yellowish. Odor and taste not distinctive.

Occurrence: Scattered or in groups on the ground and among mosses in conifer woods. Summer-fall.

Edibility: Unknown.

Microscopic Features: Spores 38-52 × 2-2.5 µm, fusiform, multiseptate, smooth. Hyaline. Paraphyses slender, forked, with curved to spiral tips.

Comments: *Flavida* means "yellow-orange." *Spathulariopsis velutipes* is similar but has a reddish-brown stalk and a base densely covered with orange mycelium. The head of *Microglossum rufum* is not so flat, and the stalk is colored like the head.

Spathulariopsis velutipes
(Cooke & Farl.) Maas Geest.
VELVETY FAIRY FAN
Description: Fruitbody up to 7 cm high,
consisting of a head and stalk. Head
1-4 cm high and 1-3 cm wide, flattened.
Surface wrinkled to folded, fan- to
spoon-shaped, yellowish to brownish-
yellow. Stalk 2-4 cm long, 6-15 mm
thick, equal or tapered downward,
solid, velvety, reddish-brown, the base
densely covered with orange mycelium.
Flesh thin, yellowish. Odor and taste
not distinctive.
Occurrence: In groups or clusters on
decaying hardwood, sometimes on
mossy soil. Summer-fall.
Edibility: Unknown.
Microscopic Features:
Spores 30-45 × 1.5-2 μm, needlelike,
multiseptate. Hyaline.
Comments: *Velutipes* means "velvety
stalk." *Spathularia velutipes* is a synonym. *Spathularia flavida* is similar but
has a pale yellow to brownish-yellow or
yellow-orange head and a whitish stalk.
The head of *Microglossum rufum* is less
flattened, and the stalk is colored like
the head.

Trichoglossum farlowii (Cooke) E. J. Durand
Description: Fruitbody up to 8 cm high,
consisting of a head and stalk. Head 1.2-
3 cm high and 3-10 mm wide, hollow,
elliptic to oval or spindle-shaped, often
flattened with a longitudinal furrow.
Surface dry, minutely velvety to spiny
(use a hand lens), blackish-brown to
black. Stalk 2-6 cm long, 2-5 mm thick,
nearly equal, slightly compressed,
often curved, densely velvety, blackish-
brown to black. Flesh thin, tough, dark
brown. Odor and taste not distinctive.
Occurrence: Solitary, in groups or clusters
on the ground, among mosses, or on
well-decayed wood. Summer-fall.
Edibility: Unknown.
Microscopic Features:
Spores 45-85 × 6-7 μm, needlelike to
cylindric, 0-6-septate, mostly 3-septate,
smooth. Grayish or brownish. Setae
more than 150 μm long, pointed, brown.
Comments: *Geoglossum difforme* (search
online) is nearly identical but has a
bald, shiny surface and spores with
12-15 septa. Several *Trichoglossum* and
Geoglossum species are similar and
require microscopic examination of
spores for positive identification.

CARBON AND CUSHION FUNGI

These species assume a variety of shapes: clubs, crusts, hard lumpy things, even an exotic, tentacle-crowned fruitbody reminiscent of the aquatic *Hydra* you may remember from high school biology class. Fertile surfaces lack gills, pores, or teeth. They are sandpapery rough due to the presence of **perithecia**, minute flask-shaped structures containing spore-producing cells called **asci**, a reproductive feature this group shares with *Cordyceps* and *Hypomyces*. Unlike them, carbon and cushion fungi are often blackish, of a hard consistency, and grow on or adjacent to decaying wood. If you don't find your mushroom here, try *Cordyceps*, earth tongues and earth clubs, clustered corals, crust fungi, and the puffballs.

Carbon and cushion fungi are not used for food.

Annulohypoxylon cohaerens
(Pers.) Y. M. Ju, J. D. Rogers & H. M. Hsieh

Description: Fruitbody 1.5-8 mm wide, cushion-shaped to rounded. Exterior dry, hard, roughened with nipplelike bumps that are not surrounded by a depression, blackish. Interior with a single layer of embedded perithecia surrounding a solid center, dark brown to blackish.

Occurrence: Scattered, in groups or crowded clusters on decaying branches, logs, and stumps of beech trees. Summer-fall.

Edibility: Inedible.

Microscopic Features:
Spores 9-12 × 4-5 µm, elliptic-inequilateral, ends narrowly rounded, smooth, brown.

Comments: *Hypoxylon cohaerens* is a synonym. *Annulohypoxylon annulatum* (search online) is very similar, but the nipplelike bumps are surrounded by small depressions, and it grows on oaks. The fruitbodies of *Annulohypoxylon multiforme* var. *multiforme* (search online) are red-brown at first, become blackish-brown in age, and grow on birch branches and logs.

Apiosporina morbosa (Schwein.) Arx
BLACK KNOT

Description: Fruitbody 3-15 cm long, 1-3 cm thick, club- to spindle-shaped or irregularly elongated. Exterior hard, roughened with nipplelike bumps, often furrowed and cracked, dark olive, becoming black. Interior brittle, white at first, black when mature, with perithecia embedded in a single layer near the surface.

Occurrence: Solitary or in groups, clasping and enveloping twigs and branches of cherry and plum trees. Year-round.

Edibility: Inedible.

Microscopic Features:
Spores 13-19 × 4-7.5 µm, narrowly elliptic to clavate, 1-3 septate, smooth. Pale yellowish-brown.

Comments: *Dibotryon morbosum* is a synonym. *Morbosa* means "diseased." It is a highly destructive pathogen of cherry and plum trees.

Camarops petersii
(Berk. & M. A. Curtis) Nannf.
DOG'S NOSE FUNGUS
Description: Fruitbody 2-6 cm wide,
stalkless, cushion-shaped, oval or
irregular. Outer surface yellowish- to
grayish-brown, splitting open to leave
a ragged collar around a shiny, black,
sandpaper-like inner surface that is
covered with black slime when actively
exuding spores. Flesh thick, firm,
reddish- to blackish-brown, containing
five or six layers of perithecia that
are not visible as colored zones.
Odor unpleasant, like creosote. Taste
unpleasant.
Occurrence: Solitary, scattered, or in
groups on decaying hardwood. Late
spring-fall.
Edibility: Inedible.
Microscopic Features:
Spores 6-8 × 3.5-4 μm, elliptical,
smooth. Bluish-black.
Comments: Commonly called the Split-
skin Carbon Cushion. *Peridoxylon
petersii* is a synonym. *Daldinia
concentrica* is similar, but the outer
surface does not split open to expose
a shiny black inner surface; the flesh
is concentrically zoned when cut
vertically.

Daldinia concentrica
(Bolton) Ces. & De Not.
CARBON BALLS
Description: Fruitbody 2-5 cm wide,
cushion-shaped to nearly round.
Surface slightly uneven and furrowed,
finely roughened, dull or shiny, often
showing minute pores (use hand lens),
reddish-brown to black. Flesh fibrous or
powdery and carbonlike, concentrically
zoned with dark purplish-brown,
blackish, and whiter layers. A single
layer of perithecia is embedded under
the surface, opening on it as pores.
Occurrence: Solitary or in clusters on
decaying beech logs, stumps, and trees.
Year-round.
Edibility: Inedible.
Microscopic Features:
Spores 12-17 × 6-9 μm, irregularly
elliptic with one side flattened and
a barely visible germination cleft
containing a single oil drop, smooth.
Dark brown.
Comments: Also called the Coal Fungus,
Cramp Balls, and King Alfred's Cakes.
The concentric zones are distinctive.
Daldinia childiae (search online) is
similar but grows on oaks and other
hardwoods. The spores have a straight,
full-length germ slit and lack oil drops.
Daldinia asphalatum (search online) has
a slender stalk.

Diatrype stigma (Hoffm.) Fr.

Description: Fruitbody up to 20 cm or more long, 1-2 mm thick, a spreading crust that is highly variable in shape and size. Exterior shiny or dull, finely roughened or nearly smooth, sometimes minutely cracked, brownish-purple to reddish-brown when young, becoming blackish-brown to black when mature. Interior whitish to brownish, fibrous or brittle, with perithecia embedded just below the surface in a single layer.

Occurrence: On decaying hardwood branches and logs. Year-round.

Edibility: Inedible.

Microscopic Features:

Spores 6-12 × 1.5-2 µm, allantoid, smooth, with 1 or 2 oil drops at each end. Hyaline.

Comments: Similar brownish-black to black spreading crust fungi tend to have more coarsely roughened surfaces and produce dark brown, rather than white, spores. Microscopic examination is usually required for positive identification. *Rhytisma americanum* (see photo on p. 33) forms raised black spots on red, silver, or sugar maple leaves and is commonly called Tar Spot of Maple. *Rhytisma acerinum* (search online) grows on Norway maple leaves.

Entonaema liquescens Möller

Description: Fruitbody 1-13 cm wide, 1-6 cm high, stalkless, cushion-shaped to rounded, typically convoluted and brainlike. Exterior powdery, bright sulfur-, olive-, or dull yellow, occasionally with orange tones, sometimes bruising greenish, easily rubbed off. The darker inner layer is roughened like sandpaper by the porelike openings of embedded perithecia; it is 1-5 mm thick, gelatinous when wet, thinner and hard when dry, surrounding a cavity filled with watery liquid that drains if the fruitbody is punctured, leaving it collapsed.

Occurrence: Scattered or in clusters on decaying wood. Summer-early winter.

Edibility: Unknown.

Microscopic Features:

Spores 8-13 × 4-7.5 µm, elliptic-inequilateral to rectangular with blunt ends, with or without a straight germ slit that runs less than the full length of the spore, typically with 2 oil drops. Pale to dark brown.

Comments: *Liquescens* refers to the watery fluid. Puffballs and earthballs are solid when young and become filled with spore mass or powder when mature.

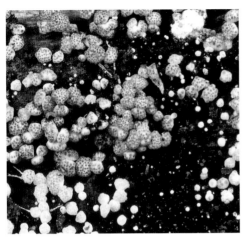

Hypocrea gelatinosa complex (Tode) Fr.
YELLOW CUSHION HYPOCREA
Description: Fruitbody 1-3 mm wide,
  cushion-shaped to nearly round.
  Exterior smooth and pale yellow when
  young, becoming slightly roughened
  and developing green dots, finally
  turning green to dark green at maturity.
  Interior soft, gelatinous, translucent,
  with embedded perithecia that appear
  as green dots.
Occurrence: In dense clusters on decaying
  wood. Summer-fall.
Edibility: Inedible.
Microscopic Features:
  Spores 4-6 × 3-4 μm, globose to elliptic,
  finely warted. Green.
Comments: Also known as the Green
  Cushion Hypocrea. *Creopus gelatinosus*
  is a synonym. This is a massive complex
  of more than forty species identifiable
  by molecular analysis.

Kretzschmaria deusta
(Hoffm.) P. M. D. Martin
CARBON CUSHION
Description: Fruitbody up to 40 cm or
  more long, 10 cm wide, and 3-6 mm
  thick when mature, a thick, spreading
  crust forming irregularly shaped
  patches. When immature (asexual
  stage) the fruitbody is soft, lobed,
  powdery, and grayish-white, with a
  white interior. At maturity (sexual
  stage) the fruitbody is black throughout
  with a finely roughened, conspicuously
  furrowed surface resembling burnt
  wood. The perithecia that develop are
  embedded beneath the surface in a
  single layer.
Occurrence: On hardwood stumps and
  roots. Year-round.
Edibility: Inedible.
Microscopic Features:
  Spores 28-36 × 7-10 μm, irregularly
  elliptic with one side flattened, smooth.
  Dark brown.
Comments: *Ustulina deusta* is a synonym.
  Compare with *Diatrype stigma*, which
  has a much more even and often
  somewhat shiny surface along with
  smaller spores.

Xylaria magnoliae J. D. Rogers
**CONE FLICKERS,
MAGNOLIA-CONE XYLARIA**
Description: Fruitbody 2.5-7.5 cm high,
1-2 mm thick, erect, spindle-shaped
or filamentous, sometimes branched,
tough. Exterior at first powdery and
whitish on the upper portion, blackish
below (asexual stage), becoming black
overall and finely roughened like sandpaper (sexual stage). Interior white, with
perithecia embedded in a single layer.
Occurrence: Singly or in quantity, only on
decaying magnolia cones. Spring-fall.
Edibility: Inedible.
Microscopic Features:
Spores 11-17 × 3-6 μm, spindle-shaped
to crescent-shaped, with an obscure
germ slit, smooth. Yellowish.
Comments: *Xylaria magnoliae* is easy
to identify because of its exclusive
association with magnolia fruits. *Xylaria
persicaria* (search online) grows on
buried peach pits. *Xylaria oxyacanthae*
(see photo on p. 33) grows on buried
hickory or pecan nuts and on hawthorn
fruits, and *X. liquidambaris* (search
online) grows on sweetgum balls. The
Candle Snuff Fungus, *Xylaria hypoxylon*
(search online) is spindle-shaped or
branched and antlerlike; it grows on
decaying hardwood.

Xylaria polymorpha (Pers.) Grev.
DEAD MAN'S FINGERS
Description: Fruitbody 2-9 cm high
and 1-3 cm thick, irregularly club- to
spindle-shaped, tough. Exterior at first
white or bluish and powdery on the
upper portion, blackish below (asexual
stage), becoming black, wrinkled, and
finely roughened like sandpaper (sexual
stage). Interior white, with perithecia
embedded in a single layer just beneath
the surface. Stalk rudimentary or
absent.
Occurrence: Solitary, in groups, or densely
clustered on decaying hardwood
stumps or buried wood. Year-round.
Edibility: Inedible.
Microscopic Features:
Spores 22-30 × 5-9 μm, spindle-shaped
or irregularly elliptic with one side
flattened, with a long straight germ slit
that extends about one-half to two-
thirds of the spore length, smooth. Dark
brown.
Comments: The larger *Xylaria poitei*
(search online) has a similar appearance
but smaller spores measuring 14-18 ×
5.5-7.5 μm. *Xylaria longipes* (search
online) usually has a long stalk; the
spores are 13-15 × 5-7 μm.

Xylaria tentaculata Berk. & Broome
FAIRY SPARKLERS

Description: Fruitbody 1.6-3.5 cm high overall, consisting of a stalk and a head crowned with tentacles. Head 3-10 mm long and 3-6 mm thick, cylindrical, scurfy (flaky), grayish, with a mouthlike opening at the apex. This opening is surrounded by 8 or more filamentous tentacles, 1.3-4 cm long and up to 0.75 mm thick, erect or spreading, pale to pinkish-gray, coated with grayish or whitish powder when mature. Stalk 1.6-2.5 cm long, 1.5-3 mm thick, nearly equal, sometimes twisted, granular to scurfy, gray to blackish, sometimes tinged with blue. Flesh thin, extremely fragile, white.

Occurrence: Solitary, scattered, or in groups among mosses or on humus or decaying wood. Summer-fall.

Edibility: Inedible.

Microscopic Features: Spores 19-22 × 7.5-9 µm, elliptic-inequilateral to crescent-shaped, with 2 large oil drops and a long germ slit, smooth. Dark brown.

Comments: *Tentaculata* means "having tentacles." This small but spectacular species is easily overlooked.

CORDYCEPS, TOLYPOCLADIUM, AND SIMILAR FUNGI

With a single exception, the Carolina representatives of this group are parasitic. Some grow on false truffles. Some attack plants. Others invade living insects, controlling their behavior and eventually killing them before sprouting like grisly antennae from the corpse. *Trichoderma alutaceum*, a recycler of wood and organic debris, is the nonparasitic exception. The fertile "head" of a *Cordyceps* has a sandpapery texture, as do fertile surfaces in the Carbon and Cushion fungi and some

Hypomyces. Distinguishing a ground-dwelling *Cordyceps* from an Earth Club may require careful excavation. The base of a parasitic *Cordyceps* will be connected, perhaps by a thin thread, to the remains of its host.

Chinese medicine employs an Asian cousin of our *Cordyceps militaris*. A Norwegian *Cordyceps* was the original source of cyclosporine, an immunosuppressant drug that made human organ transplantation possible.

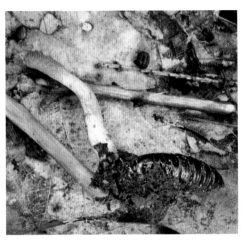

Cordyceps militaris (L.) Fr.
TROOPING CORDYCEPS
Description: Fruitbody up to 8 cm high,
6-10 mm wide, consisting of a head
and stalk. Head cylindric to spindle-
or club-shaped, finely roughened,
reddish-orange. Stalk round, tapering
downward, often curved, smooth,
orange. Flesh thin, pale orange. Odor
and taste not distinctive.

Occurrence: Solitary or in groups on larvae
and pupae of moths and butterflies
shallowly buried in soil or mosses.
Summer-fall.

Edibility: Unknown.

Microscopic Features:
Spores filiform, breaking into barrel-
shaped spores, 2.5-6 × 1-1.5 μm,
smooth. Hyaline.

Comments: The larger *Ophiocordyceps
melolonthae* grows on beetle larvae.
It has a yellowish or whitish, oval or
spindle-shaped head and yellowish
stalk. *Purpureocillium atypicola* = *Nomu-
raea atypicola* (see photo on p. 34)
has a cylindrical to spindle-shaped,
scurfy, grayish-tan to light gray-purple
fruitbody; it grows on buried woodland
spiders. The fruitbody of *Cordyceps
olivascens* (search online), which might
occur in the Carolinas, is cylindric, light
green to olive-buff, and attached to
buried or partially buried insects.

Ophiocordyceps melolonthae
(Tul. & C. Tul.) G. H. Sung, J. M. Sung,
Hywel-Jones & Spatafora
BEETLE CORDYCEPS
Description: Fruitbody consisting of a
head and stalk attached to its host.
Head 2-3 cm high, 1-1.5 cm wide, oval,
sometimes forking, finely roughened,
yellow or whitish. Stalk 5-7 cm long,
3-10 mm thick, nearly equal, spindle- or
club-shaped, smooth, yellowish. Flesh
thin, whitish to pale yellow. Odor and
taste not distinctive.

Occurrence: Solitary or several attached to
beetle larvae that are shallowly buried
in soil or decaying wood. Summer-fall.

Edibility: Unknown.

Microscopic Features:
Spores filiform, breaking into elliptical
spores, 4-8 × 1-1.5 μm, smooth. Hyaline.

Comments: *Cordyceps melolonthae* is
a synonym. The smaller *Cordyceps
militaris* grows on larvae and pupae of
moths and butterflies. It has a finely
roughened reddish-orange head and an
orange stalk.

Tolypocladium capitatum (Holmsk.) Quandt, Kepler & Spatafora
ROUND-HEADED CORDYCEPS
Description: Fruitbody consisting of a head and stalk. Head 6-20 mm tall and wide, irregularly rounded, finely roughened like sandpaper, dark reddish-brown to olive-black. Stalk 2-8 cm long, 5-16 mm thick, nearly equal, smooth to slightly ridged, fibrous, yellow to dingy yellow, becoming olive-brown in age. Flesh white, thick, firm. Odor and taste not distinctive.

Occurrence: Solitary or in groups in mixed woods on buried, walnut-shaped, reddish-brown fruitbodies of *Elaphomyces* species. Summer-fall.

Edibility: Unknown.

Microscopic Features:
Spores 16-28 × 1.5-3 μm, cylindric to filiform, smooth. Hyaline.

Comments: *Cordyceps capitata* and *Elaphocordyceps capitata* are synonyms. *Tolypocladium ophioglossoides* has a spindle-shaped to oval or club-shaped head and is connected to the *Elaphomyces* host by golden, ropelike strands. *Tolypocladium inflatum* (search online) has a whitish, very rough head and a whitish stalk; it grows on beetle larvae buried in wood.

Tolypocladium ophioglossoides (J. F. Gmel.) Quandt, Kepler & Spatafora
ADDER'S TONGUE, GOLDEN-THREAD CORDYCEPS
Description: Fruitbody consisting of a head and stalk. Head 2-2.5 cm high, 1-1.6 cm wide, spindle-shaped to oval or club-shaped, finely roughened like sandpaper, yellowish- to dark reddish-brown, becoming olive-black at maturity. Stalk 2.5-14 cm high, 1.5-10 mm thick, equal or nearly so, smooth, yellow to olive-black, with long ropelike strands of golden hyphae connecting it to the host. Flesh thick, firm, whitish. Odor and taste not distinctive.

Occurrence: Solitary or in groups in mixed woods on buried, walnut-shaped, reddish-brown fruitbodies of *Elaphomyces* species. Summer-fall.

Edibility: Unknown.

Microscopic Features: Spores 2-5 × 1.5-2 μm, cylindric, smooth. Hyaline.

Comments: *Cordyceps ophioglossoides* and *Elaphocordyceps ophioglossoides* are synonyms. *Tolypocladium capitatum* is similar but has an irregularly rounded head. *Trichoderma alutaceum* = *Podostroma alutaceum* (search online) is cylindric to club-shaped without a clearly delineated head. It is whitish to yellowish or pale yellow-orange before maturing to orange-brown; it grows on decaying wood.

These parasitic molds don't bother to produce their own mushrooms. They steal somebody else's, infecting, distorting, and converting them to their own use. Victims include gilled mushrooms, polypores, boletes, and earth clubs. In some cases what the mold lacks in structural ambition is made up for by a try-everything approach to reproduction. *Hypomyces chrysospermus*, for example, is a three-stage mold producing a different type of spore at each stage. The first and second, called **conidia** and **aleuriospores**, respectively, are asexual, containing the complete genetic information of the parent. Conidia are thin-walled and colorless (**hyaline**); aleuriospores have a color. The third type, **ascospores**, are sexually produced in flask-shaped structures called **perithecia** and contain half the parental genome. As you might anticipate, exact identification of some *Hypomyces* requires microscopy or other technical methods.

Lobster mushrooms—*Russula* or *Lactarius* species parasitized by *Hypomyces lactifluorum*—are prized edibles. The edibility of other "hypomycized" mushrooms is unknown or not recommended. Deadly poisonous *Amanitas* are among the mushrooms susceptible to infection by certain *Hypomyces*.

Hypomyces chrysospermus Tul. & C. Tul.
BOLETE MOLD,
GOLDEN HYPOMYCES

Description: This mold partially or completely coats its host and occurs in three developmental stages. The first stage is fuzzy and white and produces conidia. The second is powdery and yellow to golden-yellow and produces aleuriospores. The third is reddish-brown, is pimply in texture, and generates ascospores.

Occurrence: On boletes, gilled mushrooms, and *Rhizopogon*. Summer-fall.

Edibility: Inedible.

Microscopic Features: Conidia 10-30 × 5-12 µm, elliptic, 1-celled, smooth; hyaline. Aleuriospores 10-25 µm, globose, thick-walled, warted; yellow to brownish. Ascospores 15-30 × 4-6 µm, 2-celled, fusiform. Hyaline.

Comments: *Hypomyces microspermus* (search online) is nearly identical but has globose 8-15 µm aleuriospores, and ascospores measuring 8-15 × 2.3-4 µm. *Hypomyces chlorinigenus* (search online) is also similar but has ovoid to cylindrical conidia, 10-11 × 4-5 µm; cylindric, longitudinally ridged aleuriospores, 35-45 × 15-18 µm; and elliptic-fusiform, 2-celled ascospores, 7.5-12 × 2.5-5 µm. *Hypomyces completus* (see photo on p. 35), stays white longer and attacks *Suillus spraguei*.

Hypomyces hyalinus
(Schwein.) Tul. & C. Tul.
AMANITA MOLD

Description: A parasitic mold that partially or completely covers its host, causing it to develop abnormally and become club-shaped to rather phallic. Surface roughened like sandpaper, chalk white to yellowish or pale orange. Host up to 25 cm high, 2-7 cm wide; cap, gills, and other structures may be poorly defined or undiscernible.

Occurrence: On various species of *Amanita*, especially *A. rubescens*. Late spring-fall.

Edibility: Reportedly edible if parasitizing an edible species, such as *Amanita rubescens*, but certainly not recommended. *Amanita bisporigera* and other deadly species may also be host organisms.

Microscopic Features:
Ascospores 15-20 × 4.5-6.5 µm, spindle-shaped, 2-celled, coarsely warted. Hyaline.

Comments: The identity of the host mushroom may be hard to determine, although reddish-staining specimens are probably *Amanita rubescens*. Uniformly dull pinkish to pale pinkish-red or pale pinkish-purple specimens are most likely also parasitized by *Mycogone rosea*.

Hypomyces lactifluorum
(Schwein.) Tul. & C. Tul.
LOBSTER MUSHROOM, LOBSTER FUNGUS

Description: A hard-surfaced mold covering the cap, stalk, and gills of its deformed host. Parasitic fungus roughened like sandpaper, orange to reddish-orange or dull red, sometimes with whitish areas. Host organism up to 20 cm wide, usually partially buried in conifer debris or mosses, very dense, firm, brittle, and white-fleshed. Odor fishy to rotten in age. Taste not distinctive when raw.

Occurrence: Solitary, scattered, or in groups on species of *Russula* and *Lactarius* growing under conifers. Summer-fall.

Edibility: Good when cleaned and well-cooked.

Microscopic Features:
Ascospores 35-40 × 4.5-7 μm, spindle-shaped, coarsely warted, 2-celled. Hyaline.

Comments: A popular edible, although unparasitized mushrooms of the host species may not be; also, the host mushroom may not even be identifiable. This *Hypomyces* seems to remediate the culinary deficiencies or toxicities of its host. Stinky old Lobsters are prized as a source of dyes.

Hypomyces luteovirens (Fr.) Tul. & C. Tul.
RUSSULA MOLD

Description: A thin, hard parasite covering the deformed gills and sometimes the stalk of its host. The parasitic surface is roughened like sandpaper, yellowish-green to dark green. Host organism up to 15 cm wide, cap variously colored, flesh white.

Occurrence: Solitary, scattered, or in groups on various *Russula* species growing under conifers or hardwoods. Summer-fall.

Edibility: Unknown.

Microscopic Features:
Ascospores 28-35 × 4.5-5.5 μm, spindle-shaped, 1-celled, often coarsely warted but sometimes nearly smooth. Hyaline.

Comments: This fungus often goes unnoticed because it may grow only on the underside of its host, leaving the cap color and shape intact.

Mycogone rosea Link

Description: A very thin, somewhat uneven and roughened parasite covering the deformed gills, cap, and stalk of its host mushroom, sometimes in addition to, or a superinfection on, *Hypomyces hyalinus*. Dull pinkish to pale pinkish-red or pale pinkish-purple; host organism often a species of *Amanita*, especially *A. rubescens*, but numerous other host species may become infected.

Occurrence: Solitary, scattered, or in groups on host organisms throughout eastern North America, in grassy areas, conifer or hardwoods. Summer-fall.

Edibility: Unknown.

Microscopic Features: Asexual spores produced from the ends of vegetative hyphae, 2-celled; basal cell 7-23 × 6-20 µm, globose to subglobose, hyaline, smooth; apical cell larger, 15-35 × 13-23 µm, globose to subglobose, thick-walled, reddish pigmented, warty.

Comments: *Rosea* means "reddish." Much about this parasite remains unclear, including its relationship to *Hypomyces hyalinus* when attacking *Amanita rubescens*. *Mycogone rosea* may be the asexual stage of *Hypomyces hyalinus*.

This section presents a grab-bag of plant parasites from fungal groups not previously covered. Most species described here are agriculturally or horticulturally significant. If the plant disease you're trying to identify affects the twigs or branches of a cherry or plum tree, check *Apiosporina morbosa*. If what you see is an irregular, burnt-looking growth on birch or, rarely, on beech, elm, or ironwood, try *Inonotus obliquus*.

Members of this biologically diverse group produce a variety of different spore types. **Basidiospores** are sexually generated in the same manner as spores of gilled mushrooms or boletes. **Ascospores** are also sexually produced but in an ascus, the sort of elongated spore factory used by morels, cup fungi, and others. Complicated life cycles, which might include more than one host species along the way, can result in different types of spore at different stages. Some are asexual, duplicating the genetic material of the parent. **Conidia**, **urediospores**, and **teliospores** are among these asexual possibilities. The particular names derive, among other things, from the stage in the life cycle when the spore is produced and the evolutionary branch of kingdom Fungi where the species resides.

Corn smut, *Ustilago maydis*, makes for nasty-looking ears of corn and decreases crop yields but is also a culinary delicacy. Ergot, *Claviceps purpurea*, a parasite of agricultural rye and other grasses, can be deadly poisonous.

Claviceps purpurea (Fr.) Tul.
ERGOT
Description: Sclerotium 1.5-3.5 cm long, cylindric with tapered, rounded ends, typically curved, with shallow, longitudinal grooves. Exterior wrinkled and finely roughened like sandpaper, hard, purplish-black to brownish-black. Flesh firm, white.

Occurrence: Solitary, in groups, or in clusters on the inflorescences of many species of grasses, especially rye, wheat, and barley. Summer—overwintering until spring.

Edibility: Poisonous, causing ergotism or St. Anthony's Fire, which may be fatal.

Microscopic Features:
Ascospores 65-95 × 0.5-1 μm, hairlike, smooth. Hyaline. Asci elongated-cylindric, thick-walled, tips bluing in Melzer's reagent, 8-spored.

Comments: Ergotism produces a distinctive collection of psychological and physical symptoms. Intentional ergot ingestion may have played a role in ancient religious ceremonies. Ergotism has also been implicated in unintended episodes of mass psychosis, perhaps including the Salem witch trials of 1692-93. Modern medicine finds more prosaic uses for ergot alkaloids.

Exobasidium rhododendri
(Fuckel) C. E. Cramer
AZALEA APPLES
Description: An irregular gall-like swelling on leaves, 1-4.5 cm wide. Exterior smooth, shiny, yellow-green at first, becoming pinkish, and finally whitish and powdery in age. Flesh firm, juicy. Odor not distinctive. Taste tart to somewhat astringent.

Occurrence: Solitary or in groups on *Rhododendron* species, especially wild azalea, along streams, bogs, and moist woodlands. Spring-summer.

Edibility: Unknown.

Microscopic Features:
Basidiospores 12-16 × 2-4 μm, allantoid to nearly cylindric, with a single septum at maturity. Hyaline, inamyloid. Aseptate hyaline conidia, 5-9 × 1.5-2 μm, may also be present.

Comments: Some individuals believe the fruitlike galls are edible, but we cannot recommend eating them because of the documented toxicity of the host plant.

Exobasidium symploci Ellis & G. Martin
BUD GALL, HORSE SUGAR GALL
Description: An irregular gall-like swelling on leaf buds and flowers, 1.5-4 cm wide, rounded to highly irregular, often lobed, sometimes shaped like expanded, thickened leaf buds, stalkless. Exterior smooth or wrinkled and uneven, shiny or dull, moist, bright green to yellowish-green, sometimes with a whitish bloom, becoming dry, conspicuously distorted and yellowish-brown to grayish-brown. Flesh chambered, firm, juicy, greenish at first, becoming dull brown and powdery at maturity. Odor sweet, like apples. Taste sweet, sour apple.
Occurrence: Solitary, in groups or clusters, parasitic on developing leaf buds and flowers of Common Sweetleaf, *Symplocos tinctoriae*. Spring–early summer.
Edibility: Reportedly edible.
Microscopic Features:
 Spores 15-22 × 1.5-3 μm, cylindrical, smooth. Hyaline.
Comments: It is uncommon in the mountains, rare in the Piedmont, and more common in the Coastal Plain.

Exobasidium vaccinii (Fuckel) Woronin
BLUEBERRY GALL
Description: Moldlike, powdery, white to pale gray, greenish or reddish, surrounding and shrouding the developing leaves, shoots, and flowers of host plants, stimulating the infected parts to form swollen galls in which spores are produced.
Occurrence: Parasitic on members of the heath family, including blueberry, bilberry, and huckleberry. Spring-fall.
Edibility: Unknown.
Microscopic Features:
 Spores 11-18 × 2.5-5 μm, nearly cylindrical to allantoid, with 1-6 septa at maturity. Hyaline, inamyloid. Aseptate hyaline conidia, 5-9 × 1-2 μm, may also be present.
Comments: A serious pathogen of blueberries and a major concern of the blueberry industry in the Carolinas. Infected leaves develop light green to whitish spots. Infected fruit has firm, green areas that do not mature with the rest of the berry, making them unmarketable. Symptoms may be so severe and recurrent that blueberry fields are abandoned.

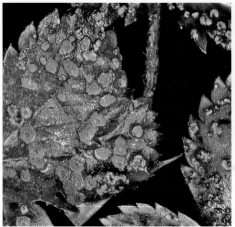

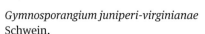

Gymnosporangium juniperi-virginianae Schwein.
CEDAR-APPLE RUST
Description: A gall, 2.5-5 cm wide when mature, at first a small, greenish-brown swelling on the upper surface of a cedar needle, rapidly enlarging to form an overwintering stage that turns reddish-brown to dark brown with small, circular depressions on the surface. In spring the depressions give rise to conspicuous orange, jellylike horns, 1-2 cm long, that become orange-brown at maturity.

Occurrence: Solitary or in groups on cedar needles. Spring–summer.

Edibility: Unknown.

Microscopic Features:
Teliospores 42-65 × 15-21 µm, 2-celled, rhombic-oval to elliptic, thick-walled, on long stalks. Brown.

Comments: The life cycle of this parasite is divided between two hosts, cedar and apple, causing considerable damage to both plants. The jellylike horns are columns of teliospores (terminal-stage spores) that infect apple leaves.

Pucciniastrum potentillae Körn.
CINQUEFOIL RUST
Description: At first tiny, rounded, reddish-brown outgrowths less than 1.5 mm wide, partially embedded in plant tissue, expanding and rupturing at maturity, forming irregular, slightly raised, bright orange, powdery pustules up to 6 mm wide.

Occurrence: In dense clusters, partially embedded in the leaves and stems of cinquefoil (*Potentilla*) species. Spring-fall.

Edibility: Inedible.

Microscopic Features:
Urediospores 14-20 × 12-15 µm, oval to globose, finely echinulate. Hyaline.

Comments: The bright orange pustules and host specificity make this fungus easy to identify. It causes considerable damage to the host plant, interfering with photosynthesis. The urediospores (summer spores) of rust fungi are asexually produced and not hardy. They germinate or die quickly.

Ustilago maydis (DC.) Corda
CORN SMUT
Description: An irregularly shaped tumorlike gall, 2-7.5 cm long, 1-6 cm wide, that swells and replaces normal corn kernels. Exterior smooth, shiny, fragile, whitish when very young, becoming silvery-gray with black tints, and finally blackish overall. Flesh firm and moist at first, whitish, becoming black and juicy, then dry, powdery and dark olive-brown, eventually rupturing and releasing the spores.

Occurrence: Solitary or in clusters on ears of corn. Summer-fall.

Edibility: Edible when the exterior is silvery-gray and the interior is black and juicy.

Microscopic Features:
Spores 9-11 × 6.5-7.5 µm, globose or subglobose, conspicuously echinulate. Pale olive-brown.

Comments: The rise of hybrid varieties of corn has reduced the frequency of Corn Smut in the United States, where it has been considered undesirable. In Mexico immature galls are a commercially grown delicacy, sold as *huitlacoche* or *cuitlacoche* and elsewhere under names including Maize Mushroom and Mexican Truffle.

First, the bad news. The Carolinas are not blessed with the crown jewels of culinary dreams. Although other truffles and related species are thought to be common, the underground lifestyle means that they are infrequently collected. Truffles typically use distinctive odors to attract spore-dispersing insect or animal predators, since spores can't be released into the air. When found near the soil surface, these fungi could be confused with puffballs, earthballs, or immature earthstars. Those species usually have a discernible stem or single point of attachment to the parent mycelium, a feature lacking in truffles and related fungi. The rounded "eggs" of Amanitas and stinkhorns might also be mistaken for truffles. Cutting them in two, from top to bottom, will clarify the situation. The interior of truffle species may be mottled, hollow, or relatively uniform in color and consistency, but it will not display the outline of an immature stinkhorn or capped mushroom.

Although truffle look-alikes may be dangerously poisonous, the truffle species themselves are thought to be free of toxicity. A few found in the Carolinas are rated as good edibles. Others are of unknown edibility or are described with terms such as "insipid" by those who've tried them.

Elaphomyces granulatus Fr. complex
FALSE TRUFFLES

Description: Fruitbody up to 2.7 cm in diameter, stalkless, consisting of a spore case and a mycelial base. Spore case rounded to somewhat flattened, often warted but sometimes smooth, with a thick wall, yellow-brown to reddish-brown, dark brown or black, thick and rindlike. Spore mass dark brown to black, homogeneous, not marbled with whitish veins. Odor described as slightly sweet to not distinctive. Taste unpleasant or not distinctive.

Occurrence: Solitary or in groups, underground beneath conifers or hardwoods. Year-round.

Edibility: Edible, inedible, or unknown, depending on the species.

Microscopic Features: Spores 27-46 μm, globose, often ornamented with spines or a reticulum. Brown.

Comments: They are often found by foragers who find *Tolypocladium* species that parasitize them. *Elaphomyces americanum* (see photo on p. 37) has a marbled spore mass. Several additional species of *Elaphomyces* occur in this complex, and microscopic examination is often required to obtain a positive identification. *Imaia gigantea* (search online) is a large, edible, warted, brown species, 3.5-15 cm wide, with a brown spore mass and whitish veins.

Pachyphlodes citrinus
(Berk. & Broome) Doweld
BERRY TRUFFLE

Description: Fruitbody 5-30 mm wide, stalkless, consisting of a spore case and mycelial base. Spore case rounded to somewhat flattened, coated with conspicuous warts, with a moderately thick wall, color variable, yellow, bright to dull orange or brown, blackening when old. Spore mass firm, white to yellowish, becoming pale olive at maturity, with whitish to grayish-olive sterile veins that darken in age. Odor not distinctive when young, becoming unpleasant or like decaying weeds. Taste not described.

Occurrence: Solitary or in groups, underground beneath hardwoods or conifers. Spring-fall.

Edibility: Unknown.

Microscopic Features:
Spores 11-21 μm, globose, initially smooth but developing golf-tee-shaped, peglike spines when mature. Yellowish.

Comments: An uncommon but very distinctive species. *Pachyphloeus citrinus* is a synonym. *Pachyphlodes* species-20 (see photo on p. 37) is similar, but its warted spore case is orange to reddish-orange. The spore mass is white when young and grayish with obscure white veins when mature.

Tuber lyonii Butters
PECAN TRUFFLE

Description: Fruitbody 1-4 cm wide, consisting of a spore case and mycelial base. Spore case rounded to irregularly lobed and furrowed, smooth or roughened in the furrows, with a thin wall, orangish-brown to reddish-brown. Spore mass white at first, becoming brown with white marbling when mature. Odor described as a complex mix of garlic, cheese, and spices. Taste not described.

Occurrence: Solitary or in groups, underground beneath oaks and pecans. Year-round, but most commonly collected in the fall.

Edibility: Edible and choice when mature.

Microscopic Features:
Spores 30-37 × 22-24 µm, elliptic, developing tall spines connected by low lines when mature. Brownish.

Comments: Sometimes spelled *Tuber lyoniae. Tuber texense* is a synonym. It is fairly common in pecan orchards, where it is frequently raked up during the pecan harvest. *Tuber canaliculatum* (see photo on p. 37) has a red-brown to orange-brown spore case and a marbled gray interior with white veins; it grows in soil with eastern white pine.

The Carolinas have figured prominently in the study of North American mushrooms for more than 200 years. Moravian minister and botanical scientist Lewis D. de Schweinitz wrote the opening chapter shortly after returning to the young United States from Europe in 1812. A Pennsylvanian by birth, Schweinitz had spent 14 years abroad improving his education, doing church work, catching the mushroom bug, and coauthoring an illustrated guide to European fungi. He settled in Salem, North Carolina, where he collected and cataloged local mushrooms in his spare time. The list he created had reached 1,373 species, 320 of them new to science, when he sent a copy to an old friend in Germany. It was published without Schweinitz's knowledge in 1822 as *Synopsis Fungorum Carolinæ Superioris*. For this and two subsequent works on American fungi, Schweinitz is considered the father of North American mycology. A new genus and several species were named in his honor. Perhaps best known to mushroomers is the Dyer's Polypore, *Phaeolus schweinitzii*.

The naming of mushrooms after colleagues or luminaries—i.e., the use of eponyms—was already common practice in the nineteenth century. Eponyms don't help depict the species in question, but that's usually the worst that can be said of them. There are, however, exceptions. Two midcentury pillars of Carolinas mycology were involved in what must surely rank among the most backhanded naming compliments in taxonomic history.

Rev. Moses Ashley (M. A.) Curtis, an Episcopal priest and amateur botanist based in Hillsborough, North Carolina, published his first mushroom paper in 1848. In 1851, during an extended church posting to Society Hill, South Carolina, he began a highly productive long-distance collaboration with the English mycologist Rev. Miles Joseph Berkeley. Few author citations appear after the scientific name of a mushroom as often as the abbreviation Berk. & M. A. Curtis. As the Civil War reduced the South to poverty, Curtis and his son advocated the use of mushrooms as food in an illustrated manuscript, but it was never printed. Curtis is remembered by *Pseudomerulius curtisii* and *Pulveroboletus curtisii*.

His friendly rival for the unofficial title of greatest living American mycologist was Henry William Ravenel of South Carolina, a one-time plantation owner and agricultural innovator whose fortunes never recovered from the Civil War. Ravenel made his mycological name between 1853 and 1860 by creating 5-volume sets of dried fungi, collectively known as *Fungi Caroliniani Exsiccati*. Each volume contained 100 specimens hand-glued to the pages. The set he forwarded to the Smithsonian Institution became a foundational contribution to the National Fungus Collection, today housed in Beltsville, Maryland. Decades later, with English botanist M. C. Cooke, Ravenel coauthored the 8-volume *Fungi Americani Exsiccati*. Throughout his career he also worked with Berkeley and Curtis.

Many species of plants and fungi are named after Ravenel, including a genus of parasitic rusts—plant diseases having been another area of interest. Two honorific species described by Berkeley and Curtis were truly special. In 1852 they named a pink and rudely tubular stinkhorn *Corynites ravenelli*. Today it is known as *Mutinus ravenelii*, a look-alike of *Mutinus elegans*, which Berkeley had attempted to name *Corynites curtisii* after Curtis's death. In that same paper Berkeley briefly resurrected his old partner to describe a different species of stinkhorn, one that Ravenel first collected and informally reported in 1846. They dubbed it *Phallus ravenelii*. If stinkhorns are the measure of a mycologist, Ravenel beats Coker by a score of two to one.

Academia was beginning to take a serious interest in the field. Toward the end of Ravenel's life, the University of North Carolina (UNC) elected him to membership in the Elisha Mitchell Scientific Society and awarded him an honorary doctorate. Ravenel probably never met George Francis Atkinson, a Cornell graduate who was at the time an active member of the Mitchell Society and a junior member of the UNC faculty. Atkinson moved on to the University of South Carolina in 1889 and eventually found his way back to Cornell in New York State. There he made a career of bringing order to the vagary and chaos of mushroom descriptions previously authored on both sides of the Atlantic. He did much to standardize acceptable written procedure and introduced photography to the process. Mushrooms named for Atkinson include the colorful *Cortinarius atkinsonianus*.

Henry Curtis Beardslee, a teacher who also served as senior master at the Asheville School for Boys (now Asheville School) from 1901 to 1919, discovered and described many new fungal genera and species. He is best known for "The Russulas of North Carolina" (1918) published in the *Journal of the Elisha Mitchell Scientific Society*. The editor of that journal and Beardslee's frequent collaborator at UNC, William Chambers Coker, became the next giant of mycology in the Carolinas.

Both North and South Carolina can legitimately claim Coker, a native son of Hartsville, South Carolina. Educated at South Carolina College and Johns Hopkins, with a postdoctoral semester in Germany, Coker joined the UNC faculty

in 1902. He rose through the ranks to become chairman of UNC's new Botany Department in 1908 and kept right on impressing people throughout the remainder of his 43-year UNC career. Along the way he established the university's arboretum and produced 137 professional books and papers, including 58 on fungi. Professional mycologists may hold his pioneering work on aquatic fungi in highest regard, but Coker's book-length treatments of *Amanita*, coral fungi, gasteromycetes including puffballs, the boletes, and stalked tooth fungi still circulate today. To top it off, his contemporaries regarded him as a generous and exemplary professor. Beardslee was one beneficiary. John Nathaniel Couch, Coker's student and eventual successor as chairman of the Botany Department, coauthored with Coker *The Gasteromycetes of the Eastern United States and Canada*. Longtime research assistant Alma Holland Beers coauthored the books *The Boletaceae of North Carolina* and *The Stipitate Hydnums of the Eastern United States*. Species honoring Coker include *Amanita cokeri* and *Lactarius subvernalis* var. *cokeri*. The Coker Arboretum at UNC is named for him as well.

The taxonomic understanding of mushrooms so diligently organized and tended by the likes of Atkinson and Coker came under threat in 1969 when ecologist Robert Whittaker of Cornell University, Atkinson's alma mater, had the nerve to suggest that fungi aren't really plants, that they deserved a biological kingdom of their own. Up in heaven, Ravenel, Berkeley, and Curtis took a breather from disputing the line between honor and mockery in the naming of species to greet Whittaker's preposterous notion with a unified howl of disapproval. But Whittaker's ideas caught on, aided by advances in molecular technology. The genetic code could now be read and compared across species. Genetic relatedness rather than morphological similarity would become the gold standard for constructing the Tree of Life on Earth.

Rytas Vilgalys, a graduate student of Orson K. Miller Jr. at Virginia Tech, took up the new DNA-based approaches for classification and later joined the faculty at Duke University in 1986. Now a full professor, Vilgalys and his graduate students have been using genomic data to infer the evolutionary history of all fungi (including mushrooms), leading to a complete reclassification of the fungal kingdom based on molecular phylogenetics. These methods are also being used to study millions of as-yet-unknown fungal species that occur in our surrounding environments. Vilgalys has contributed to more than 200 publications and oversees a strong postgraduate program to carry these projects forward.

What of mycology in the twenty-first century, and the role played by Carolinian mushroom-seekers? For everyday mushroomers the molecular revision of the Tree of Life presents obvious challenges. The sheer magnitude of the task guarantees that the present instability of scientific names will continue for some time. However, the ongoing expansion of mycological knowledge, and the delight and joy folks experience when finding mushrooms (regardless of the names we might assign them), will continue. The enthusiasm and curiosity of amateurs who roam the woods and fields enjoying the wonders of nature and wondering what they have found guarantee that. Increasingly, "nonprofessionals" are contributing to our mycological knowledge base by their involvement in Citizen Science projects. Individuals and members of local and regional mushroom clubs are collaborating in the collection and analysis of mycological data, sharing specimens, voucher collections, and species lists with researchers who may no longer have the ability to be in the field as pioneering field mycologists once were. In a very real way, the role of the amateur mycologist is now more important than ever before. The Carolinas, being among the most biodiverse regions of North America, are waiting to be explored by them.

acidic: having a sour or sharp taste

acrid: having an unpleasantly sharp and burning taste or smell

acute: having a sharp edge

agglutinated: glued together

aleuriospores: stalkless asexual spores borne laterally

allantoid: sausage-shaped

amyloid: staining grayish to blue-black in Melzer's reagent

anamorphic: pertaining to the asexual stage

angular: having one or more angles

angular-ovoid: somewhat egg-shaped with one or more angles

anise: a sweet, licorice-like odor

annulus: a band or ring on the stalk

apex, apical, apices: the uppermost portion

apical pore: a small opening in the uppermost portion of the wall of a spore

apiculate: having a projection at or near the base of a spore

arcing: a segment of a circle shaped like a curve or arch

asci, ascus: saclike structures in which ascospores are produced

ascospore(s): a sexual spore formed within an ascus

aseptate: lacking cross-walls

asexual: produced without the exchange of genetic information

astringent: tending to cause the mouth to pucker

asymmetrical, asymmetrically: not identical on both sides

attached (gills): joined to the stalk

azonate: lacking zones or bands

bald: lacking fibers, hairs, scales, etc.

basal, base: the lowest portion

basidia: typically club-shaped cells on which basidiospores are formed

basidiospores: sexual spores formed on a club-shaped cell called a basidium

beaded: having a row of exuded droplets

beveled: slanted or sloped

bog: a poorly drained, spongy, wet area composed primarily of sphagnum mosses and peat, usually surrounding a body of water

brick red: rusty red to dull rusty red

buff: dull white to very pale yellow

bulb, bulbed, bulbous: a somewhat rounded swelling

burgundy: deep red to reddish-purple

button: the immature stage of a mushroom

cadmium yellow: various shades of bright golden-yellow

cap: the upper part of a mushroom that supports gills, tubes, spines, or a smooth surface on its underside

carmine: dark red or purplish-red

Carolina bays: elliptical depressions concentrated along the Atlantic seaboard

cartilaginous: tough and fibrous, often splitting lengthwise in strands

cavitating: collapsing and forming cavities

central: at the middle

chambered: divided into distinct compartments

chamois: grayish-yellow

channeled: grooved, troughlike, or hollowed out

cinnabar: vivid reddish-orange

clavate: club-shaped

cogwheel, cogwheeling: a toothed wheel

color flash: an instantaneous and fleeting color reaction that sometimes occurs when chemicals are applied to various mushroom tissues

columella: a persistent sterile column within a spore case

compressed: flattened longitudinally

concave: shaped like a bowl

concentric, concentrically: having rings or zones within one another in a series

confluent: merging and becoming continuous together

conidia: asexual spores supported by tiny stalks

conifer: a cone-bearing tree with needlelike leaves, such as hemlock or pine

conjoined: linked together, usually at the tips

convex: curved or rounded like an inverted bowl

copious: having a large quantity

corrugated: coarsely wrinkled or ridged

cortina: a spiderweb-like partial veil

cortinaceous: consisting of spiderweb-like fibrils

crested: having a showy tuft of projecting teeth

crimped: having small, regular folds

crimson: deep purplish-red

crossveined, crossveins: having tiny wrinkles or raised ridges that connect adjoining gills

cuticle: the outermost tissue layer of the cap or stalk

cylindric, cylindrical: having the same diameter throughout the length

cylindric-ellipsoid: nearly having the same diameter throughout the length and resembling an elongated oval with similarly curved ends

cylindric-oblong: nearly having the same diameter throughout the length and longer than wide and with somewhat flattened ends

cylindric-subclavate: somewhat cylinder-like to somewhat club-shaped

cystidia, cystidial: sterile cells that project between, and usually beyond, the basidia, or on the cap or stalk surface

deciduous: having leaves that fall off every year

decurrent: running down the stalk

deliquescing: dissolving into an inky fluid

dextrinoid: staining orange to orange-brown or dark red to reddish-brown in Melzer's reagent

dimpled: with shallow depressions like the cover of a golf ball

disc: the central area of the surface of a cap

duff: decaying plant matter on the ground in woodlands

duplex: consisting of two distinct layers of different textures

eccentric: away from the center but not lateral

echinulate: having small spines

edges (gills): the sharp, free, lower portion most distant from the cap

ellipsoid, elliptic, elliptical: resembling an elongated oval with similarly curved ends

ellipsoid-cylindric: elongated and somewhat cylindric

ellipsoid-fusoid: elongated and somewhat spindle-shaped

elliptic-fusiform: more or less elliptical and somewhat spindle-shaped

elliptic-inequilateral: more or less elliptical with unequal sides

elliptic-ovoid: mostly egg-shaped but somewhat elliptic

elongated-cylindric: having the same diameter throughout the length but tapered at each end

elongate-fusoid: elongated and somewhat spindle-shaped

elongate-ovoid: elongated and somewhat egg-shaped

empirically: based on personal observation or experience, not scientific method

entire: even, not broken, serrated, or torn

ephemeral: lasting for a very short time

ergot alkaloids: fungal toxins produced by *Claviceps* species that cause irrational behavior, hallucinations, convulsions, and even death

ergotism: a neurological condition that develops after ingesting ergot alkaloids

eroded: partially worn away and appearing ragged

escarpment: a long cliff or steep slope that separates two flat or slightly sloped areas

exuded: very slowly released

faces: the sides of a gill

farinaceous: an odor variously compared to sliced watermelon rind, cucumber, meal, bread dough, or farina (think Cream of Wheat)

felty: having a texture that resembles a soft, nonwoven matted fabric

fenugreek: a Eurasian plant with a distinctive sweet odor resembling maple syrup

FeSO$_4$: iron sulfate, also called iron salt, usually a 10 percent solution

fetid: having an offensive odor

fibril(s): tiny fiber(s)

fibrillose: composed of fibrils

fibrous: composed of fibers

filamentous: composed of tiny threads

filiform: threadlike

flatwoods: low-lying, dry timberland typically containing pine trees

flesh: the inner tissue of a fruitbody

fodder: feed for livestock, especially chopped hay or straw

fork, forked, forking: divided into two or more branches

free (gills): not attached to the stalk

fringe, fringed: decorated with tiny fibrils or hairs

frondlike: resembling a leaf, often with many divisions

fruitbody: the reproductive stage of a fungus, sometimes called a mushroom

furrowed: marked by grooves

fusiform: spindle-shaped

fusiform-ellipsoid, fusiform-elliptic: mostly spindle-shaped and somewhat elongated

fusoid: somewhat spindle-shaped

fusoid-clavate: club-shaped and somewhat spindle-shaped

gelatinous: having the consistency of jelly

germ slit: a fissure or crack in the spore wall that facilitates germination

gills: thin or thick, knifeblade-like structures on the undersurface of the cap of some mushrooms

glabrous: lacking hairs or scales, bald and smooth

glance, glancing: shine like highlights in polished wood when held at a certain angle

gleba: the spore-bearing tissue of stinkhorns and puffballs, also called a spore mass

globose: round, resembling a globe

gregarious: closely scattered over a small area

hardwood: any non-cone-bearing tree with broad leaves, such as beech or oak

heath balds: highly acidic or well-drained areas typically found along narrow ridges and mountain crests dominated by evergreen shrubs

hemispheric: shaped like one-half of a sphere

hexagonal: having six angles and six sides

host: an organism that supports a parasite or pathogen; also a mycorrhizal partner

hyaline: clear and nearly colorless

hydrazines: toxic liquid or gaseous chemicals, used in making rocket fuel, that may damage the nervous system, liver, or kidneys

hygrophanous: fading markedly as the cap dries

hygroscopic: readily absorbing water

hyphae: threadlike filaments composed of fungal cells

hypomycized: attacked by species of *Hypomyces*

immunostimulant: an agent that activates an immune response

inamyloid: unchanging or staining pale yellow in Melzer's reagent

incrusted: covered with a thin, hard crust

incurved: bent inward toward the stalk

inflorescences: the flowering portion of a stem

inrolled: bent inward and upward toward the stalk

KOH: potassium hydroxide, usually a 3-5 percent concentration in water

labyrinthine: resembling a maze

lacerated: appearing as if torn

lacrimoid: shaped like a teardrop

larvae: the immature, wingless, feeding stage of an insect

lateral, laterally: on the side or edge

latex: a watery or milklike fluid that exudes from some mushrooms when cut or bruised

latticelike: crossed and arranged to form a diagonal pattern

lavender: a pale tint of purple

lilac: pale bluish-purple

lobe, lobed: a subdivision with a rounded margin

longitudinal, longitudinally: oriented along the vertical axis of the stalk

luminescent: something that glows and emits light

maitake: Japanese name for *Grifola frondosa*

marbled: having flecks or streaks of a different color

margin: the edge of a mushroom cap

marginate: having gill edges that are darker than the faces

maritime forests: ocean coastal wooded habitats

maroon: dark reddish-purple

marzipan: a confection consisting primarily of honey or sugar and almond paste, with a distinctive odor of almond extract

maze: a complex network of interconnected pathways

Melzer's reagent: a solution containing iodine, potassium iodide, chloral hydrate, and water, used to test spores and tissues for color reactions

membranous: having a membrane

mosaic: a pattern produced by arranging small pieces

mottling: spots or blotches of different shades or colors

multiseptate: having several or many cross-walls

musky: having a strong odor of musk

musty: having an unpleasant odor suggestive of mold

mycelia, mycelial, mycelium: a mass of hyphae, typically hidden in a substrate

mycophagist: a person who eats fungi

mycorrhizal: having a mutually beneficial relationship with a tree or other plant

nitrous: a reference to nitrogen-containing compounds, which are pungent and unpleasant

nondecurrent: not running down the stalk

oblanceolate: having a much greater width than length and tapering

obliquely: in a slanting direction

oblong: longer than wide and with somewhat flattened ends

oblong-elliptic: longer than wide and somewhat elliptic

obovate, obovoid: egg-shaped, with the broader end opposite to the point of attachment

obtuse: rounded or blunt

ornamented: having the surface decorated with warts, spines, reticulation, or other markings

oval: egg-shaped

ovoid: somewhat egg-shaped

paraphyses: distinctive sterile cells that keep asci erect

parasite: an organism that obtains nutrients from a living host

parasitic, parasitized, parasitizing: obtaining nutrients from a living host

partial veil: a layer of tissue that covers the gills or pores of some immature mushrooms

pathogen: a disease-producing organism

pedicel: a slender stalk

perennial: continuing growth from year to year.

peridiole(s): tiny egglike structure(s) that contains spores

peridium: one or more layers that form the wall of a spore case

perithecia: minute flask-shaped structures containing asci and ascospores

phallic: shaped like an erect penis

pinkening: becoming pink

pocosins: upland shrubby bogs of the coastal plain

pore: the open end of a tube, also called the tube mouth

pseudo-gills: false gills that are thick and blunt

psychonautic: pertaining to the exploration of the mind using intentionally induced altered states of consciousness

punctate: marked with tiny points, spots, dots, or scales

pungent: having a strong, sharp smell

punky: lacking a firm texture

pupae: the nonfeeding stage of an insect before becoming an adult

radial, radially, radiate, radiating: pointed away from a common central point, like the spokes of a wheel

rays: pointed pieces of a split spore case

resin, resinous: composed of a sticky lacquer that may solidify to form a shiny crust

resinous dots or smears: small marks or patches of a sticky resin

reticulate, reticulated, reticulation, reticulum: raised, netlike ridges found on the stalk surface or spores of some mushrooms

rhizomorph: a thick, cordlike strand of hyphae growing together as a unit

rhombic-oval: having four equal sides without right angles and somewhat oval

ring: remnants of a partial veil that remains attached to the stalk after the veil ruptures, or the uppermost flaring portion of a sheath

ring zone: faint remnants of a partial veil, usually composed of tiny fibers, attached to the stalk

rosette: arranged in the shape of rose petals

rudimentary: having a very small stature

saffron: golden-yellow

saprotroph: an organism that lives off dead or decaying matter

scabers: small, stiff, granular projections on the stalk of some boletes

scales: flattened, erect, or recurved projections or torn portions of a cap or stalk surface

scalloped: having a wavy outer edge

scarlet: a bright red to slightly orange-tinted red

sclerotium: a small, rounded to irregular structure composed of dormant hyphae

scurfy: roughened by tiny flakes or scales

septa, septate: cross-walls, divided by cross-walls

serrated: jagged or toothed like a saw blade

setae: sharply pointed, microscopic, sterile cells that are usually brown or yellow

sexual: produced with the exchange of genetic information

sheath: an outer, socklike tissue layer covering the stalk base upward, at least to the midportion

sinuous: somewhat wavy

sphagnum moss: a type of moss occurring mostly in wet, acidic habitats, especially bogs

spermatic: having the odor of semen

spinulose: having little spines

spore case: a saclike structure that contains the spore mass

spore mass: a dense layer of spores produced by puffballs or stinkhorns, also called a gleba

spore print: a deposit of spores on paper, glass, or other surface

spores: microscopic reproductive cells

stalk: the erect structure that supports the cap, head, or spore case of a fruitbody

St. Anthony's Fire: a name commonly used during the Middle Ages for ergotism

sterile margin: having cuticle tissue that extends beyond the gills, tubes, or other reproductive structures on the underside of the cap

stratified: arranged in specific layers

striate: having small and more or less parallel lines or furrows

stuffed: containing a soft tissue that usually disappears in age, leaving a hollow space

subcylindric, subcylindrical: having nearly the same diameter throughout the length

subdecurrent: extending slightly down the stalk

subdistant (gills): halfway between close and distant

subellipsoid: somewhat like an elongated oval

subelliptic, subelliptical: pertaining to a somewhat elongated oval

subfusiform, subfusoid: nearly spindle-shaped

subglobose: nearly round

suboblong: somewhat longer than wide and with more or less flattened ends

substrate: organic matter that serves as a food source for fungal mycelium, such as soil, leaves, or wood

subventricose: somewhat swollen in the middle and tapered in both directions

sulfur yellow: bright yellow

superinfection: invasion and multiplication of a different pathogen in an already infected host

swamp: an area of low-lying land that is always wet and often flooded

synonym: an alternate name that has been replaced by a more current one

tawny: dull yellowish-brown

teliomorphic: pertaining to the sexual stage

teliospores: thick-walled overwintering spores formed at the terminal stage during the life cycle of rusts and smuts

terrestrial: growing on the ground

tiers: a series of rows of different lengths

translucent: allowing light to pass through while causing structures on the other side to not be sharply visible

truncate, truncated: appearing cut off at the end

tube: a narrow, parallel, spore-producing cylinder on the underside of the cap of boletes or polypores

tufts: short, compact clusters arising from a common base

umbilicate: having a central, funnel-shaped depression

umbo: a rounded or pointed elevation at the center of some mushroom caps

undulating: more or less wavy

universal veil: a layer of tissue that completely encloses immature stages of some mushrooms

urediospores: summer spores produced during the life cycle of rust species

ventricose: swollen in the middle and tapered in both directions

verges: areas along a path, road, field, etc.

vinaceous: having the colors of red wines

virulent: highly aggressive

volva: the remains of a universal veil at the stalk base of some gilled mushrooms, or the base of some stinkhorns

warts, warted: small patches of tissue on the top of some mushroom caps, or blunt projections on the wall of some spores

wheylike: watery white

zones, zoned: concentric rings or bands on the cap or stalk of some mushrooms

Arora, D. 1979. *Mushrooms Demystified*. Berkeley, Calif.: Ten Speed Press. 959 pp.

Baird, R., L. E. Wallace, G. Baker, and M. Scruggs. 2013. "Stipitate Hydnoid Fungi of the Temperate Southeastern United States." *Fungal Diversity* 62: 41-114.

Banerjee, P., and W. J. Sundberg. 1995. "The Genus *Pluteus* (Pluteaceae, Agaricales) in the Midwestern United States." *Mycotaxon* 53:189-246.

Baroni, T. J. 2017. *Mushrooms of the Northeastern United States and Eastern Canada*. Portland, Ore.: Timber Press, Inc. 599 pp.

Bessette, A. E., A. R. Bessette, and D. W. Fischer. 1997. *Mushrooms of Northeastern North America*. Syracuse, N.Y.: Syracuse University Press. 584 pp.

Bessette, A. E., A. R. Bessette, W. C. Roody, and S. A. Trudell. 2013. *Tricholomas of North America—A Mushroom Field Guide*. Austin: University of Texas Press. 208 pp.

Bessette, A. E., D. B. Harris, and A. R. Bessette. 2009. *Milk Mushrooms of North America—A Field Identification Guide to the Genus Lactarius*. Syracuse, N.Y.: Syracuse University Press. 299 pp.

Bessette, A. E., O. K. Miller, A. R. Bessette, and H. H. Miller. 1995. *Mushrooms of North America in Color—A Field Guide Companion to Seldom-Illustrated Fungi*. Syracuse, N.Y.: Syracuse University Press. 188 pp.

Bessette, A. E., W. C. Roody, and A. R. Bessette. 2000. *North American Boletes—A Color Guide to the Fleshy Pored Mushrooms*. Syracuse, N.Y.: Syracuse University Press. 400 pp.

Bessette, A. E., W. C. Roody, A. R. Bessette, and D. L. Dunaway. 2007. *Mushrooms of the Southeastern United States*. Syracuse, N.Y.: Syracuse University Press. 375 pp.

Bessette, A. E., W. C. Roody, W. E. Sturgeon, and A. R. Bessette. 2012. *Waxcap Mushrooms of Eastern North America*. Syracuse, N.Y.: Syracuse University Press. 179 pp.

Beug, M. W. 2009. "Worldwide Mushroom Poisoning, Diagnosis and Treatment: Comments on Some of the Recent Research." *Fungi* 2, no. 3: 11-15.

Beug, M. W., A. E. Bessette, and A. R. Bessette. 2014. *Ascomycete Fungi of North America—A Mushroom Reference Guide*. Austin: University of Texas Press. 488 pp.

Binion, D. E., S. L. Stephenson, W. C. Roody, H. H. Burdsall Jr., L. N. Vasilyeva, and O. K. Miller Jr. 2008. *Macrofungi Associated with Oaks of Eastern North America*. Morgantown: West Virginia University Press. 467 pp.

Burdsall, H. H., Jr., and M. T. Banik. 2001. "The Genus *Laetiporus* in North America." *Harvard Papers in Botany* 6:43-55.

Buyck, B., and V. Hofstetter. 2011. "The Contribution of Tef-1 Sequences to Species Delimitation in the *Cantharellus cibarius* Complex in the Southeastern USA." *Fungal Diversity* 49: 35-46.

Buyck, B., V. Hofstetter, and I. Olariaga. 2016. "Setting the Record Straight on North American *Cantharellus*." *Cryptogamie, Mycologie* 37, no. 3: 405-17.

Buyck, B., I. Olariaga, B. Looney, J. Justice, and V. Hofstetter. 2016. "Wisconsin Chanterelles Revisited and First Indications for Very Wide Distributions of *Cantharellus* Species in the United States East of the Rocky Mountains." *Cryptogamie, Mycologie* 37, no. 3: 345-66.

Buyck, B., I. Olariaga, J. Justice, D. Lewis, W. Roody, and V. Hofstetter. 2016. "The Dilemma of Species Recognition in the Field When Sequence Data Are Not in Phase with Phenotypic Variability." *Cryptogamie, Mycologie* 37, no. 3: 367-89.

Coker, W. C., and J. N. Couch. 1974. *The Gasteromycetes of the Eastern United States and Canada*. Reprint. New York: Dover. 283 pp.

Freeman, A. E. H. 1979. "*Agaricus* in the Southeastern United States." *Mycotaxon* 8:50-115.

Gilbertson, R. L., and L. Ryvarden. 1986. *North American Polypores*. Vol. 1, *Fungiflora*. Oslo. 433 pp.

——. 1987. *North American Polypores*. Vol. 2, *Fungiflora*. Oslo. 451 pp.

Griffith, G. E., J. M. Omernik, J. A. Comstock, M. P. Schafale, W. H. McNab, D. R. Lenat, T. F. MacPherson, J. B. Glover, and V. B. Shelburne. 2002. "Ecoregions of North Carolina and South Carolina (color poster with map, descriptive text, summary tables, and photographs)." Reston, Va.: U.S. Geological Survey, ftp://newftp.epa.gov /EPADataCommons/ORD/Ecoregions /nc/ncsc_front.pdf.

Guzmán-Dávalos, L., G. M. Mueller, J. Cifuentes, A. N. Miller, and A. Santerre. 2003. "Traditional Infrageneric Classification of *Gymnopilus* Is Not Supported by Ribosomal DNA Sequence Data." *Mycologia* 95:1204-14.

Haygood, T. A. M. 1983. "Henry William Ravenel, 1814-1887: South Carolina Scientist in the Civil War Era." Ph.D. diss., Rice University, https:// scholarship.rice.edu/handle/1911/15756. Accessed August, 28, 2016.

Jenkins, D. T. 1986. *Amanita of North America*. Eureka, Calif.: Mad River Press. 198 pp.

Kaufman, C. H. 1918 (1971). *The Gilled Mushrooms (Agaricaceae) of Michigan and the Great Lakes Region*. 2 vols. Reprint. New York: Dover. 924 pp.

Kerrigan, R. W. 2016. *Agaricus of North America*. Bronx: New York Botanical Garden. 572 pp.

Kuo, M., and A. S. Methven. 2014. *Mushrooms of the Midwest*. Champaign: University of Illinois Press. 427 pp.

Lincoff, G. H. 1981. *The Audubon Society Field Guide to North American Mushrooms*. New York: Knopf. 926 pp.

Olariaga, I., N. Van Vooren, M. Carbone, and K. Hansen. 2015. "A Monograph of *Otidea* (*Pyronemataceae, Pezizomycetes*)." *Persoonia* 35:166-229.

Omernick, J. M., and G. E. Griffith. 2008. "Ecoregions of North Carolina and South Carolina (EPA)." *The Encyclopedia of Earth*, http://www.eoearth.org/view /article/152148/.

Peck, C. H. 1882. "An Imperfectly-Described Phalloid." *Bulletin of the Torrey Botanical Club* 9:123-24.

Petersen, R. H., and K. Hughes. 2014. "Cauliflower Tales." *McIlvainea* 23:13-15, http://www.namyco.org/publications /mcilvainea/v23/cauliflower_tales.html.

Phillips, R. 1991. *Mushrooms of North America*. Boston: Little, Brown. 319 pp.

Redhead, S. A., R. Vilgalys, J.-M. Moncalvo, J. Johnson, and J. S. Hopple Jr. 2001. "*Coprinus* Pers. and the Disposition of *Coprinus* Species *sensu lato*." *Taxon* 50: 203-41.

Roody, W. C. 2003. *Mushrooms of West Virginia and the Central Appalachians*. Lexington: University Press of Kentucky. 520 pp.

WEBSITES

https://www2.clarku.edu/faculty/dhibbett /Reprints%20PDFs/Justo&Castro _Pluteus_nothopellitus.pdf

Index Fungorum: www.indexfungorum .org

MushroomExpert.com: www.mushroom expert.com

Mushroom Observer: www.mushroom observer.org

Studies in the Amanitaceae: http://www .amanitaceae.org

PHOTO AND FIGURE CREDITS

Except for those listed below, photographs were taken by Alan E. Bessette, Arleen R. Bessette, or Michael W. Hopping.

Harley Barnhart: *Claviceps purpurea*

Jason Bolin: *Boletellus ananas*

Fabrizio (Fab) Bordo: *Retiboletus griseus*

Ryan Bouchard: *Retiboletus ornatipes*

Patricia Buchanan drew all of the line drawing illustrations.

E. J. Dwigans: *Entonaema liquescens, Mycena epipterygia* var. *viscosa*

Dan Guravich: *Pulveroboletus curtisii, Tylopilus indecisus*

Rosanne Healy: *Elaphomyces granulatus* complex, *Elaphomyces americanum, Pachyphlodes citrinus, Pachyphlodes* species-20

Josh Hutchins: *Aureoboletus russellii*

Josh Kielsmeier-Cook: *Camarops petersii*

Marty Klein: *Amanita jacksonii*

Renée Lebeuf: *Clavariadelphus truncatus, Cortinarius distans, Cudonia lutea, Gymnopus dryophilus, Humaria haemispherica, Hygrocybe cantharellus, Laccaria amethystina, Leotia viscosa, Marasmius cohaerens, Ophiocordyceps melolonthae, Rhodocollybia maculata, Strobilurus conigenoides, Tolypocladium ophioglossoides, Tricholoma subresplendens, Volvariella bombycina*

David Lewis: *Amanita hesleri*

Owen McConnell: *Boletus durhamensis, Marasmius fulvoferrugineus, Mycena leaiana, Rubroboletus dupainii, Veloporphyrellus conicus, Xylaria polymorpha*

John Plischke III: *Boletus nobilissimus, Gyromitra brunnea, Scorias spongiosa*

Alan Rockefeller: *Aseroe rubra, Psilocybe cubensis*

Bill Roody: *Abortiporus biennis, Amanita onusta, Amanita parcivolvata, Amanita ravenelii, Amanita volvata* complex, *Baeospora myriadophylla, Boletus auripes, Bothia castanella, Butyriboletus frostii, Calvatia gigantea, Cantharellus lateritius, Cantharellus velutinus, Cladomeris umbellata, Clavariadelphus americanus, Clavulinopsis aurantio-cinnabarinus, Clitocella mundula, Clitopilus prunnulus, Coltricia montagnei, Cortinarius armillatus, Cortinarius collinitus, Entoloma incanum, Entoloma serrulatum, Ganoderma tsugae, Gelatoporia dichroa, Harrya chromapes, Hypomyces hyalinus, Lactarius chrysorrheus, Lactifluus allardii, Lactifluus petersenii, Lactifluus volemus, Leccinellum crocipodium, Leccinum insigne, Leccinum scabrum, Lepiota clypeolaria, Lycoperdon americanum* (A), *Lycoperdon americanum* (B), *Lysurus periphragmoides, Marasmius nigrodiscus, Marasmius rotula, Marasmius strictipes, Multifurca furcata, Panaeolina foenisecii, Phallogaster saccatus, Pholiota flammans, Pleurotus dryinus, Psathyrella candolleana, Psathyrella rugocephala, Russula earlei, Russula redolens, Russula variata, Sebacina sparassoidea, Suillellus subvelutipes, Suillus granulatus, Suillus spraguei, Tapinella panuoides, Tylopilus atronicotianus, Tylopilus badiceps, Tylopilus ferrugineus, Tylopilus intermedius, Tylopilus sordidus, Tylopilus violatinctus, Xerocomus hortonii*

Mary Smiley: *Xerocomus sclerotiorum*

Matthew Smith: *Tuber canaliculatum, Tuber lyonii*

Walt Sturgeon: *Amanita farinosa, Coltricia cinnamomea, Coprinellus micaceus, Entoloma abortivum, Entoloma strictius, Gymnopus luxurians, Hygrophoropsis aurantiaca, Inocephalus murrayi, Inocybe rimosa, Lentinus tigrinus, Megacollybia rodmanii, Rhodocollybia butyracea*

Jeremy Ward: Frontispiece photo of Adelaide Ward holding a Giant Puffball

Michael Wood: *Gloeocantharellus purpurascens*

INDEX TO COMMON NAMES

INDEX TO SCIENTIFIC NAMES

Genera and species names that denote currently recognized classification are set in **boldface**. Page numbers of genera and species that are fully described and illustrated are also set in **boldface**. Page numbers of synonyms, cross-references, or partially described species are set in regular.

ALAN E. BESSETTE is a professional mycologist and emeritus professor of biology. He has published numerous papers and more than twenty books. A recipient of the Mycological Foray Service Award and the North American Mycological Association Award for Contributions to Amateur Mycology, Alan teaches seminars and workshops on a national level.

ARLEEN R. BESSETTE, mycologist and botanical photographer, has collected mushrooms for forty years. She has published several papers and sixteen books and has won top honors in the North American Mycological Association's photography competition. Arleen teaches seminars and workshops on mycology and dyeing with mushrooms both regionally and nationally.

MICHAEL W. HOPPING is an amateur mycologist, author, and retired medical doctor. A member of the Asheville Mushroom Club, he chaired its foray committee for several years and currently serves as one of its principal mushroom identifiers and as a community educator.

Photograph of Alan E. Bessette: Arleen R. Bessette
Photograph of Arleen R. Bessette: Alan E. Bessette
Photograph of Michael W. Hopping: Mitch Hopping

Other **Southern Gateways Guides** you might enjoy

Waterfalls and Wildflowers in the Southern Appalachians
Thirty Great Hikes

TIMOTHY P. SPIRA

Includes 125 color photos of wildflowers for plant identification

Exploring Southern Appalachian Forests
An Ecological Guide to 30 Great Hikes in the Carolinas, Georgia, Tennessee, and Virginia

STEPHANIE B. JEFFRIES AND THOMAS R. WENTWORTH

Seeing the forest as well as the trees

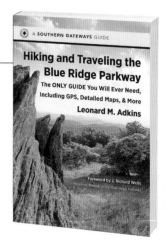

Hiking and Traveling the Blue Ridge Parkway
The Only Guide You Will Ever Need, Including GPS, Detailed Maps, and More

LEONARD M. ADKINS
FOREWORD BY J. RICHARD WELLS

The most up-to-date resource for Blue Ridge Parkway travelers

THE
BOYS
~ IN ~
CHICAGO
HEIGHTS

THE FORGOTTEN CREW
OF THE CHICAGO OUTFIT

MATTHEW J. LUZI

THE
History
PRESS

Published by The History Press
Charleston, SC 29403
www.historypress.net

Copyright © 2012 by Matthew J. Luzi
All rights reserved

Front cover: Collection of John Binder

First published 2012
Second printing 2012
Third printing 2012
Fourth printing 2013

Manufactured in the United States

ISBN 978.1.60949.733.0

Library of Congress Cataloging-in-Publication Data

Luzi, Matthew.
The boys in Chicago Heights : the forgotten crew of the Chicago Outfit / Matthew Luzi.
pages cm
Includes bibliographical references.
ISBN 978-1-60949-733-0
1. Outfit (Organization)--History--20th century. 2. Organized crime--Illinois--Chicago
Heights--History--20th century. 3. Gangsters--Illinois--Chicago Heights--Biography. 4.
Chicago Heights (Ill.)--Biography. 5. Chicago Heights (Ill.)--Social conditions--20th century.
I. Title.
HV6452.I32O875 2012
364.10609773'11--dc23
2012038838

John Luzi, on the right, bartending at the Club Cadillac on the Strip in Calumet City circa 1940.

CONTENTS

ACKNOWLEDGEMENTS

I acknowledge and thank my wife, Christine, for her indulgence, and I acknowledge and thank all of my family members for their support and encouragement.

I am grateful to John Binder, Mark Levell, Jeff Thurston, Art Bilek and Chuck Schauer. I thank John for his generosity in always including me on information related to Chicago Heights and sharing his resources. Thanks to Mark for sharing his information and connecting me with several people that contributed to my understanding of this subject. Just when I thought that most resources were tapped out of information, Jeff Thurston seemed to come up with another obscurity that helped add context and background. Art Bilek's firsthand knowledge of some of the people and places related to this subject was a great contribution. Chuck Schauer has been a great resource regarding the Thompson Submachine, not to mention a great theorist on the St. Valentine's Day Massacre. I am also grateful to Mars Eghigian Jr. for directing me to certain resources and assisting in navigating various bureaucracies.

I am fortunate to have known several people that lived through some of the events described in this work. I am very appreciative that they took time to discuss their experiences with me. It was a pleasure to have known Rio Burke. I am extremely appreciative of the information she provided as Dominic Roberto's former wife. It was also a pleasure to have known Joe Fushi. His firsthand knowledge of certain events and of the technical aspects of alcohol production was invaluable.

I would also like to acknowledge Lou Corsino. I am grateful to Lou for sharing his knowledge and information and especially for connecting me to a great bunch of guys from Chicago Heights.

Thanks to Dr. Jim Ammirati, Jim Ammirati and Mike Roberts for sharing information and photographs. Unless otherwise noted, all images appear courtesy of the author.

For anyone wishing to contact me about the boys in Chicago Heights, I may be reached at luzimjl@gmail.com.

INTRODUCTION

Chicago Heights, Illinois, is a working class suburb situated about thirty-five miles south of the Loop, downtown Chicago. It was once a "satellite city," together with Joliet, Aurora, Elgin and Waukegan. Chicago Heights grew out of farmland at the turn of the twentieth century. The community was originally planned and designed to attract businesses that desired to get away from the congestion and high costs of Chicago. The jobs created attracted emigrants from across Europe.

My own family followed the path to Chicago Heights. My great-grandfather, Ruggiero Luzi, emigrated from San Benedetto del Tronto, Italy. He arrived in Chicago Heights in 1916. My great-grandmother, Theresa Liparota, was from Sambiase, Calabria, Italy. She arrived in Chicago Heights in 1913 with her mother, sister and brother. The two met in Chicago Heights through the arrangement of Theresa's father and were married in 1919. Originally they lived on the East Side of Chicago Heights and later moved to West End Avenue, just across the tracks that separate the East Side from the West Side.

I was curious about our family heritage. I asked questions and listened to stories about what it was like in Chicago Heights during the old days. It seemed that the experiences of my family were similar to those of most other immigrants. However, there were stories that I heard about bootleggers that I thought were unique. There were stories of my great-grandmother cooking for her brother, Frank Liparota (aka LaPorte), Dominic Roberto, Jim Emery and their friends—big shots in the "Syndicate."[1] I also heard that

Frank LaPorte sometimes harbored unsavory out-of-town characters at my great-grandparents' house. Whenever these guests were present, the curtains and shades remained drawn to avoid the risk that someone might learn who was staying there. I heard about Al Capone coming to town and handing money out to children. I was told that Dominic Roberto, Jim Emery and Frank LaPorte were close to Al Capone. I also heard stories about Joliet, Illinois, and Calumet City, Illinois, during the 1940s and '50s.

Notwithstanding the stories, I had difficulty learning more because the history of Chicago Heights on this subject is often overlooked in resources. There are few references to Dominic Roberto and Jim Emery, if they are mentioned at all. Much of the history about Al Capone is recorded as if Al Capone was solely responsible for events that occurred during Prohibition across the Chicago metropolitan area. Likewise, events during Prohibition in Chicago Heights are attributed to Capone taking over bootlegging or establishing the practice. Later accounts of organized crime activities in Chicago Heights and the surrounding suburbs were attributed to Chicago Outfit bosses based in Chicago Heights. While true that by the early 1930s the Chicago Heights street crew was integrated with the Chicago Outfit, many accounts make it seem as though local bosses were transplanted from Chicago.

Federal agencies, mostly the Federal Bureau of Investigation (FBI), did not begin to investigate the Chicago Outfit until after the Apalachin, New York meeting of organized crime bosses in 1957. Prior to 1957, the FBI considered criminal organizations such as the Capone Gang to be local and therefore, outside its jurisdiction. When the FBI began to investigate organized crime, it paid little attention to the origins of the Outfit, except where it was relevant to note that the subject of an investigation was previously a member of the "old Capone Gang." I suspected that Dominic Roberto, Jim Emery and Frank LaPorte played a more important role to Al Capone, and later the Outfit, than many accounts reported. Therefore, I decided to conduct some research of my own.

The information I discovered traces the origins of organized crime in Chicago Heights from before Prohibition and brings that history forward through its last known boss, Dominick "Tootsie" Palermo. The amount of information that I discovered is such that I am not able to record all of the details in this work. I am also unable to delve into the sociological questions about why organized crime flourished in Chicago Heights. Although some of the conditions described with respect to the neighborhoods in Chicago Heights and the conditions that many were forced to work in may provide some insight, a more in-depth analysis of the sociological questions deserve further exploration. However, this work is intended to reflect salient events in the history of the Chicago Heights street crew of the Outfit. Let's start by looking at the early days of Chicago Heights, including what attracted the Italians, where in Italy they came from and some of the events leading up to Prohibition.

CHAPTER 1

CROSSROADS OF THE NATION

Chicago Heights is located about thirty-five miles south of Chicago's Loop and about seven miles west of the Indiana border. The first European settlers arrived in the area during the 1830s. They were predominantly German, French and Irish immigrants making their way westward. It was not long before other white settlers followed during the 1840s and 1850s. At that time, the area was known as Thorn Grove. Proximity to Chicago, rich farmland, access to fresh water and affordable property motivated the early settlers to stay in the area. The first public auctions for land took place in 1838. One acre sold for $1.25, and it stayed at that price until 1850. The Sauk Trail thoroughfare served as a major route for westward travelers. Many traveling from the east were enticed to stay when they realized that land was cheap and opportunity was plenty.[2]

The German immigrants contributed greatly to the growth of Thorn Grove. Their numbers caused the population to surge. By the 1850s, the area became known as Bloom after the organization of Bloom Township. In 1853, the first railroad tracks were laid through the area. The Michigan Central attracted businesses and brought postal service, which contributed to the continued development of the area. During the Civil War, there was a lull in rail development as the country preoccupied itself with the war effort. Railroad building boomed after the Civil War, to the benefit of local citizens. It was not long before the Chicago and Eastern Illinois Railroad (C&EI) to Chicago Heights was completed. By 1869, it was possible to make the trip to downtown Chicago in less than two hours. In 1887, the Elgin, Joliet and

Eastern Railroad was built through Bloom.[3] Needless to say, the railroads accelerated the growth of the area and made it attractive for development.

In 1890, Charles Wacker saw the potential of the area and formed the Chicago Heights Land Association (CHLA). Wacker started out as a brewer for his father's company in Chicago. He worked as a bank director and real estate investor before taking over the business. His more notable accomplishments included working on the 1893 Columbian Exposition Committee and the Chicago Plan Commission. Charles Wacker was the booster that Chicago Heights needed. He understood that Chicago was becoming a crowded, expensive and difficult place to do business.[4] Therefore, he embarked on a search for an area where land was relatively cheap and available with close proximity to Chicago and access to rail service. Bloom met the criteria.

Around 1890, the CHLA arranged for the purchase of four thousand acres on the east side of the C&EI railroad tracks for manufacturing development. By 1892, the CHLA had arranged for the completion of a rail beltway, which gave the area a connection to every railroad entering Chicago. The town also featured a thriving town center and boasted eight factories. The stage was almost set to start a full marketing campaign to attract additional industries. Wacker realized that Bloom was just a short train ride away from the Columbian Exposition site at Jackson Park in Chicago. In fact, the C&EI serviced both the Columbian Exposition site and Bloom. Therefore, he arranged for the CHLA to commission Louis Sullivan to build the Victoria Hotel in 1892.[5] It was a tremendous success. The hotel served not only as a place to stay while enjoying the exposition, but it also provided the CHLA with a captive audience to which it could promote the attributes of Bloom.

To further market the town, the CHLA set out to formally change the name from Bloom to Chicago Heights. In 1892, the residents voted to adopt the change and incorporated the Village of Chicago Heights. Through the 1890s, the CHLA continued to market and promote Chicago Heights with ads referring to it as the greatest manufacturing district in the world with the ability to ship products anywhere at cheap shipping rates. The CHLA also organized weekend rail excursions to Chicago Heights, chartering rail cars and hiring bands to entertain the crowds as sort of a 1890s industrial land grab.[6]

As an astute developer, Charles Wacker recognized the need for an organized plan for the village. Industries needed infrastructure. In addition, there was housing to consider, both for industry executives and for the workers. All of this needed to be supported by a thriving town center with

View of Illinois Street, downtown Chicago Heights, looking east. The Victoria Hotel with its water tower and clock tower can be seen in the distance. This photo was taken in the mid-1940s when the downtown area was thriving.

all the necessary amenities including postal service, clothing and food purveyance and healthcare. The CHLA planned Chicago Heights so that industrial facilities were located to the east of the C&EI railroad tracks. The CHLA modernized and, in some cases, provided water, gas and electric power. Concerning housing, it was planned so that the workers lived east of the C&EI tracks in neighborhoods that became known as the East Side and the Hill. The industry executives and wealthier residents lived west of the C&EI tracks. Separating the East Side from the West Side was the downtown area, with Halsted Street running down the center and Illinois Street running east and west off Halsted Street. Once the CHLA had the plan solidified, it started selling residential lots.

The CHLA's marketing efforts paid off. In 1897, there were thirty-eight railroads and twenty factories in Chicago Heights. Manufacturing companies located there included steel, plumbing, glass works, lumber, dry goods, fireproofing, paper, paint, iron works, railway specialties and roofing tile.

In 1901, the village became the City of Chicago Heights. During the first mayoral term of the newly incorporated city, an aldermanic form of government was adopted with five aldermen serving as members of the first

View of Illinois Street looking west from Halsted Street. The Victoria Hotel is in the right foreground with the Blatz Beer sign. The Lincoln Dixie Theater can be seen in the distance. The entire area has since been demolished, a victim of urban renewal and a shift away from manufacturing.

city council. The first aldermen were representative of the early German settlers and more recent business pioneers, with names like Kirgis, Belknap, VanDoren, Salisbury and Klauch. The stage was now set for an influx of workers to populate the town.[7]

The year 1913 brought more good news for the growth of Chicago Heights. That year it was announced that the nation's first major east–west roadway, Lincoln Highway, would pass through town. The announcement was coupled with the news that Dixie Highway, a major north–south roadway, would also pass through Chicago Heights and intersect Lincoln Highway. The intersection of the two major roadways put Chicago Heights at the crossroads of the nation. Chicago Heights, therefore, had a major advantage for attracting more businesses with its access to the rails and thoroughfares.[8]

The rapid growth of factories and businesses in Chicago Heights during the 1890s attracted immigrants from all over western and central Europe and attracted migrants from the South. But it would be the Italians that comprised the largest ethnic population. The earliest Italians arrived around

1890. They were mostly men searching for work. They were industrial pioneers that heard through word-of-mouth about the CHLA's marketing campaigns regarding job opportunities in Chicago Heights. Once settled with a job and a place to stay, the early Italian immigrants passed word back to relatives and friends interested in leaving for America. By 1900, there were three hundred Italians in Chicago Heights; in 1910, there were a little over three thousand; and by 1920, the Italian immigrants were the largest ethnic population in Chicago Heights.[9]

The East Side and the Hill neighborhoods became the most heavily populated and established Italian neighborhoods in Chicago Heights. The majority of the Italian population came from the central and southern Italian regions of Le Marche, Abruzzi, Lazio, Campania, Calabria and Sicily. The Italians settled in neighborhoods according to their familial and regional backgrounds. Consequently, Sicilian and Marchegiani immigrants largely populated the East Side neighborhood. A good number of the Marchegiani but also the majority of immigrants from Lazio and Calabria lived in the Hill.[10]

The settlement of the immigrants in these neighborhoods worked in favor in the CHLA's plan to have the lower class workers concentrated around the factories and away from the tonier West Side. The East Side and the Hill became densely populated with workers. Some were packed in boardinghouses with numerous others. They worked long, hard hours in oppressive conditions. The factories lacked unions, and safety conditions were nonexistent. It is not surprising that many news stories of the day indicate that the immigrants met with prejudice. The articles themselves referred to Italians in derogatory terms. Such circumstances may have led to socialist activities that were reported and perhaps an increase in crime. Murders were frequently reported by the *Chicago Heights Star* newspaper as being the result of the "Black Hand" or "the Vendetta" whenever an Italian was involved. Certainly, the majority of the Italians were law-abiding citizens. But the newly formed city with its recently arrived immigrants had an element of lawlessness. One citizen recalled that the town felt similar to an old west town where card playing, booze drinking and pool shooting were the only forms of recreation for the residents of the East Side and the Hill. It was recalled that Twenty-second Street had twenty-six saloons and men routinely carried revolvers.[11]

On the other hand, there was power in numbers, and numbers worked in favor of the Italian immigrants with Chicago Heights' aldermanic form of government. Between 1910 and 1912, a majority of the aldermen were Italians. One of the aldermen was Antonino Sanfilippo. He was elected alderman for the third ward in 1915 and reelected in 1917 and 1919. He was also elected to serve as city clerk. In 1962, the FBI was gathering information about the activities of Frank LaPorte. As part of its investigation, the FBI took the following report from a local banker regarding the early immigrants to Chicago Heights and politics:

> *At the turn of the century Chicago Heights was rapidly becoming a highly industrialized and manufacturing city. It was commonly referred to as the biggest little city in the country. As a result of this industrialization, there was an insufficient labor force to operate various manufacturing plants, and efforts were made by the leaders of commerce and industry to import cheap immigrant labor to operate various plants. When one family from a foreign country or a certain province would arrive in Chicago Heights and establish [itself], [they] would send word to [their] village regarding the job opportunities and soon others from that province or village would appear in Chicago Heights.*
>
> *In view of the language barrier and social difficulties encountered in the new country, the immigrants and their families would immediately rely upon and follow anyone who could understand the language and the customs of this country. As the years progressed, it became evident that certain families gained prominence and political power among numerous immigrant families. It appeared that one family from each of the countries represented and controlled a large number of votes and influence.*[12]

As their numbers increased and the Italian population gained a voice in local politics, they gained confidence to open their own businesses and establish social organizations. Indeed, Italians and other immigrants in the community were beginning to assimilate. However, other residents were resentful and suspicious of the immigrants, particularly the Italians, as they were the largest immigrant group. The East Side and the Hill were viewed as places rampant with vice and gambling. There was concern that the Italian aldermen on the city council were breeding corruption. Thus, on February 15, 1921, the citizens voted in favor of switching to an at-large commission form of government where the commissioners ran on a citywide basis.[13] Incentive to vote in favor of the referendum may have been provided to concerned citizens five days before the election when deputy sheriffs raided two hotels in Chicago Heights and arrested 120 people on gambling charges.

Antonino Sanfilippo lost his aldermanic seat to the commission form of government. The concerned citizens may have been justified in removing the "Italian influence," for Sanfilippo was the first crime boss to emerge in Chicago Heights. Sanfilippo used his connections in the community to secure votes. In return, he provided favors to his constituents, such as securing jobs and aiding in the process of becoming a citizen. He also used his community influence and political power to protect gambling and illegal liquor operations.

In January 1919, the Eighteenth Amendment to the Constitution was ratified. After one year of ratification, the manufacture, sale or transportation of alcohol within, importation of alcohol into or exportation of alcohol from the United States was prohibited. The Volstead Act providing the enforcement powers for the Eighteenth Amendment took effect in January 1920.

A majority of residents of Chicago Heights opposed Prohibition. Many of the immigrants were accustomed to traditions that included beer, wine and whiskey. In addition, Prohibition stripped many of their only form of recreation by closing taverns. It is not surprising that many residents would ignore the law and produce alcohol for personal consumption. It is also not surprising that others would view Prohibition as an economic opportunity or that a man like Antonino Sanfilippo would view Prohibition as an opportunity to expand his interests, especially after losing his aldermanic seat.

CHAPTER 2

PROHIBITION, ANTONINO SANFILIPPO AND PHIL PIAZZA

Antonino Sanfilippo was born in Lascari, Sicily, on May 9, 1877. He emigrated from Sicily to the United States in 1904. Sanfilippo was educated as a pharmacist and operated a drug store on East Twenty-second Street in the Hill neighborhood. He married a German woman named Gertrude Sandauer, and they had one son, born in 1907.[14] Sanfilippo's education and refined personality contributed to his success and ability to absolutely control the vote on the East Side.[15] Sanfilippo's political career ended in 1921 when he lost a bid to become a commissioner by a small margin. Around the time his political career ended, Sanfilippo emerged as the dominant boss of organized crime in Chicago Heights. Philip Piazza and Jim Lamberta, fellow Sicilians, served as Sanfilippo's top lieutenants.[16] His influence in the Italian community and political connections helped ease his transition into bootlegging. Sanfilippo used his influence to protect his own interests and those of the independent operators for a price.[17]

The Sanfilippo organization was made up of fellow Sicilians and was tied to the Unione Siciliana. A benevolent organization originally formed in Chicago, the Unione eventually had chapters around the United States. Its members were strictly Sicilian.

Other Sicilian factions at the forefront of bootlegging and gambling in Chicago Heights included the Costello brothers, the Zarante brothers, the Macaluso brothers, the DiGiovanni brothers and the Battaglia brothers.[18] The Battaglia brothers first came to notoriety in 1914 with the murder of Frank DeMaria at Death Corner in Little Sicily on Chicago's near

Pete Zarante and Charlie Costello pose for a staged photo possibly in Hot Springs, Arkansas. Each was the patriarch of their respective clans.

North Side. DeMaria was a private investigator who was looking into the murder of Chicago Heights produce vendor Isaac Levin. Levin was killed because his business threatened the Battaglias' produce business. Pietro Siatta, an employee of the Battaglia brothers, signed an affidavit that, while hanging out in a tavern on Sixteenth Street in Chicago Heights, he overheard two men conspiring to murder DeMaria for investigating the Levin killing.[19]

The Costello brothers and the Zarante brothers were the more dominant of the independent Sicilian groups of brothers. The Costellos formed close ties with Al Capone, and the Zarantes aligned with the Costellos.

There was also an Italian (non-Sicilian) faction that was headed by longtime friends and business partners Dominic Roberto and Jim Emery. Having emigrated from Calabria, the Perry brothers aligned with Roberto and Emery.[20] In the early days of Prohibition, all of these groups had their spheres of influence, but ultimately they paid the price to Sanfilippo for the protection that his significant influence could provide. Regarding these groups, the banker interviewed by the FBI reported that:

> *When the Prohibition Era came into being, the Italians seemed to be more adept at making "bathtub gin" and they soon organized family wine makers into a highly efficient distilling corporation.*
>
> *As the need for more whiskey became apparent, these families and their associates began raiding Polish and Slovakian home stills and through fear and, blackmail and extortion, acquired considerable wealth and in turn were able to bribe local officials into protecting their illegal distilling operations. They had Chicago Heights police officers acting as guards in convoying their whiskey into Chicago, Illinois, where it was sold to Chicago interests.*

The banker further reported:

> *…these families were and are able to control a sufficient number of the immigrant or labor population to sway elections. This was a well-known fact in political circles and as a consequence these families were able to direct the activities of the elected officials in Chicago Heights city government.*[21]

By the mid-1920s, the Chicago Heights bootleggers developed the sophistication of a well-run business. The Costello brothers were instrumental to other bootleggers because they operated as confectioners, which gave them access to sugar distributors. They were able to receive large shipments of sugar and re-distribute it to the various bootleggers for the manufacture of alcohol. The bootleggers used three different fermentation methods for the production of alcohol: a seven-day method, a three-day method and a sixteen-hour method. Each produced alcohol of 160 to 190 proof. The seven-day method was a natural fermentation process that produced between thirty and forty thousand gallons. These operations were very large and required two shifts of men working day and night. Due to their size, these stills were operated on farms or in warehouses. In some instances, stills of this size were placed in the basement of a house with holes cut through the first and second floors to accommodate the still. The three-day method used a chemical process to speed up the fermentation. These stills could be operated in garages. The sixteen-hour method produced the least amount of alcohol and also used a chemical process to speed fermentation. This method could be operated anywhere, and the alcohol produced was commonly referred to as "bathtub gin."[22]

The bootleggers were also adept at avoiding law enforcement. Alcohol production produced heat. During the winter months, law enforcement might try to fly over an area after a fresh snow. If they noticed a building with no snow on its roof there was a possibility that a still was operating inside. As a countermeasure, bootleggers painted the roofs white. Law enforcement also used a "smell test" for detection. Agents went to neighborhoods and walked the blocks to sniff the air because alcohol making produced fumes that were strong enough to smell from the street. In response, an inventive Chicago Heights bootlegger created a still that did not produce fumes. It was so successful that members of the Purple Gang visited from Detroit to see how it worked.[23]

In Chicago during the early 1900s, events were taking place that later impacted Chicago Heights. Jim Colosimo was rising through the seedy Chicago political ranks of the Levee district by delivering votes for First Ward aldermen John "Bathhouse John" Coughlin and Michael "Hinky Dink" Kenna. By 1908, Colosimo's criminal enterprise had grown significantly, and he amassed considerable wealth, which attracted the attention of Black Handers who extorted him for money. Realizing he needed protection from the Black Handers, Colosimo sent to New York for Johnny Torrio. Shortly after his arrival, Torrio arranged for three of Colosimo's Black Hand extortionists to be ambushed and shot to death. Colosimo was so grateful that he convinced Torrio to stay in Chicago to work for him as a brothel manager in the Levee. Torrio's ability as a manager was quickly recognized, and before long, he was Colosimo's top lieutenant.

By 1912, the winds of reform started to blow through Chicago and the Levee was most affected. The brothels in the district were closed or moved to other parts of the city within a few years. Torrio, however, had the foresight to expand operations to sustain his criminal enterprise.[24]

Chicago was saturated and suburban areas were experiencing tremendous growth as industries moved out of the city for cheaper land and labor. The automobile allowed people to live in outlying areas, commute to their jobs and travel greater distances to seek pleasure. These factors, plus the fact that suburban officials and police forces were easily corrupted, made suburban roadhouses an appealing idea for expansion. The first roadhouse Torrio opened was the Burnham Inn in Burnham, Illinois, on the Indiana border. John Patton, "the Boy Mayor" of Burnham, was a willing host and provided all of the necessary local protection. Its proximity to the steel mills and industry of Southeast Chicago, Northwest Indiana and the surrounding south suburban towns, such as Harvey and Chicago Heights, provided a steady stream of customers. Burnham's location allowed patrons to simply slip across the Indiana border to avoid arrest if there was a raid by an authority other than the Burnham police. The Burnham Inn proved to be so successful that Torrio opened the Speedway and the Arrowhead roadhouses in Burnham.[25]

Prohibition offered the possibility to consolidate the various independent gangs to form a consortium in the illegal liquor trade for the entire Chicago area. Torrio was ready to seize the moment, but Colosimo was content and no longer interested in taking on risky ventures. That posed a problem for Torrio, as he needed Colosimo's permission and support in order to capitalize on Prohibition. In their world, Colosimo left Torrio with no choice. On May 11, 1920, Big Jim Colosimo was shot to death in the front vestibule of Colosimo's Café as he waited for a supposed liquor shipment. The path was cleared for Torrio to assume control, expand his network of roadhouses throughout the suburbs and consolidate the various gangs in the metropolitan area.[26]

Torrio expanded the roadhouse network in Burnham by adding the Coney Island Café and the Barn. The Roamer Inn was established in Posen, the Burr Oak Hotel in Blue Island and the Shadow Inn in Stickney. In Chicago, Torrio was buying up breweries and making arrangements to wholesale beer to other gangs who in turn retailed the product.

Al Capone arrived in Chicago in 1919 after running into some trouble back home in New York City. Frank Yale, one of Capone's mentors, arranged for him to move to Chicago and join Torrio. Al Capone was put to work lining up various establishments in Chicago and the suburbs. By 1921, Torrio convinced the other gangs in Chicago that the best way to survive was to cooperate and implement rules of operation that they collectively enforced. In exchange for their cooperation, Torrio offered his connections so the gangs could operate openly.[27]

Peace among the gangs lasted until Dion O'Banion, North Side gang boss and flower shop owner, became restless because he felt threatened by the West Side Genna brothers' infringement on his territory. O'Banion set up Torrio by arranging for him to buy O'Banion's interest in the Seiben brewery. O'Banion received a tip that the brewery would be raided, and he arranged for his deal with Torrio to take place on the day of the raid. Torrio was taken into custody at the time of the raid, and because it was a second Prohibition violation, he had to serve time. O'Banion's treachery led to retaliation by Torrio and Capone. On November 10, 1924, O'Banion was shot to death in his flower shop by three assailants. O'Banion's successor, Hymie Weiss, tried to avenge the killing of his predecessor on Saturday, January 25, 1925, when Weiss, George "Bugs" Moran and Vincent "Schemer" Drucci ambushed Torrio outside of his apartment. Torrio survived, but he did not have the temerity to fight a gang war. Therefore, he turned over control to Al Capone who, rather than negotiate peace, used force to take control of Chicago for himself.[28]

When Torrio expanded his roadhouse operations, he looked to Chicago Heights as a prime location. Chicago Heights had all of the elements necessary for an ideal location, including a large number of factory workers that served as a customer base, a corruptible local government and an indigenous Italian population with enough of a criminal element that he could tap into their political connections and fledgling bootleg operations. He opened the Moonlight Café on Lincoln Highway in 1920, and it quickly became one of Torrio's most successful and opulent entertainment spots. It was billed as "the jazziest spot south of Chicago" and was described as "the house of a thousand windows" for the many diamond-shaped panes that adorned the place. The person Torrio selected to run the Moonlight was a known Chicago Heights character named Joe Arrigo. Arrigo had the necessary credentials for the position, exhibiting both competence as a club manager and the necessary political connections that Torrio valued. When the Moonlight was raided by the state's attorney's office in May 1923, Arrigo was arrested as the keeper and described as "a well-known host in Chicago jazz palaces." The trial for his arrest was moved across Cook County to Evanston, Illinois, to circumvent Arrigo's powerful influence in the southern part of the county.[29]

Torrio established the Moonlight Café not just as a good business opportunity but also to cement a mutually beneficial relationship with Sanfilippo and his organization. Sanfilippo could supply the protection for the Moonlight and for other ventures in the southern part of Cook County that interested Torrio. Additionally, Torrio received alcohol from Chicago Heights distillers and then wholesaled it to other gangs in Chicago and throughout the metropolitan area. Through this arrangement, Torrio provided the Chicago Heights groups with the market they needed to sell their alcohol and the cooperation of the Torrio-Capone organization. At the same time, the Chicago Heights bootleggers continued to operate independently in their territory.

In the early 1920s, the operations of the Sanfilippo organization grew and prospered. Between 1921 and 1924, the *Chicago Heights Star* ran various stories about large gambling operations, rampant vice, murders of victims on the periphery of the bootlegging operations and large-scale still operations run by the various operators.[30] It was not long before Piazza and Lamberta decided it was time to take action and thus the Chicago Heights rackets for themselves.

On the evening of April 19, 1924, Antonino Sanfilippo dropped off his son at home on East Twenty-second Street and proceeded to pick up two men. No one saw exactly what happened next, but a short while later, Sanfilippo's car was found against a tree on Seventeenth Street. He was slumped behind the wheel with four gunshots to the back of the head. The *Chicago Heights Star* reported that Sanfilippo was a very cautious man and would not let anyone ride in the rear seat of his car. Since the shots came from behind, it was suspected that two men, one in the front passenger seat and one in the rear, carried out the shooting. Given Sanfilippo's cautious nature, it was suspected that the shooters were men he trusted.[31] Lamberta was questioned as a suspect, but the evidence against him was deemed insufficient.[32]

Whether Piazza and Lamberta arranged Sanfilippo's murder or carried it out, it is almost certain that they were responsible. At the time of Sanfilippo's murder, it was commonly heard around town that Jim Lamberta killed Sanfilippo.[33] In any event, Piazza and Lamberta had the most to gain from Sanfilippo's death and indeed Piazza emerged as the boss of Chicago Heights with Lamberta and Joseph Martino as his top lieutenants. Joe Martino was a Sicilian that operated a "soft drink parlor" and pool room at the intersection of Sixteenth Street and Lowe across from the Milano Café in Chicago Heights.[34]

Just prior to Sanfilippo's murder, Al Capone's brother, Salvatore "Frank" Capone, was shot and killed in Cicero, Illinois, on April 1, 1924. Frank was in Cicero to control the Capone Gang's interests in Cicero's municipal election. He was spotted by three detectives at a polling place with Charlie Fischetti, his cousin and known Torrio-Capone gang member, and a third unknown gunman. When detectives approached, Frank pulled his weapon, fired and missed. The detectives returned fire and killed Frank. As an Italian custom, Al Capone went into mourning and stopped shaving until Frank's funeral.[35] The funeral was a hugely elaborate affair with $20,000 worth of flowers supplied by Dion O'Banion's flower shop. One of the arrangements was a six-foot-high heart made of carnations with the inscription "From the boys in Chicago Heights."[36] Among those present were John Torrio and most of the Chicago area's gangster elite. The *Southtown Economist* had this to say:

> *Powers of gangland, police officers, women, politicians, and others massed for blocks about the home to do him honor. Floral pieces and roped off*

The Capone house at 7244 South Prairie in Chicago on the day of Frank Capone's funeral in April 1924. Three carloads of the boys from Chicago Heights attended the funeral.

spaces kept back the curious. A carriage starter seated the dead man's family in their limousines, handed three delegations of Chicago Heights men into their spacious cars, and seated the less pretentious, though equally sympathetic friends of the Capon[e]'s in softly upholstered automobiles. There were more than one hundred cars in the procession.

Flowers in every conceivable funeral design filled twelve automobiles and were massed about the coffin in the hearse.[37]

The Chicago Heights delegation most likely included Sanfilippo since he had an arrangement with Torrio and the Costello brothers and Dominic Roberto and Jim Emery since they were loyal to Capone. Given that Sanfilippo was killed a little more than two weeks after the funeral of Frank Capone allows for speculation that Piazza and Lamberta seized on this time to kill Sanfilippo knowing that the Capone loyalists would be distracted by the period of mourning.

Piazza was much flashier than his predecessor. He was known for his nightspots, which were heavily advertised in the newspapers of the day. He owned the Derby Inn at 175th and Halsted Street in Homewood, Illinois, across the street from Washington Park racetrack, and he owned the Milano Café at Sixteenth Street and Lowe on the East Side of Chicago Heights. The Milano was an extremely popular restaurant and nightspot that attracted people from all over the area. In 1925, a party of sixty government marshals raided the place and found a very ornate and expensively decorated nightclub on the main floor and a massive still operating underneath the club.[38] The still operation was so big that the basement of the Milano had to be extended underneath Sixteenth Street to accommodate its size. The *Chicago Daily News* reported that the still was the largest in the county. It operated on a twenty-four-hour basis and employed fifteen people who were required to punch a time clock for their shifts. A ledger of the amounts of alcohol produced was also kept on hand.[39] Jake Lingle was arrested after the Milano Café raid with four other people for stealing furnishings and alcohol from the café. Lingle was a reporter for the *Chicago Tribune* who was killed in June 1930 at the Illinois Central commuter tunnel at Randolph and Michigan while on his way to Washington Park racetrack. At the time of his death, he was wearing a diamond-studded belt buckle given to him by Al Capone. It was suspected that he had crossed gangster Jack Zuta.[40]

Piazza set out to cement ties with the Unione Siciliana and isolate Torrio and Capone from Chicago Heights. His Unione connections were through some close associates of the Genna brothers from the West Side of Chicago. Orazio "the Scourge" Tropea was a known "terrorist" for the Genna brothers and also a regular at the Milano Café.[41] Giuseppe "Il Cavaliere" Nerone (Joseph Nerone alias Anthony Spano) was a Genna subordinate and a relative of Piazza's. Nerone had a falling out with the Genna brothers concerning the salary they paid him. When they refused to give him a percentage, Nerone moved to Chicago Heights and established himself with Piazza's bootlegging interests.[42]

Piazza put Lamberta in charge of collecting protection payments from the various bootlegging and vice operations in Chicago Heights. It was a "street tax" levied by the Piazza Gang. In exchange for the payments, Piazza was supposed to provide protection from raids and arrests.[43] Joe Martino served as Piazza's conduit between police and the gang. In the event there was a raid, it was Joe Martino who would see to it that the problem was resolved. Joe Fushi related that he was once arrested while operating a still at Twenty-second Street and East End Avenue. When agents caught him, they asked who his boss was, but he would not say. The agents indicated that they knew who his boss was and proceeded to take him to Joe Martino's pool hall. When they arrived, Fushi greeted Martino and told him that he was arrested at the still. With that Martino turned to the agents and said, "He's all right, take him back to work, boys."[44]

Piazza prospered from the time of Antonino Sanfilippo's murder until the end of 1925. However, the independent bootleggers and vice operators in Chicago Heights did not respect Piazza. They viewed Piazza as arrogant and resented having to acquiesce to him. Additionally, the appearance of Nerone in Chicago Heights was viewed as a serious infringement on their territory. By late 1925 and into early 1926, Piazza continued to have Lamberta collect tribute from the various operators, but he failed to provide protection in return. During this period of time, Prohibition agents seized eighteen stills. The independent operators were so incensed that they demanded their money back, but the demand fell on deaf ears.[45] The time was ripe for someone to step in and take over. Dominic Roberto seized the opportunity, but it was going to take cooperation from the various bootleggers in Chicago Heights, and some assistance from Chicago.

CHAPTER 3

GANG WAR AND THE RISE OF DOMINIC ROBERTO

Roberto was born Domenico Ruberto on January 15, 1896, in Sambiase, Calabria, Italy, the son of Joseph Ruberto and Caterina (Catherine) Falvo. He emigrated from Italy to Canada and crossed into the United States at International Falls, Minnesota, in November 1913. In 1917, he claimed exemption from the draft as an alien.[46] Roberto was charged with carrying a concealed weapon and robbery in connection with a clothing store heist in Kankakee, Illinois, in July 1921. He was fined $500 for the weapons charge, and the robbery charge was dropped in November 1921. On February 22, 1922, Roberto and Emery were charged with conspiracy and assault, respectively, in connection with a shooting that took place on Western Avenue in Blue Island, Illinois. The prosecution was dropped because of threats that Roberto and Emery made against the witnesses.[47]

On April 14, 1924, Roberto married Rae "Rio" Burke, a young cabaret singer that he met while she was performing at a nightclub in Chicago Heights that he owned. Roberto and Burke lived with Jim Emery and his family at their home at Twenty-sixth and Chicago Road in Chicago Heights. Rio recalled that Roberto and Emery were already allied with Capone at that time. She also recalled that it was Roberto and Emery that hid Capone after the killing of William McSwiggin, assistant state's attorney, in April 1926.[48]

By the mid-1920s, Roberto and Emery had established themselves as bootleggers and tavern, smoke shop and nightclub operators. The headquarters of their operations was the Cozy Corner tavern and the Monroe Hotel, located in the same building at Seventeenth and East End

Jim Emery and Dominic Roberto standing behind Dominic's parents, Joseph Ruberto and Caterina (Catherine) Falvo. The photo was probably taken during the mid-1920s.

Avenue in Chicago Heights. Rumrunners from Iowa, Southern Illinois, Saint Louis and Kansas City stopped at the Cozy Corner to make alcohol purchases or pick-ups for distribution.[49] The top protégé of Roberto and Emery was Roberto's cousin, Frank LaPorte.

In late 1925, it made no sense to continue to pay Piazza protection and receive nothing in return. Roberto sensed that many of the other independent operators in Chicago Heights felt the same way, including many of the Sicilian families. Roberto particularly knew that he could count on the Costello and Zarante brothers because their loyalties were with Capone. As Roberto built support in Chicago Heights, he turned to Al Capone for additional support. Capone had taken over from Torrio and gladly provided Roberto with the outside support that Roberto required. Chicago Heights was a lucrative and strategic territory and Capone recognized that he could benefit from a relationship with Roberto. After all, Chicago Heights had been a Torrio-Capone suburb. It was only after Piazza took over and allowed Nerone to operate in Chicago Heights that Capone lost his Chicago Heights

Left: Dominic Roberto posing as a respectable gentleman. His Leavenworth parole report referred to him as a habitual criminal.

Below: Dominic Roberto relaxes in Hot Springs, Arkansas, with some key figures that helped rid Chicago Heights of Philip Piazza and his supporters. *From left to right:* Sam "Black Sam" DiGiovanni (on donkey), Dominic Roberto, John Roberts, Tony Costello, Phil Bacino (on donkey) and Charlie Costello stands in the rear. Phil Bacino later owned and operated John's Pizzeria on the Strip in Calumet City. *From the collection of John Binder and Matthew Luzi.*

stream of revenue.[50] With alliances and support in place, the stage was set for Roberto to purge Chicago Heights of the Piazza Gang.

The first target was Jim Lamberta, and not only was his killing the first, but it was also perhaps the most stunning because a woman was killed with him. On the evening of June 2, 1926, Mrs. Crystal Barrier, Mrs. Violet Bass, Miss Marguerite Quintenz and Miss Mabel "Bobbie" Siemer went to the Milano Café in Chicago Heights for dinner. While there, the women met up with Jim Lamberta, Philip Piazza and Charlie Costello. Shortly after midnight, the group decided to go to the Derby Inn at 175th and Halsted Street. Piazza wanted to show off the club, which was scheduled to reopen after extensive renovation. Lamberta and Piazza drove to the club while Charlie Costello escorted Bobbie Siemer. Violet Bass drove the rest of the women. The group sat and listened to the nickel piano and conversed until about 1:00 a.m. when Charlie Costello left with Bobbie Siemer. About twenty minutes later, Lamberta, Crystal Barrier and Violet Bass headed for the door to leave while Piazza and Marguerite Quintenz remained inside. As soon as the door shut, shotgun blasts rang out. Just as Piazza opened the door to investigate the noise, Violet Bass appeared with her arm bleeding, crying, "They've killed Crystal!" Lamberta had just gotten into his car when the shots were fired. Crystal Barrier and Violet Bass were standing near the car in the path of the buckshot. When Piazza got to Lamberta's car, he was still alive. Piazza dragged him from the car and placed him next to where Crystal Barrier lay dead. Marguerite Quintenz was so frightened that she fled into a nearby cornfield and remained there until 5:00 a.m.

At the scene, the police found at least one sawed-off shotgun and eleven empty shell casings. When they searched Lamberta's body, they found $3,700 in cash and about $10,000 worth of loose diamonds in his pockets. The police rounded up all of the surviving members of the party plus the husbands of Crystal Barrier and Violet Bass for questioning and their testimony at the coroner's inquest. During questioning, Marguerite Quintenz stated that she saw a dark Cadillac tailing the party and she recognized Joe Guzzino at the wheel. Bobbie Siemer also recalled seeing Joe Guzzino tailing the party. However, when it came time to testify at the inquest, Marguerite Quintenz could not recall seeing any cars, let alone one with Joe Guzzino behind the wheel.[51]

When considering the circumstances of Lamberta's murder, it appears likely that the murder was a set up. It was widely speculated that the intended victims were Lamberta and Piazza. It is significant to note that Guzzino, a known Roberto supporter and gunman, was placed at the scene and that Charlie Costello, recently allied with Roberto, was also present. It is conceivable that the murder was planned with Costello as the set-up man, giving the signal to Guzzino when he left the Derby Inn that Lamberta and Piazza were still in the club getting ready to leave. Unfortunately, Crystal Barrier and Violet Bass, rather than Piazza, exited with Lamberta.

The next victim of the gang war was Frank Camera. Camera was a suspect in a murder. He made things worse for himself when the police went to pick him up for the murder and found him operating a still. Camera was found shot to death June 9, 1926, on Lincoln Highway, eighteen miles east of Chicago Heights in Indiana.[52] The Roberto faction got nervous that Camera might either take revenge for Lamberta or talk to authorities about what he knew of the Lamberta killing to cut a deal on his murder charge.

About six weeks after Lamberta was killed, gunmen sought Piazza and found their mark. At 10:16 p.m. on July 22, 1926, Piazza stood in the Lowe Street entranceway of his Milano Café at Sixteenth and Lowe. A car pulled up, and two gunmen in dark suits approached and fired a volley of shots at Piazza. Piazza was hit several times and killed by a shot that pierced his throat. Piazza's brother, John, heard the shooting and was first to reach his fallen brother. Just as he reached the body, he saw the two gunmen run across Sixteenth Street and get into the waiting car that then sped away.

After the coroner's inquest, Piazza's death was ruled, "death from gunshot wounds at the hands of person or persons unknown," a rather typical way for the coroner to close such cases at the time. It was reported that during his life, Piazza was hated, feared or respected by hundreds of men. His funeral procession was fitting for a man of his stature in the underworld at the time. There were thirty carloads of flowers and many carloads of people composing his funeral procession. The procession was led by a band and escorted through town by a contingent of state, county and local motorcycle policemen.[53] Piazza's killing effectively eliminated the leadership of the Piazza Gang. However, the war was not over, as Roberto moved against other Piazza and Lamberta loyalists that might pose a threat.

Joe Salvo was well known to police as a vice leader of the East Side. He was also the nephew of Jim Lamberta. At 1:00 a.m. on the morning of August 3, 1926, Joe Salvo was standing outside of his home and cigar shop at 342 East Fourteenth Street on the East Side of Chicago Heights. He was just a few feet from an eyewitness when a touring car came down Arnold Street loaded with a number of men. According to reports, the car pulled alongside Salvo and one of the occupants fired through an open window with a sawed-off shotgun. Salvo was hit four times and died later that morning at St. James Hospital.[54]

Joe "Il Cavaliere" Nerone was next and met his fate at the hands of gunmen in Chicago. Nerone was traveling through the Italian neighborhood on the North Side of Chicago on the morning of August 20, 1926, when he became suspicious of a car containing two men tailing him. Nerone pulled over in front of a barbershop at 454 West Division and tried to flee down a passageway. Nerone drew his pistol as he got out of his car, but the two men from the pursuing car fired first. Nerone managed to fire twice and miss before being shot four times by his pursuers. At first, police mistakenly identified the body as Frank Milani or Maroni but a search of the body revealed an Italian gun permit in Nerone's name. The son of the proprietor of the barbershop, twelve-year-old Nunzio Scardino, testified at the inquest that the shooter was Tony Aiello and another man he did not recognize. Nerone's involvement with the Genna brothers and Piazza was widely reported, but his death was ultimately attributed to his involvement in Chicago Heights with Piazza.[55] The best evidence that Nerone was killed because of his connections to Piazza and Chicago Heights was found on the next victim of the gang war.

The body of Frank Capello, Nerone gunman, was found on the morning of August 29, 1926, next to a car he was driving on a rural stretch of State Street near Twenty-sixth Street, just outside of Chicago Heights. The car had run into a ditch, and Capello's body was lying alongside the car. There were two men from Chicago that happened to be driving by the scene just after Capello had been shot. They testified at the coroner's inquest that, as they approached the car Capello was driving, they heard shots and observed three men running into a cornfield near the scene. However, the fleeing men did not have time to remove incriminating evidence. After a search of Capello's body, the police found the telephone number of Mrs. B. Tropea, the common-law wife of Orazio Tropea. The police also found the bankbook of Joe Nerone that showed $4,000 in recent deposits and receipts issued by banks for large sums to Joe Pavia and Peter Maggiore, two known Piazza henchmen. Police were sure the money represented profits from the illicit liquor trade. Investigators also discovered information that Dominic Roberto may have been involved. The car was originally owned by the Illinois Distributing Company and was sold to Dominic Roberto. Roberto had loaned the car to Capello as a prospective buyer of the car a few days before his murder.

The body of Antonio DeStefano Pelledrino, another Nerone subordinate, was found at the intersection of Cottage Grove and Joe Orr Road four days after the killing of Frank Capello. Pelledrino was strangled, and his remains were covered with alcohol and set on fire. The *Chicago Tribune* reported that Pelledrino acquaintances had seen him frequently in the company of Nerone

This photo was taken at Neroni's Grove at Twenty-second and State Street in Chicago Heights in 1927. It was taken to commemorate the consolidation of the Chicago Heights bootleggers under Dominic Roberto. The photo was in the possession of the author's great-grandmother but was never displayed because of its incriminating nature. *Front row, seated, left to right:* Luigi ("Louie") Angellotti, Anthony Scibi, George Zarante, Nick Costello, John Nicastro, Frank LaPorte, and Jim DiPeso. *Middle row, left to right:* James Strangis, Tony Costello, John Roberts, Sam Costello, Peter "Pete" Zarante, Dominic Roberto, Charlie Costello, Charlie Presto, Jimmy "Jim" Emery, Sam Geraci, and Nick DiGiovanni. *Back row, left to right:* Mike Roberts, Jim "Big Jim" Roberts, Sebastiano "Curly" Zarante, Saverio Liparota, J. Pulia, Joe "Joe Barrelhouse" Arrigo, John "Jack" Perry, Nicola "Nick" Neroni, Joe Guzzino, Sam "Black Sam" DiGiovanni, John Piazza, unknown, Bill Willis, Tony Sibolis.

and Capello.[56] Police believed that he was dragged for some distance from the back of an automobile and that he choked to death from the rope tied around his neck.[57] It was suspected that Pelledrino's murder was so torturous because he tried to operate independently of the local bootleggers, and they wanted to send a message to others that dared to defy them.

Pelledrino's killing on September 2, 1926, was effectively the end of the gang war to rid Chicago Heights of Piazza and his top supporters. Roberto took some time to reestablish alliances with the Costello and Zarante brothers and to bring in the rest of the independent operators in Chicago Heights. A truce was arranged in July 1927, and Roberto emerged as the boss of Chicago Heights.

Roberto's emergence as boss of Chicago Heights also signaled his elevation in the Capone Gang as Al Capone's chief lieutenant over the south suburbs. It further signaled the formation of the Chicago Heights street crew. Jim Emery was elevated to the status of Roberto's chief lieutenant. Frank LaPorte became a key subordinate. Joe Martino stayed on because of his political and law enforcement connections and because he held a position in the Unione. The Costellos, Zarantes and other groups fell in line as members of the Chicago Heights street crew. Roberto's territory stretched from Ninety-fifth Street in Chicago south to Kankakee, Illinois, which was managed by the Macaluso brothers; east to Gary, Indiana; and west to Joliet, Illinois.

The year 1927 proved to be relatively quiet, which allowed Roberto to solidify his position. However, the gang war that raged left in excess of twenty deaths. Such violence made the law-abiding citizens and civic leaders of Chicago Heights wary, and it drew the attention of authorities. In January 1928, three more bodies turned up in vicinity of Chicago Heights. The dead were Harry Fuller of Indiana, and Joseph Cagiando and Joseph Fasso, both of Chicago Heights. The three were hijackers that attempted to usurp some merchandise. As far as Chief James Devereux of the Cook County highway police was concerned, this was the last straw. The chief was quoted as saying:

> We have made progress in Cicero. Capone has left town and we have also been making it hot for the booze interests on the northwest side of Chicago. Chicago Heights has remained a sore spot. There are probably more than two dozen huge illicit distilleries in the vicinity of the suburb. Their owners have been getting richer and tougher and have come to believe that they are entirely outside the law. We intend to show differently.[58]

Throughout the early months of 1928, the *Chicago Heights Star* stepped up its editorializing against the gangster element and the corruption that went with it. The gangsters viewed the unwanted publicity as a threat and bombed the offices of the paper in August 1928. The headlines following the bombing screamed that decency had been challenged and that gang defiance of law and order was the cause of the blast.[59] In September 1928, Dominic Roberto decided to take some time to cool off and left for Italy to avoid the fallout from the demands for action, leaving Jim Emery to manage things while he was gone.

In the autumn of 1928, Alexander Jamie—a federal agent and Eliot Ness's brother-in-law—mounted an undercover investigation. He sent three of his men into Chicago Heights to pose as corrupt agents at speakeasies and other places known to be connected. They let it be known that, for a price, they could arrange for protection of the still operations. The agents hung around for days spreading the word. They were eventually approached and brought to meet Joe Martino. Martino was taken with the idea of having federal

This photo of Jim Emery and Dominic Roberto with *amici* was taken in Italy. Emery is seated third from the left, and Roberto is seated second from the right. *From the collection of John Binder and Matthew Luzi.*

protection. The agents convinced him that in order for them to provide protection, they needed to know the right still operators. Martino agreed and took the three around Chicago Heights to show them still locations and introduce them to the operators. Just before the agents completed their investigation, the gangsters became suspicious and killed Frank Basile who was acting as chauffeur for the agents. The murder of Basile caused the agents to quickly wrap up the undercover investigation.[60]

A grand jury was convened as a result of their efforts and the efforts of agents from previous raids. The grand jury probed not only the affairs of the gangsters but also the affairs of public officials that were suspected of corruption. By October 1928, the assistant United States district attorney announced that at least one hundred witnesses were expected to be called. The witnesses included anyone with knowledge of illegal alcohol running or official corruption. The testimony was initially expected to last a few weeks but stretched through the November term and was expanded to probe activities in South Chicago Heights. The probe was expanded to determine if the bootleggers and gamblers from Chicago Heights had infiltrated that town. South Chicago Heights officials, including the village president, two board members and Leroy Gilbert, chief of police of South Chicago Heights, were called to testify.

The grand jury handed down its first indictments in November 1928, charging Martino and seven others with attempting to give a federal agent $400 to protect a still.[61]

Martino's indictment was the last straw for the Chicago Heights gangsters who blamed Martino for ingratiating himself with the undercover agents and providing them detailed information. Rumors circulated that Martino might testify against them. On November 30, 1928, as Martino stood in front of his building at Sixteenth Street and Lowe, he was approached by someone he knew and shot several times in the head. Witnesses claimed the gunman approached Martino on foot, shot him and then fired several errant shots as he fled west down Sixteenth Street to distract the witnesses. Police suspected that Martino knew his killer because he fell without removing his hands from his pockets. Federal officials believed that had Martino lived, they would have uncovered a conspiracy between politicians and bootleggers. His killing took place about one hundred feet from where Phil Piazza was killed. Sam Costello was also shot and wounded in the hand a few weeks prior when standing in front of the Costello Brothers Confectioners across the street. Authorities speculated that Costello was spared because of poor marksmanship. However, it is more likely that the Costello shooting was a warning to keep quiet during the grand jury investigation. In any event, more than six bootleg killings took place at the same intersection of Sixteenth Street and Lowe, earning it the name Death Corner.[62]

The grand jury pressed ahead by calling Leroy Gilbert back for further testimony on December 7, 1928. The Chicago Heights gangsters were determined to prevent his testimony. On the evening of December 6, 1928, as Chief Gilbert read the newspaper next to his living room window at 10:00 p.m., two men rested shotguns on the window sill and fired three shots at nearly point-blank range. Chief Gilbert was killed instantly in front of his wife. She was close enough that one of her fingers was nearly taken off by the shooting. The streets of the village were closed off as quickly as possible so all cars entering and leaving could be searched. Unfortunately, the killers had already made their getaway. In a bizarre twist of events, vigilantes took to the streets to try and ferret out the killers. Instead, a worker for the *Chicago Heights Star* was killed when he was thought to be one of the killers.[63]

The inquest following Chief Gilbert's slaying provided some additional clues about the conditions in South Chicago Heights. Daniel Anderson, the assistant United States attorney conducting the grand jury's probe, testified at the inquest that his investigation uncovered threats against Chief Gilbert. He also testified that former chief of police John Erickson was ousted because of his complicity

Joe Martino's Saloon and Poolroom located on the East Side of Chicago Heights at the intersection of Sixteenth Street and Lowe on the East Side. On November 30, 1928, Martino was found shot to death just to the right of the entrance where the plate glass window would have been. This photo was taken in the late 1980s shortly before the building was demolished. The terra cotta cornice above the entrance was inscribed: J. Martino.

with the bootleggers. Furthermore, it was revealed that the village president was a supporter of Erickson's and that Erickson's brother was a bootlegger. A village trustee testified at the inquest that he was threatened for voting in favor of ousting Erickson. Three days after the vote, the trustee's house was set on fire. He suspected that the bootleggers were responsible based on the discovery at the scene of a gunnysack labeled "Clinton Corn Sugar Company."[64]

Following the inquest, state and county officials joined with Daniel Anderson in a combined effort to solve Chief Gilbert's killing. Anderson supplied state and county officials with the names of two suspects to aid in their efforts. Anderson also issued the following statement:

> *The hoodlum element has been in complete control of the city of Chicago Heights for over four years. Police and city officials have lacked the honesty and courage to make a move or give an order without first obtaining approval of the gunmen and alcohol racketeers who were in control of the town.*

Chief of Police Gilbert was slain because he showed a determination to fight this hoodlum element in his village.

Mayor Daniel Bergin of Chicago Heights issued a contradictory statement in reply. He called Anderson's charges groundless but then admitted that conditions in the city had been "turbulent" since 1918.[65]

State, county and federal officials went on the offensive on January 6, 1929. That day, one hundred federal agents and Chicago detectives swarmed the town, seized city hall, temporarily relieved the local police of their duties and fanned out across the city with search warrants. Twenty-five men were taken into custody, including some of the Battaglia, Costello, Macaluso and Zarante brothers. The agents also seized a large cache of weapons and alcohol. Authorities found correspondence on the men to suggest that they had connections to, or were acting as the headquarters for, a "mafia" ring operating in Chicago, St. Louis, New York and Cincinnati. Agents disclosed that they believed the city had fallen prey to a syndicate that made millions not only from alcohol but also from large-scale gambling. It was also disclosed that well-known Cook County officials were involved. The

Prisoners from the January 6, 1929 raid are led from the Chicago Heights jail to a waiting police wagon. They were taken to the Bureau of Identification for processing. *Courtesy of the Chicago Tribune.*

newspapers tended to focus their stories on illegal bootlegging as perhaps the sole source of the crime wave in Chicago Heights. However, the authorities seemed to recognize that gambling was also a major component of income for the Chicago Heights street crew.

The gambling revelation came during the raid on the home of Oliver G. Ellis. The Ellis home was located at 1525 Euclid Avenue on the West Side of Chicago Heights. The raiding party was immediately suspicious when they discovered nine telephone lines serving the home. In a large garage in the rear of house, the raiders found 423 slot machines, fifty gallons of alcohol, fifteen cases of whiskey and forty cases of beer.[66] The bigger find, however, was $400,000 worth of canceled checks. Ellis admitted that the canceled checks were evidence of the proceeds of the take from illegal slot machines for the past fourteen months. Ellis also admitted that his share of the take from the slots in 1928 alone was $200,000. He refused to name the other four that shared the profits.[67] However, the raiders also found a safe containing financial records that fully detailed the slot machine operations. The records showed that the return for one year's operation of the slots was $1,500,000. The payouts went up the line to high-ranking members of the Capone Gang. The records would eventually be used to build a test tax case against Ralph Capone and were then used in the tax case against Al Capone.[68]

Following the raid, authorities worked to unravel the conspiracy between the bootleggers, gamblers, syndicate members and the public officials furnishing protection. They also wanted to know who divided the money from the slot machine operations. Ellis was indicted for conspiracy on February 2, 1929.[69] In December of that year, he was charged with tax fraud and was sentenced to one year and a day in Leavenworth Federal Penitentiary.[70] While Ellis made certain admissions about the money from the slots, he never admitted who he split the profits with.

As for the fate of the bootleggers, the grand jury continued to hear testimony to bolster evidence for an indictment. In late January 1929, more than one hundred additional witnesses were called. The witness testimony before the grand jury culminated in March 1929, when Al Capone was called to testify.[71] His appearance caused a stir with the public, and thousands showed up at the federal building just to get a glimpse of him going in. His testimony lasted for one hour and twenty minutes on March 21, 1929, and he was ordered to appear again on March 26, 1929.[72] The grand jury concluded its work after Capone's testimony, and an indictment of eighty-one individuals was prepared in April and announced in May 1929.[73]

Above: Deputy Chicago police commissioner John Stege helps to destroy slot machines found in the garage behind the home of Oliver Ellis. *Courtesy of the* Chicago Tribune.

Left: Al Capone confers with his attorney in March 1929 as he waits to testify before the grand jury about what he knows of the bootlegging and gambling activities in Chicago Heights. *From the collection of John Binder.*

The indictment made for sensational headlines by including several public officials, including John Costabile, the acting chief of police, and Edward Cassidy, the former chief of police. The indictment named prominent figures, including Dominic Roberto, Jim Emery, Frank LaPorte and the Perry (aka Perri) brothers. It did not name any of the Costello brothers, the DiGiovanni brothers or the Macaluso brothers. The indictment charged the defendants with conspiracy to violate the National Prohibition Act. However, the indictment lacked charges for several major crimes that were expected to be cleared. The indictment charged none of the defendants with the murders of Chief Gilbert or Joe Martino. It did not charge any of the defendants with any of the murders that took place during the preceding three years or during the gang war. Additionally, the indictment failed to charge any of the defendants with conspiracy for illegal gambling.[74] Frank LaPorte was charged simply with allowing a still to operate; Jim Emery was charged only with possession of alcohol; and Dominic Roberto was merely charged with meeting with Edward Cassidy. In fact, the indictment was so weak that by the mid-1930s the charges were either dropped or the defendants paid a nominal fee and continued with their activities. For example, John Roberts, Dominic's brother, paid a $200 fine for violating the Prohibition Act, and Jim Emery pled guilty and was fined $500.

However, the indictment showed the scope and scale of the bootlegging and gambling operations. It charged that from January 1, 1925, through April 30, 1929, three million gallons of alcohol valued at $36 million were manufactured.[75] Coupled with the estimated gambling profits of $1.5 million per year, it is evident why Dominic Roberto was willing to take out the competition and consolidate Chicago Heights for himself under the auspices of Al Capone. It is also evident why Al Capone was eager to lend his support to ensure that Chicago Heights was once again brought under the umbrella of the Capone Gang.

Dominic Roberto lasted as the boss of Chicago Heights for a relatively short period. He returned to Chicago Heights at some point in early 1929 but left for Italy again in the summer of 1929. Upon his return to the United States in November 1929, he was detained at Ellis Island pending a conspiracy investigation that lasted until February 1930. The conspiracy case was brought to trial, and he was eventually dismissed from the case. In 1931, he wanted to return to Italy to get married but feared that the authorities would deny him reentry. He tried to reopen his Petition for Naturalization, which was originally denied. His request to reopen was also denied. Roberto was then indicted and tried on charges that he made false statements on his Petition for Naturalization, that he made false statements at his hearing on the petition and

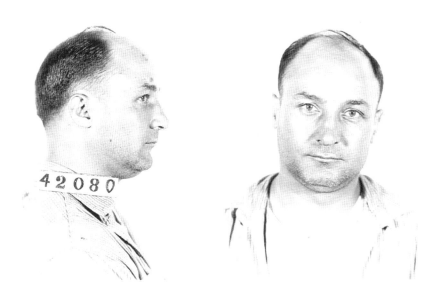

Dominic Roberto's Leavenworth Penitentiary mug shot. *From the National Archive.*

that he lied under oath about his arrest record. He was eventually convicted on May 3, 1932, and sentenced to two years at Leavenworth.

Roberto corresponded from prison with top associates Jim Emery, Sam and Charlie Costello, George Montesanti and Frank LaPorte. He also corresponded with John Mackler and Charles Baron, both key political figures. Mackler was a powerful Republican politician and construction contractor. Baron had connections to the Democratic Party through Chicago ward boss Jacob Arvey. Roberto's February 1933 parole report recommended that he not be paroled under any circumstances, noting that his associates were "gangsters and philanderers" and that he was a habitual criminal.[76] He was discharged from prison on February 28, 1934, but a warrant for his deportation was issued on July 26, 1933, and he was held pending appeal of the warrant. His appeals were denied as was his writ certiorari to the U.S. Supreme Court on November 8, 1934, and he was deported to Italy on January 5, 1935.[77]

Roberto's absence from Chicago Heights left an opening in the top spot of the Chicago Heights street crew. Such a void might have caused a spurt of violence before Roberto's efforts to consolidate the different factions. However, Roberto's efforts left in place a structure with somewhat of a succession plan that was endorsed by Al Capone. Thus, from roughly 1928, the reins of command for the Chicago Heights street crew were passed to Roberto's chief lieutenant and close friend Jim Emery.

CHAPTER 4

THE ERA OF
BIG JIM EMERY

Jim Emery's relationship in organized crime with Dominic Roberto went back to their early days in Chicago Heights. The two were not related, but their association was most likely forged in Italy where their hometowns are in the same vicinity in Calabria. The two were just four years apart, and they arrived in Chicago Heights within a year of each other. Emery, whose real name was Vincenzo Ammirati, was born November 2, 1892. He emigrated from Cosenza, Calabria, Italy, in 1912. He arrived in New York on February 17, 1912, and headed straight for Chicago Heights, arriving there four days later on the twenty-first of February. Frank LaPorte signed the Petition for Naturalization for Jim Emery and also for Dominic Roberto. Emery and his wife, Josephine, had five children: Ralph, John, Louis, George and Vera. The family was known around town for the large house they lived in at 2606 Chicago Road in Chicago Heights.[78] It was a white Victorian-style house on a large piece of property with a gazebo in back.

Emery first came to the attention of authorities in 1922 when he and Roberto were charged in connection with the shooting on Western Avenue. In that incident, Emery shot Andrew Myers, son of Blue Island, Illinois alderman Arnold Myers under the Rock Island viaduct at Western Avenue. Emery allegedly shot in defense of Roberto, claiming that Myers tried to rob them. The alibi was unlikely because the investigation showed that Myers was shot in the back without warning or cause. Emery was charged with assault with a dangerous weapon and with intent to commit murder. Roberto was charged with conspiracy.[79] Given the political connections of Myers, it

Young Jim Emery (left), and
Dominic Roberto. This photo was
probably taken around the time
of the Myers shooting in 1922.
Note the significant bulge under
Dominic's breast pocket.

is more likely that the shooting was motivated by some illegal venture for
which Roberto and Emery sought political protection. Perhaps the other
motive was that Roberto and Emery felt double-crossed by Myers and his
father for their failure to provide protection in exchange for money Roberto
and Emery previously provided. Regardless, Myers survived the shooting
and went on to serve as alderman for the Second Ward in Blue Island during
the 1930s. Myers died at the age of seventy in 1967.[80]

Emery and Roberto were co-owners of the Monroe Hotel. It was a two-
story building with sixteen rooms upstairs where prostitutes were known
to be kept. On the first floor, Emery and Roberto operated a cigar store
and the Cozy Corner tavern, both known for gambling. The building was
constructed in 1901 and was originally occupied by August Kasdorf's saloon.
Roberto and Emery acquired it from Kasdorf, a Chicago Heights alderman.
In 1928, Roberto admitted that he and Emery owned the property. In fact,
it was the headquarters of Roberto and Emery throughout Prohibition until
Roberto's troubles started in 1928. The property continued to be owned
by the two through the 1930s. Frank LaPorte managed a gas station added
to the property. By 1936, Jim Emery and Frank LaPorte had moved on to
other ventures and Roberto was back in Italy. On January 15, 1936, a huge

explosion ripped through the building, touching off a rapidly spreading fire that destroyed everything on the site. The investigating fire marshal suspected arson due to the fact that the building was unoccupied at the time of the blaze, and it appeared that an accelerant was used. The fire marshal also discovered that the property was insured for $20,000, half of which represented a nice amount to send to Dominic.[81]

Another of Emery's endeavors from the 1920s through at least the mid-1930s was boxing. He owned and operated a gym in Chicago Heights, the Emery A.C., where he trained and promoted fighters. The Emery A.C. was successful enough that Emery was the Capone Gang's conduit to the boxing world. Boxing, in turn, provided Emery with a means to launder Prohibition proceeds, and more importantly, it provided a means to control the outcome of organized gambling on boxing. His most well-known fighter was welterweight Shuffle Callahan, born Eugene Francis Patrick Callahan; he was from Hammond, Indiana. Shuffle was a southpaw known to be a powerful puncher with a solid left hook. Emery promoted Callahan's fights throughout the Chicago area and around the country. He also had associations with other boxers of the era, including Primo Carnera and Tony Canzoneri. Between 1927 and 1936, Canzoneri held titles in the featherweight, lightweight and junior welterweight classes. Primarily an East Coast fighter, he fought Charles "Bud" Taylor to a draw in March 1927 during a bantamweight title bout in Chicago. They fought again in June 1927 in New York, but Canzoneri lost. He returned to Chicago to fight Barney Ross for the dual lightweight and junior welterweight titles in 1933. Ross was an extreme underdog but surprised everyone by beating Canzoneri. *The Last Testament of Bill Bonanno*, published posthumously, claims that Tony Canzoneri was a "group leader" for the Bonanno Family.[82]

Chicago Heights in 1928 was much less tumultuous than the preceding years during gang war. There were acts of violence committed, such as the triple murder of the hijackers, but such matters were issues of enforcement or protection. Meanwhile, Al Capone continued his attempt to consolidate territories into the domain of the Capone Gang. The Moran Gang on the North Side of Chicago had been a thorn to Capone since Dion O'Banion was eliminated. Now that Chicago Heights was settled in his favor, it was a good time to start thinking about what to do about the Moran Gang. The solution played itself out when seven of the Moran Gang were eliminated on February 14, 1929.

Prior to the St. Valentine's Day Massacre, Jim Emery hosted Al Capone at his house in the fall of 1928. The meeting was memorialized with a photograph taken in the backyard of the Emery house. It shows Al Capone

From left to right: Rita, Denise and Tony Canzoneri seen here in a photo sent to Jim Emery in a Christmas card. Rita and Tony were a popular couple on the New York social scene following Tony's boxing career. Bill Bonanno posthumously claimed that Canzoneri was a group leader in the Bonanno Crime Family. *From the collection of Dr. Jim Ammirati and Jim Ammirati.*

reclining in the grass surrounded by nine others, including Frank LaPorte, Jim Emery, Claude Maddox and Sam Costello. The reason for the meeting has been the subject of much speculation. The likely possibilities are that it was taken to confirm Emery as the successor to Roberto and confirm the promotion of Frank LaPorte, or it was taken during a planning session for the massacre, or both. The confirmation of Emery and LaPorte makes sense, given that LaPorte and Emery are seated on the ground reclining with Capone and that Roberto is not in the photograph. The massacre planning session is plausible when considering that the men in the photo were the known enforcement end of the Capone Gang. There is also circumstantial evidence of the massacre linked to some of the men in the photo. For instance, a car used in the massacre was found in a burning garage on February 22, 1929, at 1723 North Wood Street. It was determined that the garage was rented by a "Frank Rogers." He provided an address at 1859 West North Avenue. That address adjoined the Circus Café, the headquarters of Claude

This photo was taken in the backyard of the Emery home at Twenty-sixth Street and Chicago Road in Chicago Heights in the autumn of 1928. Copies of the photo have circulated for years. An original has surfaced recently in the possession of Dominic Roberto's relatives. *Front row, left to right:* Frank LaPorte, Vera Emery, Al Capone, Willie Heeney and Jim Emery. *Back row, left to right:* Rocco DeGrazia, Louis "Little New York" Campagna, Claude "Screwy" Maddox, Nick Circella and Sam Costello. *From the collection of Michael Roberts.*

Maddox.[83] In addition, Frank LaPorte was known to hide Fred Burke, the only person connected to the massacre, at the home of his sister.[84]

In December 1929, Burke was wanted for shooting and killing a St. Joseph, Michigan police officer after being pulled over for a hit and run. Burke was traced to a home on the outskirts of St. Joseph, where police found two Thompson submachine guns. Tests later determined that the guns were used in the St. Valentine's Day Massacre. Burke eluded arrest until March 1931, when authorities arrested him at a farm in Green City, Missouri. Burke was tried and convicted in Michigan. He died in prison in 1940.

Two events occurred in the early 1930s that drastically changed the way the Outfit conducted business. One was the conviction of Al Capone for income tax evasion and the other was the repeal of Prohibition.

After the government's successful prosecution of Ralph Capone, the focus shifted to Al Capone. Three indictments were handed down against Capone in 1931, two for income tax evasion and one for violating the Volstead Act. The

Fred Burke, the only man connected to the St. Valentine's Day Massacre. Frank LaPorte was known to hide Burke at his sister's home in Chicago Heights. Here, he displays some attitude while in custody. *From the collection of John Binder.*

trial started October 6 and lasted until October 17, 1931, when Capone was convicted by the jury after just eight hours of deliberation. On October 24, Capone was sentenced to eleven years.[85] The high-flying flamboyant days of the roaring twenties were over. The government sent a message that it had new tools in the tax laws to go after gangsters, who would have to conduct their activities with more caution and with a lower profile than Al Capone or Dominic Roberto. The Chicago Heights banker's report to the FBI included this observation:

Until Capone was arrested for an income tax violation, none of the "syndicate" leaders utilized legitimate banking circles for their funds or operation of businesses. Soon after the Capone incident, the bank opened numerous accounts for the various individuals and it was obvious that these people had engaged adequate, intelligent accountants and business people to provide them with advice and counsel in handling their monetary affairs in order to evade prosecution for income tax violations. It was at this point these individuals began putting their money into legitimate businesses in order that they could withstand an investigation and show that they were earning sufficient income to enjoy the expensive living they were enjoying.

Shepherding the new way of doing things for the Outfit was Frank Nitti, real name Nitto. Nitti became Outfit boss in 1932. It was recognized that Nitti had the low-profile demeanor and political connections to allow the Outfit to persevere. Nitti's top lieutenant in Chicago Heights was Jim Emery.[86]

Prohibition was repealed by ratification of the Twenty-first Amendment on December 5, 1933. If it were not repealed, Capone potentially faced more jail time, but the government decided to drop the Volstead Act charges against him. The repeal of Prohibition meant the Outfit had to seek new streams of revenue. The challenge was in seeking new revenue during the Great Depression. For Jim Emery, the question was not so much where to find new revenue but how to expand a steady source of revenue that the Chicago Heights street crew enjoyed since before the days of Prohibition —organized gambling.

In the early 1930s, Emery set out to ensure the political bases were covered. During Prohibition, he had amassed considerable political power by bribing local officials to protect bootlegging and gambling operations. Knowing that he could not expand gambling without political protection, he donated considerably to politicians that provided protection during Prohibition in hope that they would continue to do so after its repeal. In Chicago Heights, his closest political ally was John Mackler, a local construction contractor who turned to politics. He eventually served as a Cook County Commissioner. In the tradition of Cook County politics, his son was endorsed to take his place after he died in February 1952. Emery backed Mackler as he was getting his start in politics, and in return, Mackler provided protection to Emery. By 1934, Mackler was head of the county central committee for the Republican Party. In September of that year, he hosted a massive Republican rally at the Lincolnshire Country Club in Crete, Illinois, to rally the voters. The event was attended by delegations throughout Cook County, and all of the major party leaders attended. The sponsor of the program was the Republican Organization of Chicago Heights, of which Jim Emery was a member. Presumably, Emery was exerting his influence to advance his favored candidate.

Whether it worked or not is subject to speculation because in May 1935, a new city administration headed by a "reform" mayor Joseph Gannon was voted in. Gannon provided a lot of press that he beat the bipartisan machine consisting of Mayor Daniel Bergin, Democrat, and John Mackler for the Republicans. However, Gannon admitted that handbooks still existed in Chicago Heights. Gannon, on the one hand, may have been playing reformer while on the other he was allowing Emery's vice and gambling interests to continue to operate. Emery was known to contribute to whatever party served his interests best. It may not have mattered much in any event, because the Chicago Heights street crew was ever expanding.

Joliet and Will County were lucrative, as were Harvey and Blue Island. But the town that represented the most potential for growth was Calumet City. The Strip, as it was known, ran along State Street from Wentworth Avenue to State Line Road. It was an ideal location with corrupt Burnham, Illinois, to the north and Hammond, Indiana, just across State Line Road. Its location next to the Indiana border made Calumet City an ideal place to avoid interference from Illinois law enforcement and vice versa. Jim Colosimo and John Torrio first recognized the potential of Calumet City with its proximity to well-paid factory workers.[87] They thoroughly corrupted local politicians so that their houses of prostitution and gambling ran without interference. Cook County was the responsible law enforcement authority, but they had enough connections in county government that the threat of raids by the Cook County sheriff was minimal.

Enter Jim Emery in the mid-1930s with an edict from Frank Nitti to find sources of income to replace the loss of Prohibition. At that time, the Strip was not operating to its full potential. Emery found that the current local politicians were just as corruptible as those that preceded them in the 1920s. The administrations of William Zick, John Jaranowski, Frank Kaminski and Stanley Bejger, from 1935 to 1956, allowed the Outfit to run the Strip unimpeded at the local level. In the case of Mayor Jaranowski, he ran into trouble with the IRS to the tune of $100,000. Jaranowski supposedly obtained the money to pay the debt from Jim Emery in exchange for letting him take over the Strip and run it wide open.

With the politicians lined up, Emery consolidated the club operators that had strayed from Outfit control. Any reluctance was met with violence and intimidation. A resistant club owner might have been paid a visit by some tough guys that might trash the place or harm the owner physically. If that did not work, a strike was called. The resistant owner usually decided to cooperate, and shortly after, one of Emery's lieutenants in Calumet City appeared on the license. Much of the muscle for this effort was obtained from Emery A.C. When Emery's fighters were not in training, he sent them to Calumet City to enforce his orders. In 1936, Emery opened the Owl Club, which became the largest gambling establishment and nightclub in Calumet City.[88]

In the late 1930s, Emery started to devote more time to horse racing and spent more of his time in Florida. As a result, several men in the Chicago Heights street crew started to rise to prominence during this period. John

Jim Emery's horse Snorky winning at Riverside Park in Kansas City, Missouri. The Muehlebach Hotel in Kansas City hosted Charles and Anne Lindbergh for the event. Anne Lindbergh is seen in the photo presenting a bouquet to the jockey. Emery named the horse after Al Capone's nickname. *From the collection of Dr. Jim Ammirati and Jim Ammirati.*

From left to right: Nick Neroni, Joe Guzzino and Frank LaPorte. This photo was probably taken in the late 1930s as the three of them were on the rise in the Chicago Heights street crew.

Roberts oversaw his brother Dominic's interests; Frank LaPorte managed slot machines; Francis Curry ran Joliet and Will County; Joe Guzzino served as Jim Emery's eyes and ears over Francis Curry and served as Curry's enforcer; and Jimmy Catuara served as the main enforcer in Calumet City. In Chicago Heights, Charlie, Sam, Tony and Nick Costello kept an eye on things, along with Sam DiGiovanni. Nick Neroni was the union representative serving as the business agent for Local 5 of the Hod Carriers Union, a precursor to the Laborers' Union. Union infiltration was another source of income for the Outfit after Prohibition.

John Roberts was born Giovanni Ruberto in Sambiase, Italy, in 1901. He emigrated from Italy to the United States in December 1920. He had a wife and daughter that stayed in Italy.[89] Judging by the timing of his entry in 1920, it is a safe assumption that he was lured to the United States upon hearing of the good fortunes brought by Prohibition. Once in Chicago Heights, John Roberts quickly went to work with Dominic. After his brother was deported,

Jim Emery, in silk robe, sits with John Roberts to his right. John Nicastro stands in back. Nicastro served as a bagman for the Chicago Heights street crew, shuttling money and messages between Chicago Heights, Chicago and Italy. *From the collection of John Binder and Matthew Luzi.*

he also assisted Jim Emery in the expansion of the operations of the Chicago Heights street crew. From the mid-1930s until his death in 1961, he was closely associated with Frank LaPorte. John Roberts was frequently seen on the Strip in Calumet City and was probably responsible for bringing Jimmy Catuara into the crew.

Jimmy Catuara was born in 1905 and was a longtime resident of the Bridgeport/Chinatown neighborhood of Chicago. He first came to prominence in April 1933, when he and William Palermo, both then associated with James "King of the Bombers" Belcastro, were pulled over by police and found to be carrying a dynamite bomb. After twenty-five continuances, the two went on trial for the incident in October 1933. They were convicted and sentenced to five to twenty-five years in prison. Before entering prison, Catuara was picked up in March 1934 as a suspect in the bombing of milk dairies. He was picked up once more in August 1934 on suspicion for yet another bombing. He finally entered prison and was released in December 1942 after serving seven years, eleven months.[90] His

John Roberts, seated, with Jimmy "the Bomber" Catuara standing beside him. The fact that John Roberts is seated suggests that he was in a position of authority or respect over Jimmy Catuara. *From the collection of John Binder and Matthew Luzi.*

exploits earned him the nickname "Jimmy the Bomber." After his release from prison, Catuara showed up in Calumet City. It was well known on the Strip in the mid-1940s that he was Emery's chief enforcer. Catuara was known to threaten recalcitrant club owners with a shotgun and so thoroughly enjoyed a life of crime that one informant told the FBI that Jimmy Catuara would rather earn $100 illegally than $1,000 legally.[91]

Emery kept a string of horses at Tropical Park racetrack in Miami during the late 1930s. When in Chicago, he spent most of his time at his horse ranch in Tinley Park, Illinois. Locally, his horses ran in high-stakes contests at all of the major tracks of the day, including Lincoln Fields, Washington Park and Arlington. His best-known horse from 1938 to 1940 was Dolly Val. In a 1938 race at Lincoln Fields, Dolly Val was a favorite at even money. However, the horse finished so far back there was a track inquiry and the jockey was suspended. Nevertheless, a week later Dolly Val was entered in Detroit and won, paying off at $89.80, which caused bookmakers around the country to shudder.[92] Such shenanigans caused a track steward at

Jim Emery's horse in the lead at Washington Park race track in Homewood, Illinois. Note the initials "JE" on the horse's hood and the jockey's cap.

Lincoln Fields to write the Illinois racing board and express his displeasure with Emery's participation in Illinois racing. Racing regulators paid no attention throughout the 1940s. During that period, Emery continued to build his stable of horses and dominate the sport for the Outfit. His horses were nominated for the Kentucky Derby in 1944 and won at Washington Park's Great Western in 1946.

Race regulators did not take action until October 1954, when the *Chicago Daily News* ran a five-month investigation into how the Outfit muscled into Illinois racing. The series of articles that followed described Emery as a mystery man of the Outfit, deeply involved in racing.[93] The newspaper investigation prompted the Illinois Racing Board to launch its own investigation. The investigations caused Emery to quickly sell off his horses, and they uncovered numerous known bookmakers working the stands at the local tracks, with twenty-five bookmakers at Lincoln Fields alone. The bookmakers and Emery were banned from the tracks. In Emery's case, the ban lasted for about a year. He was reinstated in 1955.[94]

The Chicago Heights street crew did well under Jim Emery during the Depression. The expansion of organized gambling and vice succeeded. Emery had installed enough competent lieutenants that he could pursue broader endeavors for the Outfit. He sent a delegation, which included Frank LaPorte, to Italy to meet with Dominic Roberto in 1938. The meeting was probably intended to establish the means by which Roberto would receive his share of the proceeds from the activities of the Chicago Heights street crew. Additionally, the meeting probably opened a channel for the Outfit to benefit from any activities that Roberto established in Italy on the Outfit's behalf. The relationship mutually benefited the two parties for many years to come.

Gangland killings in Chicago Heights ceased with the repeal of Prohibition. This was due in part to the Outfit's desire to stay out of the spotlight and due in part to the consolidation of the gangs. That changed on February 9, 1938, when three men entered the South Side Bakery at Twenty-second and Butler in the Hill neighborhood looking for Sam Costello. As he stepped to the counter, one of the men greeted Costello, pulled a .45 and shot him. The other two then opened fire; all three gunmen hit Costello nine times. Five men in the back of the bakery—Luigi Onofrio, Nick Costello, Nello Bagagli, Joe DiGiovanni and Chris Giordano—rushed to the front with their own weapons drawn and shot it out with the gunmen. Nick Costello was wounded, but Bagagli and Giordano made a safe getaway. Police discovered that as the

Jim Emery seen here in his 1930 V-12 Cadillac. The car was a classic even in its day. This photo was taken in the driveway at the Emery home. *From the collection of Dr. Jim Ammirati and Jim Ammirati.*

Police investigate the murder of Sam Costello at the DiGiovanni Bros. South Side Bakery Shop at Twenty-second and Butler in the Hill neighborhood of Chicago Heights. Costello was killed February 9, 1938, by three assailants disguised as hunters. He was wearing a diamond-studded belt buckle given by Al Capone to his close friends.

gunmen made their way to the bakery, they stopped at Twenty-first Street to remove the license plates from their car and that all three were dressed as hunters. Police suspected the motive stemmed from Costello trying to muscle in on gambling in Will County. However, Will County gambling was already under the control of the Chicago Heights street crew. It is more likely that with Emery spending more time away from Chicago Heights, Costello saw an opportunity to make a move against him and possibly take over as boss of Chicago Heights. Emery probably received word and made a preemptive strike against Costello. In any event, no one was ever arrested for the killing. At the time of his death, Sam Costello was wearing a diamond-studded belt buckle given by Al Capone to his close friends and associates.[95]

During the 1940s, Joe Guzzino was spending time in Louisville, Kentucky, for Jim Emery and Francis Curry. Guzzino was born in 1899 in Donaldsville, Louisiana. He and his family eventually made their way to Chicago Heights as its industry started to boom and its Italian community grew. Guzzino became associated with Dominic Roberto and Jim Emery, starting out as one of their enforcers during Prohibition. In the 1940s, Guzzino was running wire room

Jim Emery, Dominic Roberto and Charlie "Lucky" Luciano attend a horse race in Rome, Italy, in 1949. Jim Emery is second from left, Dominic Roberto is in front of Emery wearing the dark pinstripe suit and Charlie Luciano stands in front of Roberto wearing glasses. *Courtesy of © Bettman/Corbis.*

services from Louisville, Kentucky, for the handbooks in Chicago Heights, Joliet and Calumet City. The operation of the wire rooms cut down on overhead for handbooks of the crew as they were able to get results directly from Guzzino's wire services without paying a third party provider.

After World War II, Emery was using Guzzino as an emissary to Italy where Guzzino associated with "mafia" leaders.[96] No doubt that one of them was Dominic Roberto, now back in Sambiase, Italy. He also met with crime figures in other areas of Italy, such as Ottaviano, just outside of Naples. During the late 1940s, his activities and associations attracted the attention of the Federal Bureau of Narcotics. One of his associates was Frank "Three Finger Frank" Coppola. Coppola was active in Detroit, St. Louis, and Kansas City, where he was known as the slot machine king. He was deported from the United States in 1948 and spent some time in Mexico before being expelled back to Italy. Coppola established himself in the drug trade in Detroit, St. Louis and New Orleans. In 1952, the Italian government broke a story of a drug smuggling bust in San Diego with ties to Coppola.

The FBI obtained information from the Federal Bureau of Narcotics that Emery and Coppola were indicted by the Italian government in 1952 for conspiracy in connection with a narcotics smuggling ring under the auspices of Charlie Luciano.[97] It is not known if the indictment had any validity or if it resulted in a conviction for Emery. However, Emery was known to meet with Dominic Roberto and Charlie Luciano in Italy.

Emery maintained his leadership of the Chicago Heights street crew into the 1950s but took on more of an advisory role as he lived out his remaining years mostly in Florida. By 1953, he started to divest himself of some of his active interests. One interest in particular was the Co-operative Music Company, in which he was a partner with Frank LaPorte. In 1953, Co-operative spun off its cigarette operation to Emery's son Ralph and his son-in-law Joe Costello, which they operated as Regal Vending Company. Ralph Emery was also part owner of the NOLA Race Wire Service in New Orleans, Louisiana, with Carlos Marcello.

Emery was unable to reestablish his position of dominance in horse racing after his reinstatement by the Illinois Racing Board in 1955. He died in March 1957, in Fort Lauderdale, Florida. Upon Emery's death, the leadership of the Chicago Heights street crew passed to his chief lieutenant, Frank LaPorte. Dominic Roberto and Jim Emery had groomed LaPorte for the position since Prohibition. In fact, LaPorte had been the de facto leader since at least the early 1950s.

CHAPTER 5

FRANK LAPORTE

F rank LaPorte was a cousin of Dominic and John Roberto. He was born Francesco Liparota in Sambiase, Calabria, Italy, on October 7, 1901, to Saverio (Sam) and Maria Theresa Liparota. Maria's maiden name was Falvo. Her aunt was Catherine Falvo, Dominic and John Roberto's mother. LaPorte emigrated from Italy and arrived in Philadelphia with his mother and two younger sisters, Theresa and Dolly, on August 20, 1913.[98] They arrived in Chicago Heights two days later and settled in with their father in the Hill neighborhood at 412 East Twenty-second Street, where the family maintained a small grocery store. Eventually, five more sisters were added to the family. LaPorte associated with Dominic Roberto and Jim Emery around 1919 or 1920 as they were expanding into bootlegging activities. He started primarily as Roberto's driver.

He was first arrested on September 10, 1926, with Dominic Roberto and a John Locus for the murder of John Andreadis. The three had gone to the C.H. Lunch Room at Sixteenth and Halsted Street, just steps from the police station, looking for Andreadis, the cook. Roberto sought Andreadis to settle a grudge not related to his vice or bootlegging activities. According to witness James Tsoutis, Roberto entered the kitchen, followed by Locus and LaPorte. Tsoutis claimed that upon finding Andreadis cleaning the stove, one of the three pulled a gun and shot Andreadis three times. The assailants immediately left, and Tsoutis went for the police to report the crime. Tsoutis gave police a complete account of what he saw, along with the names of Roberto, LaPorte and Locus. The police ordered an extensive manhunt, but the three turned

Frank LaPorte is at far right in this 1911 photo taken in Italy. Next to him from right to left are his sisters Theresa and Dolly (the toddler) and his mother, Maria Theresa Liparota.

themselves in and admitted that they were in the lunchroom and promised to tell what they knew of the incident. The police believed they had a solid case with three suspects in custody and a witness willing to testify. They allowed Tsoutis to go home until the start of the coroner's inquest the following day. However, the case fell apart when Tsoutis took the stand and changed his story completely. He claimed that Andreadis was the only one in the kitchen when he heard the shots. Roberto, LaPorte and Locus followed Andreadis to the stand. A detailed questioning was expected, but with Tsoutis changing his story, the three suspects declined to testify to anything, including their occupations.[99] With that, the three were released. The murder of Andreadis was the first time LaPorte's name received publicity.

LaPorte was questioned in connection with another murder on December 18, 1927. This time, the body of Peter Ruffolo was found dumped alongside the road at the intersection of Halsted Street and Ridge Road north of Chicago Heights. The police developed very few clues but surmised that Ruffolo was picked up on the East Side of Chicago Heights and "taken for a ride." Robbery was ruled out as a motive since Ruffolo's money and a pistol were found on his body. At the coroner's inquest, LaPorte was questioned because he was the last person known to see Ruffolo alive. LaPorte offered nothing of value that led to a viable suspect or motive. The investigation

Frank LaPorte stands to the left of George Montesanti in this photo. LaPorte and Montesanti were picked up on suspicion with six others in 1930 by Pat Roche of the state's attorney's office.

was continued for a week, after which time the coroner's jury returned an open verdict for lack of evidence. The papers attributed Ruffolo's killing to another "booze" killing.[100] There may have been some validity to this presumption, but the police never fully explored Ruffolo's background or his candy business—a business that allowed the Costello brothers to operate successfully supplying bootleggers with the raw materials to produce alcohol.

Frank LaPorte hit the news again in October 1930, when Pat Roche, chief investigator of the state's attorney's office, raided Chicago Heights and rounded up Joe Guzzino, John Roberts, Frank LaPorte, Al Soldano, George Montesanti and three others. The eight men were rounded up on suspicion so that Roche could run them through the Bureau of Identification and check their backgrounds. Nothing came of the round-up except Roche noted that Frank LaPorte was seen frequently hanging around Al Capone's headquarters.[101] In 1951, Soldano, then the owner of the Zig Zag Club on the Strip in Calumet City, would be questioned in the suspected gangland killing of Fred Brissa.

In November 1932, Frank LaPorte appeared before another coroner's inquest. This time, it was for a personal tragedy. On Sunday evening, November 27, 1932, Sam Liparota (he used his actual name) was visiting at his friend John Sposato's home. While there, a third man, Luigi Cianpini, dropped in for a visit. Liparota was acquainted with Cianpini as a customer of his grocery store. At first, the three men visited amicably, but then the subject of a grocery bill owed by Cianpini to Sam Liparota came up. Cianpini stated that he could not pay the bill, and an argument ensued. It became so heated that Sposato had to step between the two and urge that they calm down. With that, Cianpini grabbed his coat and started to leave. However, Sam Liparota said something to which Cianpini took offense. Cianpini turned back from the door, pulled a .38 revolver and opened fire on Liparota. Liparota pulled his own .32 revolver, and a gun battle erupted. When the shooting stopped, ten shots were fired between the two. Liparota was hit in the chest; Cianpini was hit in the abdomen. Liparota died at the scene and Cianpini died later at the hospital. At the inquest Frank LaPorte testified regarding his father's background and good relationship with Cianpini, leaving the impression that there was no other reason than a heated argument for the shooting.[102]

Frank LaPorte had proven his loyalty and capability to Dominic Roberto and Jim Emery throughout Prohibition. In the late 1930s and early 1940s, Emery expanded the scope of gambling throughout the southern suburbs. He entrusted LaPorte to oversee slot machines and handbooks for the entire area. LaPorte showed that he was a capable earner by establishing some of the biggest handbooks in Cook County. Police raided one in 1938. Located at 82 Illinois Street, it had four ticket writers serving several hundred patrons on site, with another twelve telephone operators taking bets over the phone. Charged with running the place was Charles Kirgis. When asked how he managed to keep such a large-scale illegal operation running wide-open, he responded that he knew town officials and they knew him.[103] He failed to mention that not only did he know town officials, he was also related. The clerk of the city court of Chicago Heights was Edward Kirgis.

In 1941, the *Chicago Daily News* printed an exposé on illegal gambling south of Chicago. The story noted that there were no attempts to camouflage the gambling establishments in Chicago Heights. Rather, they ran wide-open with assurance of protection by local authorities. Their only threat was the occasional and expected raid by county highway police. The largest gambling operation noted was located at 1728 Halsted Street, where over

Frank LaPorte in his naval uniform, circa 1943. He served as a cook assigned to an aircraft repair unit at the Glenview Naval Air Station.

one hundred patrons gathered to view wall sheets for the races at Lincoln Fields. Charlie Costello was reportedly Emery's lieutenant in charge of the operation.[104] However, the exposé did not mention that Frank LaPorte and Jim Emery owned 1728 Halsted Street. The location later became the home office of the Co-operative Music Company, a jukebox and vending machine company established to generate legitimate income and launder illegal income. The company served as a front for distributing slot and pinball machines, which doubled as gambling devices.

By 1942, Emery wanted LaPorte to take on more responsibility in Calumet City. But that had to wait at least two years because LaPorte decided to enlist in the navy. He did not join out of patriotism; rather, he joined to gain some assurance that he would not be deported if charges were ever filed against him. LaPorte was a cook assigned to an aircraft repair unit at Glenview Naval Air Station. While there, he supposedly bribed high-ranking officers with prime steaks in exchange for favorable treatment. His unit was transferred to Bremerton, Washington, in 1944. By that time, he was over the age of forty-two, and therefore, the navy granted him an honorable discharge on November 9, 1944.[105]

When LaPorte returned to Chicago Heights in 1944, the structure of the Outfit had changed. Frank Nitti committed suicide in March 1943, upon being indicted for extortion of Hollywood film studios through the Outfit's control of the International Alliance of Theatrical Stage Employees (IATSE) union. With Nitti's death, Paul Ricca took over as boss of the Outfit. Ricca was also indicted with Nitti and was convicted in 1943. With Ricca in prison in 1944, Anthony "Tony" Accardo became acting boss, assuming full control in 1946. After his release from prison, Ricca acted as advisor to the Outfit until his death. No doubt, Accardo gave Jim Emery his full endorsement in elevating LaPorte because Accardo and LaPorte were both "up and comers" at the same time in the Capone Gang.

In 1945, Frank LaPorte was put in charge of running the strip tease, prostitution and gambling houses on the Strip in Calumet City. It was also in 1945 that Frank LaPorte founded the Co-operative Music Company with Jim Emery. Managing the clubs in Calumet City went hand in glove with the vending business. Every club used LaPorte's jukeboxes and vending machines.

Around this same period, LaPorte consolidated the gambling operations of Francis Curry in Joliet, Illinois. Francis Curry was born in Joliet, Illinois, in December 1902. A bootlegger during Prohibition, he originally allied

The Co-operative Music Company at 1728 Halsted Street is seen in this early 1950s surveillance photo. *From the National Archive.*

Francis Curry, rackets boss in charge of Joliet for Frank LaPorte, sits to the left of John Roberts in this photo taken during the early or mid-1940s. *From the collection of John Binder and Matthew Luzi.*

himself with Paul Ricca. When Ricca went to prison in 1944, Curry served as the caretaker of Ricca's Will County farm. Curry also testified on Ricca's behalf at his parole hearing. In the early 1940s, Curry was given permission to operate slot machines in Will County for the Chicago Heights street crew. Frank LaPorte recognized that Curry was doing an adequate job, but he was not doing enough to ensure that all of the machines in the incestuous world of Joliet politics and crime were under Outfit control.

Curry's biggest competition in the late 1930s was Will County deputy sheriff Leahm Kelly. In April 1938, Kelly delivered a beating to William McCabe, editor of the *Weekly Spectator*, a local newspaper, and former state's attorney in Will County. McCabe's offense was an editorial he wrote stating that Kelly should be thrown out of office as the personal bailiff of Judge Edwin L. Wilson. A few weeks after the incident, the Joliet Township board voted to place a tax on gambling devices including slot machines. Kelly protested loudly at the meeting that he owned $60,000 worth of machines and the tax would put him out of business. In 1939, Judge Wilson was indicted with Dennis Kelly, Leahm's brother, for election fraud. The indictment alleged that Dennis Kelly, business agent for the local bartender's union, hired floaters to vote multiple times for Judge

Wilson. The Kelly brothers were trying to keep Judge Wilson in office because he protected their slot machines to the extent that he was once threatened with impeachment for interfering with their removal.[106]

By 1945, Leahm Kelly had built a sizable slot and vending machine business known as Automatic Music Company. He was attempting to put his machines in Cook County in competition with Co-operative Music Company, which was unacceptable to Frank LaPorte. On October 13, 1946, as Leahm Kelly pulled into his driveway and stepped from his car, another vehicle pulled in behind him. From the second car emerged a gunman that shot Kelly several times, killing him. Following Kelly's death, the Automatic Music Company was taken over by LaPorte.[107] Curry was brought in as a partner, and the business name was changed to Wilco Music Company. When Curry testified at a congressional investigation in 1948, he stated that he was operating two to three hundred slots through Wilco. Based on estimates, the machines generated $100,000 to $120,000 annually.

Dennis Kelly and William McCabe did not fare well either. Dennis Kelly survived a shooting in April 1947, in connection with the Outfit's attempts to gain control of the bartenders' union. He was not as fortunate in March 1953, when gunmen caught Kelly leaving his girlfriend's house in Hammond, Indiana. Two shotgun blasts followed by two pistol shots killed him.[108] He had tried moving into slot machines.

William McCabe decided to run for committeeman in Joliet's Forty-sixth Precinct in April 1948. The Forty-sixth was a political stronghold for Francis Curry. As an outspoken critic of vice and gambling, McCabe was not the favored candidate. On April 8, 1948, McCabe was kidnapped, beaten and shot. Afterward, McCabe claimed that he was attacked by Curry's henchman for refusing Curry's order to withdraw from the race.[109] McCabe eventually recovered but was never the same. He remained a majority shareholder of the *Weekly Spectator* but ceded daily control to his partner, Molly Zelko. She continued the paper's crusade against gambling in Joliet until September 25, 1957, when she disappeared. When she failed to show for work, the police went to her apartment, where they found her car parked outside. It was unlocked with the keys under the seat. One of her shoes was on the trunk of the car and the other was found nearby. Police speculated that she kicked the shoes off during a struggle but later a passerby claimed to have noticed the shoe and placed it on the trunk. When police asked McCabe about Molly Zelko's disappearance, he responded that Francis Curry should be questioned because of her known hatred and crusade against him. McCabe succumbed to the stress of the investigation and his poor health in August 1958, when he died of natural causes.

An investigation into Zelko's background revealed irregularities that contributed to the intrigue surrounding her disappearance. For instance, despite meager earnings, she owned a seventeen-and-a-half-karat diamond ring valued at $37,000. She reportedly paid just $5,000 for it. Authorities thought they had a break in the case when James Rini, an ex-convict and lower-level Outfit associate, confessed to the kidnapping. Rini claimed gangsters, including Frank LaPorte and Francis Curry, hired him to execute Zelko for her anti-gaming crusades. However, when Robert Kennedy arranged for Rini to testify before a Senate Rackets Committee, he pled the Fifth. Rini later recanted his story to the press. He said that he made the story up so authorities would stop questioning him about it and reduce his sentence for providing information. However, a 1993 *Chicago Reader* article by John Conroy notes that Rini had threatened another newspaper editor, had participated in an attempted murder and was involved with the coin machine industry. Molly Zelko was never found, and authorities never charged anyone for her disappearance.[110]

Calumet City was a little less challenging to manage when Frank LaPorte returned from the navy. Most of the remaining competition was eliminated while LaPorte was away. The biggest competitor had been Frank Abbatte. Formerly from Chicago Heights, Abbatte moved to Hammond, Indiana to be closer to his nightclubs in Calumet City. Abbatte's sideline was horseracing. He left home with his horses in February 1944, to attend the races in Hot Springs, Arkansas. He was last seen alive on February 23, 1944, when he brought his car in for repairs and asked that it be ready the next day. His dead body turned up in April 1944, about thirty miles outside Hot Springs. The innovative police work of the day determined that Frank Abbatte was "taken for a ride" and killed by person or persons unknown. The elimination of Abbatte was most likely a two-for-one deal for Jim Emery. Abbatte's death meant less competition in Calumet City and in horseracing. Following Abbatte's death, his associates met with similar fates. Matt Manzo, owner of the Paddock Club, disappeared; Onofrio Vitale's body turned up in a sewer; and Thomas Neglia was killed while getting a haircut in a Chicago barbershop.[111]

The Strip in Calumet City was booming in the 1940s. The large-scale gambling operations received a boost from local factory workers flush with overtime pay as they worked round the clock during the war. World War II itself brought strippers and the skin trade to augment the gambling. No less than thirty-four clubs lined both sides of a five-block area of the Strip in the mid-1940s. Calumet City was said to have more liquor licenses per

The Strip in Calumet City from the intersection of State Line Road and State Street in the early 1950s. Clubs visible in this photo include the Chatter Box, Club Cadillac, Show Club, Rip Tide, Club Rondavoo, Zig Zag Club, Derby Club, The Paddock and the Little Club.

capita than any other city in America, with 365 operating saloons by the late-1940s and just fourteen police officers to watch over them. It earned its nicknames: "Barbary Coast of the Midwest" and "Wickedest Little Town in America."

Following the elimination of Abbatte and his associates, Phil Bacino and the Miceli brothers, aka Mitchell or Micheli, were installed to watch over interests in Calumet City. The Miceli brothers operated several clubs and managed some of the gambling. Phil Bacino was an old-line mobster who had a relationship with Jim Emery going back to Prohibition. He operated on the Strip out of his restaurant known as John's Pizzeria. He was picked up at a national meeting of Sicilian mobsters in Cleveland in 1928 under the name Tony Bello. On October 5, 1935, he shot and killed John Nickels, owner of the Town Club in Calumet City. Three days later, a coroner's verdict declared it justifiable homicide and released Bacino. He had been

John Miceli (center) talks to one of the performers at the Little Club following a raid. Miceli and his brothers Sam, Joe and Anthony were known as the Mitchell boys. They ran several Calumet City clubs, including the Brass Rail, the Little Club, the Rip Tide and the Music Box, for Frank LaPorte.

in a fight with Nickels on the evening of October 5, when Nickels went to Bacino's house to confront him about a debt that Nickels's associate Joe Morris owed to Bacino. Bacino testified at the coroner's inquest that Nickels returned to his house later in the evening and was waving a gun at him from the porch, so he shot Nickels through the front window. Nickels's wife claimed he was unarmed when he left the house.[112]

Bacino maintained the appearance of a legitimate businessman. The Outfit intended it that way because John's Pizzeria served as a sort of headquarters for the Strip. Regular meetings attended by Frank LaPorte, various club owners and upper echelon members of the Outfit were held there. Bacino also mediated disputes and was a facilitator between the Outfit and local politicians.

Calumet City offered something for everyone. The Outfit was able to attract top-name talent like Jimmy Durante and Martha Raye. Many of the clubs featured Las Vegas–style revues. The Owl Club in particular featured top-flight entertainment to go along with large-scale gambling. Jim Emery sponsored

Frank LaPorte for part ownership in the Owl Club with Tony Accardo. John Perry served as the front man and club manager, while Jim "One Armed Jimmy" Montella was the gambling manager. It was the premier location in Calumet City, and the numbers were staggering. Gross income from its handbook operation in 1948 alone was $1.8 million. In 1949, the gross income from its handbook was $1.6 million, plus $300,000 from a dice game.[113]

Frank LaPorte was doing so well in the late 1940s that he employed most of his relatives and friends. They worked collection routes for Co-operative Music Company and Wilco Music Company. They were partners or fronts in Calumet City establishments, they worked the handbooks and some were in positions of authority in the Chicago Heights street crew. It was also around this time that Frank LaPorte installed his bodyguard and driver Al Pilotto as president of the Hod Carriers Local 5 in Chicago Heights. Things were going so well that LaPorte moved into a new custom-built ranch-style home in Flossmoor, Illinois. He was surrounded on the same block with relatives that had key positions in his organization. He also started to spend more time out west, particularly in California, where he had contact with Frank Bompensiero in San Diego. Bompensiero was originally from Milwaukee, Wisconsin. LaPorte probably made contact with Bompensiero through his own Milwaukee connections, John Moroni and Frank Balistreri. LaPorte and Bompensiero were known to make trips to Tijuana, Mexico, to visit Frank Coppola before he was sent back to Italy and also to meet with Gaspare Matranga, a former Calumet City operator and known enforcer.

Senator Estes Kefauver launched a Special Committee to Investigate Organized Crime on May 3, 1950. The committee might not have otherwise attracted attention except its hearings traveled to cities thought to have heavy organized crime influence. In addition, with many of the committee's proceedings being televised, the public became captivated as nicely dressed mobsters and racketeers in sunglasses were paraded before the cameras. When the hearings reached Chicago, part of the spotlight was shown on Calumet City. For the first time, there was a public outcry to do something. Newspapers started to run stories about the town and its bawdy reputation.

The Cook County Sheriff's Police led the first raid on the Owl Club in February 1951. Thirty-five people were arrested as four hundred more fled. By July 1951, the Owl Club was raided two more times. That same month, raiders of the state's attorney's office fanned out to Blue Island and Chicago Heights. The police recognized Mike Cifelli when they raided Chicago Heights as he was arrested twice before at the Owl Club. In August, the raiders hit Calumet City

The Owl Club in Calumet City featured top-name entertainment of the day. *From left to right:* Paul Ricca, Louie Campagna, Frank LaPorte and Jimmy Durante. The photo was taken at the Owl Club in the early 1950s.

Martha Raye poses at the head of the table with her guests from Chicago Heights. The men seated around the table starting at left are Ralph Emery, John Roberts, Joe Guzzino, John Nicastro and Jimmy "One Armed Jimmy" Montella. This photo was taken at Martha Raye's 5 O'Clock Club in Miami Beach. *From the collection of John Binder and Matthew Luzi.*

This photo was taken in Tijuana, Mexico, circa 1948. *From left to right:* Frank "Three Fingered Frank" Coppola, Frank LaPorte, Diva Pilotto, Mickey LaPorte, Thelma Bompensiero, Mary Ann Bompensiero, Al Pilotto and Frank Bompensiero. Three Fingered Frank was supposedly indicted with Jim Emery by the Italian government in connection with a drug conspiracy. Frank Bompensiero was a San Diego mobster originally from Milwaukee. *Courtesy of the* San Diego Reader, *photo first published in* A Bad, Bad, Boy *by Judith Moore.*

again and raided the Four Aces, another of LaPorte's clubs. Nabbed in the raid was none other than Mike Cifelli, causing him to blurt out, "What, again?!" as the raiders burst into the club. All of this activity caused corrupt Mayor Kaminski to suspend the license of the Four Aces and several other clubs.[114] As it turned out, most of the raids were for show.

In the meantime, there was still one independent competitor, Arthur Helfer, to deal with. Helfer had been around for twenty-five years and controlled liquor licenses for eight establishments without associating with the Chicago Heights street crew. There were several attempts to eliminate Helfer but none successful until September 15, 1951, when Helfer was shot six times as he walked up the driveway to his home.[115]

By 1953, the Strip was running mostly as it was before the 1951 raids. An informant reported to the FBI that the raids occurred only until Frank LaPorte had a chance to meet with the sheriff's office and settle on an

The gambling operation at the Owl Club just before a raid in 1951. Note the number of patrons and at least four betting windows seen in the back. There was no attempt to conceal gambling operations at the Owl Club or any of the other clubs on the Strip because Frank LaPorte had thoroughly corrupted Calumet City officials and police.

amount to pay. It seemed like another cleanup might occur when Stanley Bejger was elected mayor of Calumet City in 1953. However, he was the son-in-law of former mayor John Jaranowski.

The IRS presented another threat in 1954 when it went after Frank LaPorte and Tony Accardo for understated income from the Owl Club. The case seemed to be settled in 1955, but LaPorte and Accardo asked that the case be reopened to hear further testimony. LaPorte eventually settled on an amount to pay to the IRS. However, charges for tax fraud were brought against Accardo. The government charged that Accardo set up false income as a beer salesman to hide income from gambling. The case went to trial in 1960. Accardo relied heavily on several Chicago Heights witnesses to assist his case. Testifying for Accardo were Joe Costello, John Macaluso and Al Pilotto. They all testified that Accardo was in fact selling Foxhead 400 beer. Al Pilotto admitted during his testimony that he was a partner in the Wilco Music Company with Frank LaPorte, James Ross, Marty Pulcini, Frank Franze, Mike Roberts, Sam DiGiovanni and Dominick and William Palermo. Ross, Pulcini and Franze were brothers-in-law of LaPorte. Accardo was eventually convicted of tax fraud, but the decision was reversed on appeal.

By the mid-1950s, Frank LaPorte started to distance himself from active participation in the activities of Calumet City. The raids and the tax investigation probably caused him to realize that he needed to maintain a lower profile. Ownership and management of the Owl Club changed hands to LaPorte's brother-in-law Tony Franze. Also, Joe Guzzino started to take a more active role in the operations of Calumet City during the mid-1950s. The Chicago Crime Commission obtained information that Guzzino may have been responsible for the Helfer murder and in return was promoted to take over day-to-day responsibilities in Calumet City. Many of the clubs that LaPorte directly controlled were now in the names of close associates and relatives. This freed LaPorte to explore investment opportunities for the Outfit out west and still receive a cut of the take. It was during this time period that he built a custom home for himself in Stockton, California, just north of Modesto, California.

Louie Campagna died of natural causes in 1955. He was a top Outfit figure going back to Capone's day. Supposedly, LaPorte was acknowledged as boss of the Chicago Heights street crew at Campagna's wake.[116] LaPorte's stature in the Outfit was noted by the Chicago Crime Commission in 1952, when it reported that he was known to meet once a month in Chicago Heights with top Outfit bosses Tony Accardo, Sam Giancana, Eddie Vogel and Rocco Fischetti. When Jim Emery died in 1957, Frank LaPorte took complete control of the crew and its network of gambling, vice and vending machine operations. By this time, LaPorte amassed enough wealth and power that his activities could not be questioned by anyone in the Outfit except new street boss Sam Giancana and Tony Accardo in his new role as advisor to Giancana.

The infamous meeting of La Cosa Nostra's commission in Apalachin, New York, that took place in 1957 caused the FBI to focus on organized crime. The FBI scrambled to set up its Top Hoodlum Program in cities suspected of having a strong organized crime influence. Chicago was one such city. The FBI did not become interested in Frank LaPorte as a target for the program until 1962. By that time, LaPorte had been involved in organized crime for forty years.

Calumet City did not appear willing to change its ways. In May 1959, city aldermen refused to approve the full-time appointment of acting police chief Casimir Linkiewicz to succeed Henry Wleklinski. Wleklinksi was on leave of absence after being indicted for malfeasance in office. However, the aldermen's inaction could not prevent the damage that Linkiewicz had done in two months as acting chief. During that time, he supplied enough

Frank LaPorte poses with the son of his *paisano* in Milwaukee. The photo was most likely taken to commemorate the boy's confirmation. LaPorte had forged an alliance with people from Milwaukee going back to Prohibition. *From the collection of John Binder and Matthew Luzi.*

information to Paul Newey, chief investigator for State's Attorney Benjamin Adamowski, for Newey to organize a raid on ten spots in Calumet City. These included some of Frank LaPorte's most notorious: the Folies Bergere, the Rip Tide, Four Aces and the Derby Club. The raid netted ninety-eight arrests and resulted in the seizure of a large cache of business records. It had a chilling effect on LaPorte's Calumet City operations as the state's attorney convened a grand jury. The federal government also jumped in and issued subpoenas to the ninety-eight individuals arrested.[117] Perhaps worse for Frank LaPorte, an Outfit boss who took every precaution to remain out of the spotlight, was an article in the *Chicago Daily News* on June 2, 1959, that exposed him as being behind the vice dens of Calumet City. The article noted that LaPorte had done such an excellent job avoiding the spotlight that no law enforcement agencies had a current photo of him and that he had no available arrest record. In an attempt to change that, the article

Frank LaPorte placed many of his close friends and relatives in key positions. Among those pictured in this photo are standing in the back row, starting third from the left: Tony Falvo, Tony Franze, John Roberts and Jimmy Ross. Crouched directly in front of John Roberts is Theodore Bartusiewicz. Crouched in the front on the far right is Dominic Franze. Tony Falvo was a bodyguard for LaPorte. Dominic Franze served as business agent for the Laborers' local in Joliet, Illinois, during the early 1940s.

described LaPorte's habits and exposed how he concealed his interests in three clubs by using his brothers-in-law, including Theodore Bartusiewicz and Frank Franze, as fronts.

Following the raid, many of the clubs stayed in business, but the wide-open gambling and prostitution was curtailed. By July 1959, six of the clubs on the Strip closed for good. LaPorte decided to move the Owl Club's operations over to Calumet Park, Illinois, into George "Babe" Tuffanelli's Club Corral. George Tuffanelli's given name was Constance Tuffanelli. He was a bootlegger during Prohibition and was fined $500 in 1926 for violating the Volstead Act. In 1943, Tuffanelli was sentenced to a year and a day for possession of untaxed alcohol. Tuffanelli's side gig was as a racecar owner. One of his cars qualified for the 1948 Indy 500. Locally, he was frequently

George "Babe" Tuffanelli is seen here in a 1940s police photo. Tuffanelli ran the rackets in Blue Island, Illinois, under the auspices of Frank LaPorte. When not running gambling in Blue Island, Tuffanelli occupied himself with race cars. *Courtesy of the Chicago Crime Commission.*

seen at the Calumet Park Raceway. Frank LaPorte, with the backing of the Outfit, set Tuffanelli up with the Club Corral in Calumet Park, Illinois. It was a large-scale operation that ran into the early morning hours. He was once interviewed about the club and stated that he built the place on contract for unnamed owners (presumably LaPorte and Accardo). When asked who owned the casino in the back of the club, he declined to answer.[118]

LaPorte decided to concentrate on Will County, Chicago Heights and other areas in the south suburbs where he still had influence over local authorities. Of course, the clubs that remained in Calumet City still carried vending machines supplied by Co-operative Music Company. LaPorte also continued to receive a cut from the activities of the clubs that remained open. The grand juries convened after the 1959 raid resulted in some low-level indictments. However, LaPorte, Bacino, the Micelis and other higher-ups were not charged. They were too well insulated, and most of the witnesses were strippers that had no knowledge of the business behind the Strip. As for Chief Linkiewicz, the aldermen continued to oppose confirmation of his appointment even after Mayor Joseph Nowak was elected in 1961. Mayor

Nowak took measures to ensure that gambling and prostitution remained curtailed as much as possible. As part of that effort, he re-appointed Chief Linkiewicz every thirty days as temporary chief of police.[119]

The Club Corral did not maintain the Owl Club's business for long. In November 1959, a large high-stakes gambling operation controlled by the Outfit known as the "Big Game" had moved to Will County when it was driven from Cicero, Illinois, after a raid. When the game moved, Frank LaPorte decided to consolidate the Club Corral action with the Big Game and become a member of the bank with Tony Accardo, Sam Giancana, Rocco Fischetti, Gus Alex, Les Kruse and Johnny Drew. Moving the game to Will County also meant cutting in Francis Curry. The game operated unimpeded for two years until *Chicago Tribune* reporter Sandy Smith showed up in 1961 and exposed the gambling after finding it running wide-open with two hundred patrons.[120] Supposedly, each member of the bank kicked in $20,000 to fund the operation nightly.

Frank LaPorte started a cat-and-mouse game with federal authorities in September 1961, when he was subpoenaed to appear before the McClellan Committee. The committee was chaired by Senator John McClellan and was looking into organized crime activity. The committee was interested to hear from LaPorte about his operations that had moved from Calumet City to the Thornton-Lansing, Illinois area. LaPorte successfully dodged the subpoena, but the *Chicago Tribune* claimed its investigative reporters found vice wide-open at several clubs in the area operated by Sam Miceli. It also found the Folies Bergere in Calumet City operating again.[121] The FBI opened their LaPorte file in 1962, as noted above, the year after he was subpoenaed by the McClellan Committee. LaPorte spent the next decade appearing in Chicago Heights or at his home in Flossmoor for brief periods and then traveled to California or other locales in an attempt to stay ahead of investigators and their subpoenas.

The largest raid to hit the Chicago Heights street crew occurred on April 9, 1963, when three hundred federal agents raided thirty-one handbook operations throughout south Cook County and Will County. The raid ensnared sixty people, including Ralph Emery, Art Pilotto (Al's brother), Al Pilotto, Dominick Palermo, Joe Costello and William, Raymond and Charles Kirgis. Joe Guzzino was identified as part of the upper echelon of Calumet City gambling. He and Richard Guzzino were both questioned. The raid turned up interesting information in the records of the Co-operative Music Company. The records showed that John Roberts was on the payroll for $20,000 annually even though he had passed away in 1961. Dominic

For years, no current photographs of Frank LaPorte were ever publicized. He went to great lengths to make certain that the press did not have the opportunity to take his photo and he traveled frequently in an attempt to stay one step ahead of investigators and their subpoenas. However, he was caught by surveillance photographers in these photos. *Courtesy of the Chicago Crime Commission.*

Roberto was on the payroll for a $20,000 annual salary even though he was deported to Italy in 1935. Dominic was probably collecting his share and John's as tribute. The federal investigators took note that it was Dominic that met and conferred with Tony Accardo and Chicago police lieutenant Anthony DeGrazia in Rome in 1959. Once again, the raid resulted in low-level indictments, but LaPorte, Pilotto and other high-ranking members of the crew escaped indictment.

There was a potential casualty resulting from the raid when Joe Costello committed suicide in August 1963. Rumors circulated around Chicago Heights before Costello's suicide that hit man Anthony Panzica was in town to "take care of someone." Panzica was an ex-convict from Chicago Heights living in Florida. He was known to show up for "jobs" and was once pulled over by Chicago police at the home of Outfit enforcer and loan shark Felix "Milwaukee Phil" Alderisio. The police noted that Panzica's car was a

John Nicastro (left) visits Dominic Roberto (center) in Italy on one of his many trips as a bagman between the Outfit and Dominic Roberto.

"work car" rigged with secret compartments for the concealment of weapons. Another rumor placed Dominick Palermo at the scene just before Costello's suicide. However, police did not find any validity to the rumors and ruled Costello's death a suicide, noting that a .38 belonging to Costello was found next to his body. Police also found a suicide note that was attributed to Costello. The most likely reason for the suicide was that Costello had lost roughly $200,000 on failed gambling ventures, some in connection with the recent raid, and Ralph Emery and Frank LaPorte were pressuring him for the money.[122]

"Milwaukee" Phil Alderisio was rumored by the press to be involved in a power struggle for control over Frank LaPorte's territory in 1963. Cook County sheriff's detectives reported that Alderisio was seen meeting with Frank LaPorte at the Co-operative Music Company. Sheriff's detectives concluded that

Alderisio had taken control of Co-operative Music Company based on their observations. However, the information was suspect when considering that the source was Richard Cain. The notoriously corrupt Cain was considered by some to be a double agent for the Outfit. He was executed at Rose's Sandwich Shop on Grand Avenue in 1973. In any event, if there was a power struggle within the Outfit, it was coming from Jimmy Catuara, not "Milwaukee" Phil Alderisio. Alderisio was probably sent at the behest of Sam Giancana and Tony Accardo to help keep things under control following the 1963 raid and to offer assistance to LaPorte while he spent time away from Chicago Heights. In 1965, Frank Luzi was observed in conversation with Alderisio discussing different matters regarding Chicago Heights and Co-operative Music Company. Luzi was a nephew of Frank LaPorte. He was a bail bondsman and also LaPorte's driver and bodyguard. There was no animosity on the part of Alderisio and no indication that Alderisio had taken the company over during their conversation. The nature of the conversation was such that Luzi seemed to be reporting to Alderisio on various activities and the whereabouts of his uncle. At one point, Luzi inquired about Alderisio's trips to Italy, and Alderisio reported that he had visited with Dominic Roberto. If Alderisio was in a power struggle for Frank LaPorte's territory and had taken control of the Co-operative Music Company, he certainly did not act as if he had taken over during the conversation with Luzi.[123]

Jimmy Catuara left Calumet City sometime during the 1950s and returned to his old haunts on the South Side where he carved out his own niche. By the mid-1960s, he was living in Oak Lawn, Illinois, and his rackets extended from the South Side down through the southwest suburbs. Considering that much of his territory was within the domain of Frank LaPorte, Catuara was subordinate to him, but Catuara considered LaPorte a partner. By 1964, Catuara was frustrated with LaPorte and let it be known in Outfit circles. One informant reported to the FBI that animosity developed between the two when Catuara became aggressive in his efforts to take over some gambling operations that were under LaPorte's control. Catuara also expressed frustration to the informant that LaPorte was rarely around and that the "G" was getting to him. He also was frustrated that LaPorte had so many of his relatives on the payroll and indicated that when LaPorte died, his in-laws would be thrown out.[124]

As Catuara stirred the pot in Chicago, LaPorte was spending quite a bit of time in California. Failed schemes in California caused him unwanted publicity, legal trouble and loss of considerable investments. Over the years, LaPorte had invested proceeds from Prohibition and gambling for himself and on behalf of the Outfit. He had considerable real estate holdings in northern California, Nevada and Arizona. He was always interested in ways to invest in other ventures.

San Diego mobster and LaPorte's old friend Frank Bompensiero introduced LaPorte to Jimmy "The Weasel" Fratianno so that Fratianno could sell LaPorte on the merits of his trucking business. LaPorte decided to invest in the business. He secured $225,000 in loans from the Mercantile Bank and the Exchange National Bank in Chicago and brought his brothers-in-law Tony Franze and Jimmy Ross into the business.[125] The business initially did well until 1966 when Fratianno contracted for a road job in El Centro, California, just north of the Mexican border. Fratianno needed some new equipment for the job and once again turned to LaPorte for money. This time, LaPorte came up with $304,000. Fratianno ended up in a convoluted sub-hauling deal that cost him money over California's pay rate for the drivers. He then tried restructuring his deal with the drivers to make them owner operators. One of the drivers showed resistance and was beaten by one of Fratianno's goons. The driver went to the press, and the losing deal went from bad to worse when the local paper exposed the whole operation. The federal government opened an investigation in San Diego. LaPorte was subpoenaed and ordered to appear, as was the fired president of the Mercantile Bank of Chicago where LaPorte secured one of the loans. LaPorte employed his usual tactics and dodged the subpoena by staying out of California. Charges were not brought against LaPorte. However, Fratianno and Bompensiero were both charged. The charges against Bompensiero were dropped, and Fratianno received probation and a fine. LaPorte was out nearly $400,000 for his efforts.[126]

Fratianno also pitched a scheme to Joseph Alioto, chairman of the board of First San Francisco Bank, where Fratianno had secured his portion of the capital for the trucking deal. Joseph Alioto later served as the mayor of San Francisco. The idea was to buy the Crystal Bay casino in Lake Tahoe. In order to purchase the casino, Fratianno needed LaPorte to invest. However, LaPorte was reticent to invest because of the mounting pressure from the trucking deal and suggested that Fratianno find a "straight buyer" before LaPorte considered investing. Fratianno's front was Alioto. LaPorte, concerned with Fratianno's ability to deliver, ultimately turned it down because of the terms that Alioto proposed. LaPorte instead agreed to invest in the Tallyho Casino, which was Fratianno's fallback plan. That deal did not work out either as Fratianno failed to obtain the license to operate the Tallyho.[127] Matters were made worse in 1969 when *Look Magazine* exposed much of the scheming between Fratianno, LaPorte, Bompensiero, Joseph Alioto and other top California mobsters. The article damaged Alioto's career, resulting in his bringing a libel suit against *Look*. The article damaged LaPorte, as it brought unwanted publicity, including his photo. The photo was the first time that LaPorte's picture appeared in public since a 1945 Decatur, Illinois mug shot.

Frank LaPorte was given control of Lake County, Indiana, in the mid-1960s. The area was previously overseen by Anthony Pinelli, a Capone-era gangster from Gary, Indiana, and Jim DeGeorge, originally from Chicago Heights.[128] Their chief lieutenants were Tommy Morgano and Frank Zizzo. Pinelli got into some tax trouble with the IRS and decided to move to Los Angeles in semi-retirement. DeGeorge also went into semi-retirement, spending most of his time at his Triple D Ranch in Wisconsin. Tommy Morgano was the natural successor, but he attempted to bribe a Porter County, Indiana official to allow gambling to operate there. He was deported back to Sicily for his actions. Frank LaPorte was the natural choice to take over Lake County since it bordered his territory to the east of Chicago Heights. However, by the time LaPorte became the boss of Lake County, he was spending so much time away that oversight was handed off to his lieutenants, Dominick Palermo and Al Pilotto. Palermo would one day control Lake County for the Outfit, and Pilotto had a close relationship with Frank Zizzo.

Authorities put so much pressure on gambling in Illinois during the mid-1960s that the Outfit was once again forced to explore other areas of revenue. Frank LaPorte decided to expand his vending machine operations further into Kane and Will Counties. The mayor of Aurora, Illinois, got wind of the expansion and notified the Illinois Investigation Commission. The commission identified Chuck English, an Outfit boss involved in vending machines; Francis Curry; Frank LaPorte; his brother-in-law Frank Franze; and Ralph Emery as those behind the expansion effort. Frank Franze was identified as the one who spearheaded the effort. Frank LaPorte must have been slowing down when the subpoenas were issued in 1966 because this time he was actually served. LaPorte, Ralph Emery and Frank Franze, who were also served, appeared at the commission hearing with their attorney Eugene Bernstein (the same attorney that represented LaPorte and Accardo during the Owl Club tax trial). The questioning lasted just twenty minutes as the three refused to answer questions. Once again, no charges were filed.[129]

The year 1966 was rough for Frank LaPorte. In addition to having to appear before the Illinois Investigation Commission, there were two murders linked to the growing animosity between Jimmy Catuara and LaPorte. A third was committed in early 1967. The first murder was that of Clarence Forrest. Forrest was a bartender at the Eagles A-Go-Go in Calumet Park. The Eagles A-Go-

Go was operated by George Tuffanelli and was formerly the Club Corral. The body of Clarence Forrest was found shot and stuffed in the trunk of his car near St. John, Indiana. A diary detailing the activities at the Eagles A-Go-Go was found on his body, leading authorities to believe that Forrest was a plant for West Side mob boss Fiore "Fifi" Buccieri. Catuara persuaded Buccieri to join him in his attempt to wrest control from LaPorte over the territory of the Chicago Heights street crew. Louis Pratico, a former Chicago Heights police officer and muscleman for LaPorte, was the prime suspect in Forrest's murder. Pratico had been the manager of the Eagles A-Go-Go at the time Forrest worked there. Six months later, the body of Pratico was found in a ditch along West End Avenue in Chicago Heights. He was beaten and shot in the head. This time, the authorities suspected that Catuara struck in retaliation for Forrest. The third murder linked to the feud was that of Wesley Funicella. Funicella's body was found stuffed in the trunk of his car left in Blue Island, Illinois. He was beaten and strangled. Funicella was a LaPorte associate that worked at the R&B Collection Agency. The agency was partly owned by Jimmy Catuara, and the name of Billy Dauber, Catuara's chief enforcer, was found on his body.[130]

At the time of the feud between Catuara and LaPorte, Tony Accardo and Paul Ricca replaced Sam Giancana with Sam Battaglia as the Outfit's new boss. This would bode well for LaPorte because he had a good relationship with Sam Battaglia. Informants reported to the FBI that a sit-down was to be called by Accardo and Ricca to settle things. There is no information to confirm that the meeting took place. However, it is safe to assume that it did and that LaPorte came out intact because he never relinquished the Co-operative Music Company and he remained the acknowledged boss of the Chicago Heights street crew. It stands to reason that as long as Ricca and Accardo were around, LaPorte was safe from having his territory taken away because their roots ran back to Capone.

For the remainder of the 1960s, LaPorte continued to travel but was more cautious about going to California, if not avoiding it altogether. In late 1966, he suffered a setback when Joe Guzzino passed away suddenly of natural causes. Guzzino was with LaPorte since Prohibition and was one of his most trusted lieutenants.

When in Chicago Heights, LaPorte concentrated on the Co-operative Music Company but authorities were keeping a close eye on the company. In 1969, state revenue investigators confiscated vending machines owned by Co-operative for not displaying tax stamps.[131]

LaPorte took on the role of emissary for Accardo and Ricca. He traveled frequently at their behest wherever they needed assistance. He traveled to

California in April 1970 to carry a message that there should be no efforts to extort Moe Dalitz, a top mobster from Cleveland, Ohio, operating in Las Vegas. He also traveled to San Diego with St. Louis boss Tony Giordano to conduct some business and report back to Accardo and Ricca. In 1971, he served as a messenger for Accardo and Ricca regarding the federal investigation of John Roselli.

Another murder occurred in 1972 that some reports attributed to the feud between Catuara and LaPorte. On August 8, 1972, Guido Fidanzi pulled into Malizia's gas station on Lincoln Highway in Chicago Heights. As he walked into the station, a gold Chrysler pulled up. The driver held a handkerchief to his face and told the patrons to get down. A man got out on the passenger side and walked toward the station's office. Fidanzi caught his eye as the man approached and drew a .22 caliber pistol. Fidanzi went for the washroom and tried to lock himself in, but the gunman kicked in the door. He then drew a larger caliber weapon and shot Fidanzi twice in the head.[132] By this time, the feud between Catuara and LaPorte had passed.

It was more likely that Fidanzi was killed for Catuara's own protection. Fidanzi was indicted in February 1972 with Jimmy Catuara and sixteen others for a loan racket. Fidanzi had also worked for Catuara on other loan scams. It was reported that Catuara had been seen in the vicinity of the gas station prior to the murder with known Outfit killer Frank "The German" Schweihs. Therefore, Catuara probably had Fidanzi killed for fear that he might testify against Catuara. If that was not the motive, then Catuara had plenty of others because Fidanzi was running amok carrying out schemes unsanctioned by the Outfit.

The late 1960s and early 1970s was a time of transition for the Outfit. Heightened federal scrutiny contributed to a succession of street bosses after Sam Giancana was removed. Attrition also took its toll on the Outfit during the early 1970s. Francis Curry died May 6, 1970. "Milwaukee" Phil Alderisio died in 1971. Sam Battaglia died in 1973.

The year 1972 was particularly tough on the Outfit when Ross Prio, Paul Ricca and Frank LaPorte died. LaPorte moved the Co-operative Music Company from its 1728 Halsted Street location to property he purchased on Western Avenue in Chicago Heights in August 1972. On October 30, 1972, LaPorte spent the day at the new location and left mid-afternoon. He died that night at home in Flossmoor of an apparent heart attack. His death came just about two weeks after the death of Paul Ricca. The dilemma for Tony Accardo was installing a new boss for the Chicago Heights street crew.

CHAPTER 6

THE AL PILOTTO YEARS

1972–1982

Frank LaPorte's wake was well attended, as expected for someone of his stature and longevity with the Outfit. A funeral mass was originally scheduled to take place at St. Rocco Church on Twenty-second Street in the Hill neighborhood. However, the priest denied Catholic burial rites for LaPorte as a person of questionable character. Those in attendance included: Charles "Specs" DiCaro, an operative for South Side gambling boss, Ralph Pierce; Henry Pilotto, Chicago Heights chief of police at the time; his brother Al Pilotto; two Chicago Heights officials, Nick Pagoria and Joe Faso; and Tony Accardo and Joey Aiuppa. The *Chicago Tribune* noted that the mix of political, labor and Outfit characters gave the citizens of Chicago Heights a glimpse of the way their community worked because the attendees represented a hint of the alliance between the underworld and politics.[133]

Accardo and Aiuppa represented two-thirds of the Outfit leadership. Gus Alex was the other third. Accardo had put the three of them in charge as a result of the void created at the top by federal investigations and attrition. During LaPorte's wake, Accardo and Aiuppa reportedly huddled in the corner of the Hirsch's West End Funeral Home holding court and in conference to determine the next leader of the Chicago Heights street crew. The choices for consideration were Al Pilotto, Jimmy Catuara and Albert Tocco, most likely in that order. Jimmy Catuara was facing the loan racket indictment and may have been viewed by Accardo as a troublemaker for his feud with LaPorte. Albert Tocco was an enforcer and was showing some leadership promise but was not fully developed as a leader. Pilotto represented the best choice for Accardo. He started with Frank LaPorte during the 1930s. His relationship with Accardo went back to the 1950s, and he possessed a low-key demeanor that, no doubt, Accardo sought at a time of heightened scrutiny. Besides, Pilotto cut his teeth in the Calumet City clubs during the 1940s and '50s and had been in charge of day-to-day functions of the crew since the 1960s.

Al Pilotto was born in Chicago Heights on January 16, 1911, to Giuseppe and Angela Pilotto. His birth certificate showed his birth name as Orfeo Pilotto. His grammar school teacher had trouble with his name and took to calling him Alfred.[134] The name stuck, and he used it the rest of his life. His brothers were Henry, Leo and Arthur.

In the late 1920s or early 1930s, Pilotto worked as a bricklayer for the Chicago Heights Construction Company. He admitted that when he could not find work he was a bookmaker for the horse races. As such, he became acquainted with Frank LaPorte, Jimmy Catuara, John Roberts and others. He was corresponding with Pete Licavoli, a top Detroit mobster, when Licavoli served a sentence at Leavenworth from 1933 to 1935. On cross-examination during the Accardo tax trial, Pilotto testified that he was employed at the Owl Club in 1936 and 1937. In 1944, Frank LaPorte got him elected president of the International Hod Carriers, Building and Common Laborers' Union, Local 5. Sometime in the 1950s, he purchased the Club Palace in Calumet City from Tony Accardo. Pilotto admitted that the Club Palace operated as a bookie joint and that poker games were operated at the club. He expanded his gambling activities in Calumet City by forming the Palermo and Pilotto partnership with Dominick Palermo. In the late 1950s, he acquired an interest in the Club Corral with Frank LaPorte and George Tuffanelli.[135]

By the late 1950s, Pilotto was Frank LaPorte's chief lieutenant in charge of gambling. At that time, the two were known to frequent the Fagman's Men's Store at 108 West Randolph Street in Chicago. The store served as the Chicago headquarters for LaPorte and Pilotto. They traveled there at least once week and spent a few hours meeting with Outfit counterparts from around the city and making phone calls concerning Outfit business. Pilotto was trusted enough by LaPorte to conduct the business of the Chicago Heights street crew at Fagman's on LaPorte's behalf when he was out of town. Pilotto was known to confer with Murray Humphreys, Tony Accardo, Ralph Pierce and Paul Ricca.[136]

When Tony Accardo's tax case went to trial in September 1960, he needed witnesses to testify that he did, in fact, sell beer to them using his little red Mercedes sports car. The case hinged on charges that he did not work as a

Above: Al Pilotto relaxes at the Old Heidelberg restaurant in Miami, Florida, with several of the boys from Chicago Heights. The men seated around the table from left to right are: Joe Guzzino, Ralph Emery, Al Pilotto, John Nicastro and John Roberts. *From the collection of John Binder and Matthew Luzi.*

Left: Al Pilotto (left) with Frank LaPorte in this photo taken either in Florida, where Pilotto had a home, or California, where the two spent considerable time. Al Pilotto was once Frank LaPorte's driver and bodyguard. He worked his way up to be LaPorte's most trusted lieutenant.

beer salesman for Premium Beer Sales, Inc., and wrongly deducted his car as a business expense. The government attempted to subpoena Frank LaPorte because it contended Accardo arranged a phony salary from Premium Beer Sales, Inc. to hide his true income from the Owl Club. The government was hoping to get LaPorte to testify as to the true source of Accardo's income. However, LaPorte left for California to avoid service of the subpoena. With LaPorte safely ensconced, Accardo began selecting witnesses that were most favorable to him. Al Pilotto represented such a witness because he presented a semi-respectable air as a union official and restaurant-tavern owner. Accardo must have been pleased when Pilotto testified that not only did Accardo sell beer, he offered to help him sell it as well. He also testified that Accardo came around to several locations in Chicago Heights and Calumet City to sell beer and brought bar accessories along in his Mercedes. The government damaged Pilotto's credibility on cross-examination when Pilotto admitted that he was a partner in the Wilco Music Company. That admission provided a glimpse into the extent to which the crew had infiltrated Joliet rackets.[137]

The tax trial was the first time that Pilotto surfaced in public. The next time his name appeared was in connection with the 1963 gambling raid in south Cook County and Will County. The raid was largely developed by agents tailing a man known only as "Tish." Tish told agents that he furnished race results to taverns in the area, so agents simply followed him wherever he went and placed bets to confirm illegal activity. They also linked Tish to the home of Ralph Emery, where he was observed meeting with Emery, Al Pilotto and Joe Costello. Through the investigation, agents determined that Pilotto was Frank LaPorte's lieutenant in charge of gambling. Pilotto managed to elude the federal raiding party but volunteered to appear before the grand jury later. He appeared without an attorney and disclosed nothing about gambling in Chicago Heights. During the investigation, FBI agents interviewed Pilotto at his home. He admitted a friendship with Frank LaPorte but disclaimed any connection with prostitution and claimed that there were no horse books operating in Chicago Heights. Pilotto also claimed that he was no longer associated with the Hod Carriers Union.[138] That was news to federal investigators. After all, Al Pilotto was in charge of Local 5 since 1944. It was a primary source of influence and income.

The reason LaPorte did not have a difficult time installing Pilotto as president was because Nick Neroni had organized the union long ago and acted as the union's business agent. Neroni remained with the union until the early 1950s, when he embezzled $100,000 from it and returned to Italy. Normally, such an affront resulted in dire consequences. Rather than go after Neroni, LaPorte and other Outfit leaders acknowledged that Neroni was largely responsible for bringing Local 5 under Outfit control and decided that Neroni deserved the money. Since the Outfit had free reign over the union, investigators were dubious when Pilotto said he was no longer associated with it. Further investigation found that Pilotto was in fact succeeded by Nicolas Cuda in April 1962. However, Pilotto continued to frequent the union's office daily to use the phones and make appointments. While the office workers insisted that Pilotto's activities had nothing to do with the union, investigators remained skeptical. The pressure applied by investigations in the late 1950s and early 1960s forced Pilotto's removal from office to reduce his profile and allow him to control the union without the title.[139] Pilotto remained out of union office until 1966, when a vacancy occurred. The vacancy allowed Frank LaPorte to appoint Al Pilotto as successor. That same year, the union changed its name to Local 5, Laborers' International Union of North America.

During the mid-1960s, Pilotto attempted to stay out of the spotlight. He made great efforts to appear as respectable as possible and to be accepted by the community. He joined the Lincolnshire Country Club in Crete, Illinois, to augment the appearance of respectability. He was considered a good member and a big spender. However, Pilotto was not the first or only Outfit type to gain membership at the club. Supposedly, Phil D'Andrea, an old Capone Gang member, attempted to join in the late 1930s when he moved to Crete. He was refused membership because of his reputation. Soon after his denial, the club experienced a rash of vandalism to its greens and tees. D'Andrea then returned to the club and stated that he heard about the vandalism and felt that he could prevent it if he were given membership. The officers relented and admitted D'Andrea.[140]

Pilotto enjoyed a friendly relationship with the Chicago Heights Police Department during the 1960s. He had enough friends on the force that he did not worry about raids by local police. In 1967, negotiations began to bring his brother Henry over from the Illinois State Police to be chief of the Chicago Heights Police Department. Henry Pilotto's appointment as Chicago Heights police chief was confirmed in 1971. Embarrassment followed quickly when Art Pilotto was arrested in August 1971 by the Cook County sheriff's office during a gambling raid. Also arrested were Anthony "Dago Tony" Berretoni, Tony Montella, John Costello and Joe Barrett Jr., all of them known associates of the Chicago Heights street crew. The charges were later dropped for insufficient evidence.[141]

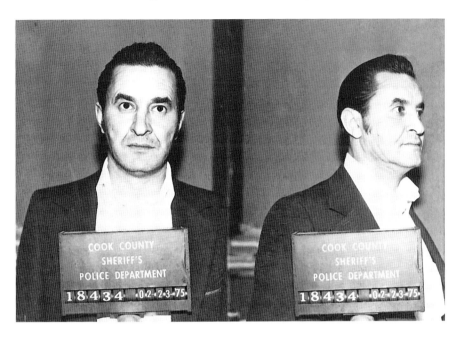

Anthony "Dago Tony" Berretoni in a 1975 arrest photo. He helped run gambling under
Al Pilotto. A 1983 Outfit organization chart listed him as a lieutenant under Albert Tocco.
Courtesy of the Chicago Crime Commission.

After Frank LaPorte died, Pilotto was left with the task of shoring up the
crew. In his later years, LaPorte spent so much time away from Chicago
Heights dodging subpoenas and doing the bidding of Accardo and Ricca
that discipline within the crew started to fray. Constant surveillance and
investigations also took a toll. Although Accardo and Ricca had put a stop
to the feud between LaPorte and Catuara, the latter continued to display
animosity and operated with an air of independence. In January 1971, the
body of Ross Corriero, a South Side Outfit bookmaker working under the
auspices of Ralph Pierce, was found in Crete, Illinois. He was shot once in
the head and once in the chest. His body was found after an anonymous
phone call was placed to a service station in Chicago Heights. The FBI
developed information that Corriero was killed on orders from Jimmy
Catuara. It was suspected that Corriero may have become an informant.
If Catuara was responsible, it could be interpreted as a way for Catuara to
eliminate a possible informant and make it look as if other members of the
crew were responsible.[142]

By 1973, Pilotto completely reorganized the Chicago Heights street crew.
He reined in Jimmy Catuara. Dominick Palermo was placed in charge of

Calumet City, and he shared some responsibility in Northwest Indiana. Pilotto's primary lieutenant in charge of Northwest Indiana was Frank Nick Zizzo. In Chicago Heights, Pilotto made Mike Paoletta his chief lieutenant. Pilotto bossed it all under cover of his position as president of Local 5.

In 1974, Pilotto turned his attention to the business of Co-operative Music Company. When LaPorte died, ownership passed to his wife and his sister. The business was operated by Martin Pulcini, LaPorte's brother-in-law, and Robert Curry, Francis Curry's son. All of them fought for control, and Pilotto got involved to mediate the dispute. The business remained important to the Outfit as a revenue generator and as a means to launder money. Therefore, Pilotto could not afford any unnecessary bickering about it. Things came to a head in March 1974, when Pilotto called a sit-down at the Hinsdale Holiday Inn. Whatever he decided to placate those involved remains unknown, however; beginning in 1975, Dino Valente, a South Holland, Illinois vending machine operator was running Co-operative Music Company.[143]

Al Pilotto visited Italy in September 1974 to take care of some business on behalf of Tony Accardo. The primary purpose of the trip was to visit Dominic Roberto. By this time, Roberto owned a large estate in Southern Italy, and he was a very influential citizen in the community. Tony Accardo and the Chicago Outfit were suspected of financing Roberto's ventures in Italy since the time of his deportation. Roberto served as the Outfit's contact with Italian organized crime groups in exchange.[144] Pilotto was the natural choice to send. The two had much to talk about regarding the death of Frank LaPorte and the current state of his affairs. Pilotto probably provided Roberto with a current report of the Chicago Heights street crew that Roberto had founded under the auspices of Al Capone nearly fifty years prior. The FBI attempted to learn more about Pilotto's visit, but the Italian government reported that no information could be developed regarding the whereabouts of Al Pilotto while in Italy or of the reputation of Roberto.

A new tool for federal prosecutors in the 1970s was the Racketeer Influenced and Corrupt Organizations Act (RICO). RICO was designed to allow prosecutors to go after organized crime figures for illegal acts or a pattern of racketeering sustained for a year or more. In order to bring a RICO case, prosecutors must show that individual crimes were committed as part of a larger pattern. Until the late 1970s, RICO was largely untested in court, but prosecutors were building cases to test it.

Al Pilotto stymied federal investigators in their efforts to find anything illegal for which they could charge him. He frustrated federal investigators by hiding behind the cover of the Local 5. In February 1976, Chicago Strike Force attorney James Walsh, the United States Department of Labor and the Internal Revenue Service held a meeting. The purpose of this meeting was to outline a joint effort to pursue Al Pilotto by targeting the activities of Local 5. The IRS agreed to consider an audit of Pilotto's personal income and conduct an intelligence investigation of his activities. The Department of Labor was in the midst of a personnel shortage but committed to audit the union's records when it had the staffing in place. The FBI agreed to look into the possibility that Pilotto misappropriated pension funds.[145]

Meanwhile, Al Pilotto busied himself with the affairs of the union and the Chicago Heights street crew. His top lieutenant, Mike Paoletta, died in June 1975, which left Pilotto to make the decision of a replacement. Indications are that the replacement was Albert Tocco. Tocco was past a three-year sentence for his part in an auto theft ring, and it was around this time that Tocco began to gain some notoriety.

Like the old days, Pilotto was using John's Pizzeria in Calumet City as his preferred spot for meetings with Dominick Palermo and Dino Valente.[146] He

Al Pilotto takes his seat at the table of the Outfit's hierarchy in this photo, known as the "Last Supper." *Back, left to right:* Joey Aiuppa, Dominic DiBella, Vince Solano, Al Pilotto, Jack Cerone and Joey Lombardo. *Front, left to right:* Anthony Accardo, Joe Amato, Joe DiVarco and James Torello. *From the collection of John Binder.*

was known to meet there frequently in the late 1970s when he had business to discuss regarding Northwest Indiana, Calumet City and the affairs of Co-operative Music Company.

Dino Valente managed Co-operative Music Company well until he placed Co-operative's machines in places controlled by Albert Tocco. In March 1978, Tocco summoned Valente to a meeting as a guise to settle their differences. However, Valente was gunned down with a twelve-gauge shotgun as he left the meeting at the Rukavina restaurant in Calumet City. The murder was attributed to Al Pilotto. However, it was learned later that Tocco was responsible when Doug Hardin, a government witness, testified that Tocco was responsible for ordering Valente's murder after meeting at the restaurant.[147]

Between 1976 and May 1981, the government continued to investigate the affairs of Local 5. The scope of the investigation spread to other mob figures and union officials. A sweeping RICO indictment was returned by a federal grand jury in Miami naming sixteen defendants on June 3, 1981. The key defendants were Tony Accardo, Al Pilotto and Santo Trafficante, a mob boss from Tampa, Florida, and Angelo Fosco, head of the Laborers' International Union. The indictment charged the defendants with a pattern of racketeering to control the union's insurance funds and collect over $2,000,000 in kickbacks. The scheme involved setting up dummy insurance companies to which contracts were awarded. One of the companies was controlled by Pilotto's son-in-law.[148] Once again, Accardo and Pilotto found themselves involved in a court proceeding, but this time as co-defendants. The case was set for trial on July 25, 1981.

Two days before the trial, as Pilotto golfed at Lincolnshire Country Club with Nick Fushi, Sam Guzzino and Rudy Bamonti, a gunman jumped from the bushes on the eighth tee and fired. Pilotto was hit in his left arm, elbow and shoulder and the right thigh. He underwent surgery at St. James Hospital in Chicago Heights, where his brother ordered his room guarded by Chicago Heights police officers.[149]

Several theories for the shooting emerged. One was that other mob bosses viewed him as weakened by the federal indictment and were challenging Pilotto. Another had it that the shooting was the result of Chicago Heights street crew infighting. Albert Tocco, in particular, had been wreaking havoc in recent years. Yet another was that Tony Accardo ordered a hit on Pilotto for fear he might become an informant in connection with the federal indictment.

Whatever theory was true, things unraveled over the next few months. First, the body of Nicholas J. D'Andrea was found in Crete, Illinois, in the trunk of his burning car on September 14, 1981. D'Andrea was a reputed associate and enforcer for Albert Tocco. D'Andrea's brother Armand was closely associated with Frank LaPorte and was established in Joliet. In the mid-1970s, Armand D'Andrea invested heavily in Arizona real estate.[150]

On October 4, 1981, the body of Sam Guzzino was found in a ditch near Beecher, Illinois. He was shot, and his throat slit. Sam Guzzino had owned an interest in the Vagabond Lounge and the Sands Motel in Chicago Heights. He also had an interest in a cab company. The cab company was known to shuttle johns and gamblers between the motel and the Vagabond.[151] Guzzino was also known as a top associate of Albert Tocco. Investigators discovered that, at the time Pilotto was shot, Guzzino pulled his own weapon and returned fire. However, Guzzino fired ten seconds after the attack and then gave a description of the shooter that conflicted with Pilotto's description. It appeared that the Outfit was suspicious of Guzzino and pressed D'Andrea for information leading to Guzzino prior to killing him. With information in hand, the Outfit then went after Guzzino.

As pressure from the Outfit and investigators mounted, it was not long before Pilotto's would-be assassin cracked and turn himself in. Daniel Bounds, Sam Guzzino's son-in-law, contacted William Lambie of the Chicago Crime Commission in late 1981and confessed that he was recruited by Sam Guzzino to kill Pilotto. Bounds turned himself in because he knew that the Outfit was after him. He told investigators that it was his understanding that Accardo ordered the hit because he was concerned that Pilotto might testify against him. Bounds also implicated Sam Guzzino's brother, Richard Guzzino (Sam and Richard Guzzino were nephews of Joe Guzzino), and Robert Ciarrocchi.[152] Richard Guzzino also had an interest in the cab company with Sam. Bounds was a cab driver for the company.

By the time Dan Bounds's story broke in August 1982, the RICO case had concluded. Tony Accardo was acquitted and thus continued his track record of successfully beating prosecution. Al Pilotto, on the other hand, was convicted and sentenced to twenty years. In determining Pilotto's sentence, the judge relied heavily on testimony from an FBI agent that worked undercover at the Show Club in Chicago Heights where members and associates of the Chicago Heights street crew were known to hang out.[153] The agent gathered what he thought was information linking Al Pilotto to all sorts of crimes including the murder of Dino Valente. However, it was discovered much later that the "Al" being referred to was Albert Tocco, not Al Pilotto. Pilotto's appeal was supported by 4,000 signatures of Chicago Heights citizens who petitioned that he be released pending appeal. Release was denied.

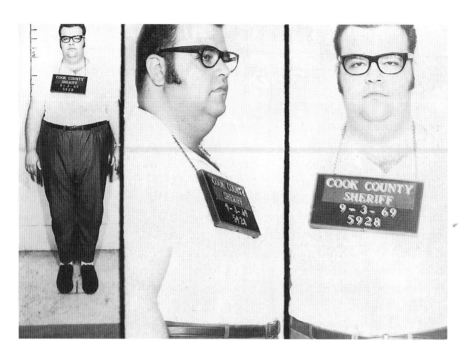

Richard Guzzino in an arrest photo from 1969. He was to be convicted in 1985 for participating in the botched hit on Al Pilotto at the Lincolnshire Country Club in 1981. *Courtesy of the Chicago Crime Commission.*

Richard Guzzino and Robert Ciarrocchi were indicted for the plot to kill Pilotto in 1984. The first trial resulted in a mistrial when Ciarrocchi suffered a heart attack. The two were tried again, and each was convicted. Guzzino received fifteen years, and Ciarrocchi received twenty-five years, which was later reduced to sixteen. The two were convicted largely on the testimony of Bounds. He took the jurors through a conspiracy to kill Pilotto that, had it not been real, would have been comedic. As they planned the caper, Bounds testified that they initially thought that he would use a bicycle to escape after the shooting, but the idea was scrapped when the twenty-dollar bike they bought from a yard sale failed to work properly. He testified he was such a poor shot with a rifle that a pistol had to be used instead. He also said that Richard Guzzino, who weighed nearly four hundred pounds, told him that he himself wanted to do it but he was too fat. Bounds further testified that they thought he needed boots for the job but instead of buying a pair that fit, Richard Guzzino loaned Bounds his boots. When the shooting finally occurred, Bounds nearly shot himself in the foot. He also testified that Sam Guzzino told him that Pilotto had to die because it was feared that Pilotto would "spill some names" and that the hit was "blessed." Sam Guzzino never mentioned Accardo specifically. Bounds assumed that Guzzino implied Accardo was the person that ordered the hit.[154] However, during his testimony under grant of immunity, Al Pilotto insisted that he was never asked to be a government witness in the RICO case and that the thought of testifying never crossed his mind.[155]

It is a safe assumption that Pilotto was shot because of the misguided ambitions of Sam Guzzino. During the 2007 Family Secrets trial, Nick Calabrese, the Outfit hit man who testified against his brother Frank, stated that when Pilotto was shot, the other Outfit bosses were upset and sought information. That is an indication that other Outfit bosses were not trying to move into Pilotto's territory. It also indicates that Tony Accardo did not order the hit. It is also safe to assume that Albert Tocco was not responsible for the shooting because nothing happened to him. In fact, he would eventually take over as a boss of the Chicago Heights street crew.

CHAPTER 7

TURMOIL AND
THE YEARS OF DECLINE

The most common theory of succession for the Chicago Heights street crew is that Albert Tocco took over in 1982 after the conviction of Al Pilotto. However, the FBI developed information that Frank Zizzo assumed leadership of the crew after Pilotto's conviction. Zizzo had risen up through the ranks in Northwest Indiana until he became Pilotto's top lieutenant for that area. Zizzo kept a low profile, a trait no doubt admired by Pilotto and senior Outfit bosses. Nick Calabrese told authorities that Frank Zizzo was present during at least the planning stages of Nick D'Andrea's killing. Apparently, Zizzo was one of those upset with Pilotto's shooting and was looking for answers. Pilotto had a say, if not the final word, in the naming of his successor after his conviction. Given that Pilotto went back years with Zizzo, that Zizzo was low profile and that he sought answers in the wake of Pilotto's shooting, it makes sense that Pilotto approved Zizzo as boss of the crew. After Zizzo died in March 1986 of natural causes, Pilotto divided leadership responsibilities between Albert Tocco and Dominick Palermo. Tocco oversaw the crew's interests in Chicago Heights and the southern suburbs of Chicago. Palermo oversaw of the crew's interests in Northwest Indiana.

Albert Tocco was born on August 9, 1929, to Michael and Laura Tocco. He had a brother named Joseph and two sisters. Michael Tocco was born in Chicago in 1895 and moved to Chicago Heights with his family in 1903. He served in World War I and received the Purple Heart. He established a successful trucking company in 1923 and operated the business successfully until his death in 1948.[156]

Michael Tocco's brother (Albert's uncle) Pasquale, however, had a more colorful background. Pasquale was a bootlegger during Prohibition. He was named in the same 1929 indictment as Frank LaPorte, Dominic Roberto and Jim Emery. Pasquale associated with the infamous Barrett Gang from Chicago Heights in the early 1930s. The gang's leaders were James Barrett and his brother Joseph. Despite the Irish last name, the Barretts indicated that their parents were Italian-born on the 1930 census records. In April 1932, thirteen members of the gang, including Pasquale Tocco, were rounded up in connection with four bank robberies and the kidnapping of Howard Wolverton, a wealthy South Bend, Indiana businessman and his wife. Joseph Barrett surfaced again in the 1950s running a bordello in Godley, Illinois, for Frank LaPorte. Joe Barrett Jr. served in the same line of work during the 1970s and early 1980s for Albert Tocco.[157]

Albert Tocco's arrest record dated to 1945 when he spent time in a juvenile home. He was picked up in April 1949 for general investigation, meaning that he was on the radar of law enforcement. His first real notoriety occurred in 1951 when he was convicted of rape for assaulting an eighteen-year-old woman. He was sentenced to twenty-five years, but the conviction was overruled by the Illinois Supreme Court when it found that there was no evidence of forcible attack.[158] By the 1960s, Tocco was on the rise in the Chicago Heights street crew under Frank LaPorte. He was a known enforcer for the crew and worked in Harvey, Illinois, to keep an eye on the gambling joints there.[159]

Albert's brother Joseph "Papa Joe" Tocco was also an Outfit figure dispatched to Arizona by Frank LaPorte to oversee operations in the Phoenix–Tucson area. He had been in Arizona since at least the mid-1960s. His world came crashing down in 1982 when charges were filed in Maricopa Superior Court by a joint state task force looking into his activities. The complaint against Joe Tocco alleged that he directed a criminal syndicate of eleven people involved in extortion, prostitution and trafficking of stolen property among other things. He eventually pled guilty and received a fifteen-year sentence. In exchange for a reduced sentence for crimes that could have cost him sixty years, he provided the government with some useful information.[160]

In 1975, Louis Bombacino was living in hiding in Tempe, Arizona, under the alias Joe Nardi. Bombacino was hiding out from the Outfit after acting as a cooperating witness for the government against some big Outfit names, including Jack Cerone and Dominic Cortina. His testimony helped to convict the defendants in 1970. Louis Bombacino was killed on the morning of October 6, 1975, when a bomb exploded as he climbed into his Lincoln Continental. Perhaps by 1975 Bombacino felt that the Outfit had moved on and forgotten about him. He should have heeded the lesson in the fate of William Bioff who was killed in Arizona by a car bomb in 1955, several years after Bioff helped convict several Outfit bosses. In any event, Joe Tocco reportedly told the government that the man responsible for ferreting out Bombacino was Anthony Amadio. Amadio went back with Frank LaPorte to the heydays of Calumet City when he owned the Derby Club on the Strip for LaPorte. When Joe Tocco provided the information connecting Amadio to Bombacino in 1984, Amadio was serving a term in California for disposing of stolen securities.[161]

In 1965, the FBI charged Albert Tocco and nine others with taking part in an interstate stolen car ring. The FBI alleged that the ring stole the cars to order, altered their VIN numbers and then shipped them out of state for resale. Tocco was convicted and sentenced in June 1967 to three years in prison and fined $1,000.[162] Al Pilotto attempted to intercede on his behalf but could not arrange an acquittal for Tocco. Tocco won a small victory when he was allowed to remain free pending appeal. The appeals process was eventually exhausted, and Tocco served his time. He was back on the street by 1974 and ready to pick up where he left off with chop shops. His major obstacle was Jimmy Catuara.

Catuara remained active in the 1970s. He caught a break in 1973 when he was acquitted in the case where he was indicted with Guido Fidanzi. Catuara was suspected in 1974 of taking part in the planning of the Purolator Security, Inc. heist, one of Chicago's most infamous crimes. Purolator was an armored car service that was robbed of over $4 million in cash. Agents of the Illinois Bureau of Investigation observed Catuara attend several meetings prior to the heist with Peter Gushi and Luigi DiFronzo, two of the six men charged with the crime. Gushi was Catuara's neighbor and a convicted cartage thief. DiFronzo was supposedly a relative of Catuara and had knowledge of laundering money in the Cayman Islands. Gushi was previously involved in schemes with Catuara associates, Gus Rubino and Billy Dauber. In 1975, authorities claimed to have recovered nearly all of the money except for $300,000. Gushi claimed the money was given to him so that he could arrange to move it out of the country. However, before he got the money out, Gushi claimed the Outfit shook him down by demanding he turn it over or die. He supposedly asked Jimmy Catuara to intervene, but Catuara told him he was on his own. Feeling he had no choice, Gushi did as the Outfit demanded and packed the money in a suitcase and left it in the alley behind his house for pick up.[163]

The term "chop shop" was used for various independent car thieves and/ or salvage yards that cut up stolen cars and resold the parts or resold cars built with chopped parts and clean VIN numbers. In some cases, the Outfit pressured independent operators into paying street tax to operate or suffer serious harm. In other cases, an independent operator might be indebted to the Outfit, in which case the operator was squeezed out and replaced with a frontman who paid the tax. If the operator missed a payment or was short, the Outfit simply treated it as a juice loan and attached interest. The Chicago Crime Commission noted in 1978 that Cook County reported 42,000 auto thefts. Translating that the majority of thefts went to chop shops, the Chicago Crime Commission estimated that they generated millions of dollars and, therefore, motive for the Outfit.

Albert Tocco must have learned from the 1965 stolen car case that it would be more effective to disassociate from stealing cars and concentrate on organizing the chop shops in order to collect street tax. He may have also picked up on the idea from Jimmy Catuara, because Catuara started collecting street tax from the chop shops in the early 1970s. His chief enforcer at the time was Billy Dauber. Dauber was particularly effective because he was feared, even by other enforcers. A chop shop operator testified at a Senate Subcommittee that Dauber "would sometimes just snap and turn on you and from then on your life was in danger."[164] Regardless, it was not long before Tocco was credited with sparking a gang war for control of the chop shops.

From the mid-1970s to around 1980, as many as fourteen murders were attributed to the chop shop wars. Many of the murders were related to the effort to force the chop shops to pay street tax. However, several murders were evidence of Tocco's efforts to take control from Jimmy Catuara. Between October 1976 and July 1977, three known enforcers and collectors of Jimmy Catuara were gunned down: Steve Ostrowsky, October 1976; James Palaggi, August 1977; and Sam Annerino, July 1977. A fourth, Richard Ferrara, disappeared in June 1977 and was never found. It was apparent that Jimmy Catuara was in jeopardy. Al Pilotto and other Outfit bosses may have finally decided that Catuara's time had passed. Perhaps they had grown wary of some of Catuara's antics or perhaps they believed that he was holding back on what he was earning as suspected. Whatever the case, Tocco would have been unable to go after someone of Catuara's stature without backing from the bosses. It was reported in October 1977 that Catuara's rackets were taken over by Angelo "The Hook" LaPietra, the Twenty-sixth Street crew boss. Investigators learned the switch came after Catuara was kidnapped, stuffed in the trunk of a car and held prisoner for few days.[165] The chop shops were left to Albert Tocco.

Catuara initially seemed to get the message because he rarely left his house until July 1978 when he began to revisit his old neighborhood. The

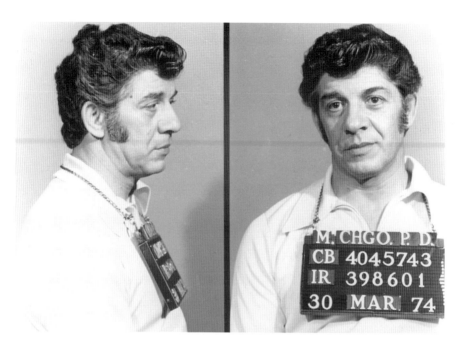

Albert Tocco in a 1974 police photo just as the chop shop war was heating up. *From the collection of Wayne Johnson.*

The body of Jimmy Catuara is loaded onto a stretcher by police after he was ambushed by two gunmen while in his Cadillac at Hubbard and Ogden in Chicago. Catuara was pushed out by Albert Tocco. *From the collection of Jeff Jabaay.*

106

Outfit took notice that Catuara was coming around again and apparently decided that further messages would be futile. On Friday morning, July 28, 1978, Catuara was sitting in his Cadillac at Hubbard and Ogden on the near West Side when two men ran up to the car and fired from both the passenger and driver sides. Catuara managed to open the passenger side door and fall to the pavement, where one of the gunmen fired the final shot, killing him.[166] Catuara's demise was widely credited to Albert Tocco.

Tocco controlled the chop shops but not without attracting attention. The chop shop war produced more gangland murders than anything since Prohibition. That level of violence sparked government investigations. One of the targets was Billy Dauber.

Initially Catuara's main enforcer, Dauber had a falling-out with Catuara and switched allegiance to Tocco after getting out of prison in the mid-1970s. State and federal agents executed two search warrants on Dauber's Crete, Illinois home in 1979. They found a hidden room in the basement with a police monitor and confiscated eleven guns and a small amount of cocaine. It was enough to bring weapons and drug charges against him. To make matters worse, a Senate Subcommittee heard testimony linking Dauber to three murders. By early 1980, the pressure was getting to him. He began drinking heavily in Chicago Heights bars frequented by Albert Tocco and other members of the Chicago Heights street crew. On at least one occasion, Tocco admonished him to stop drinking and running his mouth off. His behavior soon raised suspicions that Dauber was an informant and rumors began to circulate that a hit was ordered on him. Dauber went back to the mid-1960s as a top enforcer and collector and had plenty of information on Al Pilotto, Albert Tocco and others.[167]

On July 2, 1980, Dauber left the Will County Courthouse with his wife, Charlotte, after an appearance related to the weapons and drug charges. He attempted to take rural back roads to his home as a precaution. However, an Outfit hit team in two vehicles caught up with the couple. The team consisted of Frank Calabrese Sr. in the blocking vehicle and Ron Jarrett driving a van with gunmen Butch Petrocelli and Gerald Scarpelli. Calabrese wheeled in front of the Daubers to slow them down, giving Jarrett the opportunity to pull alongside so that Petrocelli and Scarpelli were able to open fire, causing the Daubers to veer off the road and into an apple tree. Jarrett then pulled over so that Scarpelli could fire several rounds from his shotgun at close range. Billy Dauber and his wife were both killed. It was later reported that Dauber had met on several occasions with the Federal Bureau of Alcohol, Tobacco and Firearms as a cooperating witness.[168]

Left: Billy Dauber was once the most feared enforcer for Jimmy Catuara and later Al Tocco. By the late 1970s, he was feeling the pressure from investigations into his activities and agreed to meet with the Federal Bureau of Alcohol, Tobacco and Firearms. He and his wife were killed in July 1980 as they left a court appearance in Joliet, Illinois. *Courtesy of the U.S. Department of Justice.*

Right: Albert Tocco is seen here in the mid-1970s. *Courtesy of the U.S. Department of Justice.*

Before his death, Dauber had provided investigators with information related to Albert Tocco's gambling activities and police corruption. Using Dauber's information, investigators acted swiftly. In August 1980, agents executed a search warrant at Tocco's home. They then organized a raid comprised of one hundred agents in December 1980 to gather more evidence of Tocco's gambling operations. The agents swept through locations throughout Chicago Heights and South Cook County including Tocco's home and his City Vending Company. Agents confiscated $14,000 in cash, five bags of diamonds and one bag of colored stones from Tocco's home. [169] It was the largest raid in the area since 1963.

Gambling charges against Tocco and eleven others were finally announced in 1983. The case was handed to the jury after six weeks of trial in April 1984. The government was disappointed when the jury acquitted Tocco and three others after just sixteen hours of deliberation. The remaining defendants were convicted of minor charges. Tocco was acquitted just in time for him to attend the farewell testimonial dinner at the Alcazar restaurant in Chicago Heights for outgoing police chief Henry Pilotto. The affair was attended by two hundred guests, including many area politicians and the new police chief. [170]

The acquittal steeled the government's resolve to bring a better case against Tocco. By 1983, not only was the government aware of Tocco's extensive criminal activities but it was also apparent that he had succeeded in corrupting city government by taking over the waste disposal contract for

Chicago Heights. He simply let the existing contractor know that he was taking over. Not wanting any trouble from Tocco, the existing contractor did not re-bid for the contract and then sold itself out to Albert Tocco's Chicago Heights Disposal Company. The deal for the contract and the company was consummated with assistance from certain city officials.

If Frank Zizzo succeeded Al Pilotto until Zizzo died in 1986, then Tocco enjoyed just two years at the top. On October 26, 1988, Tocco was indicted on forty-eight counts of racketeering and for filing false income tax returns. The government announced that the indictment was the result of the first phase of an extensive investigation into organized crime and political corruption in the southern suburbs. Tocco went missing when he heard of the pending indictment. The FBI went on alert to find him, and he was added to the Ten Most Wanted List.[171] Agents finally caught Tocco in January 1989. He had been hiding out in Greece since the indictment was unsealed. Agents were tipped to Tocco's whereabouts by tracking Tocco's young son who was going to visit his father. Agents learned that Tocco was in the company of a Greek underworld figure while there.[172]

Just before the case went to trial, the government dropped a bombshell that Betty Tocco, Albert's wife, agreed to cooperate and testify against him. Among other things, she was ready to testify that Tocco, Dominick Palermo, Al Roviaro and Nick Guzzino buried Tony Spilotro and his brother Michael in an Indiana cornfield. Roviaro was with the Chicago Heights street crew operating in Northwest Indiana. He was convicted in 1966 for directing the importation of millions of dollars' worth of heroin from Montreal, Canada.

The Spilotros fell into disfavor for botching the Outfit's operations in Las Vegas. The Spilotros' murder was a compartmentalized hit that involved several Outfit figures tasked with different aspects of the job. Tocco, Palermo, Roviaro and Guzzino were tasked with the burial.[173] The bodies of the Spilotros turned up in June 1986, when a farmer happened to find the makeshift grave site. Betty Tocco provided information that her husband called her frantically to pick him up in Enos, Indiana, near where the Spilotros were buried. Tocco explained to his wife that as they dug the grave, something caused them to panic and scatter. When Tocco heard that the grave was discovered, he went into hiding in Florida, fearing that Outfit boss Joseph Ferriola would have him killed for not completing the job. He did not return to Chicago Heights until receiving word that Ferriola had forgiven him.[174]

The trial began November 9, 1989, and lasted for a month. The jurors heard from an array of witnesses, including Dino Valente's wife, former street tax collectors, nightclub operators and the star witness, Betty Tocco. He was linked to the murders of Billy Dauber, Dino Valente and August Maniaci, a Milwaukee mobster indebted to Tocco. When the trial concluded, the jury took just nine and a half hours to convict Tocco of thirty-four felony counts. On May 14, 1990, Tocco was sentenced to two hundred years in prison and fined $2 million.[175]

The government then turned to the corruption phase of its investigation. Cases were brought against Chicago Heights Finance Commissioner Nick LoBue and former South Chicago Heights mayor Don Prisco. They pleaded guilty and agreed to testify. Their pleas allowed for charges against Chicago Heights mayor Charles Panici and commissioners John Gliottoni and Louise Marshall. Each was convicted and received prison sentences and fines. Despite his conviction, Charles Panici maintains his innocence. Bloom Township supervisor Robert Grossi was also charged and received four years for misuse of funds. The government then charged several police officers, including Chicago Heights deputy police chief Sam Mangialardi. Mangialardi was charged with receiving payoffs from drug dealers. He received ten and a half years.

Dominick Palermo took control of the Chicago Heights street crew at the time that Albert Tocco was indicted. With Al Pilotto in prison, Frank Zizzo dead and the prospect that Tocco would be acquitted slim, Palermo was essentially the last boss standing. In the early 1940s, he operated the Black Steer restaurant near the Chicago Stockyards, the same neighborhood that bred Jimmy Catuara. He came to Calumet City after World War II and worked in that area for the rest of his days with the crew. At first, he served as a bodyguard for Frank LaPorte but quickly moved up through the ranks in the Calumet City area. He operated various clubs and also served as the payoff man for a while in Calumet City. Palermo's name surfaced in 1957 in connection with the Molly Zelko case when an anonymous caller contacted the *Weekly Spectator* office and reported that Palermo may have had something to do with the case. Eventually, he and Al Pilotto became partners, and from then on, he served as one of Pilotto's top lieutenants for Calumet City and Northwest Indiana. After Pilotto took over from LaPorte and reorganized the crew, he made Palermo a paid representative of Local 5, Laborers' International Union.[176] A retired laborer said about Palermo:

> *That son of a bitch signed me up for a union while he was wearing a fedora, sunglasses and pointy shoes. I was Irish, but all my friends at the time were Italian. I turned to my friend, and said, "That guy is mobbed up." My friend said, "Welcome to the union." [Palermo] was used to getting the contractors to unionize. You either did it the way organized crime wanted, or you had problems.[177]*

Above: Dominick "Tootsie" Palermo appears on the left in this 1944 police lineup photo. Next to him in the middle is Albert "Obie" Frabotta. At right is Ernest Manno. This photo was taken before Palermo headed to Calumet City to work the clubs for the Chicago Heights street crew. Frabotta is often credited as getting his start on the West Side of Chicago with the 42-Gang. However, he got his start in crime in the late 1920s when he associated with a gang of bank robbers from Chicago Heights. He was born in Steger, Illinois, just south of Chicago Heights. *From the collection of John Binder*.

Left: There must be something important in the case. Watching over it are Dominick "Tootsie" Palermo (left), John Nicastro seated with his hands on the case and Jimmy Catuara standing over John Nicastro's shoulder. *From the collection of John Binder and Matthew Luzi*.

111

Dominick Palermo as he appeared later in life, probably in the 1980s. *Courtesy of the U.S. Department of Justice.*

The government wasted no time indicting Palermo. While the Orland Park FBI office was investigating Tocco, its counterparts in Northwest Indiana were investigating Palermo. On December 18, 1990, just seven months after Tocco's sentencing, an indictment against Palermo and fourteen of his associates was announced in the Hammond, Indiana Federal District Court. Those indicted with Palermo included Nick Guzzino, Pete "Cadillac Pete" Petros and Bernard "Snooky" Morgano. Morgano was the nephew of deported Northwest Indiana mob boss Tommy Morgano. The indictment included charges of racketeering, conspiracy and extortion in connection with their efforts to collect street tax from vice and gambling operators. The case went to trial in July 1991 and lasted three and a half weeks. The jurors heard from witnesses that included an Indiana businessman forced to routinely pay street tax for installing poker machines; a former madam from Gary, Indiana; and an undercover FBI agent that took notes of conversations she overheard between Morgano and others. The most damaging evidence consisted of two hundred taped conversations, many made from a wiretap installed at Dominick Palermo's booth at his favorite Italian restaurant. The jury returned guilty verdicts in August 1991 against Palermo, Guzzino, Morgano and several others. Palermo received a thirty-two-year sentence and was fined $250,000; Guzzino received thirty-nine years and was fined $185,000; and Morgano received sixteen years and was fined $177,000.[178] The convictions represented a blow from which the Chicago Heights street crew would not recover.

EPILOGUE

The importance of the Chicago Heights street crew to the Outfit cannot be underestimated. The territory of the crew was one of the main sources of alcohol revenue during Prohibition for the Capone Gang. After Frank Nitti took over from Al Capone, the crew had less difficulty making adjustments to the repeal of Prohibition. They operated illegal gambling since before Prohibition and infiltrated the Laborers' Union, two areas that became staples for the Outfit.

Profits from bootlegging and gambling made Dominic Roberto, Jim Emery, Frank LaPorte and others from Chicago Heights quite wealthy. They used their wealth and connections to expand their reach and corrupted politicians in order to protect their operations. This was especially the case in Calumet City, where they ran the town wide-open, rivaling Las Vegas. It was not until 1993 that Calumet City took control of the Strip by acquiring the land and demolishing the buildings. In its place, the city created a tax increment financing (TIF) district, which allowed the city to reallocate funds from property taxes to attract legitimate businesses to the area.

Will County was a key area managed by Francis Curry. He corrupted Joliet officials so thoroughly that his gambling operations ran with impunity. Likewise, in Northwest Indiana which was overseen by Anthony Pinelli, James DeGeorge, Tom Morgano and Frank Zizzo before taken over directly by Frank LaPorte. They controlled large-scale horse and sports betting operations and, through the efforts of Joe Guzzino and Ralph Emery, had exclusive access to the wire services that supplied race results.

Even though deported, Dominic Roberto remained a key figure for the Chicago Heights street crew and the Outfit. Often underestimated or even ignored, his importance cannot be denied. Throughout his years in Italy, his known visitors included Jim Emery, Frank LaPorte, Tony Accardo, Phil Alderisio and Al Pilotto. In addition to Outfit big shots, he was frequently visited by bagmen from Chicago Heights, such as John Nicastro. They shuttled money and messages back and forth between Chicago, Chicago Heights and Italy. Roberto established contact with Italian gangsters such as Charlie Luciano on behalf of the Outfit and served the Outfit's interests in Italy from his deportation in 1935 until his death in Italy on December 17, 1975.

Frank LaPorte earned enough money for the Outfit that he was able to put up capital and expand into places such as California, Arizona and Nevada. He was known to have large real estate holdings and interests in mining operations. He used some of his profits to invest in the development of a subdivision on the North End of Chicago Heights. He also controlled numerous bars and restaurants throughout his territory in the southern suburbs. In order to protect his interests, he systematically paid off top politicians and policemen wherever necessary. The FBI noted that LaPorte controlled Chicago Heights by supporting both parties so he always had a winner. In some cases, he put up money to finance the campaigns of certain officials. At least one police chief of Chicago Heights was loyal to LaPorte for thirty years. Under Frank LaPorte, the Chicago Heights street crew had representatives in California, Arizona, Wisconsin, Florida and Mexico.

Al Pilotto served Tony Accardo well by testifying on his behalf at the 1960 tax trial and then not testifying against him in the 1982 RICO case. However, despite his attempts to keep a low profile and surviving a shooting, Al Pilotto was unable to avoid the government's resolve to build a RICO case against him. He was paroled in September 1992. He lived out his remaining days in Chicago Heights and Florida, where he had maintained a home before going to prison. Due to the terms of his parole, he had to be cautious about the people he associated with. When his parole was complete, he was too old to effectively run a street crew for the Outfit. He was, however, seen around Chicago Heights and in Chicago visiting with old friends and having meals where there were familiar faces. Alfred Pilotto died July 20, 1999, of natural causes at the age of eighty-eight.

Albert Tocco succeeded in forcing the pervasive chop shops of the 1970s to pay street tax to the Outfit. Additionally, he generated a lot of revenue from sports gambling and vice operations, which caused Outfit bosses to notice. He rose quickly through the ranks until taking over the crew with Dominick

Palermo. However, his violent tenure jeopardized the Chicago Heights street crew by bringing federal scrutiny on the crew and its influence in local government, long the protector and enabler of organized crime in Chicago Heights. Albert Tocco died at the age of seventy-seven on September 21, 2005, in federal prison at Terre Haute, Indiana.

Dominick "Tootsie" Palermo's reign as boss lasted just five years. However, he was involved in organized crime for at least forty-seven years. He died in prison in April 2005 at the age of eighty-eight. The federal convictions of Tocco and Palermo decimated the Chicago Heights street crew. After the conviction of Palermo and several of his subordinates, there was no one capable or willing to step in and carry on the criminal enterprise that was the Chicago Heights street crew.

The FBI opened an investigation in April 1993 to determine if a viable Chicago Heights street crew would emerge after the convictions of Tocco and Palermo. The FBI developed intelligence that the crew failed to develop or recruit new members. However, illegal horse and sports gambling by independent bookmakers continued to thrive and, therefore, the FBI operated under the premise that the crew would re-emerge. A follow up report in September 1994 noted that Pilotto was in no position to reorganize the crew because of the terms of his parole. The report failed to identify a viable crew operating in the far south suburbs. It also noted that there was no attempt by other Outfit crews to collect street tax from the independent bookmakers operating in the area.

Intelligence was later developed that the remnants of the Chicago Heights street crew were absorbed by the Twenty-sixth Street crew under John Monteleone. For a while, Jim DiForti, one of his lieutenants, served as secretary-treasurer of Local 5, Laborers' International Union in Chicago Heights. However, DiForti died in 2000, and Monteleone died in 2001. At the news conference in April 2005, announcing the Family Secrets indictment of Joey Lombardo, Frank Calabrese, James Marcello and several others, federal prosecutors declared the Chicago Heights street crew defunct.

The Family Secrets case relied heavily on the testimony of Frank Calabrese Jr. and Nick Calabrese, Frank Sr.'s brother. Nick Calabrese's testimony helped clear the infamous Dauber murders. He also helped shed some light on what happened to Nick D'Andrea and Sam Guzzino. The D'Andrea murder was included in the indictment and brought to trial, but the Guzzino murder was not. The jury deadlocked on the D'Andrea charges against James Marcello.

The disappearance of Tony "Little Tony" Zizzo serves as a footnote to the Family Secrets indictment and is possibly the last link to the Chicago

Heights street crew. Zizzo was last seen at a Melrose Park restaurant on August 31, 2006, just about a year after the indictment was announced. The most common theories about his disappearance are that he voluntarily disappeared to avoid being indicted himself or that he was eliminated because of a dispute with another mobster. Tony Zizzo was the son of Frank Zizzo, who the FBI believes took over the Chicago Heights street crew when Al Pilotto went to prison.

NOTES

INTRODUCTION

1. The spelling of names changed frequently between aliases used, news reports and official documents that recorded events in the lives of the subjects. For purposes of identification, the most commonly occurring spelling or usage appears. Traditional organized crime in Chicago is referred to as the "Syndicate," the "Chicago Outfit" or the "Outfit" as opposed to the mafia or La Cosa Nostra.

CHAPTER 1

2. See Candeloro and Paul, *Chicago Heights: At the Crossroads of the Nation*, 33, 39–40. See also Candeloro and Paul, *Chicago Heights*, 7-9, and *Chicago Heights Revisited*, 9–14.
3. See Candeloro and Paul, *Chicago Heights: At the Crossroads*, 33, 39–40. See also Candeloro and Paul, *Chicago Heights*, 7-9, and *Chicago Heights Revisited*, 9–14.
4. See University of Illinois, Chicago website: http://www.uic.edu/depts/lib/specialcoll/exhibits/fpdcc/People/CHARLESWACKER.html
5. See Candeloro and Paul, *Chicago Heights: At the Crossroads*, 39–46.
6. Ibid.
7. Ibid.
8. Ibid.
9. Ibid.
10. See Candeloro, *Italians in Chicago Heights*.

11. See Candeloro and Paul, *Chicago Heights: At the Crossroads*, 99. See also Dominic Candeloro, *Chicago Heights, 1890–1975* (Originally appeared in Holli and Jones's *Ethnic Chicago*, 1984).

12. See FBI Subject File Number 92-5793-130, subject, Frank LaPorte.

13. See Candeloro and Paul, *Chicago Heights: At the Crossroads*, 50.

CHAPTER 2

14. See Antonino Sanfilippo Petition for Naturalization, November 29, 1907.

15. See *Chicago Tribune*, January 7, 1929.

16. Ibid.

17. See Binder and Luzi, "Al Capone and Friends."

18. The true spelling of Costello was Castelli. See Charles Costello nee Castelli Declaration of Intention, filed April 24, 1916. The name was probably changed to Costello so that it would sound Irish. The name Zarante in various accounts and official documents appears as Zeranti, Zaranti and Zerante. Zarante is used here because it is the spelling most frequently found.

19. See *Chicago Tribune*, June 24, 1914.

20. John Perry's Petition for Naturalization listed his town of origin as "Gastro" and his obituary listed his town of origin as "Bella Nicastro" Italy. Neither of these towns was found in the author's research. However, there is a town named Nicastro in Calabria, Italy.

21. See FBI Subject File Number 92-5793-155, subject: Frank LaPorte.

22. Author's interview with Joe Fushi.

23. Ibid.

24. See Schoenberg, *Mr. Capone*, 41–65, 112 and 115–122. See also John Kobler, *Capone*, 37, 70–78, 124–133 and 146.

25. See Schoenberg, *Mr. Capone*, 41–65, 112 and 115–122. See also John Kobler, *Capone*, 37, 70–78, 124–133 and 146.

26. See Schoenberg, *Mr. Capone*, 41–65, 112 and 115–122. See also John Kobler, *Capone*, 37, 70–78, 124–133 and 146.

27. See Schoenberg, *Mr. Capone*, 41–65, 112 and 115–122. See also John Kobler, *Capone*, 37, 70–78, 124–133 and 146.

28. See Schoenberg, *Mr. Capone*, 41–65, 112 and 115–122. See also John Kobler, *Capone*, 37, 70–78, 124–133 and 146.

29. See *Chicago Heights Star*, May 31, 1923.

30. Ibid., February 10, 1921, June 22, 1922, and March 9, 1923.

31. Ibid., April 24, 1924.

32. Ibid., June 4, 1926.

33. Author's interview with Joe Fushi.

34. See Joseph Martino Declaration of Intention filed, April 4, 1924.

35. See Schoenberg, *Mr. Capone*, 98–99.

36. See also Kobler, *Capone*, 116.

37. See *Southtown Economist*, April 9, 1924.

38. See *Chicago Heights Star*, April 23, 1925.

39. See *Chicago Daily News*, July 23, 1926.

40. See Schoenberg, *Mr. Capone*, 277–286.

41. See *Chicago Tribune*, July 23, 1926.

42. It should be noted that Joseph Nerone is not related to Nick Neroni who appears elsewhere in this work.

43. See *Chicago Herald and Examiner*, June 3, 1926.

44. Interview with Joe Fushi.

45. See *Chicago Herald and Examiner*, June 3, 1926, and July 24, 1926.

CHAPTER 3

46. See FBI Subject File Number 92-5793-155, subject: Frank LaPorte. See Also Dominic Roberto Petition for Naturalization, August 29, 1927.

47. See FBI Subject File Number 92-5793-155, subject: Frank LaPorte.

48. See *Chicago Tribune*, April 13, 1986. Also, author's interviews with Rio Burke.

49. Eliot Ness notes of his pursuit of Al Capone, Case Western Reserve Historical Society, Cleveland, Ohio.

50. See Schoenberg, *Mr. Capone*, 133.

51. For information contained in this paragraph see *Chicago Heights Star*, June 4, 1926, *Chicago Tribune* June 4, 1926 and *Chicago Herald and Examiner*, June 3, 1926. The *Chicago Tribune* reported that police found one sawed-off shotgun while the Chicago *Herald and Examiner* reported that two shotguns, a twenty-gauge and a sixteen-gauge, were found.

52. See *Chicago Heights Star*, June 11, 1926.

53. For the information contained in this paragraph see *Chicago Heights Star*, July 23, 1926 and July 24, 1926; *Chicago Daily News*, July 23, 1926; *Chicago Tribune*, July 23, 1926; and *Chicago Herald and Examiner*, July 24, 1926.

54. See *Chicago Heights Star*, August 3, 1926.

55. Ibid., August 20 and 21, 1926; *Chicago Tribune*, August 20 and 21, 1926; and see *Chicago Herald and Examiner*, August 21, 1926.

56. See *Chicago Tribune*, September 3, 1926.

57. See *Chicago Heights Star*, September 3, 1926.

58. See *Chicago Tribune*, January 19, 1928.

59. See *Chicago Heights Star*, August 28, 1928.
60. See Foster, "Black Hand War Rages in Chicago Heights." See also Chicago *Herald and Examiner*, December 1, 1928.
61. See *Chicago Heights Star*, October 26, 1928 and November 2, 1928. See also *Chicago Herald and Examiner*, December 1, 1928.
62. See *Chicago Heights Star*, November 30, 1928 and December 4, 1928. See also *Chicago Herald and Examiner*, December 1, 1928.
63. See *Chicago Heights Star*, December 7, 1928.
64. See *Chicago Herald and Examiner*, December 7, 1928. See also *Chicago Tribune*, December 8, 1928.
65. See *Chicago Tribune*, December 9, 1928.
66. Ibid., January 7, 1929.
67. See *Chicago Daily News*, January 8, 1929.
68. See *Chicago Daily News*, February 24, 1936.
69. See *Chicago Tribune*, January 8, 1929.
70. Ibid., November 17, 1934.
71. See *Chicago Heights Star*, March 22, 1929.
72. See *Chicago Tribune*, March 21, 1929.
73. See *Chicago Heights Star*, May 3, 1929.
74. See Grand Jury Indictment, In the District Court of the United States of America for The Northern District of Illinois, Eastern District, No. 19444.
75. See *Chicago Herald and Examiner*, May 4, 1929.
76. See United States Penitentiary, Leavenworth, Kansas; File No. 42080, Record of Dominic Roberto.
77. See FBI Subject File Number 92-5793-155, subject: Frank LaPorte.

CHAPTER 4

78. See Vincenzo Ammirati Petition for Naturalization, March 30, 1927. Note that Ammirati was buried under the name "Ammirato." However, he signed his Petition for Naturalization "Ammirati" which is also the name used in court documents. See also Dominic Roberto Petition for Naturalization, August 29, 1927.
79. See Chicago Crime Commission Memorandum, January 12, 1960.
80. See *Blue Island Sun Standard*, December 7, 1967.
81. See *Chicago Heights Star*, January 17, 1936.
82. See websites: boxrec.com and International Boxing Hall of Fame ibhof.com for information about these boxers. See also Bonanno and Abromowitz, *Last Testament of Bill Bonanno*, 265.
83. See Kobler, *Capone*, 249.

84. As told to the author by a resident of the home.

85. See Kobler, *Capone*, 320–346. See also Schoenberg, *Mr. Capone*, 309–325.

86. See Eghigian, *After Capone* pgs. 209-212. See also *Chicago Tribune*, February 9, 1936.

87. See Stephen Hull, *America's Wickedest City*, Spur, 1950.

88. See FBI Subject File Number 92-5793-155, subject: Frank LaPorte.

89. See John Roberto Declaration of Intention filed June 4, 1941.

90. See *Chicago Tribune*, April 20, 1933, May 21, 1933, October 30, 1933, November 2 and 3, 1933, March 28, 1934, March 29, 1934, August 30, 1934, and December 3, 1942.

91. See FBI Subject File Number 92-5793-155, subject: Frank LaPorte.

92. See *Chicago Daily News*, October 14, 1954. See also John J. Binder, *The Chicago Outfit*.

93. See *Chicago Daily News*, October 14, 1954.

94. See *Chicago Tribune*, March 7, 1957.

95. See *Chicago Heights Star*, February 11, 1938, and February 15, 1938. See Also the *Chicago Daily Times*, February 10, 1938 and *Chicago Tribune*, February 10, 1938.

96. See FBI Subject File Number 92-2012, subject: Joe Guzzino.

97. See FBI File Number 92-7148-1, subject: Sammy Paxton.

CHAPTER 5

98. See Frank LaPorte Petition for Naturalization, May 20, 1926.

99. See *Chicago Heights Star*, September 10, 1926 and September 14, 1926.

100. Ibid., December 20, 1927 and December 30, 1927.

101. See *Chicago Tribune*, October 6, 1930.

102. See *Chicago Heights Star*, November 29, 1932.

103. See *Chicago Tribune*, August 26, 1938.

104. See *Chicago Daily News*, May 27, 1941.

105. See FBI Subject File Number 92-5793-155, subject: Frank LaPorte.

106. See *Chicago Tribune*, April 17, 1938, April 20, 1938, and July 26, 1939.

107. See *Chicago Herald American*, October 16, 1948. See also FBI Subject File Number 92-5793-155, subject: Frank LaPorte.

108. See *Chicago Tribune*, March 6, 1953.

109. Ibid., April 8, 1948. See *Chicago Herald American*, October 18, 1948.

110. See *Chicago Tribune*, September 28, 1957, September 29, 1957, October 2, 1957 October 3, 1957, and October 10, 1957.

111. See *Chicago Tribune* May 4, 1944 and *Spur* Magazine, July, 1950.

112. See *Hammond Times*, October 8, 1935.

113. See *Chicago Tribune*, June 30, 1955.

114. Ibid., February 11, 1951, July 28, 1951, and July 31, 1951. *Chicago Daily News*, August 16, 1951. *Hammond Times*, May 23, 1951.

115. *Chicago Daily News*, September 15, 1951.

116. Ibid., June 20, 1959.

117. Ibid., May 29, 1959.

118. See FBI Subject File Number 92-5793-155, subject: Frank LaPorte.

119. See *Chicago Sun-Times*, June 22, 1962.

120. See *Chicago Tribune*, September 25, 1961.

121. Ibid., November 16, 1961.

122. Ibid., May 27, 1964. See also FBI Subject File Number 92-5793-155, subject: Frank LaPorte.

123. See *Chicago Tribune*, August 8, 1963. See also FBI Subject File Number 92-782-21, subject: Joseph Stein.

124. FBI Subject File Number 92-5793-155, subject: Frank LaPorte.

125. See Demaris, *The Last Mafioso*, pgs. 116-118.

126. Ibid., 176–180. *Chicago Tribune*, June 20, 1967.

127. See Ovid Demaris, *The Last Mafioso*, 149–157.

128. See *Chicago Tribune*, February 4, 1965.

129. Ibid., September 13, 1966, September 24, 1966, and April 14, 1967.

130. Ibid., August 31, 1966. See also *A Report on Crime for 1966* published by the Chicago Crime Commission and *Chicago Tribune*, March 1, 1967. Informants also stated to the FBI that Catuara was responsible for Pratico's murder.

131. See *Chicago Tribune*, May 8, 1969.

132. Ibid., February 16, 1972.

CHAPTER 6

133. See *Chicago Tribune*, November 13, 1972.

134. See FBI Subject File Number 92-7815-2, subject: Alfred Pilotto.

135. See FBI Subject File Number 92-7815-2, subject: Alfred Pilotto. See also summary of testimony from Accardo Tax trial.

136. See FBI Subject File Number 92-7815-2, subject: Alfred Pilotto.

137. See *Chicago's American*, October 25, 1960 and the *Chicago Tribune*, October 27, 1960.

138. See *Chicago Tribune*, April 4, 1963 and *Chicago Sun-Times*, April 4, 1963. See also FBI Subject File Number 92-7815-2, subject: Alfred Pilotto.

139. See FBI Subject File Number 92-5793-155, subject: Frank LaPorte. See also *Chicago Tribune*, April, 1963.

140. See FBI Subject File Number 92-7815-2, subject: Alfred Pilotto. See also parole report number 58-194 re: Phil D'Andrea, undated.

141. See *Chicago Tribune*, August 2, 1971, March 27, 1975 and *Chicago Sun-Times*, November 10, 1971.

142. See FBI Subject File Number 92-7815-2, subject: Alfred Pilotto. See also *Chicago Daily News*, January 9, 1971.

143. See FBI Subject Files Numbered 92-7815-2 and 92-2306-88, subjects: Alfred Pilotto and Sammy Paxson respectively.

144. See FBI Subject File Number 92-7815-2, subject: Alfred Pilotto.

145. Ibid.

146. Ibid.

147. See *Chicago Sun-Times*, March 18, 1978 and *Chicago Heights Star*, November 23, 1989.

148. See *Chicago Tribune*, June 5, 1981. See also United States of America v. Anthony Accardo et al., No. 81-23 O-CR-ALH, United Stated District Court, Southern District of Florida.

149. See *Chicago Tribune*, July 25, 1981 and July 27, 1981.

150. See *Chicago Heights Star*, September 17, 1981. See also *Arizona Republic*, undated from 1973.

151. See *Chicago Tribune*, October 5, 1981. See also *Chicago Heights Star* October 8, 1981.

152. See *Chicago Tribune*, August 21 and 22, 1982.

153. Ibid., September 19, 1982.

154. See United States of America v. Richard Guzzino and Robert Ciarrocchi, Nos. 85-2413, 85-3099, United States Court of Appeals for the Seventh Circuit.

155. See also *Chicago Sun-Times*, May 23, 1985.

CHAPTER 7

156. See *Chicago Heights Star*, January 30, 1948.

157. See *Chicago Tribune*, April 24, 1932, *The Chicago Heights Star*, April 26, 1932, *Chicago Tribune*, September 23, 1961, and *Chicago Tribune* June 10, 1979.

158. See *Chicago Tribune* August 28, 1951 and November 21, 1952.

159. References to Tocco in Harvey were found in FBI Subject File Number 92-5793-155, subject: Frank LaPorte. The Chicago Crime Commission developed information that Tocco was an enforcer for the Chicago Heights street crew in the 1960s.

160. See *Arizona Republic*, September 17, 1982.

161. See *Chicago Sun-times*, February 27, 1984 and December 19, 1952.

162. See the Chicago Crime Commission's *Searchlight*, May, 1979 and *Chicago Tribune* June 16, 1967.

163. See *Chicago Tribune*, January 16, 1973, October 24, 1974, November 3, 1974, and February 2, 1975.

164. Ibid., November 29, 1979.

165. Ibid., October 1, 1977.

166. Ibid., July 29, 1978 and August 6, 1978.

167. Ibid., July 3, 1980 and July 4, 1980 and See also Jeff Coen, *Family Secrets* pgs. 194-195.

168. See *Chicago Tribune*, July 3, 1980 and July 4, 1980 and See also Jeff Coen, *Family Secrets* pgs. 194-195.

169. See *Chicago Heights Star*, December 18, 1980.

170. See *Chicago Tribune*, April 1, 1984 and *Chicago Sun-Times*, April 22, 1984.

171. See *Chicago Heights Star*, October 27, 1988 and October 30, 1988.

172. See *Chicago Tribune*, January 9, 1989.

173. Ibid., October 14, 1989, March 23, 1966 and Coen, *Family Secrets*, 241-247.

174. See *Chicago Tribune*, April 1, 1990.

175. See *Chicago Sun-Times*, December 8, 1989 and *Chicago Tribune*, May 17, 1990.

176. See *Chicago Sun-Times*, October 7, 1988 and October 2, 1957. See also FBI Subject File Number 92-5793-155, subject: Frank LaPorte.

177. See *Chicago Heights Star*, April 21, 2005.

178. See *Chicago Tribune*, August 17, 1991 and March 27, 1992.

BIBLIOGRAPHY

Abramovitz, Gary and Bill Bonanno. *The Last Testament of Bill Bonanno, The Final Secrets of a Life in the Mafia.* New York: HarperCollins Publishers, 2011.

"Antonino Sanfilippo Petition fo Naturalization." November 29, 1907.

Arizona Republic

Binder, John J. *The Chicago Outfit.* Chicago: Arcadia, 2003.

Binder, John J. and Matthew J. Luzi. "Al Capone and Friends." *IASOC Criminal Organizations* 10, no. 3.

Box Rec website. June 2012. http://boxrec.com/media/ (accessed 2012).

Brisson, Lance, and Richard Carlson. "The Web that Links San Francisco's Mayor Alioto and the Mafia." *Look Magazine*, September 23, 1969.

Candeloro, Dominic. "Italians in Chicago Heights 1890–1975." In *Ethnic Chicago*, by Holli and Jones. Erdmanns, 1984.

Candeloro, Dominic, and Barbara Paul. *Chicago Heights.* Charleston, South Carolina: Arcadia Publishing, 1998.

———. *Chicago Heights Revisited.* Charleston, South Carolina: Arcadia Publishing, 2000.

———. *Chicago Heights: At the Crossroads of the Nation.* Charleston, South Carolina: Arcadia Publishing , 2004.

"Charles Costello (Castelli) Declaration of Intention." April 24, 1916.

Chicago Crime Commission. "Albert Tocco." *Searchlight*, 1979.

Chicago Daily News

Chicago Daily Times

Chicago Heights Signal

Chicago Heights Star
Chicago Herald American
Chicago Herald and Examiner
Chicago Reader
Chicago Sun-Times
Chicago Tribune
Chicago's American

Coen, Jeff. *Family Secrets: The Case That Crippled the Chicago Mob.* Chicago: Chicago Review Press Incorporated, 2009.

Demaris, Ovid. *Captive City.* New York: Lyle Stuart, Inc., 1969.

———. *The Last Mafioso.* New York: Times Books, 1981.

"Dominic Roberto Petition for Naturalization." August 29, 1927.

Eghigian, Mars, Jr.. *After Capone: The Life and World of Chicago Mob Boss Frank "The Enforcer" Nitti.* Nashville, TN: Cumberland House Publishing, Inc., 2006.

FBI Subject File Number 92-2012, Subject: Joseph Guzzino.

FBI Subject File Number 92-2306-88, Subject: Sammy Paxson.

FBI Subject File Number 92-5793-155, Subject: Frank LaPorte.

FBI Subject File Number 92-7815-2, Subject: Alfred Pilotto.

FBI Subject File Number 92-782-21, Subject: Joseph Stein.

Foster, Ralph. "Black Hand War Rages in Chicago Heights." *Startling Detective*, December 1932.

"Frank LaPorte Petition for Naturalization." May 20, 1926.

Hammond (Indiana) *Times*

Hull, Stephen. "America's Wickedest Town." *Spur*, July 1950.

International Boxing Hall of Fame. June 2012. http://www.ibhof.com.

"John Roberto Declaration of Intention." June 4, 1941.

"Joseph Martino Declaration of Intention." April 4, 1924.

Kobler, John. *Capone: The Life and World of Al Capone.* New York: Da Capo Press, 1992.

Ness, Eliot. "Notes of his pursuit of Al Capone." Cleveland, OH: Case Westen Reserve Historical Society, n.d.

Northwest Indiana Times. 2009. http://www.nwitimes.com/app/sinstrip/virtualtour/ (accessed June 2012).

"Parole Report Number 58-194 re: Phil D'Andrea." n.d.

"Record of Dominic Roberto." *United States Penitentiary, Leavenworth Kansas, File No. 42080.* n.d.

Schoenberg, Robert J. *Mr. Capone: The Real-and Complete-Story of Al Capone.* New York: William Morrow and Company, Inc., 1992.

Southtown Economist

United States of America v. Anthony Accardo et al. 81-23 O-CR-ALH (United States District Court, Southern District of Florida , 1981).

United States of America v. Richard Guzzino and Robert Ciarrocchi. Nos. 85-2413, 85-3099 (United States Court of Appeals for the Seventh Circuit, 1985).

University of Illinois, Chicago. 2012. http://www.uic.edu/depts/lib/specialcoll/ exhibits/fpdcc/people/charleswacker.html (accessed 2012)

ABOUT THE AUTHOR

 Matthew "Matt" Luzi first became interested in the organized crime history of Chicago Heights when he heard stories of Al Capone visiting the town. Unable to find details to explain Capone's presence in Chicago Heights, he began to research its organized crime history twenty-five years ago. Matt majored in criminal justice during college, and he interned with the Chicago Crime Commission, which helped further his research. He has served as secretary-treasurer of the Merry Gangsters Literary Society, a group of Chicago-area historians and writers committed to the research of Chicago's Prohibition era history. His research has been acknowledged in several books and articles on the subject. Matt currently resides in Chicago and continues to research the history of organized crime in Chicago Heights.